These safety symbols are used in laboratory and field investigations in this book to indicate possible hazards. Learn the meaning of each symbol and refer to this page often. *Remember to wash your hands thoroughly after completing lab procedures.*

PROTECTIVE EQUIPMENT   Do not begin any lab without the proper protection equipment.

GOGGLES Proper eye protection must be worn when performing or observing science activities that involve items or conditions as listed below.	**APRON** Wear an approved apron when using substances that could stain, wet, or destroy cloth.	**SOAP** Wash hands with soap and water before removing goggles and after all lab activities.	**GLOVES** Wear gloves when working with biological materials, chemicals, animals, or materials that can stain or irritate hands.

LABORATORY HAZARDS

Symbols	Potential Hazards	Precaution	Response
DISPOSAL	contamination of classroom or environment due to improper disposal of materials such as chemicals and live specimens	• DO NOT dispose of hazardous materials in the sink or trash can. • Dispose of wastes as directed by your teacher.	• If hazardous materials are disposed of improperly, notify your teacher immediately.
EXTREME TEMPERATURE	skin burns due to extremely hot or cold materials such as hot glass, liquids, or metals; liquid nitrogen; dry ice	• Use proper protective equipment, such as hot mitts and/or tongs, when handling objects with extreme temperatures.	• If injury occurs, notify your teacher immediately.
SHARP OBJECTS	punctures or cuts from sharp objects such as razor blades, pins, scalpels, and broken glass	• Handle glassware carefully to avoid breakage. • Walk with sharp objects pointed downward, away from you and others.	• If broken glass or injury occurs, notify your teacher immediately.
ELECTRICAL	electric shock or skin burn due to improper grounding, short circuits, liquid spills, or exposed wires	• Check condition of wires and apparatus for fraying or uninsulated wires, and broken or cracked equipment. • Use only GFCI-protected outlets	• DO NOT attempt to fix electrical problems. Notify your teacher immediately.
CHEMICAL	skin irritation or burns, breathing difficulty, and/or poisoning due to touching, swallowing, or inhalation of chemicals such as acids, bases, bleach, metal compounds, iodine, poinsettias, pollen, ammonia, acetone, nail polish remover, heated chemicals, mothballs, and any other chemicals labeled or known to be dangerous	• Wear proper protective equipment such as goggles, apron, and gloves when using chemicals. • Ensure proper room ventilation or use a fume hood when using materials that produce fumes. • NEVER smell fumes directly. • NEVER taste or eat any material in the laboratory.	• If contact occurs, immediately flush affected area with water and notify your teacher. • If a spill occurs, leave the area immediately and notify your teacher.
FLAMMABLE	unexpected fire due to liquids or gases that ignite easily such as rubbing alcohol	• Avoid open flames, sparks, or heat when flammable liquids are present.	• If a fire occurs, leave the area immediately and notify your teacher.
OPEN FLAME	burns or fire due to open flame from matches, Bunsen burners, or burning materials	• Tie back loose hair and clothing. • Keep flame away from all materials. • Follow teacher instructions when lighting and extinguishing flames. • Use proper protection, such as hot mitts or tongs, when handling hot objects.	• If a fire occurs, leave the area immediately and notify your teacher.
ANIMAL SAFETY	injury to or from laboratory animals	• Wear proper protective equipment such as gloves, apron, and goggles when working with animals. • Wash hands after handling animals.	• If injury occurs, notify your teacher immediately.
BIOLOGICAL	infection or adverse reaction due to contact with organisms such as bacteria, fungi, and biological materials such as blood, animal or plant materials	• Wear proper protective equipment such as gloves, goggles, and apron when working with biological materials. • Avoid skin contact with an organism or any part of the organism. • Wash hands after handling organisms.	• If contact occurs, wash the affected area and notify your teacher immediately.
FUME	breathing difficulties from inhalation of fumes from substances such as ammonia, acetone, nail polish remover, heated chemicals, and mothballs	• Wear goggles, apron, and gloves. • Ensure proper room ventilation or use a fume hood when using substances that produce fumes. • NEVER smell fumes directly.	• If a spill occurs, leave area and notify your teacher immediately.
IRRITANT	irritation of skin, mucous membranes, or respiratory tract due to materials such as acids, bases, bleach, pollen, mothballs, steel wool, and potassium permanganate	• Wear goggles, apron, and gloves. • Wear a dust mask to protect against fine particles.	• If skin contact occurs, immediately flush the affected area with water and notify your teacher.
RADIOACTIVE	excessive exposure from alpha, beta, and gamma particles	• Remove gloves and wash hands with soap and water before removing remainder of protective equipment.	• If cracks or holes are found in the container, notify your teacher immediately.

INTEGRATED
ⓘSCIENCE

GLENCOE

INDIANA

GRADE 7

Mc
Graw
Hill
Education

COVER: yevgeniy11/shutterstock

mheducation.com/prek-12

Copyright © 2018 McGraw-Hill Education

Send all inquiries to:
McGraw-Hill Education
8787 Orion Place
Columbus, OH 43240

ISBN: 978-0-07-898599-7
MHID: 0-07-898599-4

Printed in the United States of America.

2 3 4 5 6 7 QVS 21 20 19 18 17

Contents in Brief

Authors

American Museum of Natural History
New York, NY

Michelle Anderson, MS
Lecturer
The Ohio State University
Columbus, OH

Juli Berwald, PhD
Science Writer
Austin, TX

John F. Bolzan, PhD
Science Writer
Columbus, OH

Rachel Clark, MS
Science Writer
Moscow, ID

Patricia Craig, MS
Science Writer
Bozeman, MT

Randall Frost, PhD
Science Writer
Pleasanton, CA

Lisa S. Gardiner, PhD
Science Writer
Denver, CO

Jennifer Gonya, PhD
The Ohio State University
Columbus, OH

Mary Ann Grobbel, MD
Science Writer
Grand Rapids, MI

Whitney Crispen Hagins, MA, MAT
Biology Teacher
Lexington High School
Lexington, MA

Carole Holmberg, BS
Planetarium Director
Calusa Nature Center and Planetarium, Inc.
Fort Myers, FL

Tina C. Hopper
Science Writer
Rockwall, TX

Jonathan D. W. Kahl, PhD
Professor of Atmospheric Science
University of Wisconsin-Milwaukee
Milwaukee, WI

Nanette Kalis
Science Writer
Athens, OH

S. Page Keeley, MEd
Maine Mathematics and Science Alliance
Augusta, ME

Cindy Klevickis, PhD
Professor of Integrated Science and Technology
James Madison University
Harrisonburg, VA

Kimberly Fekany Lee, PhD
Science Writer
La Grange, IL

Michael Manga, PhD
Professor
University of California, Berkeley
Berkeley, CA

Devi Ried Mathieu
Science Writer
Sebastopol, CA

Elizabeth A. Nagy-Shadman, PhD
Geology Professor
Pasadena City College
Pasadena, CA

William D. Rogers, DA
Professor of Biology
Ball State University
Muncie, IN

Donna L. Ross, PhD
Associate Professor
San Diego State University
San Diego, CA

Marion B. Sewer, PhD
Assistant Professor
School of Biology
Georgia Institute of Technology
Atlanta, GA

Julia Meyer Sheets, PhD
Lecturer
School of Earth Sciences
The Ohio State University
Columbus, OH

Michael J. Singer, PhD
Professor of Soil Science
Department of Land, Air and Water Resources
University of California
Davis, CA

Karen S. Sottosanti, MA
Science Writer
Pickerington, Ohio

Paul K. Strode, PhD
I.B. Biology Teacher
Fairview High School
Boulder, CO

Jan M. Vermilye, PhD
Research Geologist
Seismo-Tectonic Reservoir Monitoring (STRM)
Boulder, CO

Judith A. Yero, MA
Director
Teacher's Mind Resources
Hamilton, MT

Dinah Zike, MEd
Author, Consultant, Inventor of Foldables
Dinah Zike Academy; Dinah-Might Adventures, LP
San Antonio, TX

Margaret Zorn, MS
Science Writer
Yorktown, VA

Consulting Authors

Alton L. Biggs
Biggs Educational Consulting
Commerce, TX

Ralph M. Feather, Jr., PhD
Assistant Professor
Department of Educational Studies
and Secondary Education
Bloomsburg University
Bloomsburg, PA

Douglas Fisher, PhD
Professor of Teacher Education
San Diego State University
San Diego, CA

Edward P. Ortleb
Science/Safety Consultant
St. Louis, MO

Series Consultants

Science

Solomon Bililign, PhD
Professor
Department of Physics
North Carolina Agricultural and
Technical State University
Greensboro, NC

John Choinski
Professor
Department of Biology
University of Central Arkansas
Conway, AR

Anastasia Chopelas, PhD
Research Professor
Department of Earth and Space
Sciences
UCLA
Los Angeles, CA

David T. Crowther, PhD
Professor of Science Education
University of Nevada, Reno
Reno, NV

A. John Gatz
Professor of Zoology
Ohio Wesleyan University
Delaware, OH

Sarah Gille, PhD
Professor
University of California San Diego
La Jolla, CA

David G. Haase, PhD
Professor of Physics
North Carolina State University
Raleigh, NC

Janet S. Herman, PhD
Professor
Department of Environmental Sciences
University of Virginia
Charlottesville, VA

David T. Ho, PhD
Associate Professor
Department of Oceanography
University of Hawaii
Honolulu, HI

Ruth Howes, PhD
Professor of Physics
Marquette University
Milwaukee, WI

Jose Miguel Hurtado, Jr., PhD
Associate Professor
Department of Geological Sciences
University of Texas at El Paso
El Paso, TX

Monika Kress, PhD
Assistant Professor
San Jose State University
San Jose, CA

Mark E. Lee, PhD
Associate Chair & Assistant Professor
Department of Biology
Spelman College
Atlanta, GA

Linda Lundgren
Science writer
Lakewood, CO

Keith O. Mann, PhD
Ohio Wesleyan University
Delaware, OH

Charles W. McLaughlin, PhD
Adjunct Professor of Chemistry
Montana State University
Bozeman, MT

Katharina Pahnke, PhD
Research Professor
Department of Geology and Geophysics
University of Hawaii
Honolulu, HI

Jesús Pando, PhD
Associate Professor
DePaul University
Chicago, IL

Hay-Oak Park, PhD
Associate Professor
Department of Molecular Genetics
Ohio State University
Columbus, OH

David A. Rubin, PhD
Associate Professor of Physiology
School of Biological Sciences
Illinois State University
Normal, IL

Toni D. Sauncy
Assistant Professor of Physics
Department of Physics
Angelo State University
San Angelo, TX

Welcome to

iSCIENCE

We are your partner in learning by meeting your diverse 21st century needs. Designed for today's tech-savvy middle school students, the McGraw-Hill Education Indiana *iScience* program offers hands-on investigations, rigorous science content, and engaging, real-world applications to make science fun, exciting, and stimulating.

Login information

1 Go to **connected.mcgraw-hill.com.**

2 Enter your registered Username and Password.

3 For **new users** click here to create a new account.

4 Get **ConnectED Help** for creating accounts, verifying master codes, and more.

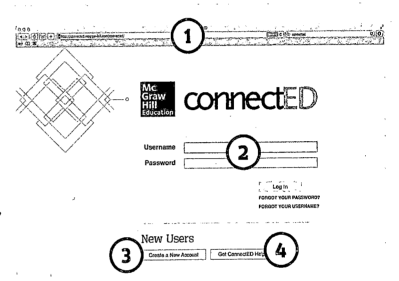

Your ConnectED Center

5 Scroll down to find the program from which you would like to work.

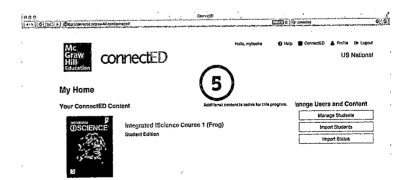

Quick Start Guide
Indiana iScience | Student Center

(1) The Menu allows you to easily jump to anywhere you need to be.

(2) Click the **program icon** at the top left to **return to the main page** from any screen.

(3) **Select a Chapter and Lesson** Use the drop down boxes to quickly jump to any lesson in any chapter.

(4) Return to your **My Home** page for all your **ConnectED** content.

(5) The **Help** icon will guide you to online help. It will also allow for a quick logout.

(6) The **Search Bar** allows you to search content by topic or standard.

(7) **Access the eBook** **Use** the **Student Edition** to see content.

(5) (6) (8)

 eBook (7)

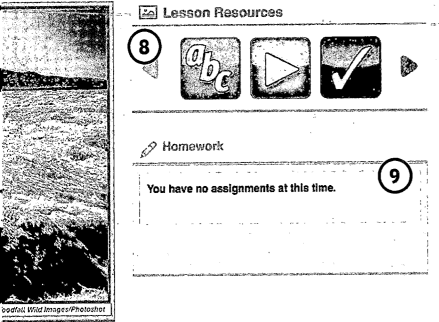

Lesson Resources

(8)   ▶

✎ Homework

You have no assignments at this time. (9)

oodfall Wild Images/Photoshot

Legal   Privacy and Cookie Notice   Technical Support   Minimum Requirements   Help

---

(8) Quickly access helpful links to **multiple resources**, such as:

 LearnSmart

 Chapter Resources Files, Reading Essentials, Get Ready to Read, Quick Vocabulary

 Animations, Videos, Interactive tables

 Self-check quizzes, online and standardized test practice

PBL Project-Based Learning activities

 Lab manuals, safety videos, virtual labs & other tools

 Vocabulary, Multilingual eGlossary, Vocab eGames, Vocab eFlashcards

 Personal Tutors

 Classroom Presentation Toolkit with Powerpoints

 Dinah Zike's Foldables and more

 eGames

Science Notebook

(9) Check your **Homework** assignments here.

connected.mcgraw-hill.com

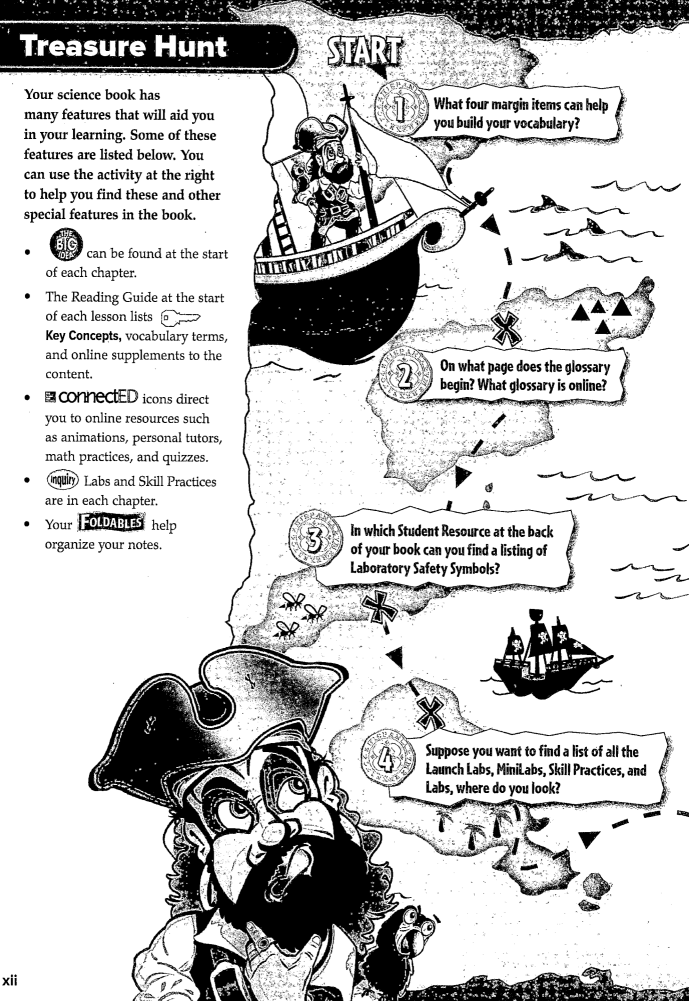

Treasure Hunt

START

Your science book has many features that will aid you in your learning. Some of these features are listed below. You can use the activity at the right to help you find these and other special features in the book.

- **BIG IDEA** can be found at the start of each chapter.

- The Reading Guide at the start of each lesson lists 🔑 **Key Concepts,** vocabulary terms, and online supplements to the content.

- **connectED** icons direct you to online resources such as animations, personal tutors, math practices, and quizzes.

- **(Inquiry)** Labs and Skill Practices are in each chapter.

- Your **FOLDABLES** help organize your notes.

1 What four margin items can help you build your vocabulary?

2 On what page does the glossary begin? What glossary is online?

3 In which Student Resource at the back of your book can you find a listing of Laboratory Safety Symbols?

4 Suppose you want to find a list of all the Launch Labs, MiniLabs, Skill Practices, and Labs, where do you look?

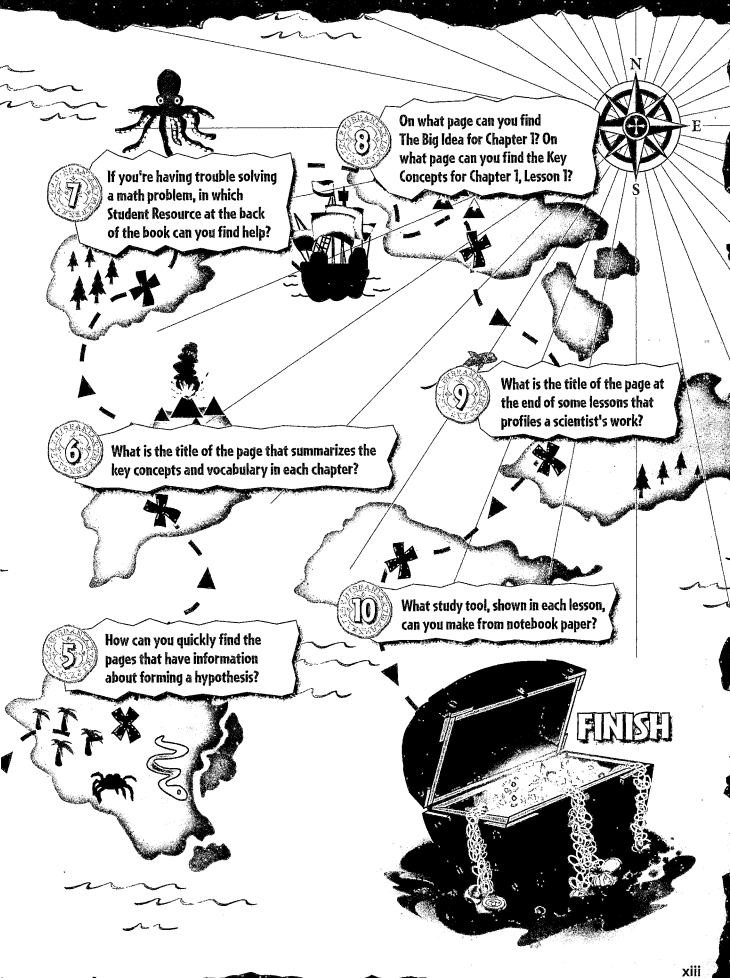

Table of Contents

Table of Contents

Table of Contents

Student Resources

TABLE OF CONTENTS

Launch Labs

Inquiry

MiniLabs

Skill Practice

Inquiry

HOW IT WORKS

TABLE OF CONTENTS

GREEN SCIENCE

SCIENCE & SOCIETY

CAREERS in SCIENCE

Scientific Explanations

THE BIG IDEA

Inquiry Vacuuming Corals?

No, these two divers are collecting data about corals in waters near Sulawesi, Indonesia. They are marine biologists, scientists who study living things in oceans and other saltwater environments.

- What information about corals are these scientists collecting?

- What questions do they hope to answer?

- How can science provide answers to their questions and your questions?

Methods of SCIENCE

This chapter begins your study of the nature of science, but there is even more information about the nature of science in this book. Each unit begins by exploring an important topic that is fundamental to scientific study. As you read these topics, you will learn even more about the nature of science.

Mc Graw Hill Education | connectED

Your one-stop online resource
connectED.mcgraw-hill.com

 LearnSmart®

 Project-Based Learning Activities

 Chapter Resources Files, Reading Essentials, Get Ready to Read, Quick Vocabulary

 Lab Manuals, Safety Videos, Virtual Labs & Other Tools

 Animations, Videos, Interactive Tables

 Vocabulary, Multilingual eGlossary, Vocab eGames, Vocab eFlashcards

 Self-checks, Quizzes, Tests

 Personal Tutors

Reading Guide

Key Concepts 🔑
ESSENTIAL QUESTIONS

- What is scientific inquiry?

- What are the results of scientific investigations?

- How can a scientist minimize bias in a scientific investigation?

Vocabulary

science p. NOS 4

observation p. NOS 6

inference p. NOS 6

hypothesis p. NOS 6

prediction p. NOS 7

technology p. NOS 8

scientific theory p. NOS 9

scientific law p. NOS 9

critical thinking p. NOS 10

  Multilingual eGlossary

 ▷ **BrainPOP®**

🖋 SEPS.1, SEPS.4, SEPS.8, 6-8.E.1, 6-8.E.2, 6-8.E.3, 6-8.E.4, 6-8.LST.4.2

Understanding Science

What is science?

The last time that you watched squirrels play in a park or in your yard, did you realize that you were practicing science? Every time you observe the natural world, you are practicing science. **Science** *is the investigation and exploration of natural events and of the new information that results from those investigations.*

When you observe the natural world, you might form questions about what you see. While you are exploring those questions, you probably use reasoning, creativity, and skepticism to help you find answers to your questions. People use these behaviors in their daily lives to solve problems, such as how to keep a squirrel from eating bird seed, as shown in **Figure 1.** Similarly, scientists use these behaviors in their work.

Scientists use a reliable set of skills and methods in different ways to find answers to questions. After reading this chapter, you will have a better understanding of how science works, the limitations of science, and scientific ways of thinking. In addition, you will recognize that when you practice science at home or in the classroom, you use scientific methods to answer questions just as scientists do.

Figure 1 Someone used reasoning and creativity to design each of these squirrel-proof bird feeders. However, some solutions don't work. Scientists use similar methods to try to solve problems.

Branches of Science

No one person can study all the natural world. Therefore, people tend to focus their efforts on one of the three fields or branches of science—life science, Earth science, or physical science, as described below. Then people or scientists can seek answers to specific problems within one field of science.

WORD ORIGIN

biology
from Greek bios, means "life"; and logia, means "study of"

Life Science

Biology, or life science, is the study of all living things. This aquatic ecologist, a life scientist who studies interactions in aquatic ecosystems, is sampling invertebrates in the water. Biologists ask questions such as

- How do plants produce their own food?
- Why do some animals give birth to live young and others lay eggs?
- How are reptiles and birds related?

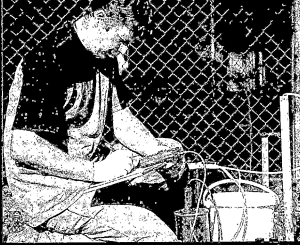

Earth Science

The study of Earth, including its landforms, rocks, soil, and forces that shape Earth's surface, is Earth science. These Earth scientists are collecting soil samples in Africa. Earth scientists ask questions such as

- How do rocks form?
- What causes earthquakes?
- What substances are in soil?

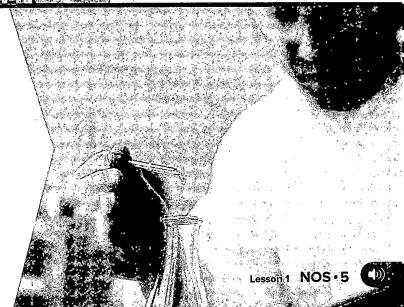

Physical Science

The study of chemistry and physics is physical science. Physical scientists study the interactions of matter and energy. This chemist is preparing antibiotic solutions. Physical scientists ask questions such as

- How do substances react and form new substances?
- Why does a liquid change to a solid?
- How are force and motion related?

Scientific Inquiry

As scientists study the natural world, they ask questions about what they observe. To find the answers to these questions, they usually use certain skills, or methods. The chart in Figure 2 shows a sequence of the skills that a scientist might use in an investigation. However, it is important to know that, sometimes, not all of these skills are performed in an investigation, or performed in this order. Scientists practice scientific inquiry–a process that uses a variety of skills and tools to answer questions or to test ideas about the natural world.

Ask Questions

Like a scientist, you use scientific inquiry in your life, too. Suppose you decide to plant a vegetable garden. As you plant the vegetable seeds, you water some seeds more than others. Then, you weed part of the garden and mix fertilizer into some of the soil. After a few weeks, you observe that some vegetable plants are growing better than others. *An observation is using one or more of your senses to gather information and take note of what occurs.*

Observations often are the beginning of the process of inquiry and can lead to questions such as "Why are some plants growing better than others?" As you are making observations and asking questions, you recall from science class that plants need plenty of water and sunlight to grow. Therefore you infer that perhaps some vegetables are receiving more water or sunlight than others and, therefore, are growing better. *An* **inference** *is a logical explanation of an observation that is drawn from prior knowledge or experience.*

Hypothesize

After making observations and inferences, you are ready to develop a hypothesis and investigate why some vegetables are growing better than others. *A possible explanation about an observation that can be tested by scientific investigations is a* **hypothesis.** Your hypothesis might be: Some plants are growing taller and more quickly than others because they are receiving more water and sunlight. Or, your hypothesis might be: The plants that are growing quickly have received fertilizer because fertilizer helps plants grow.

Figure 2 This flow chart shows steps you or a scientist might use during a scientific investigation.

Ⓥ **Visual Check** What happens if a hypothesis is not supported?

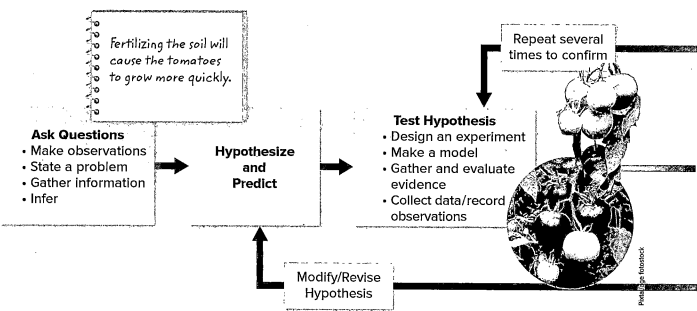

Fertilizing the soil will cause the tomatoes to grow more quickly.

Ask Questions
- Make observations
- State a problem
- Gather information
- Infer

Hypothesize and Predict

Test Hypothesis
- Design an experiment
- Make a model
- Gather and evaluate evidence
- Collect data/record observations

Repeat several times to confirm

Modify/Revise Hypothesis

Predict

After you state a hypothesis, you might make a prediction to help you test your hypothesis. *A prediction is a statement of what will happen next in a sequence of events.* For instance, based on your hypotheses, you might predict that if some plants receive more water, sunlight, or fertilizer, then they will grow taller and more quickly.

Test your Hypothesis

When you test a hypothesis, you often are testing your predictions. For example, you might design an experiment to test your hypothesis on the fertilizer. You set up an experiment in which you plant seeds and add fertilizer to only some of them. Your prediction is that the plants that get the fertilizer will grow more quickly. If your prediction is confirmed, it supports your hypothesis. If your prediction is not confirmed, your hypothesis might need revision.

Analyze Results

As you are testing your hypothesis, you are probably collecting data about the plants' rates of growth and how much fertilizer each plant receives. Initially, it might be difficult to recognize patterns and relationships in data. Your next step might be to organize and analyze your data.

You can create graphs, classify information, or make models and calculations. Once data are organized, you more easily can study the data and draw conclusions. Other methods of testing a hypothesis and analyzing results are shown in Figure 2.

Draw Conclusions

Now you must decide whether your data support your hypothesis and then draw conclusions. A conclusion is a summary of the information gained from testing a hypothesis. If your hypothesis is supported, repeat your experiment several times. A repeated experiment is performed by the same scientist and ensures that results are accurate. If your hypothesis is not supported, you can modify it and repeat the scientific inquiry process.

Communicate Results

Scientists communicate new information to others by writing scientific articles, speaking at conferences, or exchanging information. Other scientists can use this new information in their research. This is also how other scientists learn of experiments that need to be replicated. During experiment replication, different scientists repeat an experiment to verify results.

Key Concept Check What is scientific inquiry?

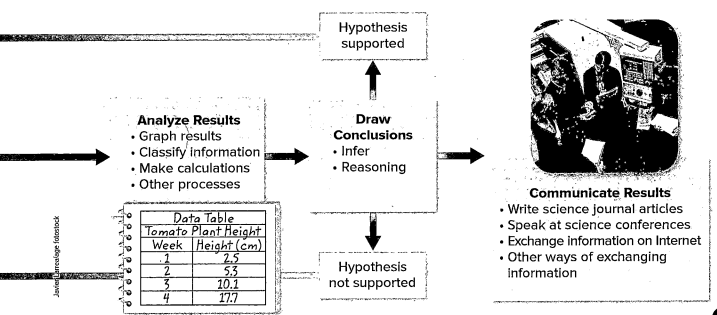

Hypothesis supported

Analyze Results
- Graph results
- Classify information
- Make calculations
- Other processes

Data Table	
Tomato Plant Height	
Week	Height (cm)
1	2.5
2	5.3
3	10.1
4	17.7

Draw Conclusions
- Infer
- Reasoning

Hypothesis not supported

Communicate Results
- Write science journal articles
- Speak at science conferences
- Exchange information on Internet
- Other ways of exchanging information

Javier Larrea/age fotostock

Results of Scientific Inquiry

Both you and scientists perform scientific inquiry to find answers to questions. There are many outcomes of scientific inquiry, such as technology, materials, and explanations, as shown below.

 Key Concept Check What are the results of scientific investigations?

Technology

The practical use of scientific knowledge, especially for industrial or commercial use is technology. Televisions, smartphones, and computers are examples of technology. The C-Leg, shown to the right, is one of the latest designs of computer-aided limbs. The prosthetic leg has sensors that anticipate the user's next move, which prevents him or her from stumbling or tripping. In addition, this new technology has several modes that can enable the user to walk, stand for long periods of time, and even ride a bike.

New Materials

Another possible outcome of an investigation is a new material. For example, scientists have developed a bone bioceramic. A bioceramic is a natural calcium-phosphate mineral complex that is part of bones and teeth. This synthetic bone mimics natural bone's structure. Its porous structure allows a type of cell to grow and develop into new bone tissue. The bioceramic can be shaped into implants that are treated with certain cells from the patient's bone marrow. It then can be implanted into the patient's body to replace missing bone.

Possible Explanations

Many times, scientific investigations answer the questions: *who, what, when, where,* or *how.* For example, who left fingerprints at a crime scene? When should fertilizer be applied to plants? What organisms live in rain forests?

During an expedition in the Colombian Amazon rainforest in 2008, scientists discovered a new species of titi monkey.

Scientific Theory and Scientific Laws

Scientists often repeat scientific investigations to verify that the results for a hypothesis or a group of hypotheses are correct. This can lead to a scientific theory.

Scientific Theory The everyday meaning of the word *theory* is an untested idea or an opinion. However, *a **scientific theory** is an explanation of observations or events based on knowledge gained from many observations and investigations.* For example, about 300 years ago, scientists began looking at samples of trees, water, and blood through the first microscopes. They noticed that all of these organisms were made of tinier units, or cells, as shown in **Figure 3**. As more scientists observed cells in other organisms, their observations became known as the cell theory. This theory explains that all living things are made of cells. A scientific theory is assumed to be the best explanation of observations unless it is disproved. The cell theory will continue to explain the makeup of all organisms until an organism is discovered that is not made of cells.

Scientific Laws Scientific laws are different from societal laws, which are agreements on a set of behaviors. *A **scientific law** describes a pattern or an event in nature that is always true.* A scientific theory might explain how and why an event occurs. But a scientific law states only that an event in nature will occur under specific conditions. For example, the law of conservation of mass states that the mass of materials will be the same before and after a chemical reaction. This scientific law does not explain why this occurs—only that it will occur. **Table 1** compares a scientific theory and a scientific law.

Figure 3 When you view blood using a microscope, you will see that it contains red blood cells.

FOLDABLES

Make a vertical two-column chart book. Label it as shown. Use it to organize your notes on scientific investigations.

Results of Scientific Investigations | Examples

Table 1 Comparing Scientific Theory and Scientific Law	
Scientific Theory	**Scientific Law**
A scientific theory is based on repeated observations and scientific investigations.	Scientific laws are observations of similar events that have been observed repeatedly.
If new information does not support a scientific theory, the theory will be modified or rejected.	If many new observations do not follow the law, the law is rejected.
A scientific theory attempts to explain why something happens.	A scientific law states that something will happen.
A scientific theory usually is more complex than a scientific law and might contain many well-supported hypotheses.	A scientific law usually is based on one well-supported hypothesis that states that something will happen.

Skepticism in Media

When you see scientific issues in the media, such as newspapers, radio, television, and magazines, it is important to be skeptical. When you are skeptical, you question information that you read or hear, or events you observe. Is the information truthful? Is it accurate? It also is important that you question statements made by people outside their area of expertise, and claims that are based on vague statements.

Evaluating Scientific Evidence

An important skill in scientific inquiry is critical thinking. **Critical thinking** *is comparing what you already know with the information you are given in order to decide whether you agree with it.* Identifying and minimizing bias also is important when conducting scientific inquiry. To minimize bias in an investigation, sampling, repetition, and blind studies can be helpful, as shown below.

 Key Concept Check How can a scientist minimize bias in a scientific investigation?

① Sampling

A method of data collection that involves studying small amounts of something in order to learn about the larger whole is sampling. A sample should be a random representation of the whole.

② Bias

It is important to reduce bias during scientific investigations. Bias is intentional or unintentional prejudice toward a specific outcome. Sources of bias in an investigation can include equipment choices, hypothesis formation, and prior knowledge.

Suppose you were a part of a taste test for a new cereal. If you knew the price of each cereal, you might think that the most expensive one tastes the best. This is a bias.

③ Blind Study

A procedure that can reduce bias is a blind study. The investigator, subject, or both do not know which item they are testing. Personal bias cannot affect an investigation if participants do not know what they are testing.

④ Repetition

If you get different results when you repeat an investigation, then the original investigation probably was flawed. Repetition of experiments helps reduce bias.

Science cannot answer all questions.

You might think that any question can be answered through a scientific investigation. But there are some questions that science cannot answer, such as the one posed in **Figure 4.** Questions about personal opinions, values, beliefs, and feelings cannot be answered scientifically. However, some people use scientific evidence to try to strengthen their claims about these topics.

Safety in Science

Scientists follow safety procedures when they conduct investigations. You too should follow safety procedures when you do any experiments. You should wear appropriate safety equipment and listen to your teacher's instructions. Also, you should learn to recognize potential hazards and to know the meaning of safety symbols. Read more about science laboratory safety in the Science Skill Handbook at the back of this book.

Ethics are especially important when using living things during investigations. Animals should be treated properly. Scientists also should tell research participants about the potential risks and benefits of the research. Anyone can refuse to participate in scientific research.

Figure 4 Science cannot answer questions based on opinions or feelings, such as which paint color is the prettiest.

ACADEMIC VOCABULARY
ethics
(noun) *rules of conduct or moral principles*

Lesson 1 Review

☑ **Online Quiz**

Virtual Lab

Use Vocabulary

1. **Explain** the relationship between observations and hypotheses.

2. **Use the terms** *technology, scientific law,* and *scientific theory* in complete sentences.

3. **Contrast** inference and prediction.

4. **Compare and contrast** critical thinking and inference.

Understand Key Concepts 🔑

5. Which should NOT be part of scientific inquiry?
   A. bias
   B. *analysis*
   C. hypothesis
   D. testing

6. **Describe** four real-life examples of the results of scientific investigations.

7. **Discuss** *four ways a scientist can reduce bias in scientific investigations.*

Interpret Graphics

8. **Draw** a graphic organizer like the one below. In each oval, list an example of how to test a hypothesis using scientific inquiry.

Test Hypothesis

Critical Thinking

9. **Suggest** Why do you think people believe some theories even if they are not supported by credible evidence?

10. **Evaluate** In a magazine, you read that two scientific investigations attempted to answer the same question. However, the two teams of scientists came to opposite conclusions. How do you decide which investigation was valid?

The Design Process

Create a Solution

Take a look at all the human-made items around you. All the furniture, vehicles, technology, and even clothing that we have is the result of engineering processes. Recall that scientists use the process of scientific inquiry to investigate and explore the natural world. Engineers investigate and explore the human-made world by using the design process. This enables them to design, construct, and maintain things that do not occur naturally. The design process is a set of methods used to find and create a solution to a problem or need.

The Steps

Identify a Problem or Need

- Determine a problem or a need.
- Document all questions, research, and procedures throughout the process.

Research the Problem & Brainstorm Solutions

- Research any existing solutions that address the problem or need.
- Brainstorm all possible solutions.

Design Solutions

- Suggest limitations of the solutions.
- Look at all solutions and select the best one.
- Create a design of the solution.

Redesign the Solution

- Redesign and modify solution, as needed.
- Construct final solution.

Construct a Prototype

- Estimate materials, costs, resources, and time to develop the solution.
- Construct a prototype.

Test & Evaluate the Solution

- Use models to test the solutions.
- Use graphs, charts, and tables to evaluate results.
- Analyze and evaluate strengths and weaknesses of the solution.

Communicate the Results

- Communicate your designed solution and results to others.

Identify a Problem

Providing enough electricity to power a large city can be difficult. Not only is it expensive, but it can also involve building power plants that can pollute the environment. One way cities get electricity is through the use of wind generators. As the wind blows, the generator's turbines spin and generate electricity, which can be used inside the city. These turbines result in little pollution, but do not always provide enough electricity to fulfill the city's needs.

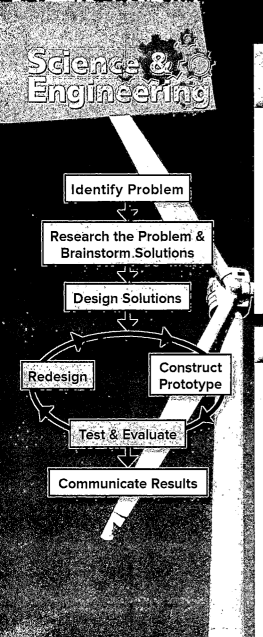

Identify Problem

↓

Research the Problem & Brainstorm Solutions

↓

Design Solutions

↓

Redesign ← → Construct Prototype

Test & Evaluate

↓

Communicate Results

Research the Problem & Brainstorm Solutions

Creating an effective solution first requires finding out more about the problem. The first step is finding out what other people have done to try to solve the same problem. This prevents an engineer from trying a solution that has failed in the past. It also allows the engineer to gain more information for use in the design process. Researching solutions that have been tested is critical in determining if the problem statement is still accurate. Once engineers have gathered enough information, they can begin brainstorming new solutions to the problem.

Design Solutions

After several possible solutions have been brainstormed, engineers can create complex designs. Part of creating a realistic design means taking its constraints into consideration. Constraints are limitations put on the product from outside factors. Factors that can affect the product include cost, ethical issues such as animal testing, environmental impacts, social and political issues, product safety, or attractiveness. For example, wind generators are generally placed in fields where many people can see them. If a design is considered too unattractive, people might not be willing to install them.

It is especially important for engineers to consider the properties of the materials used in designs. These materials should be chosen based on their chemical, physical, and mechanical properties as well as how the materials interact. For example, a very fragile material that can be damaged by strong winds would be a poor choice for a turbine.

Construct a Prototype

Before mass producing the design, engineers first construct a prototype. A prototype is the first example of the design and is used to test the design under real conditions. Prototypes are sometimes also called models.

Models are used to demonstrate processes that happen too slowly, too quickly, or on too small of a scale to observe directly, as well as ones that are potentially dangerous or too large to otherwise study. Engineers frequently study more than one model of a design to

gather as much information as possible. Types of models include physical, mathematical, and computer simulations.

Limitations of Models

Models are good for gathering information about a design, but they cannot give engineers all the information needed. Models do not always behave exactly the way a real product would. This is why it is important to test designs with more than one model.

Conceptual Model

During a brainstorming session, the engineer describes how the wind turbines will function on the top of a hill. To show his team members what this will look like, he draws an image, similar to what is shown on the left. This drawing is called a conceptual model. Conceptual models are sketches or drawings that represent ideas or concepts that describe how someone thinks about something in the natural world. The equation that the engineer placed next to his sketch allows him to show how he calculated the amount of energy that could be produced by his conceptual model.

Computer Simulation

This engineer is using a computer model or computer simulation to determine where to place wind turbines to produce the most energy possible. A computer simulation is a model that combines many mathematical equations. It is used to collect data or to test a process or a procedure. A computer simulation often can be done before anything is actually built or made.

Physical Model

A pinwheel can be considered a physical model of a wind turbine. When the wind blows, the pinwheel moves, just like the blades of the wind turbine. Physical models are those that you can see and touch. Physical models show the relationship between the parts. Other examples of physical models are model cars, a globe of Earth, and a gumdrop-toothpick model of a chemical compound.

Science & Engineering

Identify Problem

Research the Problem & Brainstorm Solutions

Design Solutions

Redesign

Construct Prototype

Test & Evaluate

Communicate Results

Test & Evaluate

Without testing, it is impossible to accurately analyze how well a design solves a problem. By testing and evaluating the design at all stages, engineers can identify problems and solve or prevent them. It is important to test a design many times to identify uncommon and unexpected errors. It would be a good idea to test a model wind generator in many simulated rainstorms rather than just one, because they are frequently rained on.

Redesign

Sometimes testing reveals errors or unexpected results. In other cases, new information is gathered that was not there during the original development. This can mean that the model needs to be redesigned. After the model is redesigned, it is tested and evaluated again.

Communicate Results

After testing the wind turbine, data is shared with the other engineers and scientists. They might need to conduct more research, modify the prototype, and test again. Engineers may go through this process many times before they develop a solution that meets their needs. The final design and prototype are then sent to manufacturing for production.

(bkgd)Design Pics/David Chapman, (inset)Steve Cole/Getty Images

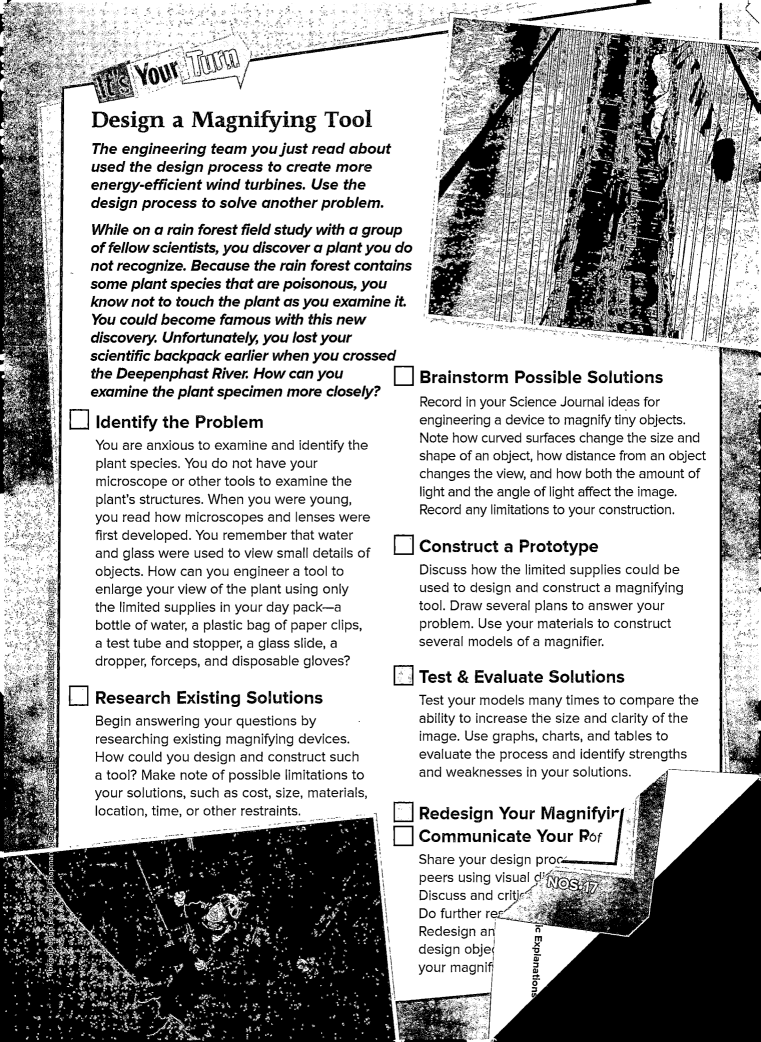

Design a Magnifying Tool

The engineering team you just read about used the design process to create more energy-efficient wind turbines. Use the design process to solve another problem.

While on a rain forest field study with a group of fellow scientists, you discover a plant you do not recognize. Because the rain forest contains some plant species that are poisonous, you know not to touch the plant as you examine it. You could become famous with this new discovery. Unfortunately, you lost your scientific backpack earlier when you crossed the Deepenphast River. How can you examine the plant specimen more closely?

☐ Identify the Problem

You are anxious to examine and identify the plant species. You do not have your microscope or other tools to examine the plant's structures. When you were young, you read how microscopes and lenses were first developed. You remember that water and glass were used to view small details of objects. How can you engineer a tool to enlarge your view of the plant using only the limited supplies in your day pack—a bottle of water, a plastic bag of paper clips, a test tube and stopper, a glass slide, a dropper, forceps, and disposable gloves?

☐ Research Existing Solutions

Begin answering your questions by researching existing magnifying devices. How could you design and construct such a tool? Make note of possible limitations to your solutions, such as cost, size, materials, location, time, or other restraints.

☐ Brainstorm Possible Solutions

Record in your Science Journal ideas for engineering a device to magnify tiny objects. Note how curved surfaces change the size and shape of an object, how distance from an object changes the view, and how both the amount of light and the angle of light affect the image. Record any limitations to your construction.

☐ Construct a Prototype

Discuss how the limited supplies could be used to design and construct a magnifying tool. Draw several plans to answer your problem. Use your materials to construct several models of a magnifier.

☐ Test & Evaluate Solutions

Test your models many times to compare the ability to increase the size and clarity of the image. Use graphs, charts, and tables to evaluate the process and identify strengths and weaknesses in your solutions.

☐ Redesign Your Magnifyir
☐ Communicate Your R

Share your design proc
peers using visual d'
Discuss and criti
Do further re
Redesign an
design obje
your magnif

ic Explanations

Lesson 2

Reading Guide

Key Concepts

ESSENTIAL QUESTIONS

- What is the difference between accuracy and precision?

- Why should you use significant digits?

- What are some tools used by life scientists?

Vocabulary

description p. NOS 18

explanation p. NOS 18

International System of Units (SI) p. NOS 18

accuracy p. NOS 20

precision p. NOS 20

significant digits p. NOS 21

 Multilingual eGlossary

SEPS.2, SEPS.6, 6-8.E.1, 6-8.E.2, 6-8.E.3, 6-8.E.4

Measurement and Scientific Tools

Description and Explanation

How would you describe the squirrel's activity in **Figure 5**? A **description** *is a spoken or written summary of observations.* Your description might include information such as: the squirrel buried five acorns near a large tree. A qualitative description uses your senses (sight, sound, smell, touch, taste) to describe an observation. *A large tree* is a qualitative description. However, a quantitative description uses numbers to describe the observation. *Five acorns* is a quantitative description. You can use measuring tools, such as a ruler, a balance, or a thermometer, to make quantitative descriptions.

How would you explain the squirrel's activity? An **explanation** *is an interpretation of observations.* You might explain that the squirrel is storing acorns for food at a later time. When you describe something, you report what you observe. But when you explain something, you try to interpret your observations. This can lead to a hypothesis.

Figure 5 A description and an explanation of a squirrel's activity contain different information.

The International System of Units

Suppose you observed a squirrel searching for buried food and recorded that it traveled about 200 ft from its nest. Someone who measures distances in meters might not understand how far the squirrel traveled. The scientific community solved this problem in 1960. It adopted *an internationally accepted system for measurement called the* **International System of Units (SI).**

Richard Peters/Alamy

SI Base Units and Prefixes

Like scientists and many others around the world, you probably use the SI system in your classroom. All SI units are derived from seven base units, as listed in **Table 2**. For example, the base unit for length, or the unit most commonly used to measure length, is the meter. However, you have probably made measurements in kilometers or millimeters before. Where do these units come from?

A prefix can be added to a base unit's name to indicate either a fraction or a multiple of that base unit. The prefixes are based on powers of ten, such as 0.01 and 100, as shown in **Table 3**. For example, one centimeter (1 cm) is one one-hundredth of a meter and a kilometer (1 km) is 1,000 meters.

 Interactive Table

Table 2 SI Base Units

Quantity Measured	Unit (symbol)
Length	meter (m)
Mass	kilogram (kg)
Time	second (s)
Electric current	ampere (A)
Temperature	Kelvin (K)
Substance amount	mole (mol)
Light intensity	candela (cd)

Table 3 Prefixes

Prefix	Meaning
Mega– (M)	1,000,000 (10^6)
Kilo– (k)	1,000 (10^3)
Hecto– (h)	100 (10^2)
Deka– (da)	10 (10^1)
Deci– (d)	0.1 (10^{-1})
Centi– (c)	0.01 (10^{-2})
Milli– (m)	0.001 (10^{-3})
Micro– (μ)	0.000 001 (10^{-6})

Conversion

It is easy to convert from one SI unit to another. You either multiply or divide by a power of ten. You also can use proportion calculations to make conversions. For example, a biologist measures an Emperor goose in the field. Her triple-beam balance shows the goose has a mass of 2.8 kg. She could perform the calculation below to find its mass in grams, X.

$$\frac{X}{2.8\,kg} = \frac{1,000\,g}{1\,kg}$$

$$(1\,kg)X = (1,000\,g)(2.8\,kg)$$

$$X = \frac{(1,000\,g)(2.8\,kg)}{1\,kg}$$

$$X = 2,800\,g$$

Notice that the answer has the correct units.

Accurate	Precise but not accurate	Accurate and precise	Not accurate or precise

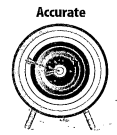 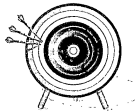 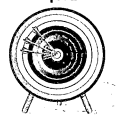 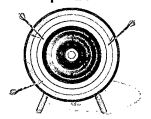

| An arrow in the center indicates high accuracy. | Arrows far from the center indicate low accuracy. Arrows close together indicate high precision. | Arrows in the center indicate high accuracy. Arrows close together indicate high precision. | Arrows far from the center indicate low accuracy. Arrows far apart indicate low precision. |

Figure 6 The archery target illustrates accuracy and precision. An accurate shot is in the bull's-eye.

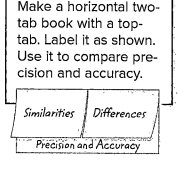

Make a horizontal two-tab book with a top-tab. Label it as shown. Use it to compare precision and accuracy.

Similarities	Differences
Precision and Accuracy	

Precision and Accuracy

Suppose your friend Simon tells you that he will call you in one minute, but he calls you a minute and a half later. Sarah tells you that she will call you in one minute, and she calls exactly 60 seconds later. What is the difference? Sarah is accurate and Simon is not. **Accuracy** *is a description of how close a measurement is to an accepted or true value.* However, if Simon always calls about 30 seconds later than he says he will, then Simon is precise. **Precision** *is a description of how similar or close measurements are to each other,* as shown in **Figure 6.**

Table 4 illustrates the difference between precise and accurate measurements. Students were asked to find the melting point of sucrose, or table sugar. Each student took three temperature readings and calculated the mean, or average, of his or her data. As the recorded data in the table shows, student A had more accurate data. The melting point mean, 184.7°C, is closer to the scientifically accepted melting point, 185°C. Although not accurate, Student C's measurements are the most precise because they are similar in value.

Key Concept Check How do accuracy and precision differ?

Table 4 The data taken by student A are more accurate because each value is close to the accepted value. The data taken by student C are more precise because the data are similar.

Table 4 Student Melting Point Data	Student A	Student B	Student C
Trial 1	183.5°C	190.0°C	181.2°C
Trial 2	185.9°C	183.3°C	182.0°C
Trial 3	184.6°C	187.1°C	181.7°C
Mean	184.7°C	186.8°C	181.6°C
Sucrose Melting Point (accepted value) 185°C			

Measurement and Accuracy

The tools used to take measurements can limit the accuracy of the measurements. Suppose you are measuring the temperature at which sugar melts, and the thermometer's measurements are divided into whole numbers. If your sugar sample melts between 183°C and 184°C, you can estimate the temperature between these two numbers. But, if the thermometer's measurements are divided into tenths, and your sample melts between 183.2°C and 183.3°C, your estimate between these numbers would be more accurate.

Significant Digits

In the second example above, you know that the temperature is between 183.2°C and 183.3°C. You could estimate that the temperature is 183.25°C. When you take any measurement, some digits you know for certain and some digits you estimate. **Significant digits** *are the number of digits in a measurement that are known with a certain degree of reliability.* The significant digits in a measurement include all digits you know for certain plus one estimated digit. Therefore, your measurement of 183.25°C would contain five significant digits, as explained in Table 5. Using significant digits lets others know how certain your measurements are. Figure 7 shows an example of rounding to 3 significant digits?

 Key Concept Check Why should you use significant digits?

Figure 7 Since the ruler is divided into tenths, you know the rod is between 5.2 cm and 5.3 cm. You can estimate that the rod is 5.25 cm.

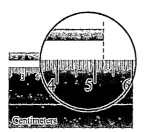

Math Skills

Significant Digits
The number 5,281 has 4 significant digits. Rule 1 in **Table 5** below states that all nonzero numbers are significant.

Practice
Use the rules in **Table 5** to determine the number of significant digits in each of the following numbers: 2.02; 0.0057; 1,500; and 0.500.

 Math Practice

 Personal Tutor

SCIENCE USE V. COMMON USE

digital
Science Use of, pertaining to, or using numbers (numerical digits)

Common Use of or pertaining to a finger

Table 5 Significant Digits

Rules
1. All nonzero numbers are significant.
2. Zeros between nonzero digits are significant.
3. Final zeros used after the decimal point are significant.
4. Zeros used solely for spacing the decimal point are not significant. The zeros indicate only the position of the decimal point.

* The blue numbers in the examples are the significant digits.

Example	Significant Digits	Applied Rules
1.234	4	1
1.2	2	1
0.023	2	1, 4
0.200	3	1, 3
1,002	4	1, 2
3.07	3	1, 2
0.001	1	1, 4
0.012	2	1, 4
50,600	3	1, 2, 4

Scientific Tools

Scientific inquiry often requires the use of tools. Scientists, including life scientists, might use the tools listed on this page and the next page. You might use one or more of them during a scientific inquiry, too. For more information about the proper use of these tools, see the Science Skill Handbook at the back of this book.

Science Journal ▷

In a science journal, you can record descriptions, explanations, plans, and steps used in a scientific inquiry. A science journal can be a spiral-bound notebook or a loose-leaf binder. It is important to keep your science journal organized so that you can find information when you need it. Make sure you keep thorough and accurate records.

◁ Balances

You can use a triple-beam balance or an electric balance to measure mass. Mass usually is measured in kilograms (kg) or grams (g). When using a balance, do not let objects drop heavily onto the balance. Gently remove an object after you record its mass.

Thermometer ▷

A thermometer measures the temperature of substances. Although the Kelvin (K) is the SI unit for temperature, in the science classroom, you measure temperature in degrees Celsius (°C). Use care when you place a thermometer into a hot substance so that you do not burn yourself. Handle glass thermometers gently so that they do not break. If a thermometer does break, tell your teacher immediately. Do not touch the broken glass or the thermometer's liquid. Never use a thermometer to stir anything.

◁ Glassware

Laboratory glassware is used to hold, pour, heat, and measure liquids. Most labs have many types of glassware. For example, flasks, beakers, petri dishes, test tubes, and specimen jars are used as containers. To measure the volume of a liquid, you use a graduated cylinder. The unit of measure for liquid volume is the liter (L) or milliliter (mL).

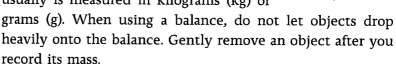

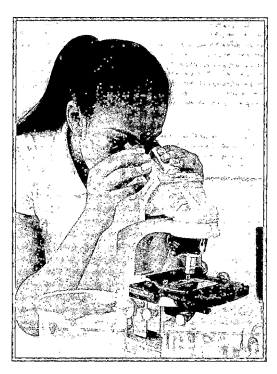

◁ Compound Microscope

Microscopes enable you to observe small objects that you cannot observe with just your eyes. Usually, two types of microscopes are in science classrooms—dissecting microscopes and compound light microscopes, such as the one shown to the left. The girl is looking into two eyepieces to observe a magnified image of a small object or organism. However, some microscopes have only one eyepiece.

Microscopes can be damaged easily. It is important to follow your teacher's instructions when carrying and using a microscope. For more information about how to use a microscope, see the Science Skill Handbook at the back of this book.

 Animation

Computers—Hardware and Software ▷

Computers process information. In science, you can use computers to compile, retrieve, and analyze data for reports. You also can use them to create reports and other documents, to send information to others, and to research information.

The physical components of computers, such as monitors and keyboards, are called hardware. The programs that you run on computers are called software. These programs include word processing, spreadsheets, and presentation programs. When scientists write reports, they use word processing programs. They use spreadsheet programs for organizing and analyzing data. Presenta ation programs can be used to explain information to others.

Tools Used by Life Scientists

Magnifying Lens

A magnifying lens is a hand-held lens that magnifies, or enlarges, an image of an object. It is not as powerful as a microscope and is useful when great magnification is not needed. Magnifying lenses also can be used outside the lab where microscopes might not be available.

Slide

To observe items using a compound light microscope, you must place it on a thin, rectangular piece of glass called a slide. You must handle slides gently to avoid breaking them.

Dissecting Tools

Scientists use dissecting tools, such scalpels and scissors, to examine tissues, organs, or prepared organisms. Dissecting tools are sharp, so always use extreme caution when handling them.

Pipette

A pipette is similar to an eyedropper. It is a small glass or plastic tube used to draw up and transfer liquids.

Key Concept Check What are some tools used by life scientists?

Lesson 2 Review

Online Quiz

Use Vocabulary

1 **Define** *description* and *explanation* in your own words.

2 **Use the term** *International System of Units (SI)* in a sentence.

Understand Key Concepts

3 Which tool would a scientist use to view a tiny organism?

A. computer
B. compound microscope
C. test tube
D. triple-beam balance

4 **Describe** the difference between accuracy and precision.

5 **Explain** why scientists use significant digits.

Interpret Graphics

6 **Draw** a graphic organizer like the one below. Write the name of an SI base unit in each circle. Add additional circles to the graphic organizer as needed.

SI Base Unit

Critical Thinking

7 **Recommend** ways that computers can assist life scientists in their work.

 Math Skills **Math Practice**

8 **Suppose** you measure the mass of a book and it is 420.0890 g. How many significant digits are in this measurement?

Materials

500-mL Erlenmeyer flask

rubber tubing, 15 cm

2-hole stopper

500-mL beaker

Also needed:
short piece of plastic tubing, water, 100-mL graduated cylinder, plastic wrap (10 cm × 30 cm), bendable straws, food coloring (optional)

Safety

How can you build your own scientific instrument?

All organisms take in and release gases. Your cells take in oxygen and release carbon dioxide just like the cells of other animals, plants, fungi, protists, and some bacteria. However, many plant cells, some protists, and some bacteria also can take in carbon dioxide and release oxygen. In this lab, you will follow a procedure and build your own scientific instrument that measures the change in the volume of a gas.

Learn It

Scientists often **follow procedures** developed by other scientists to collect data. A procedure is a step-by-step explanation of how to accomplish a task. The steps in a procedure tell you what materials to use, how to them, and in what order to perform specific tasks. Some procedures are simple, while others are more complicated and require a lot of practice and skill.

Try It

① Read and complete a lab safety form.

② Into each, an Erlenmeyer flask and a beaker, pour 350 mL of water. Pour 100 mL of water into a graduated cylinder.

③ Seal the graduated cylinder with plastic wrap. Place your hand over the plastic wrap and turn the cylinder upside down. Carefully place the sealed end of the graduated cylinder into the beaker of water. Pull off the plastic wrap without losing any water from the graduated cylinder. Have a team member hold the it so that it doesn't tip over.

④ Place one end of a straw in one hole of a 2-hole stopper. Insert the plastic tubing into the other hole. Place one end of the rubber tubing over the plastic tubing.

⑤ Without lifting the cylinder above the water's surface, insert the free end of the rubber tubing inside the cylinder. Have a team continue to hold the cylinder.

⑥ Put the stopper in the flask. Record the initial reading of the water in the graduated cylinder in your Science Journal.

⑦ Gently blow into the straw and watch the change in volume of the water. Continue blowing into the straw until the graduated cylinder contains 50 mL of gas (air).

Apply It

⑧ **Draw a diagram** of your set-up, also known as a eudiometer. Label all the parts, and describe their functions.

⑨ 🔑 **Key Concept** Describe a scenario in which a life scientist would use this instrument to measure gases.

(t to b, 4, r)Hutchings Photography/Digital Light Source; (2-3)McGraw-Hill Education

Case Study

Reading Guide

Key Concepts

ESSENTIAL QUESTIONS

* How do independent and dependent variables differ?

* How is scientific inquiry used in a real-life scientific investigation?

Vocabulary

variable p. NOS 26

dependent variable p. NOS 26

independent variable p. NOS 26

constants p. NOS 26

 Multilingual eGlossary

 SEPS.3

Biodiesel from Microalgae

For the last few centuries, fossil fuels have been the main sources of energy for industry and transportation. But, scientists have shown that burning fossil fuels negatively affects the environment. Also, some people are concerned about eventually using up the world's reserves of fossil fuels.

During the past few decades, scientists have explored using protists to produce biodiesel. Biodiesel is a fuel made primarily from living organisms. Protists, shown in Figure 8, are a group of microscopic organisms that usually live in water or moist environments. Some of these protists are plantlike because they make their own food using a process called photosynthesis. Microalgae are plantlike protists.

Designing a Controlled Experiment

The scientists in this case study used scientific inquiry to investigate the use of protists to make biodiesel. They designed controlled experiments to test their hypotheses. In the margins of this lesson are examples of how scientists in the study practiced inquiry and the skills you read about in Lesson 1. The notebook pages contain information that a scientist might have written in a science journal.

A controlled experiment is a scientific investigation that tests how one variable affects another. *A* **variable** *is any factor in an experiment that can have more than one value.* In controlled experiments, there are two types of variables. *The* **dependent variable** *is the factor measured or observed during an experiment.* The **independent variable** *is the factor that you want to test. It is changed by the investigator to observe how it affects a dependent variable.* **Constants** *are the factors in an experiment that remain the same.*

Key Concept Check How do independent and dependent variables differ?

A controlled experiment has two groups—an experimental group and a control group. The experimental group is used to study how a change in the independent variable changes the dependent variable. The control group contains the same factors as the experimental group, but the independent variable is not changed. Without a control, it is difficult to know whether your experimental observations result from the variable you are testing or from another factor.

Figure 8 Microalgae are plantlike organisms that can make oils.

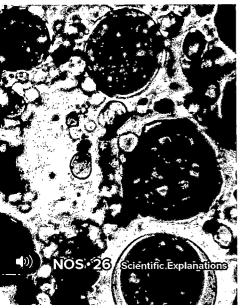

 NOS·26 Scientific Explanations

NREL/US Department of Energy/Science Source

Biodiesel

The idea of engines running on fuel made from plant or plantlike sources is not entirely new. Rudolph Diesel, shown in **Figure 9**, invented the diesel engine. He used peanut oil to demonstrate how his engine worked. However, when petroleum was introduced as a diesel fuel source, it was preferred over peanut oil because it was cheaper.

 Reading Check What did Rudolph Diesel use as fuel?

Oil-rich food crops, such as soybeans, can be used as a source of biodiesel. However, some people are concerned that crops grown for fuel sources will replace crops grown for food. If farmers grow more crops for fuel, then the amount of food available worldwide will be reduced. Because of food shortages in many parts of the world, replacing food crops with fuel crops is not a good solution.

Aquatic Species Program

In the late 1970s, the U.S. Department of Energy began funding its Aquatic Species Program (ASP) to investigate ways to remove air pollutants. Coal-fueled power plants produce carbon dioxide (CO_2), a pollutant, as a by-product. In the beginning, the study examined all aquatic organisms that use CO_2 during photosynthesis–their food-making process. These included large plants, commonly known as seaweeds, plants that grow partially underwater, and microalgae. It was hoped these organisms might remove excess CO_2 from the atmosphere. During the studies, however, the project leaders noticed that some microalgae produced large amounts of oil. The program's focus soon shifted to using microalgae to produce oils that could be processed into biodiesel.

Figure 9 Rudolph Diesel invented the first diesel engine in the early 1900s.

Scientific investigations often begin when someone observes an event in nature and wonders why or how it occurs.

A hypothesis is a tentative explanation that can be tested by scientific investigations. A prediction is a statement of what someone expects to happen next in a sequence of events.

Observation A:
While testing microalgae to discover if they would absorb carbon pollutants, ASP project leaders noticed that some species of microalgae had high oil content.

Hypothesis A:
Some microalgae species can be used as a source of biodiesel fuel because the microalgae produce a large amount of oil.

Prediction A:
If the correct species is found and the growing conditions are isolated, then large oil amounts will be collected.

(l)Science Source; (r)A3419 Stefan Puchner Deutsche Presse-Agentur/Newscom

Design an Experiment and Collect Data:
The ASP scientists developed a rapid screening test to discover which micro-algae species produced the most oil.
Independent Variable:
amount of nitrogen available
Dependent Variable:
amount of oil produced
Constants: the growing conditions of algae (temperature, water quality, exposure to the Sun, etc.)

Observation B:
Based on previous microalgae studies, starving microalgae of nutrients could result in more oil production.
Hypothesis B:
Microalgae grown with inadequate amounts of nitrogen alter their growth processes and produce more oil.
Prediction B:
If microalgae receive inadequate amounts of nitrogen then they will produce more oil.

Figure 10 Green microalgae and diatoms showed the most promise during testing for biodiesel production.

Which Microalgae?

Microalgae are microscopic organisms that live in marine (salty) or freshwater environments. Like many plants and other plantlike organisms, they use photosynthesis and make sugar. The process requires light energy. Microalgae make more sugar than they can use as food. They convert excess sugar to oil. Scientists focused on these microalgae because their oil then could be processed into biodiesel.

The scientists began their research by collecting and identifying promising microalgae species. The search focused on microalgae in shallow, inland, saltwater ponds. Scientists predicted that these microalgae were more resistant to changes in temperature and salt content in the water.

By 1985, a test was in place for identifying microalgae with high oil content. Two years later, 3,000 microalgae species had been collected. Scientists checked these samples for tolerance to acidity, salt levels, and temperature and selected 300 species. Of these 300 species, green microalgae and diatoms, as shown in Figure 10, showed the most promise. However, it was obvious that no one species was going to be perfect for all climates and water types.

Oil Production in Microalgae

Scientists also began researching how microalgae produce oil. Some studies suggested that starving microalgae of nutrients, such as nitrogen, could increase the amount of oil they produced. However, starving microalgae also caused them to be smaller, resulting in no overall increase in oil production.

Outdoor Testing v. Bioreactors

By the 1980s, the ASP scientists were growing microalgae in outdoor ponds in New Mexico. However, outdoor conditions were very different from those in the laboratory. Cooler temperatures in the outdoor ponds resulted in smaller microalgae. Native algae species also invaded the ponds, forcing out the high-oil-producing laboratory microalgae species.

The scientists continued to focus on growing microalgae in open ponds, such as the one shown in Figure 11. Many scientists still believe that these open ponds are better for producing large quantities of biodiesel from microalgae. But, some researchers are now growing microalgae in closed glass containers called bioreactors, also shown in Figure 11. Inside these bioreactors, organisms live and grow under controlled conditions. This method avoids many of the problems associated with open ponds. However, bioreactors are more expensive than open ponds.

A biofuel company in the western United States has been experimenting with a low-cost bioreactor. A scientist at the company explained that they examined the ASP program and hypothesized that they could use long plastic bags instead of closed glass containers. However, microalgae grown in plastic bags are very expensive to harvest.

Figure 11
These methods of growing microalgae are examples of different hypotheses that are being tested in controlled experiments.

Open ponds are less expensive than bioreactors for growing microalgae.

Microalgae grow under controlled conditions in glass bioreactors.

Why So Many Hypotheses?

According to Dr. Richard Sayre, a biofuel researcher, all the ASP research was based on forming hypotheses. Dr. Sayre says, "It was hypothesis-driven. You just don't go in and say 'Well, I have a feeling this is the right way to do it.' You propose a hypothesis. Then you test it."

Dr. Sayre added, "Biologists have been trained over and over again to develop research strategies based on hypotheses. It's sort of ingrained into our culture. You don't get research support by saying, 'I'm going to put together a system, and it's going to be wonderful.' You have to come up with a question. You propose some strategies for answering the question. What are your objectives? What outcomes do you expect for each objective?"

Reading Check Why is it important for a scientific researcher to develop a good hypothesis?

Increasing Oil Yield

Scientists from a biofuel company in Washington State thought of another way to increase oil production. Researchers knew microalgae use light energy, water, and carbon dioxide and make sugar. The microalgae eventually convert sugar into oil. The scientists wondered if they could increase microalgae oil production by distributing light to all microalgae. The experimental lab setup to test this idea is shown in **Figure 12**.

Observation C:
Microalgae use light energy, water, and carbon dioxide to make sugar, which is converted to oil.
Hypothesis C:
Microalgae will produce more oil if light is distributed evenly throughout because they need light energy to grow and produce more oil.
Prediction C:
If light is distributed more evenly then more microalgae will grow, and more oil will be produced.

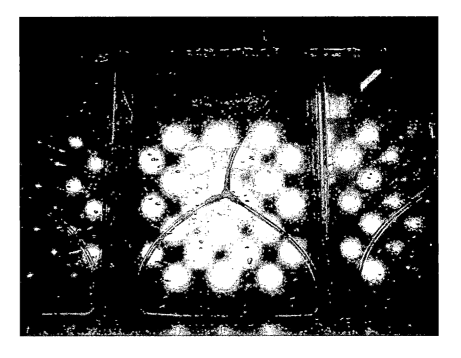

Figure 12 Acrylic rods distribute light to microalgae below the water's surface. If microalgae receive light, they can photosynthesize and eventually produce oils. Without light, microalgae are not productive.

Colin Braley/AP Images

Bringing Light to Microalgae

Normally microalgae grow near the surface of a pond. Any microalgae about 5 cm below the pond's surface will grow less. Why is this? First, water blocks light from reaching deep into a pond. Second, microalgae at the top of a pond block light from reaching microalgae below them. Only the top part of a pond is productive.

Experimental Group

Researchers decided to assemble a team of engineers to design a light-distribution system. Light rods distribute artificial light to microalgae in a bioreactor. The bioreactor controls the environmental conditions that affect how the microalgae grow. These conditions include temperature, nutrient levels, carbon dioxide level, airflow, and light.

 Reading Check In the experimental group, what variables are controlled in the bioreactor?

Data from their experiments showed scientists how microalgae in well-lit environments grow compared to how microalgae grow in dimmer environments. Using solar data for various parts of the country, the scientists concluded that the light rod would significantly increase microalgae growth and oil production in outdoor ponds. These scientists next plan to use the light-rod growing method in outdoor ponds.

Field Testing

Scientists plan to take light to microalgae instead of moving microalgae to light. Dr. Jay Burns is chief microalgae scientist at a biofuel company. He said, "What we are proposing to do is to take the light from the surface of a pond and distribute it throughout the depth of the pond. Instead of only the top 5 cm being productive, the whole pond becomes productive."

 Reading Check What is the benefit of the light-distribution system?

Scientists tested their hypothesis, collected data, analyzed the data, and drew conclusions.

Analyze Results:
The experimental results showed that microalgae would produce more oil using a light-rod system than by using just sunlight.
Draw a Conclusion:
The researchers concluded that the light-rod system greatly increased microalgae oil production.

Research scientists and scientists in the field rely on scientific methods and scientific inquiry to solve real-life problems. When a scientific investigation lasts for several years and involves many scientists, such as this study, many hypotheses can be tested. Some hypotheses are supported, and other hypotheses are not. However, information is gathered and lessons are learned. Hypotheses are refined and tested many times. This process of scientific inquiry results in a better understanding of the problem and possible solutions.

Another Way to Bring Light to Microalgae

Light rods are not the only way to bring light to microalgae. Paddlewheels can be used to keep the microalgae's locations changing. Paddlewheels continuously rotate microalgae to the surface. This exposes the organisms to more light.

Key Concept Check Describe three ways in which scientific inquiry was used in this case study.

Why Grow Microalgae?

While the focus of this case study is microalgae growth for biodiesel production, there are other benefits of growing microalgae, as shown in **Figure 13**. Power plants that burn fossil fuels release carbon dioxide into the atmosphere. Evidence indicates that this contributes to global warming. During photosynthesis, microalgae use carbon dioxide and water, release oxygen, and produce sugar, which they convert to oil. Not only do microalgae produce a valuable fuel, they also remove pollutants from and add oxygen to the atmosphere.

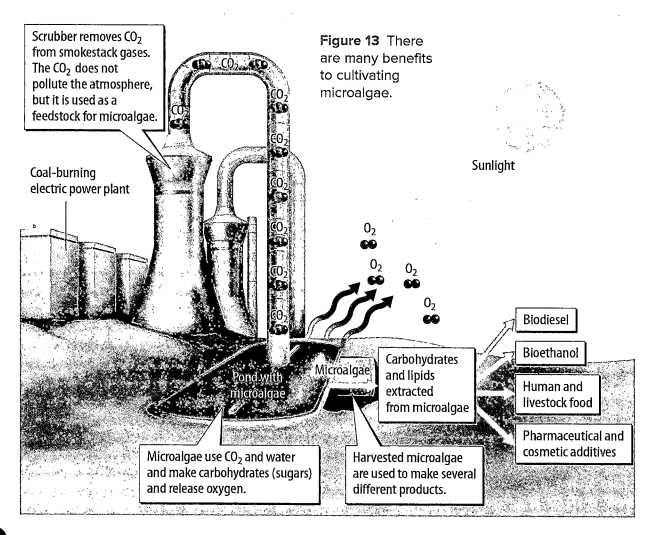

Scrubber removes CO_2 from smokestack gases. The CO_2 does not pollute the atmosphere, but it is used as a feedstock for microalgae.

Coal-burning electric power plant

Figure 13 There are many benefits to cultivating microalgae.

Sunlight

Microalgae use CO_2 and water and make carbohydrates (sugars) and release oxygen.

Harvested microalgae are used to make several different products.

Carbohydrates and lipids extracted from microalgae

Biodiesel

Bioethanol

Human and livestock food

Pharmaceutical and cosmetic additives

Are microalgae the future?

Scientists face many challenges in their quest to produce biodiesel from microalgae. For now, the costs of growing microalgae and extracting their oils are too high to compete with petroleum-based diesel. However, the combined efforts of government-funded programs and commercial biofuel companies might one day make microalgae-based biodiesel an affordable reality in the United States. In fact, a company in Israel has a successful test plant in operation, as shown in Figure 14. Plans are underway to build a large-scale industrial facility to convert carbon dioxide gases released from an Israeli coal-powered electrical plants into useful microalgae products. If this technology performs as expected, microalgae cultivation might occur near coal-fueled power plants in other parts of the world, too.

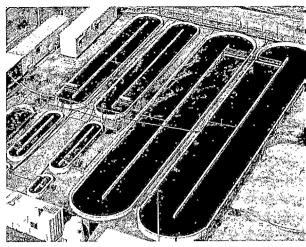

Figure 14 This microalgae test facility in Israel is reducing the amount of carbon dioxide pollution in the atmosphere.

Currently, scientists have no final conclusions about using microalgae as a fuel source. As long as petroleum remains relatively inexpensive and available, it probably will remain the preferred source of diesel fuel. However, if petroleum prices increase or availability decreases, new sources of fuel will be needed. Biodiesel made from microalgae oils might be one of the alternative fuel sources used.

Lesson 3 Review

 Online Quiz

Use Vocabulary

1 **Define** *variable* in your own words.

2 **Contrast** the terms *dependent variable, independent variable,* and *constants.*

Understand Key Concepts

3 Which factor does the investigator change during an investigation?
   A. constant
   B. dependent variable
   C. independent variable
   D. variable

4 **Give an example** of a scientific inquiry used in a real-life scientific investigation that is not mentioned in this chapter.

Interpret Graphics

5 **Organize Information** Copy and fill in a graphic organizer like the one below with information about the three types of oil production discussed in the study.

Critical Thinking

6 **Hypothesize** other methods to either increase the oil content of microalgae or to grow greater amounts of microalgae for biodiesel production.

7 **Evaluate** scientists' efforts to increase the oil content of microalgae and to grow microalgae more quickly. What would you do differently?

Materials

500-mL Erlenmeyer flask

one-hole stopper with a short pieces of plastic tubing in the hole

500-mL beaker

Also needed: rubber tubing (15 cm), water, 100-mL graduated cylinder, plastic wrap (10 cm × 30 cm), scissors, bendable straw, yeast, sugar, triple-beam balance, stopwatch, ice, thermometer

Safety

How can you design a bioreactor?

You are part of scientific team studying how yeast grows in a bioreactor. In a bioreactor, yeast uses sugar as an energy source and releases carbon dioxide gas as a waste product. One way you can tell how fast yeast grows is to measure the volume of gas the yeast produces.

Ask a Question

How do water temperature and sugar concentration affect yeast growth?

Make Observations

① Read and complete a lab safety form.

② Copy the data table shown on the next page into your Science Journal.

③ Place weighing paper or waxed paper on the triple-beam balance, and then zero the balance. Do not place solids directly on the balance. Measure 3 g of yeast. Use the paper to transport the yeast back to your lab station.

④ Repeat step 3 to measure 4 g of sugar.

⑤ Measure and pour 350 mL of water into both the Erlenmeyer flask and the beaker. Measure 100 mL of water in the graduated cylinder.

⑥ Seal the graduated cylinder with plastic wrap. Place you hand over the plastic wrap, and turn the graduated cylinder upside down. Carefully place the sealed end of the graduated cylinder into a beaker of water. Pull off the plastic wrap without losing any water from the cylinder. Have a team member hold the graduated cylinder so that it doesn't tip over.

⑦ Place one end of a 15-cm piece of rubber tubing over the short plastic or glass tubing in the stopper. Without lifting the cylinder above the water's surface, insert the free end of the long piece of tubing inside the graduated cylinder. Have a team continue to hold it. Record the initial reading of the water level in the graduated cylinder in your Science Journal.

⑧ Add the sugar and then the yeast to the Erlenmeyer flask. Place the stopper in the flask and swirl it to mix the contents. This flask is your bioreactor.

⑨ Record the volume of gas produced every 10 min for half an hour. To calculate the volume of gas produced for each 10 min time interval, subtract the initial volume from the final volume.

Form a Hypothesis

10 As a class, form a hypothesis that explains how a change in the amount of sugar in your bioreactor affects carbon dioxide production. Form a second hypothesis that explains how a change in temperature of the water affects carbon dioxide production.

Test Your Hypotheses

11 As a class, develop procedures to test your hypotheses. Use a range of temperatures and different amounts of sugar in your tests.

12 With your teammates, set up several bioreactors with the conditions you outlined in your procedures. Record the results from each bioreactor in a separate data table.

13 Using the class data, create two line graphs—one graph for each hypothesis.

Analyze and Conclude

14 **Analyze** What conditions resulted in the fastest growth of yeast?

15 **Compare** Which of the two variables had a greater influence on the growth of yeast? How did you draw that conclusion?

16 **The Big Idea** Which scientific processes did you use in your investigation of bioreactors?

Communicate Your Results

Present your team's results to your class. Include visual aids and at least one graph.

As part of your presentation, propose future research that your team will conduct on bioreactors. Describe other variables or other organisms your team will investigate. Explain the goal of your future research. Will you develop a product that can be marketed? Will you provide an explanation to solve a scientific problem? Will you develop a new technology?

Gas Produced

Temperature of water _____

Amount of sugar _____

Time (min)	Eudiometer Reading (mL)
0	
10	
20	
30	

Lab Tips

☑ Make sure the graduated cylinder is not tilted when you take readings.

☑ If you use a recycled water bottle as your bioreactor, do not squeeze the bottle once you place the stopper in it or you can force air into the eudiometer.

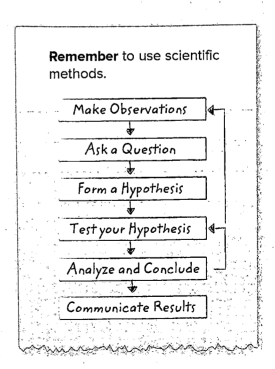

Remember to use scientific methods.

Make Observations

Ask a Question

Form a Hypothesis

Test your Hypothesis

Analyze and Conclude

Communicate Results

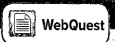

The process of scientific inquiry and performing scientific investigations can provide answers to questions about your world.

Key Concepts Summary	Vocabulary
Lesson 1: Understanding Science • Scientific inquiry, also known as scientific methods, is a collection of skills that scientists use in different combinations to perform scientific investigations. • Scientific investigations often result in new **technology,** new materials, newly discovered objects or events, or answers to questions. • A scientist can help minimize bias in a scientific investigation by taking random samples, doing blind studies, repeating an experiment several times, and keeping accurate and honest records.	**science** p. NOS 4 **observation** p. NOS 6 **inference** p. NOS 6 **hypothesis** p. NOS 6 **prediction** p. NOS 7 **technology** p. NOS 8 **scientific theory** p. NOS 9 **scientific law** p. NOS 9 **critical thinking** p. NOS 10
Lesson 2: Measurement and Scientific Tools • **Precision** is a description of how similar or close measurements are to each other. **Accuracy** is a description of how close a measurement is to an accepted value. • **Significant digits** communicate the precision of the tool used to make measurements. • Life scientists use many tools, such as science journals, microscopes, computers, magnifying lenses, slides, and dissecting tools.	**description** p. NOS 18 **explanation** p. NOS 18 **International System of Units (SI)** p. NOS 18 **precision** p. NOS 20 **accuracy** p. NOS 20 **significant digits** p. NOS 21
Lesson 3: Case Study: Biodiesel from Microalgae • The **independent variable** is a factor in an experiment that is manipulated or changed by the investigator to observe how it affects a dependent variable. The **dependent variable** is the factor measured or observed during an experiment. • Scientific inquiry is used to gain information and find solutions to real-life problems and questions.	**variable** p. NOS 26 **dependent variable** p. NOS 26 **independent variable** p. NOS 26 **constants** p. NOS 26

Use Vocabulary

Explain the relationship between each set of terms.

1 scientific law, scientific theory

2 observation, explanation

3 hypothesis, scientific theory

4 description, explanation

5 International System of Units (SI), significant digits

6 variable, constant

Understand Key Concepts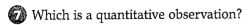

7 Which is a quantitative observation?

   A. 15 m long

   B. red color

   C. rough texture

   D. strong odor

8 Which is one way scientists indicate how precise and accurate their experimental measurements are?

   A. They keep accurate, honest records.

   B. They make sure their experiments can be repeated.

   C. They use significant figures in their measurements.

   D. They record small samples of data.

9 Which is NOT a source of bias?

   A. accurate records

   B. equipment choice

   C. funding source

   D. hypothesis formation

Critical Thinking

10 **Explain** What would be the next step in the scientific inquiry process below?

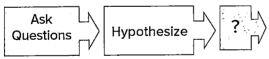

11 **Select** a science career that uses technology. Explain how that career would be different if the technology had not been invented.

12 **Identify** the experimental group, the control group, and controls in the following example. Explain your decision.

A scientist tests a new cough medicine by giving it to a group who have colds. The scientist gives another group with colds a liquid and tells them it is cough medicine. The people in both groups are women between the ages of 20 and 30 who normally are in good health.

Writing in Science

13 **Write** a five-sentence paragraph that includes examples of how bias can be intentional or unintentional and how scientists can reduce bias. Be sure to include topic and concluding sentences in your paragraph.

REVIEW THE BIG IDEA

14 What process do scientists use to perform scientific investigations? List a possible sequence of steps in a scientific inquiry and explain your reasoning.

15 What next step of scientific methods might these marine biologists perform?

Math Skills ✓ **Math Practice**

Significant Digits

16 How many significant figures are in 0.00840, 15.7, and 13.040?

ENERGY AND FORCES

1875

1895
The first X-ray photograph is taken by Wilhelm Konrad Roentgen of his wife's hand. It is now possible to look inside the human body without surgical intervention.

1898
Chemist Marie Curie and her husband Pierre discover radioactivity. They are later awarded the Nobel Prize in Physics for their discovery.

1900

1917
Ernest Rutherford, the "father of nuclear physics," is the first to split atoms.

1925

1934
Nuclear fission is first achieved experimentally in Rome by Enrico Fermi when his team bombards uranium with neutrons.

1939
The Manhattan Project, a code name for a research program to develop the first atomic bomb, begins. The project is directed by American physicist J. Robert Oppenheimer.

1950	1975	2000	

1945
American-led atomic bomb attacks on the Japanese cities of Hiroshima and Nagasaki bring about the end of World War II.

1954
Obninsk Nuclear Power Plant, located in the former USSR, begins operating as the world's first nuclear power plant to generate electricity for a power grid. It produces around 5 megawatts of electric power.

2015
Eleven percent of the world's electricity now comes from nuclear power.

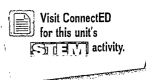

Visit ConnectED for this unit's **STEM** activity.

Unit 1 • 3

Systems

For Valentine's Day, stores display colorful, candy hearts that have words on them, like the ones in **Figure 1**. Where do those millions of candy hearts come from? How are they made? A manufacturing system produces the candy hearts. A **system** is a collection of parts that influence or interact with one another.

There are many kinds of systems. A social systems, such as a political or educational system, involves interactions among people. Systems such as ecosystems, a human body system, and the solar system are natural systems. Transportation systems, communication systems, and manufacturing systems are designed systems that provide services or products to people.

▲ **Figure 1** Whether U R A QT or a TRUE FRIEND, the candy hearts you read on Valentine's Day are produced by a manufacturing system.

Characteristics of a System

Systems often attempt to achieve a goal or are developed with a specific purpose in mind. Like most systems, the manufacturing system, the packaging system, and the transportation system shown in **Figure 2** are described in terms of the system's input, processing, output, and feedback.

Input: material, energy, or information that enters a system **Processing:** the changes that the system makes to the input **Output:** material, energy, or information that leaves a system **Feedback:** information a system uses to monitor and regulate the input, the process, and the output.

Figure 2 Follow the steps in the systems that bring candy hearts to grocery stores every February. ▼

Manufacturing System

Input: Ingredients go into a giant mixing machine. Another input, energy, moves the machine's parts.

Processing: The mixer processes the ingredients into a doughlike candy. Rollers and cutters process the candy dough into separate pieces of candy.

Output: The finished candy hearts travel down a conveyor belt. The candy hearts then become input for the packaging system.

Interactions Among Systems

Often, the output from one system becomes the input to another system. For example, the output from the manufacturing system, finished candy hearts, becomes the input to the packaging system. The outputs from the this system are cases of candy. These cases of candy become the input to the transportation system that carries the product to stores.

Order and Change in Systems

The manufacturing, packaging, and transportation systems can be thought of as subsystems to the overall candy-making system. A change in one subsystem can affect the others. Suppose a packaging machine stops working. The packaging system must provide information about the broken machine to the manufacturing system. This information is feedback. After the manufacturing system receives the feedback, it slows down production. Otherwise, there will be candy hearts all over the floor! Also, a breakdown in the packaging system can affect the systems that follow packaging, such as causing delays in the transportation system.

Feedback: If candy sales are low, feedback is sent to the manufacturing system, signaling that less candy should be produced.

MiniLab — 25 minutes

Can you design a system?

① Select an object that you use every day.

② List the inputs, the processing steps, and the outputs in the system that produces the object.

③ Draw a diagram of the object's manufacturing system.

Analyze and Conclude

1. **Identify** What are the inputs, the processing steps, and the outputs in your system?

2. **Predict** What feedback might be necessary to keep your system working well?

3. **Decide** With what other systems would your system interact?

Transportation System

Input: Cartons of boxed candy hearts become the input to the transportation system.

Process: This system transports and tracks the delivery of cartons of candy hearts to stores.

Output: The output of this system is boxes of candy hearts on shelves of stores throughout the country.

Packaging System

Input: The candy hearts become input for the packaging system.
Processing: This system processes the hearts by packaging them into boxes and cartons.
Output: These boxes and cartons are the output of the packaging system.

Chapter 1

7.PS.4, 7.PS.5, 7.PS.6, 7.PS.7, SEPS.2, SEPS.5, SEPS.6, 6-8.LST.4.1

The Laws of Motion

THE BIG IDEA How do forces change the motion of objects?

Inquiry Why move around?

Imagine the sensations these riders experience as they swing around. The force of gravity pulls the riders downward. Instead of falling, however, they move around in circles.

- What causes the riders to move around?

- What prevents the riders from falling?

- How do forces change the motion of the riders?

Get Ready to Read

What do you think?

Before you read, decide if you agree or disagree with each of these statements. As you read this chapter, see if you change your mind about any of the statements.

1. You pull on objects around you with the force of gravity.

2. Friction can act between two unmoving, touching surfaces.

3. Forces acting on an object cannot be added.

4. A moving object will stop if no forces act on it.

5. When an object's speed increases, the object accelerates.

6. If an object's mass increases, its acceleration also increases if the net force acting on the object stays the same.

7. If objects collide, the object with more mass applies more force.

8. Momentum is a measure of how hard it is to stop a moving object.

Mc Graw Hill Education connectED

Your one-stop online resource
connectED.mcgraw-hill.com

 LearnSmart*

 Chapter Resources Files, Reading Essentials, Get Ready to Read, Quick Vocabulary

 Animations, Videos, Interactive Tables

 Self-checks, Quizzes, Tests

 Project-Based Learning Activities

 Lab Manuals, Safety Videos, Virtual Labs & Other Tools

 Vocabulary, Multilingual eGlossary, Vocab eGames, Vocab eFlashcards

 Personal Tutors

Lesson 1

Reading Guide

Key Concepts

ESSENTIAL QUESTIONS

- What are some contact forces and some noncontact forces?
- What is the law of universal gravitation?
- How does friction affect the motion of two objects sliding past each other?

Vocabulary

force p. 9

contact force p. 9

noncontact force p. 10

gravity p. 11

mass p. 11

weight p. 12

friction p. 13

 Multilingual eGlossary

 What's Science Got to do With It?

 SEPS.6, 6-8.LST.4.1

Gravity and Friction

Inquiry) Why doesn't he fall?

This astronaut is on an aircraft that flies at steep angles and provides a sense of weightlessness. Why doesn't he fall? He does! Earth's gravity pulls the astronaut down, but the aircraft moves downward at the same speed.

NASA

Can you make a ball move without touching it?

You can make a ball move by kicking it or throwing it. Is it possible to make the ball move even when nothing is touching the ball?

1. Read and complete a lab safety form.
2. Roll a **tennis ball** across the floor. Think about what makes the ball move.
3. Toss the ball into the air. Watch as it moves up and then falls back to your hand.
4. Drop the ball onto the floor. Let it bounce once, and then catch it.

Think About This

1. What made the ball move when you rolled, tossed, and dropped it? What made it stop?

2. 🔑 **Key Concept** Did something that was touching the ball or not touching the ball cause it to move in each case?

Types of Forces

Think about all the things you pushed or pulled today. You might have pushed toothpaste out of a tube. Maybe you pulled out a chair to sit down. *A push or a pull on an object is called a* **force.** An object or a person can apply a force to another object or person. Some forces are applied only when objects touch. Other forces are applied even when objects do not touch.

Contact Forces

The hand of the karate expert in **Figure 1** applied a force to the stack of boards and broke them. You have probably also seen a musician strike the keys of a piano and an athlete hit a ball with a bat. In each case, a person or an object applied a force to an object that it touched. A **contact force** is a push or a pull on one object by another that is touching it.

Contact forces can be weak, like when you press the keys on a computer keyboard. They also can be strong, such as when large sections of underground rock suddenly move, resulting in an earthquake. The large sections of Earth's crust called plates also apply strong contact forces against each other. Over long periods of time, these forces can create mountain ranges if one plate pushes another plate upward.

WORD ORIGIN

force
from Latin *fortis,* means "strong"

Figure 1 The man's hand applies a contact force to the boards.

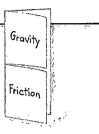

FOLDABLES

Make a vertical two-tab book from a sheet of paper. Label it as shown. Use it to organize your notes on gravity and friction.

Gravity

Friction

▲ **Figure 2** A noncontact force causes the girl's hair to stand on end.

Noncontact Forces

Lift a pencil and then release it. What happens? The pencil falls toward the floor. A parachutist falls toward Earth even though nothing is touching him. *A force that one object can apply to another object without touching it is a* **noncontact force.** Gravity, which pulled on your pencil and the parachutist, is a noncontact force. The magnetic force, which attracts certain metals to magnets, is also a noncontact force. In **Figure 2**, another noncontact force, called the electric force, causes the girl's hair to stand on end.

Key Concept Check What are some contact forces and some noncontact forces?

Strength and Direction of Forces

Forces have both strength and direction. If you push your textbook away from you, it probably slides across your desk. What happens if you push down on your book? It probably does not move. You can use the same strength of force in both cases. Different things happen because the direction of the applied force is different.

As shown in **Figure 3**, arrows can be used to show forces. The length of an arrow shows the strength of the force. Notice in the figure that the force applied by the tennis racquet is stronger than the force applied by the table-tennis paddle. As a result, the arrow showing the force of the tennis racquet is longer. The direction that an arrow points shows the direction in which force was applied.

The SI unit for force is the newton (N). You apply a force of about 1 N when lifting a stick of butter. You use a force of about 20 N when lifting a 2-L bottle of water. If you use arrows to show these forces, the water's arrow would be 20 times longer.

Figure 3 Arrows can indicate the strength and direction of a force. ▼

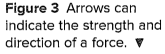
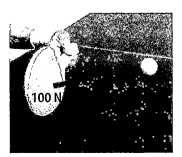

Visual Check How are the lengths of the arrows related to the different forces on the two balls?

Change in Mass	Change in Distance
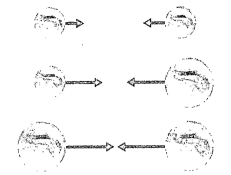	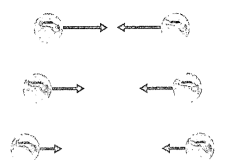
Gravitational force increases if the mass of at least one of the objects increases.	The gravitational force between objects decreases as the objects move apart.

What is gravity?

Objects fall to the ground because Earth exerts an attractive force on them. Did you know that you also exert an attractive force on objects? **Gravity** *is an attractive force that exists between all objects that have mass.* **Mass** *is the amount of matter in an object.* Mass is often measured in kilograms (kg).

The Law of Universal Gravitation

In the late 1600s, an English scientist and mathematician, Sir Isaac Newton, developed the law of universal gravitation. This law states that all objects are attracted to each other by a gravitational force. The strength of the force depends on the mass of each object and the distance between them.

 Key Concept Check What is the law of universal gravitation?

Gravitational Force and Mass The way in which the mass of objects affects gravity is shown in **Figure 4.** When the mass of one or both objects increases, the gravitational force between them also increases. Notice that the force arrows for each pair of marbles are the same size even when one object has less mass. Each object exerts the same attraction on the other object.

Gravitational Force and Distance The effect that distance has on gravity is also shown in **Figure 4.** The attraction between objects decreases as the distance between the objects increases. For example, if your mass is 45 kg, the gravitational force between you and Earth is about 440 N. On the Moon, about 384,000 km away, the gravitational force between you and Earth would only be about 0.12 N. The relationship between gravitational force and distance is shown in the graph in **Figure 5.**

 Reading Check What effect does distance have on gravity?

▲ **Figure 4** The gravitational force between objects depends on the mass of the objects and the distance between them.

📢 **Personal Tutor**

Effect of Distance on Gravity

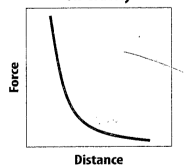

▲ **Figure 5** The gravitational force between objects decreases as the distance between the objects increases.

Weight—A Gravitational Force

Earth has more mass than any object near you. As a result, the gravitational force Earth exerts on you is greater than the force exerted by any other object. **Weight** *is the gravitational force exerted on an object.* Near Earth's surface, an object's weight is the gravitational force exerted on the object by Earth. Because weight is a force, it is measured in newtons.

The Relationship Between Weight and Mass An object's weight is proportional to its mass. For example, if one object has twice the mass of another object, it also has twice the weight. Near Earth's surface, the weight of an object in newtons is about ten times its mass in kilograms.

 Reading Check What is the relationship between mass and weight?

Weight and Mass High Above Earth You might think that astronauts in orbit around Earth are weightless. Their weight is about 90 percent of what it is on Earth. The mass of the astronaut in **Figure 6** is about 55 kg. Her weight is about 540 N on Earth and about 500 N on the space station 350 km above Earth's surface. Why is there no significant change in weight when the distance increases so much? Earth is so large that an astronaut must be much farther away for the gravitational force to change much. The distance between the astronaut and Earth is small compared to the size of Earth.

 Reading Check Why is the gravitational force that a friend exerts on you less than the gravitational force exerted on you by Earth?

ACADEMIC VOCABULARY

significant
(adjective) important, momentous

Figure 6 As she travels from Earth to the space station, the astronaut's weight changes, but her mass remains the same.

Mass: 55 kg
Weight: 540 N

Mass: 55 kg
Weight: 500 N

350 km

NASA

Visual Check What would be the weight of a 110-kg object on Earth? On the space station?

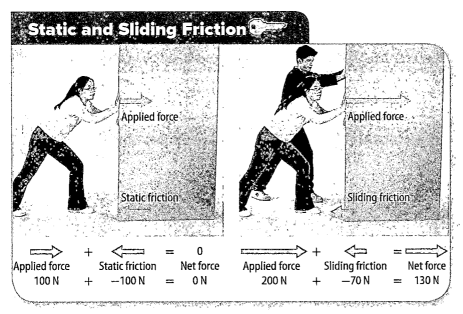

Static and Sliding Friction

Applied force

Static friction

Applied force

Sliding friction

Applied force		Static friction		Net force		Applied force		Sliding friction		Net force
100 N	+	−100 N	=	0 N		200 N	+	−70 N	=	130 N

◁ **Figure 7** Static friction prevents the box on the left from moving. Sliding friction slows the motion of the box on the right.

Friction

If you slide across a smooth floor in your socks, you move quickly at first and then stop. The force that slows you is friction. **Friction** *is a force that resists the motion of two surface that are touching.* There are several types of friction.

Static Friction

The box on the left in **Figure 7** does not move because the girl's applied force is balanced by static friction. Static friction prevents surfaces from sliding past each other. Up to a limit, the strength of static friction changes to match the applied force. If the girl increases the applied force, the box still will not move because the static friction also increases.

Sliding Friction

When static friction reaches its limit between surfaces, the box will move. As shown in **Figure 7**, the force of two students pushing is greater than the static friction between the box and the floor. Sliding friction opposes the motion of surfaces sliding past each other. As long as the box is sliding, the sliding friction does not change. Increasing the applied force makes the box slide faster. If the students stop pushing, the box will slow and stop because of sliding friction.

Fluid Friction

Friction between a surface and a fluid–any material, such as water or air, that flows–is fluid friction. Fluid friction between a surface and air is air resistance. Suppose an object is moving through a fluid. Decreasing the surface area toward the oncoming fluid decreases the air resistance against the object. The crumpled paper in **Figure 8** falls faster than the flat paper because it has less surface area and less air resistance.

(tl tr)Horizons Companies, (b)Hutchings Photography/Digital Light Source

SCIENCE USE V. COMMON USE ⋯

static
Science Use at rest or having no motion

Common Use noise produced in a radio or a television

Figure 8 Air resistance is greater on the flat paper.
▽

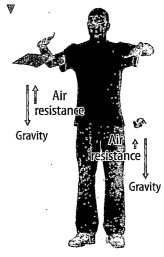

Air resistance

Gravity

Air resistance

Gravity

How does friction affect motion?

Friction affects the motion of an object sliding across a surface.

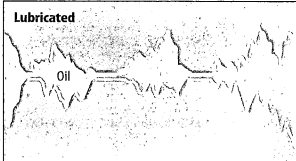

1. Read and complete a lab safety form.
2. Use **tape** to fasten **sandpaper** to a table. Attach a **spring scale** to a **wooden block** with an **eyehook** in it.
3. Record in your Science Journal the force required to gently pull the block at a constant speed on the sandpaper and then on the table.

Analyze and Conclude

1. **Compare** the forces required to pull the block across the two surfaces.

2. 🔑 **Key Concept** How did reducing friction affect the motion of the block?

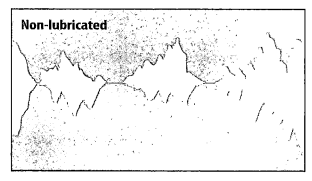

Non-lubricated

Lubricated

Oil

Figure 9 Lubricants such as oil decrease friction caused by microscopic roughness.

What causes friction?

Rub your hands together. What do you feel? If your hands were soapy, you could slide them past each other easily. You feel more friction when you rub your dry hands together than when you rub your soapy hands together.

What causes friction between surfaces? Look at the close-up view of surfaces in **Figure 9.** Microscopic dips and bumps cover all surfaces. When surfaces slide past each other, the dips and bumps on one surface catch on the dips and bumps on the other surface. This microscopic roughness slows sliding and is a source of friction.

📝 **Key Concept Check** How does friction affect the motion of two objects sliding past each other?

In addition, small particles—atoms and molecules—make up all surfaces. These particles contain weak electrical charges. When a positive charge on one surface slides by a negative charge on the other surface, an attraction occurs between the particles. This attraction slows sliding and is another source of friction between the surfaces.

✓ **Reading Check** What are two causes of friction?

Reducing Friction

When you rub soapy hands together, the soapy water slightly separates the surfaces of your hands. There is less contact between the microscopic dips and bumps and between the electrical charges of your hands. Soap acts as a lubricant and decreases friction. With less friction, it is easier for surfaces to slide past each other, as shown in **Figure 9.** Motor oil is a lubricant that reduces friction between moving parts of a car's engine.

Look again at the effect of air resistance on the falling paper in **Figure 8.** Reducing the paper's surface area reduces the fluid friction between it and the air.

Hutchings Photography/Digital Light Source

Visual Summary

 Forces can be either contact, such as a karate chop, or noncontact, such as gravity. Each type is described by its strength and direction.

Gravity is an attractive force that acts between any two objects that have mass. The attraction is stronger for objects with greater mass.

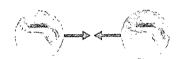

 Friction can reduce the speed of objects sliding past each other. Air resistance is a type of fluid friction that slows the speed of a falling object.

FOLDABLES

Use your lesson Foldable to review the lesson. Save your Foldable for the project at the end of the chapter.

What do you think

You first read the statements below at the beginning of the chapter.

1. You pull on objects around you with the force of gravity.

2. Friction can act between two unmoving, touching surfaces.

Did you change your mind about whether you agree or disagree with the statements? Rewrite any false statements to make them true.

Use Vocabulary

1. **Define** *friction* in your own words.

2. **Distinguish** between weight and mass.

Understand Key Concepts

3. **Explain** the difference between a contact force and a noncontact force.

4. You push a book sitting on a desk with a force of 5 N, but the book does not move. What is the static friction?
   - **A.** 0 N
   - **B.** 5 N
   - **C.** between 0 N and 5 N
   - **D.** greater than 5 N

5. **Apply** According to the law of universal gravitation, is there a stronger gravitational force between you and Earth or an elephant and Earth? Why?

Interpret Graphics

6. **Interpret** Look at the forces on the feather.

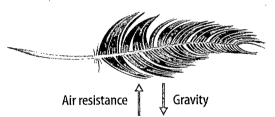

Air resistance ↑ ↓ Gravity

In terms of these forces, explain why the feather falls slowly rather than fast.

7. **Organize Information** Copy and fill in the table below to describe forces mentioned in this lesson. Add as many rows as you need.

Force	Description

Critical Thinking

8. **Decide** Is it possible for the gravitational force between two 50-kg objects to be less than the gravitational force between a 50-kg object and a 5-kg object? Explain.

(t)Terje Rakke/Getty Images, (b)Hutchings Photography/Digital Light Source

Avoiding an Asteroid Collision

Gravity to the rescue!

Everything in the universe—from asteroids to planets to stars—exerts gravity on every other object. This force keeps the Moon in orbit around Earth and Earth in orbit around the Sun. Gravity can also send objects on a collision course—a problem when those objects are Earth and an asteroid. Asteroids are rocky bodies found mostly in the asteroid belt between Mars and Jupiter. Jupiter's strong gravity can change the orbits of asteroids over time, occasionally sending them dangerously close to Earth.

Astronomers use powerful telescopes to track asteroids near Earth. More than a thousand asteroids are large enough to cause serious damage if they collide with Earth. If an asteroid were heading our way, how could we prevent the collision? One idea is to launch a spacecraft into the asteroid. The impact could slow it down enough to cause it to miss Earth. But if the asteroid broke apart, the pieces could rain down onto Earth!

Scientists have another idea. They propose launching a massive spacecraft into an orbit close to the asteroid. The spacecraft's gravity would exert a small tug on the asteroid. Over time, the asteroid's path would be altered enough to pass by Earth. Astronomers track objects now that are many years away from crossing paths with Earth. This gives them enough time to set a plan in motion if one of the objects appears to be on a collision course with Earth.

The force of gravity can change the path of an asteroid moving through the solar system.

The Spacewatch telescope in Arizona scans the sky for near-Earth asteroids. Other U.S. telescopes with this mission are in Hawaii, California, and New Mexico.

Meteor Crater in Arizona was created when an asteroid about 50 m wide collided with Earth about 50,000 years ago.

It's Your Turn

PROBLEM SOLVING With a group, come up with a plan for avoiding an asteroid's collision with Earth. Present your plan to the class. Include diagrams and details that explain exactly how your plan will work.

(t)NASA/Goddard Space Flight Center Scientific Visualization Studio, (c)Digital Vision/Alamy, (b)Chris Sauli/Getty Images, (bkgd)StockTrek/Getty Images

Newton's First Law

Reading Guide

Key Concepts

ESSENTIAL QUESTIONS

- What is Newton's first law of motion?

- How is motion related to balanced and unbalanced forces?

- What effect does inertia have on the motion of an object?

Vocabulary

net force p. 19

balanced forces p. 20

unbalanced forces p. 20

Newton's first law of motion p. 21

inertia p. 22

 Multilingual eGlossary

▷ **BrainPOP®**

 7.PS.4, 7.PS.7, SEPS.2, SEPS.6

 Go to the resource tab in ConnectED to find the PBL *Build a Better Mousetrap Car.*

Inquiry How does it balance?

You probably would be uneasy standing under Balanced Rock near Buhl, Idaho. Yet this unusual rock stays in place year after year. The rock has forces acting on it. Why doesn't it fall over? The forces acting on the rock combine, and the rock does not move.

yan Mullennix/Getty Images

Can you balance magnetic forces?

Magnets exert forces on each other. Depending on how you hold them, magnets either attract or repel each other. Can you balance these magnetic forces?

1. Read and complete a lab safety form.

2. Have your lab partner hold a **ring magnet** vertically on a **pencil,** as shown in the picture.

3. Place **another magnet** on the pencil, and use it to push the first magnet along the pencil.

4. Place a **third magnet** on the same pencil so that the outer magnets push against the middle one. Does the middle magnet still move along the pencil?

Think About This

1. Describe the forces that the other magnets exert on the first magnet in steps 3 and 4.

2. 🔑 **Key Concept** Describe how the motion of the first magnet seemed to depend on whether each force on the magnet was balanced by another force.

Identifying Forces

Ospreys are birds of prey that live near bodies of water. Perhaps several minutes ago, the mother osprey in **Figure 10** was in the air in a high-speed dive. It might have plunged toward a nearby lake after seeing a fish in the water. As it neared the water, it moved its legs forward to grab the fish with its talons. It then stretched out its wings and used them to climb high into the air. Before the osprey comes to rest on its nest, it will slow its speed and land softly on the nest's edge, near the young birds waiting for food.

Forces helped the mother osprey change the speed and direction of its motion. Recall that a force is a push or a pull. Some of the forces were contact forces, such as air resistance. When soaring, the osprey spread its wings, increasing air resistance. In a dive, it held its wings close to its body, changing its shape, decreasing its surface area and air resistance. Gravity also pulled the osprey toward the ground.

To understand the motion of an object, you need to identify the forces acting on it. In this lesson you will read how forces change the motion of objects.

Figure 10 Forces change the motion of this osprey.

(t)Hutchings Photography/Digital Light Source, (b)Marvin E. Newman/Getty Images

Combining Forces—The Net Force

Suppose you try to move a piece of heavy furniture, such as the dresser in **Figure 11.** If you push on the dresser by yourself, you have to push hard on the dresser to overcome the static friction and move it. If you ask a friend to push with you, you do not have to push as hard. When two or more forces act on an object, the forces combine. *The combination of all the forces acting on an object is the* **net force.** The way in which forces combine depends on the directions of the forces applied to an object.

Combining Forces in the Same Direction

When the forces applied to an object act in the same direction, the net force is the sum of the individual forces. In this case, the direction of the net force is the same as the direction of the individual forces.

Because forces have direction, you have to specify a reference direction when you combine forces. In **Figure 11,** for example, you would probably choose "to the right" as the positive reference direction. Both forces then would be positive. The net force on the dresser is the sum of the two forces pushing in the same direction. One person pushes on the dresser with a force of 200 N to the right. The other person pushes with a force of 100 N to the right. The net force on the dresser is 200 N + 100 N = 300 N to the right. The force applied to the dresser is the same as if one person pushed on the dresser with a force of 300 N to the right.

Reading Check How do you calculate the net force on an object if two forces are acting on it in the same direction?

REVIEW VOCABULARY ·····

reference direction
a direction that you choose from a starting point to describe an object's position

 Personal Tutor

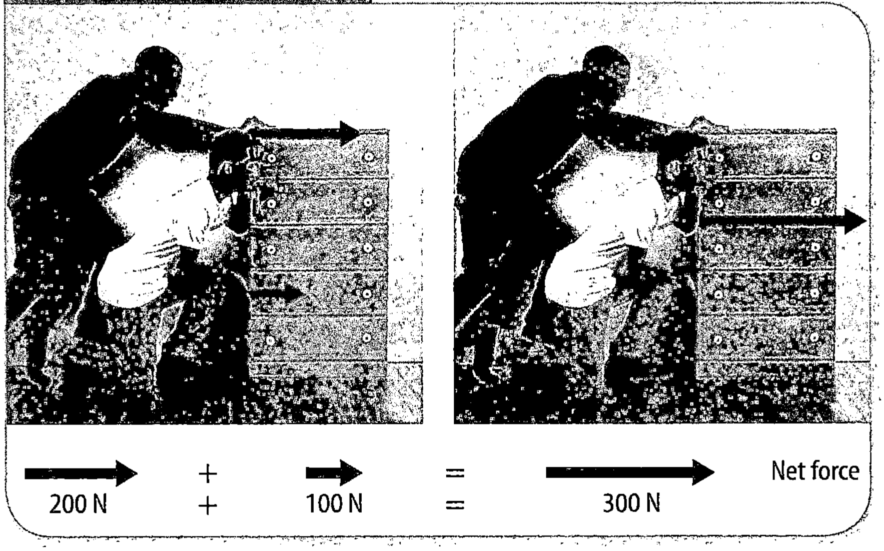

Figure 11 When forces in the same direction combine, the net force is also in the same direction. The strength of the net force is the sum of the forces.

Visual Check What would the net force be if one boy pushed with 250 N and the other boy pushed in the same direction with 180 N?

Combining Forces

200 N + 100 N = 300 N Net force

Hutchings Photography/Digital Light Source

Figure 12 When two forces acting on an object in opposite directions combine, the net force is in the same direction as the larger force. The strength of the net force is the sum of the positive and negative forces. ▷

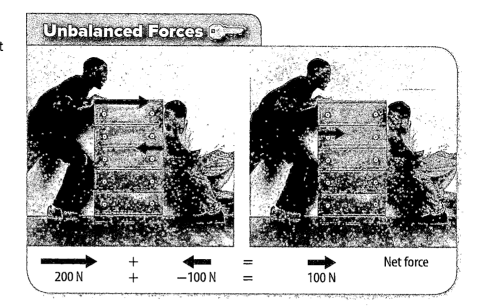

Unbalanced Forces

200 N   +   −100 N   =   100 N   Net force

Combining Forces in Opposite Directions

When forces act in opposite directions on an object, the net force is still the sum of the forces. Suppose you choose "to the right" again as the reference direction in **Figure 12.** A force in that direction is positive, and a force in the opposite direction is negative. The net force is the sum of the positive and negative forces. The net force on the dresser is 100 N to the right.

Balanced and Unbalanced Forces

When equal forces act on an object in opposite directions, as in **Figure 13,** the net force on the object is zero. The effect is the same as if there were no forces acting on the object. *Forces acting on an object that combine and form a net force of zero are* **balanced forces.** Balanced forces do not change the motion of an object. However, the net force on the dresser in **Figure 12** is not zero. There is a net force to the right. *Forces acting on an object that combine and form a net force that is not zero are* **unbalanced forces.**

Figure 13 When two forces acting on an object in opposite directions are the same strength, the forces are balanced. ▷

⊘ **Visual Check** How are the force arrows for the balanced forces in the figure alike? How are they different?

Balanced Forces

200 N   +   −200 N   =   0 Net force   0 N

Hutchings Photography/Digital Light Source

Newton's First Law of Motion

Sir Isaac Newton studied how forces affect the motion of objects. He developed three rules known as Newton's laws of motion. *According to* **Newton's first law of motion,** *if the net force on an object is zero, the motion of the object does not change.* As a result, balanced forces and unbalanced forces have different results when they act on an object.

Key Concept Check What is Newton's first law of motion?

Balanced Forces and Motion

According to Newton's first law of motion, balanced forces cause no change in an object's velocity (speed in a certain direction). This is true when an object is at rest or in motion. Look again at **Figure 13.** The dresser is at rest before the boys push on it. It remains at rest when they apply balanced forces. Similarly, because the forces in **Figure 14**—air resistance and gravity—are balanced, the parachutist moves downward at his terminal velocity. Terminal velocity is the constant velocity reached when air resistance equals the force of gravity acting on a falling object.

Reading Check What happens to the velocity of a moving car if the forces on it are balanced?

Unbalanced Forces and Motion

Newton's first law of motion only applies to balanced forces acting on an object. When unbalanced forces act on an object at rest, the object starts moving. When unbalanced forces act on an already moving object, the object's speed, direction of motion, or both change. You will read more about how unbalanced forces affect an object's motion in the next lesson.

Key Concept Check How is motion related to balanced and unbalanced forces?

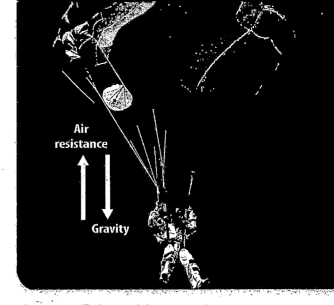

Figure 14 Balanced forces acting on an object do not change the object's speed and direction.

MiniLab 15 minutes

How do forces affect motion?

The motion of an object depends on whether balanced or unbalanced forces act on it.

1. Read and complete a lab safety form.

2. Attach **spring scales** to opposite sides of a **wooden block** with **eyehooks.**

3. With a partner, gently pull the scales so that the block moves toward one of you. Sketch the setup in your Science Journal, including the force readings on each scale.

4. Repeat step 3, pulling on the block so that it does not move.

Analyze and Conclude

1. **Explain** Use Newton's first law of motion to explain what occurred in steps 3 and 4.

2. **Key Concept** How was the block's motion related to balanced and unbalanced forces?

Figure 15 Inertia causes the crash-test dummy to keep moving forward after the car stops.

Visual Check What effect would a shoulder belt and a lap belt have on the inertia of the crash-test dummy?

WORD ORIGIN

inertia
from Latin *iners*, means "without skill, inactive"

FOLDABLES

Make a chart with six columns and six rows. Use your chart to define and show how this lesson's vocabulary terms are related. Afterward, fold your chart in half and label the outside *Newton's First Law.*

	Net force	Balanced forces	Unbalanced forces	Newton's First Law	Inertia
Net force					
Balanced forces					
Unbalanced forces					
Newton's First Law					
Inertia					

Inertia

According to Newton's first law, the motion of an object will not change if balanced forces act on it. *The tendency of an object to resist a change in its motion is called* **inertia** (ihn UR shuh). Inertia explains the motion of the crash-test dummy in **Figure 15.** Before the crash, the car and dummy moved with constant velocity. If no other force had acted on them, the car and dummy would have continued moving with constant velocity because of inertia. The impact with the barrier results in an unbalanced force on the car, and the car stops. The dummy continues moving forward because of its inertia.

Key Concept Check What effect does inertia have on the motion of an object?

Why do objects stop moving?

Think about how friction and inertia together affect an object's movement. A book sitting on a table, for example, stays in place because of inertia. When you push the book, the force you apply to the book is greater than static friction between the book and the table. The book moves in the direction of the greater force. If you stop pushing, friction stops the book.

What would happen if there were no friction between the book and the table? Inertia would keep the book moving. According to Newton's first law, the book would continue to move at the same speed in the same direction as your push.

On Earth, friction can be reduced but not totally removed. For an object to start moving, a force greater than static friction must be applied to it. To keep the object in motion, a force at least as strong as friction must be applied continuously. Objects stop moving because friction or another force acts on them.

©Caspar Benson/age fotostock

Visual Summary

Unbalanced forces cause an object to move.

According to Newton's first law of motion, if the net force on an object is zero, the object's motion does not change.

Inertia is a property that resists a change in the motion of an object.

FOLDABLES

Use your lesson Foldable to review the lesson. Save your Foldable for the project at the end of the chapter.

What do you think

You first read the statements below at the beginning of the chapter.

3. Forces acting on an object cannot be added.

4. A moving object will stop if no forces act on it.

Did you change your mind about whether you agree or disagree with the statements? Rewrite any false statements to make them true.

Use Vocabulary

1 **Define** *net force* in your own words.

2 **Distinguish** between balanced forces and unbalanced forces.

Understand Key Concepts

3 Which causes an object in motion to remain in motion?
- **A.** friction
- **B.** gravity
- **C.** inertia
- **D.** velocity

4 **Apply** You push a coin across a table. The coin stops. How does this motion relate to balanced and unbalanced forces?

5 **Explain** Use Newton's first law to explain why a book on a desk does not move.

Interpret Graphics

6 **Analyze** What is the missing force?

135 N ⟶   ⟵ ? N

Net force ⟹ 25 N

7 **Organize Information** Copy and fill in the graphic organizer below to explain Newton's first law of motion in each case.

Object at rest	
Object in motion	

Critical Thinking

8 **Extend** Three people push a piano on wheels with forces of 130 N to the right, 150 N to the left, and 165 N to the right. What are the strength and direction of the net force on the piano?

9 **Assess** A child pushes down on a box lid with a force of 25 N. At the same time, her friend pushes down on the lid with a force of 30 N. The spring on the box lid pushes upward with a force of 60 N. Can the children close the box? Why or why not?

How can you model Newton's first law of motion?

According to Newton's first law of motion, balanced forces do not change an object's motion. Unbalanced forces change the motion of objects at rest or in motion. You can model different forces and their effects on the motion of an object.

Materials

markers
(red, blue,
black, green)

Learn It

When you **model** a concept in science, you act it out, or imitate it. You can model the effect of balanced and unbalanced forces on motion by using movements on a line.

Try It

1. Draw a line across a sheet of lined notebook paper lengthwise. Place an X at the center. Each space to the right of the X will model a force of 1 N east, and each space to the left will model 1 N west.

2. Suppose a force of 3 N east and a force of 11 N west act on a moving object. Model these forces by starting at X and drawing a red arrow three spaces to the right. Then, start at that point and draw a blue arrow 11 spaces to the left. The net force is modeled by how far this point is from X, 8 N west.

3. Are the forces you modeled balanced or unbalanced? Will the forces change the object's motion?

Apply It

4. Suppose a force of 8 N east, a force of 12 N west, and a force of 4 N east act on a moving object. Use different colors of markers to model the forces on the object.

5. What is the net force on the object? Are the forces you modeled balanced or unbalanced? Will the forces change the object's motion?

6. **Model** other examples of balanced and unbalanced forces acting on an object. In each case, decide which forces will act on the object.

7. 🔑 **Key Concept** For each of the forces you modeled, determine the net force, and decide if the forces are balanced or unbalanced. Then, decide if the forces will change the object's motion.

Net Force 8 N West

(t) Jacques Cornell/McGraw-Hill Education, (b) Hutchings Photography/Digital Light Source

Reading Guide

Key Concepts 🔑
ESSENTIAL QUESTIONS

- What is Newton's second law of motion?

- How does centripetal force affect circular motion?

Vocabulary

Newton's second law of motion p. 29

circular motion p. 30

centripetal force p. 30

 Multilingual eGlossary

 7.PS.4, 7.PS.5, 7.PS.7, SEPS.5

Go to the resource tab in ConnectED to find the PBL *Putting the Shot in Motion.*

Newton's Second Law

Inquiry) What makes it go?

The archer pulls back the string and takes aim. When she releases the string, the arrow soars through the air. To reach the target, the arrow must quickly reach a high speed. How is it able to move so fast? The force from the string determines the arrow's speed.

Michael Steele/Getty Images

Launch Lab

10 minutes

What forces affect motion along a curved path?

When traveling in a car or riding on a roller coaster, you can feel different forces acting on you as you move along a curved path. What are these forces? How do they affect your motion?

1. Read and complete a lab safety form.

2. Attach a piece of **string** about 1 m long to a rolled-up **sock.**

   WARNING: Find a spot away from your classmates for the next steps.

3. While holding the end of the string, swing the sock around in a circle above your head. Notice the force tugging on the string.

4. Repeat step 3 with two socks rolled together. In your Science Journal, compare the force of swinging one sock to the force of swinging two socks.

Think About This

1. Describe the forces acting along the string while you were swinging it. Classify each force as balanced or unbalanced.

2. 🔑 **Key Concept** How does the force from the string seem to affect the sock's motion?

How do forces change motion?

Think about different ways that forces can change an object's motion. For example, how do forces change the motion of someone riding a bicycle? The forces of the person's feet on the pedals cause the wheels of the bicycle to turn faster and the bicycle's speed to increase. The speed of a skater slowly sliding across ice gradually decreases because of friction between the skates and the ice. Suppose you are pushing a wheelbarrow across a yard. You can change its speed by pushing with more or less force. You can change its direction by pushing it in the direction you want to move. Forces change an object's motion by changing its speed, its direction, or both its speed and its direction.

Unbalanced Forces and Velocity

Velocity is speed in a certain direction. Only unbalanced forces change an object's velocity. A bicycle's speed will not increase unless the forces of the person's feet on the pedals is greater than friction that slows the wheels. A skater's speed will not decrease if the skater pushes back against the ice with a force greater than the friction against the skates. If someone pushes the wheelbarrow with the same force but in the opposite direction that you are pushing, the wheelbarrow's direction will not change.

In the previous lesson, you read about Newton's first law of motion—balanced forces do not change an object's velocity. In this lesson you will read about how unbalanced forces affect the velocity of an object.

Hutchings Photography/Digital Light Source

Unbalanced Forces on an Object at Rest

An example of how unbalanced forces affect an object at rest is shown in **Figure 16.** At first the ball is not moving. The hand holds the ball up against the downward pull of gravity. Because the forces on the ball are balanced, the ball remains at rest. When the hand moves out of the way, the ball falls downward. You know that the forces on the ball are now unbalanced because the ball's motion changed. The ball moves in the direction of the net force. When unbalanced forces act on an object at rest, the object begins moving in the direction of the net force.

Unbalanced Forces on an Object in Motion

Unbalanced forces change the velocity of a moving object. Recall that one way to change an object's velocity is to change its speed.

Speeding Up If the net force acting on a moving object is in the direction that the object is moving, the object will speed up. For example, a net force acts on the sled in **Figure 17.** Because the net force is in the direction of motion, the sled's speed increases.

Slowing Down Think about what happens if the direction of the net force on an object is opposite to the direction the object moves. The object slows down. When the boy sliding on the sled in **Figure 17** pushes his foot against the snow, friction acts in the direction opposite to his motion. Because the net force is in the direction opposite to the sled's motion, the sled's speed decreases.

Reading Check What happens to the speed of a wagon rolling to the right if a net force to the right acts on it?

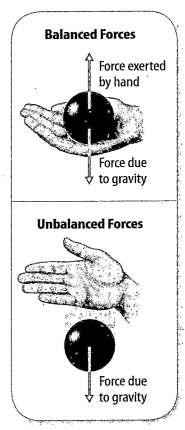

△ **Figure 16** When unbalanced forces act on a ball at rest, it moves in the direction of the net force.

Speeding up

Net force

Slowing down

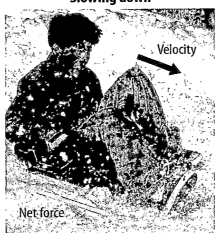

Net force

◁ **Figure 17** Unbalanced forces can cause an object to speed up or slow down.

Visual Check How would the net force and velocity arrows in the left photo change if the girl pushed harder?

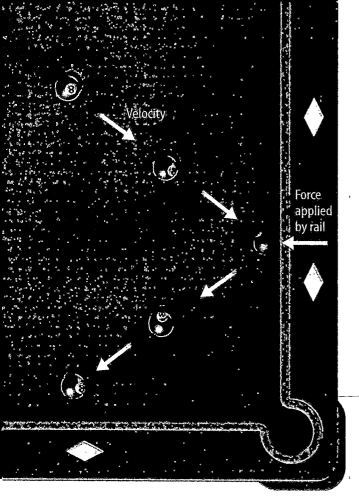

Figure 18 Unbalanced forces act on the billiard ball, causing its direction to change.

Changes in Direction of Motion

Another way that unbalanced forces can change an object's velocity is to change its direction. The ball in **Figure 18** moved at a constant velocity until it hit the rail of the billiard table. The force applied by the rail changed the ball's direction. Likewise, unbalanced forces change the direction of Earth's crust. Recall that the crust is broken into moving pieces called plates. The direction of one plate changes when another plate pushes against it with an unbalanced force.

Unbalanced Forces and Acceleration

You have read how unbalanced forces can change an object's velocity by changing its speed, its direction, or both its speed and its direction. Another name for a change in velocity over time is acceleration. When the girl in **Figure 17** pushed the sled, the sled accelerated because its speed changed. When the billiard ball in **Figure 18** hit the side of the table, the ball accelerated because its direction changed. Unbalanced forces can make an object accelerate by changing its speed, its direction, or both.

Reading Check How do unbalanced forces affect an object at rest or in motion?

🏷️ MiniLab

10 minutes

How are force and mass related? 🖼️ 📊

Unbalanced forces cause an object to accelerate. If the mass of the object increases, how does the force required to accelerate the object change?

① Read and complete a lab safety form.

② Tie a **string** to a **small box.** Pull the box about 2 m across the floor. Notice the force required to cause the box to accelerate.

③ Put **clay** in the box to increase its mass. Pull the box so that its acceleration is about the same as before. Notice the force required.

Analyze and Conclude

1. **Compare** the strength of the force needed to accelerate the box each time.

2. 🔑 **Key Concept** How did the mass affect the force needed to accelerate the box?

Newton's Second Law of Motion

Isaac Newton also described the relationship between an object's acceleration (change in velocity over time) and the net force that acts on an object. *According to* **Newton's second law of motion,** *the acceleration of an object is equal to the net force acting on the object divided by the object's mass.* The direction of acceleration is the same as the direction of the net force.

 Key Concept Check What is Newton's second law of motion?

Make a half-book from a sheet of notebook paper. Use it to organize your notes on Newton's second law.

Newton's Second Law

Newton's Second Law Equation

$$\text{acceleration (in m/s}^2) = \frac{\text{net force (in N)}}{\text{mass (in kg)}}$$

$$a = \frac{F}{m}$$

Notice that the equation for Newton's second law has SI units. Acceleration is expressed in meters per second squared (m/s^2), mass in kilograms (kg), and force in newtons (N). From this equation, it follows that a newton is the same as kg·m/s^2.

 Math Practice

 Personal Tutor

Math Skills ✕➗ Newton's Second Law Equation

Solve for Acceleration You throw a 0.5-kg basketball with a force of 10 N. What is the acceleration of the ball?

❶ This is what you know: mass: $m = 0.5$ kg

force: $F = 10$ N or 10 kg·m/s^2

❷ This is what you need to find: acceleration: a

❸ Use this formula: $a = \dfrac{F}{m}$

❹ Substitute:
the values for F and m
into the formula and divide.

$$a = \frac{10\text{ N}}{0.5\text{ kg}} = 20\ \frac{\text{kg·m/s}^2}{\text{kg}} = 20\text{ m/s}^2$$

Answer: The acceleration of the ball is 20 m/s^2.

Practice

1. A 24-N net force acts on an 8-kg rock. What is the acceleration of the rock?

2. A 30-N net force on a skater produces an acceleration of 0.6 m/s^2. What is the mass of the skater?

3. What net force acting on a 14-kg wagon produces an acceleration of 1.5 m/s^2?

WORD ORIGIN · · · · · · · · · · ·

centripetal
from Latin *centripetus*, means "toward the center"
· · · · · · · · · · · · · · ·

Figure 19 Inertia of the moving object and the centripetal force acting on the object produce the circular motion of the ball and the Moon.

Visual Check How does the direction of the velocity of a satellite differ from the direction of its acceleration?

Circular Motion

Newton's second law of motion describes the relationship between an object's change in velocity over time, or acceleration, and unbalanced forces acting on the object. You already read how this relationship applies to motion along a line. It also applies to circular motion. **Circular motion** *is any motion in which an object is moving along a curved path.*

Centripetal Force

The ball in **Figure 19** is in circular motion. The velocity arrows show that the ball has a tendency to move along a straight path. Inertia—not a force—causes this motion. The ball's path is curved because the string pulls the ball inward. *In circular motion, a force that acts perpendicular to the direction of motion, toward the center of the curve, is* **centripetal** (sen TRIH puh tuhl) **force.** The figure also shows that the ball accelerates in the direction of the centripetal force.

 Key Concept Check How does centripetal force affect circular motion?

The Motion of Satellites and Planets

Another object that experiences centripetal force is a satellite. A satellite is any object in space that orbits a larger object. Like the ball in **Figure 19**, a satellite tends to move along a straight path because of inertia. But just as the string pulls the ball inward, gravity pulls a satellite inward. Gravity is the centripetal force that keeps a satellite in orbit by changing its direction. The Moon is a satellite of Earth. As shown in **Figure 19**, Earth's gravity changes the Moon's direction. Similarly, the Sun's gravity changes the direction of its satellites, including Earth.

Circular Motion ◐━━

▷ **Animation**

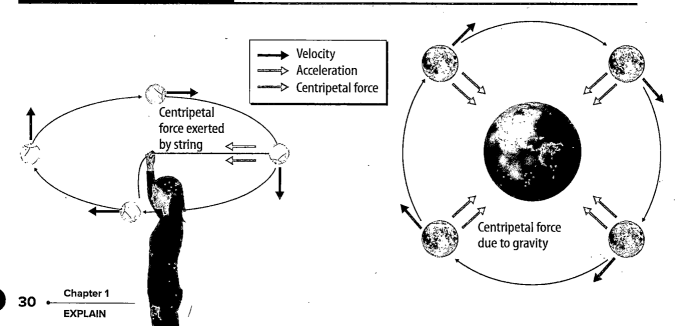

Visual Summary

Unbalanced forces cause an object to speed up, slow down, or change direction.

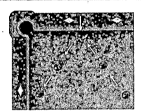

Newton's second law of motion relates an object's acceleration to its mass and the net force on the object.

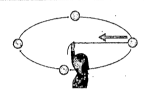

Any motion in which an object is moving along a curved path is circular motion.

FOLDABLES

Use your lesson Foldable to review the lesson. Save your Foldable for the project at the end of the chapter.

What do you think NOW?

You first read the statements below at the beginning of the chapter.

5. When an object's speed increases, the object accelerates.

6. If an object's mass increases, its acceleration also increases if the net force acting on the object stays the same.

Did you change your mind about whether you agree or disagree with the statements? Rewrite any false statements to make them true.

Use Vocabulary

1. **Explain** Newton's second law of motion in your own words.

2. **Use the term** *circular motion* in a sentence.

Understand Key Concepts

3. A cat pushes a 0.25-kg toy with a net force of 8 N. According to Newton's second law what is the acceleration of the ball?
   A. 2 m/s^2 C. 16 m/s^2
   B. 4 m/s^2 D. 32 m/s^2

4. **Describe** how centripetal force affects circular motion.

Interpret Graphics

5. **Apply** Copy and fill in the graphic organizer below. Give examples of unbalanced forces on an object that could cause an object to accelerate.

Unbalanced Forces and Acceleration

6. **Complete** Copy the graphic organizer below and complete each equation according to Newton's second law.

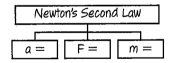

Newton's Second Law

$a =$ $F =$ $m =$

Critical Thinking

7. **Design** You need to lift up a 45-N object. Draw an illustration that explains the strength and direction of the force used to lift the object.

Math Skills   Math Practice

8. The force of Earth's gravity is about 10 N downward. What is the acceleration of a 15-kg backpack if lifted with a 15-N force?

How does a change in mass or force affect acceleration?

Materials

baseball

foam ball

meterstick

Safety

Force, mass, and acceleration are all related variables. In this activity, you will use these variables to study Newton's second law of motion.

Learn It

Vary means "to change." A **variable** is a quantity that can be changed. For example, the variables related to Newton's second law of motion are force, mass, and acceleration. You can find the relationship between any two of these variables by changing one of them and keeping the third variable the same.

Try It

1. Read and complete a lab safety form.

2. Hold a baseball in one hand and a foam ball in your other hand. Compare the masses of the two balls.

3. Lay both balls on a flat surface. Push a meterstick against the balls at the same time with the same force. Compare the accelerations of the ball.

4. Using only the baseball and the meterstick, lightly push the ball and observe its acceleration. Again observe the acceleration as you push the baseball with a stronger push. Compare the accelerations of the ball when you used a weak force and when you used a strong force.

Apply It

5. Answer the following questions for both step 3 and step 4. What variable did you change? What variable changed as a result? What variable did you keep the same?

6. Using your results, state the relationship between acceleration and mass if the net force on an object does not change. Then, state the relationship between acceleration and force if mass does not change.

7. **Key Concept** How do your results support Newton's second law of motion?

Hutchings Photography/Digital Light Source

Lesson 4

Reading Guide

Key Concepts 🔑
ESSENTIAL QUESTIONS

- What is Newton's third law of motion?

- Why don't the forces in a force pair cancel each other?

- What is the law of conservation of momentum?

Vocabulary

Newton's third law of motion p. 35

force pair p. 35

momentum p. 37

law of conservation of momentum p. 38

 Multilingual eGlossary

7.PS.4, 7.PS.5, 7.PS.6, 7.PS.7, SEPS.2

Newton's Third Law

Inquiry Why move up?

To reach the height she needs for her dive, this diver must move up into the air. Does she just jump up? No, she doesn't. She pushes down on the diving board and the diving board propels her into the air. How does pushing down cause the diver to move up?

©Patrik Giardino/Corbis

How do opposite forces compare?

If you think about forces you encounter every day, you might notice forces that occur in pairs. For example, if you drop a rubber ball, the falling ball pushes against the floor. The ball bounces because the floor pushes with an opposite force against the ball. How do these opposite forces compare?

1. Read and complete a lab safety form.
2. Stand so that you face your lab partner, about half a meter away. Each of you should hold a **spring scale.**
3. Hook the two scales together, and gently pull them away from each other. Notice the force reading on each scale.
4. Pull harder on the scales, and again notice the force readings on the scales.
5. Continue to pull on both scales, but let the scales slowly move toward your lab partner and then toward you at a constant speed.

Think About This

1. Identify the directions of the forces on each scale. Record this information in your Science Journal.

2. 🔑 **Key Concept** Describe the relationship you noticed between the force readings on the two scales.

Figure 20 When the skater pushes against the wall, the wall applies a force to the skater that pushes him away from the wall.

Opposite Forces

Have you ever been on in-line skates and pushed against a wall? When you pushed against the wall, like the boy is doing in Figure 20, you started moving away from it. What force caused you to move?

You might think the force of the muscles in your hands moved you away from the wall. But think about the direction of your push. You pushed against the wall in the opposite direction from your movement. It might be hard to imagine, but when you pushed against the wall, the wall pushed back in the opposite direction. The push of the wall caused you to accelerate away from the wall. When an object applies a force on another object, the second object applies a force of the same strength on the first object, but the force is in the opposite direction.

✓ **Reading Check** When you are standing, you push on the floor, and the floor pushes on you. How do the directions and strengths of these forces compare?

Hutchings Photography/Digital Light Source

Newton's Third Law of Motion

Newton's first two laws of motion describe the effects of balanced and unbalanced forces on one object. Newton's third law relates forces between two objects. *According to* **Newton's third law of motion,** *when one object exerts a force on a second object, the second object exerts an equal force in the opposite direction on the first object.* An example of forces described by Newton's third law is shown in **Figure 21.** When the gymnast pushes against the vault, the vault pushes back against the gymnast. Notice that the lengths of the force arrows are the same, but the directions are opposite.

Key Concept Check What is Newton's third law of motion?

Force Pairs

The forces described by Newton's third law depend on each other. *A* **force pair** *is the forces two objects apply to each other.* Recall that you can add forces to calculate the net force. If the forces of a force pair always act in opposite directions and are always the same strength, why don't they cancel each other? The answer is that each force acts on a different object. In **Figure 22,** the girl's feet act on the boat. The force of the boat acts on the girl's feet. The forces do not result in a net force of zero because they act on different objects. Adding forces can only result in a net force of zero if the forces act on the same object.

Key Concept Check Why don't the forces in a force pair cancel each other?

Action and Reaction

In a force pair, one force is called the action force. The other force is called the reaction force. The girl in **Figure 22** applies an action force against the boat. The reaction force is the force that the boat applies to the girl. For every action force, there is a reaction force that is equal in strength but opposite in direction.

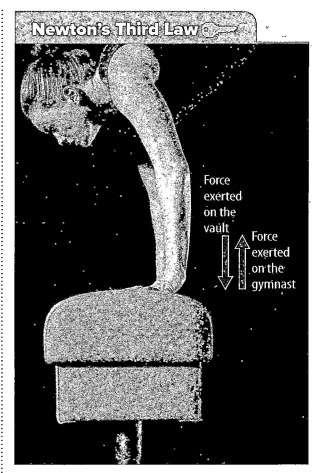

Force exerted on the vault

Force exerted on the gymnast

△ **Figure 21** The force of the vault propels the gymnast upward.

Action force exerted by the girl on the boat

Reaction force exerted by the boat on the girl

△ **Figure 22** The force pair is the force the girl applies to the boat and the force that the boat applies to the girl.

Visual Check How can you tell that the forces don't cancel each other?

Using Newton's Third Law of Motion

When you push against an object, the force you apply is called the action force. The object then pushes back against you. The force applied by the object is called the reaction force. According to Newton's second law of motion, when the reaction force results in an unbalanced force, there is a net force, and the object accelerates. As shown in **Figure 23**, Newton's third law explains how you can swim and jump. It also explains how rockets can be launched into space.

Reading Check How does Newton's third law apply to the motion of a bouncing ball?

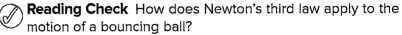

Action and Reaction Forces

Figure 23 Every action force has a reaction force in the opposite direction.

◁ **Swimming** When you swim, you push your arms against the water in the pool. The water in the pool pushes back on you in the opposite (forward) direction. If your arms push the water back with enough force, the reaction force of the water on your body is greater than the force of fluid friction. The net force is forward. You accelerate in the direction of the net force and swim forward through the water.

▷ **Jumping** When you jump, you push down on the ground, and the ground pushes up on you. The upward force of the ground combines with the downward force of gravity to form the net force acting on you. If you push down hard enough, the upward reaction force is greater than the downward force of gravity. The net force is upward. According to Newton's second law, your acceleration is in the same direction as the net force, so you accelerate upward.

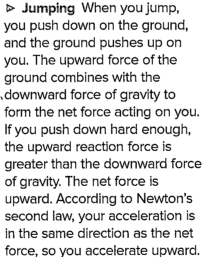

◁ **Rocket Motion** The burning fuel in a rocket engine produces a hot gas. The engine pushes the hot gas out in a downward direction. The gas pushes upward on the engine. When the upward force of the gas pushing on the engine becomes greater than the downward force of gravity on the rocket, the net force is in the upward direction. The rocket then accelerates upward.

Visual Check On what part of the swimmer's body does the water's reaction force push?

Momentum

Because action and reaction forces do not cancel each other, they can change the motion of objects. A useful way to describe changes in velocity is by describing momentum. **Momentum** *is a measure of how hard it is to stop a moving object.* It is the product of an object's mass and velocity. An object's momentum is in the same direction as its velocity.

WORD ORIGIN

momentum
from Latin *momentum*, means "movement, impulse"

Momentum Equation

momentum (in kg·m/s) = **mass** (in kg) × **velocity** (in m/s)

$$p = m \times v$$

If a large truck and a car move at the same speed, the truck is harder to stop. Because it has more mass, it has more momentum. If cars of equal mass move at different speeds, the faster car has more momentum and is harder to stop.

Newton's first two laws relate to momentum. According to Newton's first law, if the net force on an object is zero, its velocity does not change. This means its momentum does not change. Newton's second law states that the net force on an object is the product of its mass and its change in velocity. Because momentum is the product of mass and velocity, the force on an object equals its change in momentum.

Math Skills   Finding Momentum   **Math Practice**   **Personal Tutor**

Solve for Momentum What is the momentum of a 12-kg bicycle moving at 5.5 m/s?

❶ This is what you know:
   mass: m = 12 kg
   velocity: v = 5.5 m/s

❷ This is what you need to find: momentum: p

❸ Use this formula: $p = m \times v$

❹ Substitute: p = **12 kg** × **5.5** m/s = 66 kg·m/s
the values for m and v
into the formula and multiply.

Answer: The momentum of the bicycle is 66 kg·m/s in the direction of the velocity.

Practice

1. What is the momentum of a 1.5-kg ball rolling at 3.0 m/s?

2. A 55-kg woman has a momentum of 220 kg·m/s. What is her velocity?

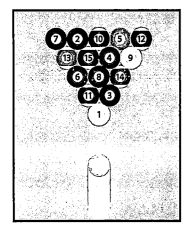

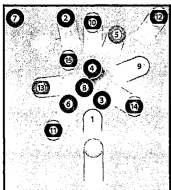

Figure 24 🔍⇒ The total momentum of all the balls is the same before and after the collision.

Conservation of Momentum

You might have noticed that if a moving ball hits another ball that is not moving, the motion of both balls changes. The cue ball in **Figure 24** has momentum because it has mass and is moving. When it hits the other balls, the cue ball's velocity and momentum decrease. Now the other balls start moving. Because these balls have mass and velocity, they also have momentum.

The Law of Conservation of Momentum

In any collision, one object transfers momentum to another object. The billiard balls in **Figure 24** gain the momentum lost by the cue ball. The total momentum, however, does not change. *According to the* **law of conservation of momentum,** *the total momentum of a group of objects stays the same unless outside forces act on the objects.* Outside forces include friction. Friction between the balls and the billiard table decreases their velocities, and they lose momentum.

🔲✓⇒ **Key Concept Check** What is the law of conservation of momentum?

Types of Collisions

Objects collide with each other in different ways. When colliding objects bounce off each other, it is an elastic collision. If objects collide and stick together, such as when one football player tackles another, the collision is inelastic. No matter the type of collision, the total momentum will be the same before and after the collision.

🔧 MiniLab
15 minutes

Is momentum conserved during a collision? 📷

(1) Read and complete a lab safety form.

(2) Make a track by using **masking tape** to secure two **metersticks** side by side on a table, about 4 cm apart.

(3) Place two **tennis balls** on the track. Roll one ball against the other. Then, roll the balls at about the same speed toward each other.

(4) Place the balls so that they touch. Observe the collision as you gently roll **another ball** against them.

Analyze and Conclude

1. **Explain** how you know that momentum was transferred from one ball to another.

2. 🔑⇒ **Key Concept** What could you measure to show that momentum is conserved?

☑ Online Quiz

Virtual Lab

Visual Summary

Newton's third law of motion describes the force pair between two objects.

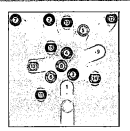

For every action force, there is a reaction force that is equal in strength but opposite in direction.

In any collision, momentum is transferred from one object to another.

Use your lesson Foldable to review the lesson. Save your Foldable for the project at the end of the chapter.

What do you think NOW?

You first read the statements below at the beginning of the chapter.

7. If objects collide, the object with more mass applies more force.

8. Momentum is a measure of how hard it is to stop a moving object.

Did you change your mind about whether you agree or disagree with the statements? Rewrite any false statements to make them true.

Use Vocabulary

1 **Define** *momentum* in your own words.

2 The force of a bat on a ball and the force of a ball on a bat are a(n) —————.

Understand Key Concepts 🔑

3 **State** Newton's third law of motion.

4 A ball with momentum 16 kg·m/s strikes a ball at rest. What is the total momentum of both balls after the collision?
   A. −16 kg·m/s   **C.** 8 kg·m/s
   B. −8 kg·m/s   **D.** 16 kg·m/s

5 **Identify** A child jumps on a trampoline. The trampoline bounces her up. Why don't the forces cancel each other?

Interpret Graphics

6 **Predict** what will happen to the velocity and momentum of each ball when the small ball hits the heavier large ball?

7 **Organize** Copy and fill in the table.

Event	Action Force	Reaction Force
A girl kicks a soccer ball.		
A book sits on a table.		

Critical Thinking

8 **Decide** How is it possible for a bicycle to have more momentum than a truck?

Math Skills ✕ ➕   ☑ Math Practice

9 A 2.0-kg ball rolls to the right at 3.0 m/s. A 4.0-kg ball rolls to the left at 2.0 m/s. What is the momentum of the system after a head-on collision of the two balls?

Modeling Newton's Laws of Motion

Materials

plastic lid

golf ball

modeling clay

2.5-N spring scales (2)

Safety

Newton's first and second laws of motion describe the relationship between unbalanced forces and motion. These laws relate to forces acting on one object. Newton's third law describes the strength and direction of force pairs. This law relates to forces on two different objects. You can learn about all three of Newton's laws of motion by modeling them.

Question

How can you model Newton's laws of motion?

Procedure

1. Read and complete a lab safety form.
2. Attach a spring scale to a plastic lid. Add mass to the lid by placing a ball of modeling clay on it.
3. Slowly pull the lid along a table with the spring scale. Record the force reading on the scale in your Science Journal.
4. Try to use the spring scale to pull the lid with constant force and constant speed.
5. Try pulling the lid with increasing force and constant speed.
6. Pull the lid so that it accelerates quickly.
7. Increase the mass of the lid by adding more modeling clay. Repeat steps 3–6.
8. Replace the modeling clay with a golf ball. Try pulling the lid slowly. Then, try pulling it from a standstill quickly. What happens to the ball in each case? Record your results.

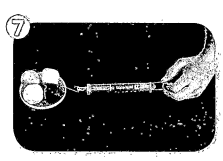

9. To model Newton's first law of motion, design an activity using the lid and the spring scales that shows that a net force of zero does not change the motion of an object. Consider how friction affects velocity in your model.

10. To model Newton's second law of motion, design an activity that shows that if the net force acting on an object is not zero, the object accelerates.

11. To model Newton's third law of motion, plan an activity that shows action and reaction forces on an object.

12. After your teacher approves your plan, perform the activities.

Analyze and Conclude

13. **Identify** the variables in each of your models. Which variables changed and which remained constant?

14. **Describe** how your model demonstrates Newton's first law of motion and how friction affected your model.

15. **Summarize** the relationships among force, mass, and acceleration and between action and reaction forces shown by your models.

16. **The Big Idea** For each law of motion that you modeled, how did the force applied to the lid relate to the motion of the lid?

Communicate Your Results

Choose one of the laws of motion, and model it for the class. Compare your model with the method of modeling used by other lab groups.

Describe another way you could model Newton's three laws of motion using materials other than those used in this lab. For example, for Newton's first law of motion, you could pedal a bicycle at a constant speed.

Lab Tips

☑ Use a smooth surface so that the lid moves easily.

☑ You might want to make a data table in which you can record your observations and the force readings.

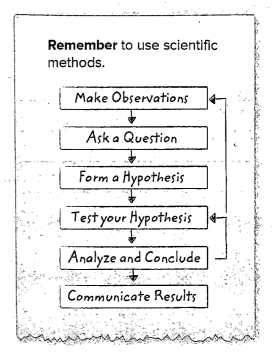

Remember to use scientific methods.

> Make Observations
> ↓
> Ask a Question
> ↓
> Form a Hypothesis
> ↓
> Test your Hypothesis
> ↓
> Analyze and Conclude
> ↓
> Communicate Results

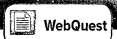

An object's motion changes if a net force acts on the object.

Key Concepts Summary

Lesson 1: Gravity and Friction

- Friction is a **contact force**. Magnetism is a **noncontact force.**
- The law of universal gravitation states that all objects are attracted to each other by **gravity.**
- **Friction** can stop or slow down objects sliding past each other.

Lesson 2: Newton's First Law

- An object's motion can only be changed by **unbalanced forces.**
- According to **Newton's first law of motion,** the motion of an object is not changed by **balanced forces** acting on it.
- **Inertia** is the tendency of an object to resist a change in its motion.

Lesson 3: Newton's Second Law

- According to **Newton's second law of motion,** an object's acceleration is the net force on the object divided by its mass.
- In **circular motion,** a **centripetal force** pulls an object toward the center of the curve.

Lesson 4: Newton's Third Law

- **Newton's third law of motion** states that when one object applies a force on another, the second object applies an equal force in the opposite direction on the first object.
- The forces of a **force pair** do not cancel because they act on different objects.
- According to the **law of conservation of momentum,** momentum is conserved during a collision unless an outside force acts on the colliding objects.

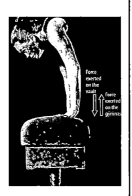

Vocabulary

force p. 9
contact force p. 9
noncontact force p. 10
gravity p. 11
mass p. 11
weight p. 12
friction p. 13

net force p. 19
balanced forces p. 20
unbalanced forces p. 20
Newton's first law of motion p. 21
inertia p. 22

Newton's second law of motion p. 29
circular motion p. 30
centripetal force p. 30

Newton's third law of motion p. 35
force pair p. 35
momentum p. 37
law of conservation of momentum p. 38

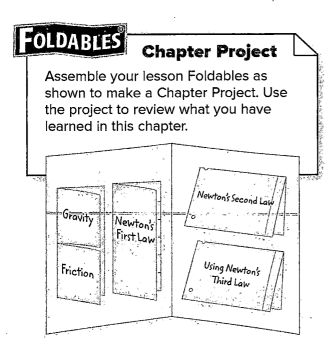

FOLDABLES

Chapter Project

Assemble your lesson Foldables as shown to make a Chapter Project. Use the project to review what you have learned in this chapter.

Use Vocabulary

1 The kilogram is the SI unit for _____.

2 The force of gravity on an object is its _____.

3 The sum of all the forces on an object is the _____.

4 An object that has _____ acting on it acts as if there were no forces acting on it at all.

5 A car races around a circular track. Friction on the tires is the _____ that acts toward the center of the circle and keeps the car on the circular path.

6 A heavy train requires nearly a mile to come to a complete stop because it has a lot of _____.

Link Vocabulary and Key Concepts

 Interactive Concept Map

Copy this concept map, and then use vocabulary terms from the previous page to complete the concept map.

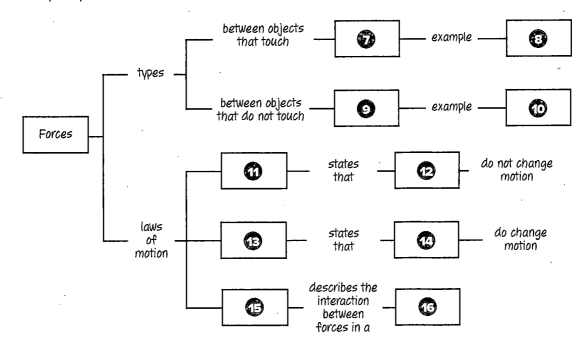

Understand Key Concepts

1 The arrows in the figure represent the gravitational force between marbles that have equal mass.

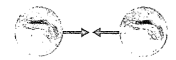

How should the force arrows look if a marble that has greater mass replaces one of these marbles?

A. Both arrows should be drawn longer.
B. Both arrows should stay the same length.
C. The arrow from the marble with less mass should be longer than the other arrow.
D. The arrow from the marble with less mass should be shorter than the other arrow.

2 A person accelerates a box across a flat table with a force less than the weight of the box. Which force is weakest?

A. the force of gravity on the box
B. the force of the table on the box
C. the applied force against the box
D. the sliding friction against the box

3 A train moves at a constant speed on a straight track. Which statement is true?

A. No horizontal forces act on the train as it moves.
B. The train moves only because of its inertia.
C. The forces of the train's engine balances friction.
D. An unbalanced force keeps the train moving.

4 The Moon orbits Earth in a nearly circular orbit. What is the centripetal force?

A. the push of the Moon on Earth
B. the outward force on the Moon
C. the Moon's inertia as it orbits Earth
D. Earth's gravitational pull on the Moon

5 A 30-kg television sits on a table. The acceleration due to gravity is 10 m/s². What force does the table exert on the television?

A. 0.3 N
B. 3 N
C. 300 N
D. 600 N

6 Which does NOT describe a force pair?

A. When you push on a bike's brakes, the friction between the tires and the road increases.
B. When a diver jumps off a diving board, the board pushes the diver up.
C. When an ice skater pushes off a wall, the wall pushes the skater away from the wall.
D. When a boy pulls a toy wagon, the wagon pulls back on the boy.

7 A box on a table has these forces acting on it.

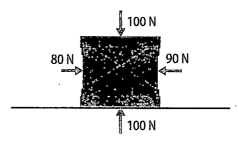

What is the static friction between the box and the table?

A. 0 N
B. 10 N
C. greater than 10 N
D. between 0 and 10 N

8 A 4-kg goose swims with a velocity of 1 m/s. What is its momentum?

A. 4 N
B. 4 kg·m/s²
C. 4 kg·m/s
D. 4 m/s²

Critical Thinking

⑨ Predict If an astronaut moved away from Earth in the direction of the Moon, how would the gravitational force between Earth and the astronaut change? How would the gravitational force between the Moon and the astronaut change?

⑩ Analyze A box is on a table. Two people push on the box from opposite sides. Which of the labeled forces make up a force pair? Explain your answer.

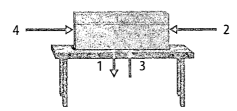

⑪ Conclude A refrigerator has a maximum static friction force of 250 N. Sam can push the refrigerator with a force of 130 N. Amir and André can each push with a force of 65 N. How could they all move the refrigerator? Will the refrigerator move with constant velocity? Why or why not?

⑫ Give an example of unbalanced forces acting on an object.

⑬ Infer Two skaters stand on ice. One weighs 250 N, and the other weighs 500 N. They push against each other and move in opposite directions. Describe the momentum of each skater after they push away from each other.

Writing in Science

⑭ Imagine that you are an auto designer. Your job is to design brakes for different automobiles. Write a four-sentence plan that explains what you need to consider about momentum when designing brakes for a heavy truck, a light truck, a small car, and a van.

REVIEW THE BIG IDEA

⑮ Explain how balanced and unbalanced forces affect objects that are not moving and those that are moving.

⑯ The photo below shows people on a carnival swing ride. How do forces change the motion of the riders?

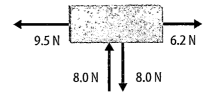

Math Skills ✕÷ ✓ Math Practice

Solve One-Step Equations

⑰ A net force of 17 N is applied to an object, giving it an acceleration of 2.5 m/s². What is the mass of the object?

⑱ A tennis ball's mass is about 0.60 kg. Its velocity is 2.5 m/s. What is the momentum of the ball?

⑲ A box with a mass of 0.82 kg has these forces acting on it.

What is the strength and direction of the acceleration of the box?

Record your answers on the answer sheet provided by your teacher or on a sheet of paper.

Multiple Choice

1 A baseball has an approximate mass of 0.15 kg. If a bat strikes the baseball with a force of 6 N, what is the acceleration of the ball?

A 4 m/s^2

B 6 m/s^2

C 40 m/s^2

D 60 m/s^2

Use the diagram below to answer question 2.

2 The person in the diagram above is unable to move the crate from its position. Which is the opposing force?

A gravity

B normal force

C sliding friction

D static friction

3 The mass of a person on Earth is 72 kg. What is the mass of the same person on the Moon where gravity is one-sixth that of Earth?

A 12 kg

B 60 kg

C 72 kg

D 432 kg

4 A swimmer pushing off from the wall of a pool exerts a force of 1 N on the wall. What is the reaction force of the wall on the swimmer?

A 0 N

B 1 N

C 2 N

D 10 N

Use the diagram below to answer questions 5 and 6.

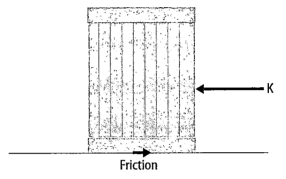
Friction

5 Which term applies to the forces in the diagram above?

A negative

B positive

C reference

D unbalanced

6 In the diagram above, what happens when force K is applied to the crate at rest?

A The crate remains at rest.

B The crate moves back and forth.

C The crate moves to the left.

D The crate moves to the right.

7 What is another term for change in velocity?

A acceleration

B inertia

C centripetal force

D maximum speed

Use the diagram below to answer question 8.

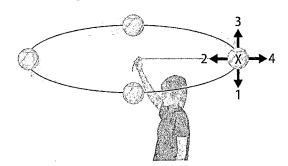

8 The person in the diagram is spinning a ball on a string. When the ball is in position X, what is the direction of the centripetal force?

  A 1
  B 2
  C 3
  D 4

9 Which is ALWAYS a contact force?

  A electric
  B friction
  C gravity
  D magnetic

10 When two billiard balls collide, which is ALWAYS conserved?

  A acceleration
  B direction
  C force
  D momentum

Constructed Response

Use the table below to answer question 11.

Newton's Laws of Motion	Explanation
First	
Second	
Third	

11 Explain each of Newton's laws of motion. What is one practical application of each law?

Use the diagram below to answer questions 12 and 13.

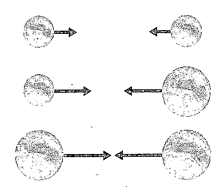

12 The arrows in the diagram above represent forces. What scientific law does the diagram illustrate? What does the law state?

13 Using the diagram, explain how marble mass affects gravitational attraction.

NEED EXTRA HELP?												
If You Missed Question...	1	2	3	4	5	6	7	8	9	10	11	12	13
Go to Lesson...	3	1	1	4	2	2	3	3	1	4	2–4	1	1

Chapter 2

7.PS.2, 7.PS.8, 7.PS.9, SEPS.1, SEPS.2, SEPS.5, SEPS.8, 6-8.LST.4.1, 6-8.LST.7.1

Using Energy and Heat

THE BIG IDEA

What are energy transfers and energy transformations?

asseck/Corbis

Inquiry Energy Transformations?

When you look at this photo, do you think of electricity? This power plant transforms the energy stored in coal to the electric energy that people use in their homes and businesses.

- How do you use energy in your home?

- Can you think of other types of energy?

- What are energy transfers and energy transformations?

What do you think?

Before you read, decide if you agree or disagree with each of these statements. As you read this chapter, see if you change your mind about any of the statements.

1. An object sitting on a high shelf has no energy.

2. There are many forms of energy.

3. In most systems, no energy is transferred to the environment.

4. Some forms of energy are replenished naturally.

5. Only particles that make up moving objects are in motion.

6. Thermal energy can be transferred in several ways.

Your one-stop online resource
connectED.mcgraw-hill.com

 LearnSmart™

 Chapter Resources Files, Reading Essentials, Get Ready to Read, Quick Vocabulary

 Animations, Videos, Interactive Tables

 Self-checks, Quizzes, Tests

 Project-Based Learning Activities

 Lab Manuals, Safety Videos, Virtual Labs & Other Tools

 Vocabulary, Multilingual eGlossary, Vocab eGames, Vocab eFlashcards

 Personal Tutors

Multilingual eGlossary

 BrainPOP®
Science Video
What's Science Got to do With It?

SEPS.1, 6-8.LST.4.1

Forms of Energy

Fuse/Getty Images

Inquiry) Got Energy?

This horse and rider need energy to move and to perform their life processes, such as breathing, digesting food, and transporting nutrients and wastes throughout their bodies. The source of energy for both the horse and the rider are the same. It comes from the foods they eat. What form of energy is found in foods? Are there other forms of energy?

Can you transfer energy?

You can transfer energy to a ball when you throw it. What are other ways you transfer energy?

1. Read and complete a lab safety form.
2. Hold the handle of a **tuning fork,** and gently strike one arm of the tuning fork with a **mallet.** (Use only the mallet provided for this purpose.)
3. Dip the arms of the tuning fork in a **beaker** of water. Observe what happens, and record your observations in your Science Journal.

Think About This

1. What is the source of energy that produced sound from the tuning fork? How do you think the tuning fork produced the sound?

2. **Key Concept** What happened to the water when the tuning fork was placed in it? Explain what you think happened to the water, the tuning fork, and the energy.

Energy

Some breakfast cereals promise to give you enough energy to get your day off to a great start. News reports often mention the price of oil, which is an energy source that provides fuel for cars and for transporting goods around the world. Meteorologists talk about the approach of a storm system with a lot of energy. News anchors report on earthquakes and tsunamis, which carry so much energy they cause great damage. Politicians talk about the nation's energy policy and the need to conserve energy and to find new energy sources. Energy influences everything in your life, including the climate, the economy, and your body. Scientists define **energy** as *the ability to cause change.*

Potential Energy

Have you ever seen an object perched on the edge of a ledge, such as the one in **Figure 1?** The object's position could easily change, which means it has energy. **Potential energy** *is stored energy due to the interaction between objects or particles.* Objects have potential energy if they have the potential to cause change. Examples of potential energy include objects that could fall due to gravity (interactions between objects–Earth and the egg) and particles that could move because of electric or magnetic forces (interactions between particles–protons and electrons).

Figure 1 The egg has potential energy because gravitational force can pull it to the ground. A simple nudge could send it falling to the floor.

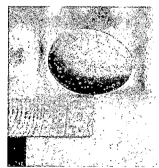

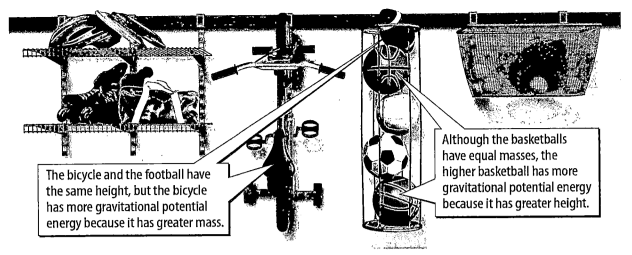

The bicycle and the football have the same height, but the bicycle has more gravitational potential energy because it has greater mass.

Although the basketballs have equal masses, the higher basketball has more gravitational potential energy because it has greater height.

△ **Figure 2** All of these objects have gravitational potential energy because they have mass and height.

△ **Figure 3** Your body breaks the chemical bonds in the foods you eat and uses the energy for life processes, including movement.

△ **Figure 4** In stars, including the Sun, atoms combine or fuse together to form heavier atoms.

Gravitational Potential Energy

Do the items stored on the garage organizer in **Figure 2** have potential energy? The answer is yes, every item– including the shelves and the brackets–has gravitational potential energy. Objects have gravitational potential energy if they have mass and height above Earth's surface.

The gravitational potential of an object energy depends on two factors–the mass of an object and the distance the object is from Earth, as shown in **Figure 2**.

Chemical Energy

Suppose you take the skates from the shelf and play hockey with your friends. Where does your body get the energy it needs? Energy in your body comes from the foods you eat. All objects, including your body and the apple in **Figure 3**, are made of atoms that are joined by chemical bonds. **Chemical energy** *is the energy stored in and released from the bonds between atoms.* Your body breaks chemical bonds in foods and converts the released energy into other forms of energy that your body can use.

Nuclear Energy

The energy stored in and released from the nucleus of an atom is called **nuclear energy**. If you watch a beautiful sunset like the one in **Figure 4**, you experience nuclear energy. The Sun's energy is released through the process of nuclear fusion. During nuclear fusion, the nuclei of atoms join together and release large amounts of energy. Nuclear energy also is released when an atom breaks apart. This breaking apart of an atom is called nuclear fission. Some power plants use nuclear fission to generate, or make, electricity.

mass = 3.6 kg
speed = 0 m/s

mass = 4.5 kg
speed = 8.0 m/s

mass = 5.5 kg
speed = 8.0 m/s

Kinetic Energy

Are you moving your hand as you take notes? Are you squirming in your chair trying to find a comfortable position? If so, you have **kinetic energy**–*energy due to motion.* All objects that have motion have kinetic energy.

Kinetic Energy of Objects

An object's kinetic energy is related to the mass and the speed of the object. For example, suppose you are bowling like the people in **Figure 5.** The girl on the left is holding a 3.6-kg bowling ball. Because the ball is not moving, it has no speed and therefore, no kinetic energy. The bowling balls shown in the other two photos have the same speed, 8.0 m/s, but the ball on the right has a greater mass. Therefore, the ball on the right has greater kinetic energy than the ball in the middle.

Electric Energy

Even objects you can't see have kinetic energy. Recall that all materials are made of atoms. In an atom, electrons move around a nucleus. Sometimes electrons even move from one atom to another. Because electrons are moving, they have kinetic energy. When electrons move, they create an electric current. *The energy in an electric current is* **electric energy.** In **Figure 6,** electrons move from one terminal of the battery through the copper wire and bulb to the other terminal of the battery. As the electrons move, their energy is transformed into light. Your brain and the nerves in your body that tell your arm and leg muscles to move also use electric energy.

Key Concept Check How do potential energy and kinetic energy differ?

△ **Figure 5** The kinetic energy (KE) of an object is related to the object's mass and speed.

Visual Check Which of the bowling balls has gravitational potential energy? Explain.

Animation

REVIEW VOCABULARY ·····

speed
the distance an object moves per unit of time

Figure 6 Electric energy is kinetic energy because the electrons have both mass and motion. ▽

Figure 7 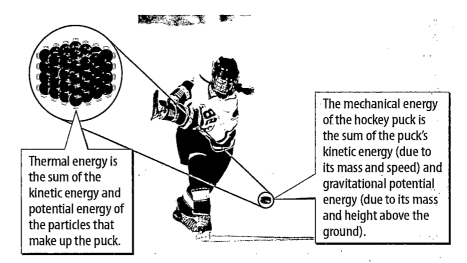 Mechanical energy is due to large-scale motions and object interactions. Thermal energy is due to atomic-scale motions and particle interactions.

Thermal energy is the sum of the kinetic energy and potential energy of the particles that make up the puck.

The mechanical energy of the hockey puck is the sum of the puck's kinetic energy (due to its mass and speed) and gravitational potential energy (due to its mass and height above the ground).

©David Stoecklein/Corbis

FOLDABLES

Make a horizontal four-column chart book. Label it as shown. Use it to organize your notes on the different forms of energy that fall into each of the categories.

Kinetic Energy	Potential Energy	Both kinetic and Potential Energies	Energy from Waves

Combined Kinetic Energy and Potential Energy

Your school is part of an educational system. Earth is part of the solar system. A system is a collection of parts that interact and act together as a whole. In science, everything that is not in a given system is the environment. For example, the hockey player, the hockey stick, the hockey puck, and the ice under the player in **Figure 7** can be considered a system.

Mechanical Energy

Does the hockey puck in **Figure 7** have kinetic energy or potential energy? It has mass and motion, so it has kinetic energy. It also has height above Earth, so it has gravitational potential energy. Scientists often study the energy of systems, such as the one described above. *The sum of the potential energy and the kinetic energy in a system is* **mechanical energy.** You might think of mechanical energy as the ability to move another object. What happens when the hockey puck hits the net? The net moves. The hockey puck has mechanical energy that causes another object to move.

Thermal Energy

Even when the hockey puck is lying on the floor with no obvious motion, the particles that make up the solid puck are in motion–they vibrate back and forth in place. Therefore, the particles have kinetic energy. The particles also have potential energy because of attractive forces between the particles. An object's **thermal energy** *is the sum of the kinetic energy and the potential energy of the particles that make up the object.* Thermal energy of an object increases when the potential energy, the kinetic energy, or both increase.

 Key Concept Check Compare mechanical energy and thermal energy.

Figure 8 ☞ When a raindrop falls into water, waves form. The waves carry energy, not matter, across the pond.

Energy Carried by Waves

Have you ever watched a raindrop fall into a still pool of water, as shown in Figure 8? The raindrop disturbs the surface of the water and produces waves that move away from the place where the raindrop hit. A **wave** *is a disturbance that transfers energy from one place to another without transferring matter.* Energy, not matter, moves outward from the point where the raindrop hits the water.

✓ **Reading Check** What do waves carry?

Sound Energy

When the raindrop hits the water, you hear a splash. The raindrop not only disturbs the surface of the water, it also disturbs the air. When the raindrop hits the water, it creates a sound wave in the air similar to water waves. Sound waves are waves that move through matter. The wave travels from particle to particle as the particles bump into each other, similar to falling dominoes. **Sound energy** *is energy carried by sound waves.*

As the sound wave travels, it eventually reaches your ear. The sound energy moves tiny hairs inside your ear. This movement is transformed into an electric signal that travels to your brain. Your brain interprets the signal as the sound of a water splash.

 **MiniLab**   **15 minutes**

How do waves transfer energy?

You know that sound energy travels through matter. Does sound travel faster through a solid, a liquid, or a gas?

1. Read and complete a lab safety form.
2. Place a **ruler** on top of a sheet of **newspaper.**
3. Stand **20 dominoes** on end with the sides 1 cm apart. The narrow edges should touch the ruler.
4. Hold the ruler in place. Have your partner start a **stopwatch** as you tip the first domino toward the others. Turn the stopwatch off when the last domino falls. Record the time in your Science Journal.
5. Repeat steps 3 and 4 with the dominoes 2 cm apart. Record the time.

Analyze and Conclude

1. **Identify Relationships** Is there a relationship between how far apart the dominoes are and the time it takes them to transfer energy?

2. ☞ **Key Concept** Particles in a solid are closer together than particles in a liquid. Particles in a liquid are closer together than particles in a gas. If sound waves travel by transferring energy from particle to particle in matter, would sound waves travel faster through a solid, a liquid, or a gas? Explain.

Radiant Energy

Have you ever wondered what light is? Light is a form of energy carried by electromagnetic waves, which are electric and magnetic waves moving perpendicularly to one another, as shown in **Figure 9.** *The energy carried by electromagnetic waves is* **radiant energy.** Electromagnetic waves travel through matter and through spaces with little or no matter, such as outer space. Electromagnetic waves often are described by their wavelengths. Wavelength is the distance from one point on a wave to the nearest point just like it.

Visible light is only one form of radiant energy. Gamma rays and X-rays are electromagnetic waves with very short wavelengths. Gamma rays and X-rays often are used in medical procedures. Ultraviolet rays have wavelengths that are a little shorter than those of light. This form of radiant energy is what gives you sunburn. Infrared rays are the energy used by many television remote controls to change channels. They also provide the warmth you feel when the Sun shines on you. Radar, television, and radio waves have long wavelengths compared to visible light.

 Key Concept Check What two forms of energy are carried by waves?

Figure 9 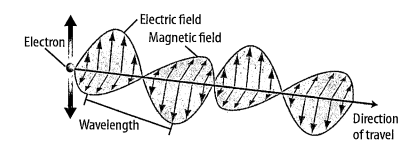 Radiant energy is carried by electromagnetic waves (also called rays) with different wavelengths.

Visual Check Determine one type of radiant energy that has a shorter wavelength than visible light and another type that has a longer wavelength.

Electromagnetic Wave

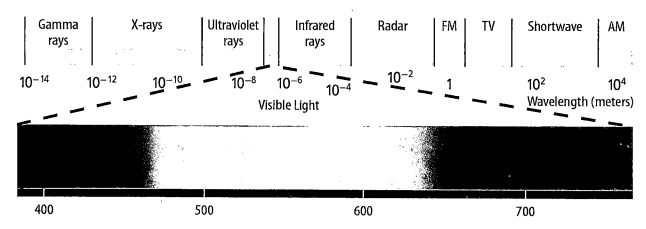

Electromagnetic Spectrum

| Gamma rays | X-rays | Ultraviolet rays | Infrared rays | Radar | FM | TV | Shortwave | AM |

10^{-14} 10^{-12} 10^{-10} 10^{-8} 10^{-6} 10^{-4} 10^{-2} 1 10^{2} 10^{4}

Visible Light   Wavelength (meters)

400   500   600   700

Wavelength (nanometers)

✓ Online Quiz

Visual Summary

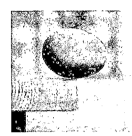

Objects can have potential energy (stored energy) and kinetic energy (energy due to movement).

Mechanical energy is due to large-scale motions and interactions in a system. Thermal energy is due to atomic-scale motions and interactions in particles.

Two kinds of energy carried by waves are sound energy and radiant energy.

FOLDABLES

Use your lesson Foldable to review the lesson. Save your Foldable for the project at the end of the chapter.

What do you think NOW?

You first read the statements below at the beginning of the chapter.

1. An object sitting on a high shelf has no energy.

2. There are many forms of energy.

Did you change your mind about whether you agree or disagree with the statements? Rewrite any false statements to make them true.

Use Vocabulary

1 The ability to cause change is _____.

2 Energy can be carried by _____, but matter cannot.

Understand Key Concepts 🔑

3 **Compare** How are thermal energy and mechanical energy similar?

4 Which form of energy does NOT involve kinetic energy?
 A. chemical   C. mechanical
 B. electric   D. thermal

5 **Explain** why an airplane flying from New York to Los Angeles has both kinetic energy and potential energy.

6 **Compare** how sound waves and electromagnetic waves transfer energy.

Interpret Graphics

7 **Identify** Where are kinetic energy and potential energy the greatest in the loop?

8 **Summarize** Copy and fill in the following graphic organizer to show forms of potential energy.

Critical Thinking

9 **List** Which has more kinetic energy: a 5-kg object moving at 5 m/s, 1 m off the ground or a 5-kg object at rest 2 m off the ground?

(t)Dimitri Vervitsiotis/Getty Images, (r)Tommaso di Girolamo/age fotostock, (b)l©David Stoecklein/Corbis

How can you classify different types of energy?

Materials

magnifying lens

musical greeting card

Safety

When you open a musical greeting card, you probably don't think about how many different forms of energy it uses. What types of energy are used in a musical greeting card?

Learn It

To **classify** means to sort objects into groups based on common features or functions. You can sort different types of energy based on the definitions of each type of energy and your experiences using them. Use this knowledge as you classify the different types of energy used in a musical greeting card.

Try It

① Read and complete a lab safety form.

② Carefully observe a musical greeting card before and during its operation. Ask questions such as: "What makes it start? What makes it stop? What is the energy source? What produces the sound?"

③ Write a hypothesis about how you think the greeting card works. What forms of energy are involved in its operation?

④ Carefully dismantle a second musical greeting card. Make a scientific illustration of the electronic parts. Label as many parts as you can. Use a magnifying lens if necessary.

⑤ Set the dismantled card in operation. Observe any motion. Gently touch parts of the card as it produces sound.

⑥ Using the card and your illustration, identify and label the different types of energy involved in the card's operation from the time it turns on until it turns off. Record your observations in your Science Journal.

Apply It

⑦ **Identify Cause and Effect** What causes the card to turn on? What causes it to turn off?

⑧ **Classify** List all of the types of energy involved in the operation of your card.

⑨ **Infer** What produces the sound? How does the sound from the card reach your ear?

⑩ 🔑 **Key Concept** What are some examples of potential energy and kinetic energy in the operation of your card? Explain.

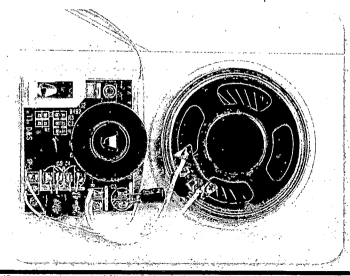

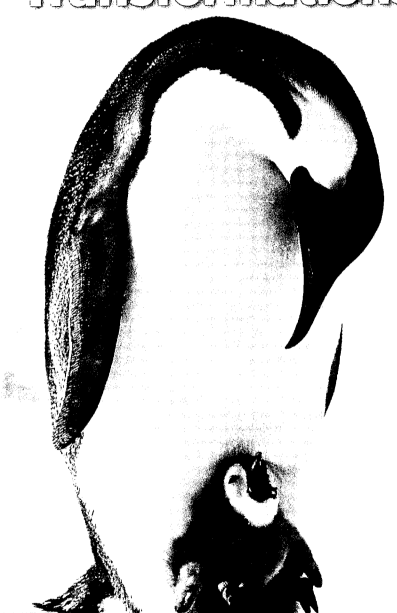

Energy Transfers and Transformations

Reading Guide

Key Concepts 🔑
ESSENTIAL QUESTIONS

- What is the law of conservation of energy?

- How is energy transformed and transferred?

- What are renewable and nonrenewable energy resources?

Vocabulary

law of conservation of energy p. 60

energy transfer p. 61

energy transformation p. 61

work p. 61

open system p. 63

closed system p. 63

renewable energy resource p. 64

nonrenewable energy resource p. 66

 Multilingual eGlossary

 7.PS.8, SEPS.5, SEPS.8, 6-8.LST.7.1

Inquiry Warm and Cozy?

This penguin chick lives in one of the coldest places on Earth—Antarctica. The chick is standing on its parent's feet to insulate its feet from the ice. This helps prevent thermal energy of the chick's body from transferring to the ice. The chick cuddles with its parent to absorb thermal energy from its parent's body. Without receiving thermal energy from the parent, the baby would quickly die.

Keith Szafranski/E+/Getty Images

How does a flashlight work?

If the lights go out, you might turn on a flashlight. When you push the switch, the light will go on. What happens? How does the flashlight work?

① Read and complete a lab safety form.

② Examine a **flashlight.** List the parts that you can see. Predict the types of energy involved in the operation of the flashlight.

③ Use the switch to turn the flashlight on. What do you think happened inside the flashlight to produce the light? Write your ideas in your Science Journal.

④ Take the flashlight apart. Discuss the kinds of energy involved in producing light.

Think About This

1. Was light the only type of energy produced? Why or why not?

2. 🔑 **Key Concept** Describe the different types of energy involved in a flashlight. Draw a sequence diagram showing how each form of energy changes to the next form.

Figure 10 Several energy changes occur in a flashlight.

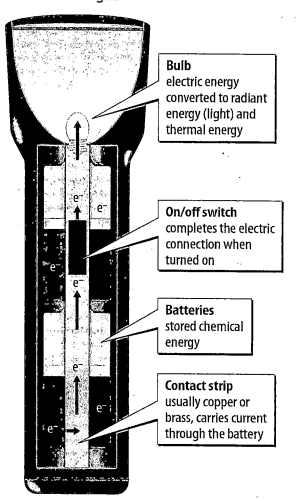

Bulb
electric energy converted to radiant energy (light) and thermal energy

On/off switch
completes the electric connection when turned on

Batteries
stored chemical energy

Contact strip
usually copper or brass, carries current through the battery

Law of Conservation of Energy

Think about turning on the flashlight in the Launch Lab. The **law of conservation of energy** *says that energy can be transformed from one form to another, but it cannot be created or destroyed.* In the flashlight shown in Figure 10, chemical energy of the battery is transformed to electric energy (moving electrons) that moves through the contact strip to the bulb. The electric energy is transformed into radiant energy and thermal energy in the lightbulb. The law of conservation of energy indicates that the amount of radiant energy that shines out of the flashlight cannot be greater than the chemical energy stored in the battery.

🔑 **Key Concept Check** What is the law of conservation of energy?

The amount of radiant energy given off by the flashlight is less than the chemical energy in the battery. Where is the missing energy? As you read this lesson, you will learn that in every energy transformation, some energy transfers to the environment.

Chemical energy is transformed to mechanical energy.

Mechanical energy is transferred to the tennis ball.

Figure 11 Energy transfers and transformations take place when the tennis player hits the ball.

Visual Check Identify at least one energy transformation that occurs as the ball moves through the air.

Energy Transfer

What happens when the tennis player in **Figure 11** hits the ball with the racket? The mechanical energy of the racket changes the movement of the ball, and the ball's mechanical energy increases. *When energy moves from one object to another without changing form, an* **energy transfer** *occurs.* The tennis racket transfers mechanical energy to the tennis ball.

Energy Transformation

Where does the mechanical energy in the tennis player's racket come from? Chemical energy stored in the player's muscles changes to mechanical energy when she swings her arm. *When one form of energy is converted to another form of energy, an* **energy transformation** *occurs.*

 Key Concept Check Identify an energy transfer and an energy transformation that occurs when someone plays a guitar.

Energy and Work

You might think that reading about energy is a lot of work. But to a scientist, it's not work at all. To a scientist, **work** *is the transfer of energy that occurs when a force makes an object move in the direction of the force.* Work is only being done while the force is acting on the object. As the tennis player swings the racket, the racket applies a force to the ball for about a meter. Although the ball moves 10 m, work is done by the racket only during the time the racket applies a force to the ball. When the ball separates from the racket, the racket no longer does work.

Suppose the tennis player is standing still before she serves the ball. She is using her muscles to hold the ball. Is she doing work on the ball? No; because the ball is not moving, she is not doing work. If a force does not make an object move in the direction of the force, it does no work on the object.

Inefficiency of Energy Transformations

When a tennis player hits a ball with a racket, most of the mechanical energy of the racket transfers to the ball, but not all of it. You know when a ball hits a racket because you can hear a sound. Some of the mechanical energy of the racket is transformed to sound energy. In addition, some of the mechanical energy of the racket is transformed to thermal energy. The temperature of the racket, the ball, and the air surrounding both objects increases slightly. Anytime there is an energy transformation or energy transfer, some energy is transformed into thermal energy.

Reading Check Summarize the energy transformations that occur when a tennis racket hits a tennis ball.

Recall the flashlight at the beginning of the lesson. The transformation of chemical energy of the battery to radiant energy from the lightbulb is inefficient, too. As the electric energy moves through the circuit, some electric energy transforms to thermal energy. When electric energy transforms to radiant energy in the lightbulb, more energy transforms to thermal energy. In some flashlights, the bulb is warm to the touch.

Recall that the law of conservation of energy says that energy cannot be created or destroyed. When scientists say that energy transformations are inefficient, they do not mean that energy is destroyed. Energy transformations are inefficient because not all the energy that is transformed to another form of energy is usable.

MiniLab

20 minutes

How can you transfer energy?

When you ride your bicycle, pushing the pedals with your feet makes the wheels turn. However, your feet don't touch the wheels. How can you transfer energy to another object without touching it?

1. Read and complete a lab safety form.
2. Place a **cork** at one edge of a **rectangular pan** half-filled with water.
3. Discuss with your teammates how you can make the cork move to the opposite edge of the pan without touching it. Possible tools include a **drinking straw,** a **plastic spoon,** and a **length of string,** but you can't physically touch the cork with these items. You also may use any other methods you can think of without touching the cork.
4. Try each of your ideas. Record your results in your Science Journal.

Analyze and Conclude

1. **Explain** which method that you tried was the most effective and the least effective.
2. **Hypothesize** What would make the cork easier to move? Explain.
3. **Key Concept** What form of energy did you start with to move the cork? In what ways was the energy transferred and transformed during each trial?

Hutchings Photography/Digital Light Source

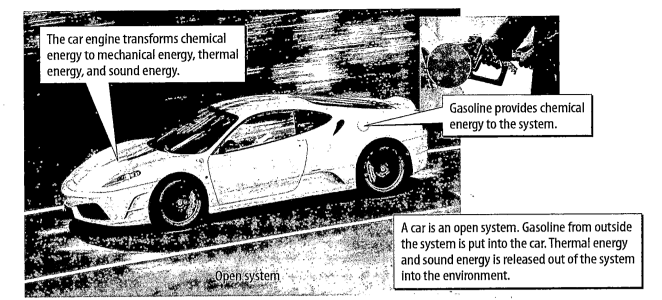

The car engine transforms chemical energy to mechanical energy, thermal energy, and sound energy.

Gasoline provides chemical energy to the system.

A car is an open system. Gasoline from outside the system is put into the car. Thermal energy and sound energy is released out of the system into the environment.

Open system

Figure 12 A car is an open system. Gasoline is an input. Thermal energy and sound energy are outputs.

Open Systems

In Lesson 1, you read that scientists often study the energy of systems. A car, as shown in Figure 12, is a system. Chemical energy of the fuel is transformed to mechanical energy of the moving car. Because energy transformations are inefficient, some of the chemical energy transforms to thermal energy and sound energy that are released to the environment. An **open system,** such as a car engine, *is a system that exchanges matter or energy with the environment.*

Closed Systems

Can you think of a system that does not exchange energy with the environment? What about a flashlight? A flashlight releases radiant energy and thermal energy into the environment. What about your body? You eat food, which contains chemical energy and comes from the environment. Your body also releases several types of energy into the environment, including thermal energy, mechanical energy, and sound energy. *A* **closed system** *is a system that does not exchange matter or energy with the environment.* In reality, there are no closed systems. Every physical system transfers some energy to or from its environment. Scientists use the idea of a closed system to study and model the movement of energy.

Energy Transformations and Electric Energy

You probably have heard someone say, "turn off the lights, you're wasting energy." This form of energy is electric energy. Most appliances you use every day require electric energy. Where does this energy come from?

Personal Tutor

 **Applying Practices**

How far will it go? Go online to investigate a process that involves energy changing from one form to another and examine what happens to the total amount of energy.

WORD ORIGIN

system
from Greek *systema*, means "whole made of several parts"

(l)Hans Dieter Seufert/c/age fotostock; (inset)Frederic Charpentier/Alamy

Renewable Energy Resources

If you think about all of the energy used in the United States, you realize that people need a lot of energy to continue living the way they do. This huge demand for energy and the desire to protect the environment has resulted in a search for renewable energy resources. *A renewable energy resource is an energy resource that is replaced as fast as, or faster than, it is used.* There are several different kinds of renewable energy resources.

Solar Radiant energy from the Sun, or solar energy, is one energy resource that can be converted into electric energy. Some solar energy plants, such as the one in **Figure 13**, transform radiant energy into electric energy with photovoltaic (foh toh vohl TAY ihk), or solar, cells. Photovoltaic cells are made from thin wafers of the element silicon. When radiant energy from the Sun hits the cells, it knocks electrons away from the silicon atoms. This movement of electrons is electric energy. Some homes, businesses, and small appliances, such as calculators, use photovoltaic cells to provide electricity.

In some solar energy plants, radiant energy from the Sun is transformed into thermal energy. The thermal energy is used to convert water to steam. The steam turns a generator, which transforms mechanical energy into electric energy.

△ **Figure 13** Solar power plants transform radiant energy from the Sun to electric energy.

Wind Have you ever driven along a highway and seen wind turbines such as those in **Figure 14?** Wind turbines are built in places where winds blow almost continuously, such as the vast open spaces of the southwestern United States. Wind moves the blades of the turbine, turning a generator that transforms kinetic energy of the wind to electric energy. One of the drawbacks of wind energy is that wind does not blow steadily at all times. This source of electric energy is not very consistent or predictable.

△ **Figure 14** Wind turbines transform kinetic energy from the wind to electric energy.

Hydroelectric If you ever have stood underneath a shower, you have felt the energy of falling water. In hydroelectric plants, falling water from rivers and dams is channeled through a turbine. When the turbine spins, mechanical energy is transformed to electric energy. Most of the hydroelectric energy produced in the United States comes from the western part of the country. The hydroelectric plant shown in **Figure 15** is at Shasta Lake in California.

The major drawback of hydroelectric energy is that dams and turbines can interrupt the natural movements of animals in rivers and lakes. Also, there are a limited number of places where rivers are large enough for these energy plants to be built.

Geothermal Earth's temperature increases as you go deeper below the surface. But in a few places, Earth is very hot close to the surface. Geothermal plants are built where thermal energy from Earth is near Earth's surface. In these energy plants, thermal energy is transferred to water creating steam. The steam turns turbines in electric generators. The states with the most geothermal reservoirs are Alaska, Hawaii, and California. The geothermal reservoir shown in **Figure 16** has been producing geothermal power in California since 1921.

Biomass Wood, plants, and even manure and garbage are considered biomass. These sources of stored chemical energy can be transformed to electric energy in energy plants like the one in **Figure 17**. Burning biomass releases carbon dioxide into the atmosphere. Some scientists believe this contributes to climate change and global warming. However, when biomass crops are grown, the plants use carbon dioxide during photosynthesis, reducing the overall amount of carbon dioxide produced in the process.

 Reading Check Which energy plant is usually built on a lake or a river?

△ **Figure 15** Potential energy stored in elevated water is transformed into electric energy in some energy plants.

△ **Figure 16** In geothermal energy plants thermal energy inside Earth is transformed into electric energy.

▷ **Animation**

△ **Figure 17** Chemical energy stored in biomass, such as wood, plants, manure, and garbage, is used to generate electric energy in some locations.

Electrical Energy Resources

Renewable resources
13.5%

Nonrenewable resources
86.5%

Table 1 Electric Energy Net Generation by Resources as of 2015				
Nonrenewable Resources			**Renewable Resources**	
Resource	Percentage		Resource	Percentage
petroleum	0.7		biomass	1.6
natural gas	33		hydroelectric	6.1
coal	33		geothermal	0.4
other gases	0.3		wind	4.7
uranium (nuclear power)	19.5		solar and other	0.7
Total	**86.5**		**Total**	**13.5**

Table 1 ☞ Most of the energy used in the United States comes from nonrenewable energy resources.

⊘ Visual Check Which resource is used to produce the most electric energy in the United States?

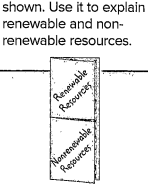

Nonrenewable Energy Resources

Most of the energy used in homes, schools, stores, and businesses comes from fossil fuels and nuclear energy, as shown in Table 1. Fossil fuels and nuclear energy are **nonrenewable energy resources**—*an energy resource that is available in limited amounts or that is used faster than it can be replaced in nature.*

Fossil Fuels Petroleum, natural gas, propane, and coal are fossil fuels. Ancient plants stored radiant energy from the Sun as chemical energy in their molecules. This chemical energy was passed on to the animals that ate the plants. Over millions of years, geological processes converted the remains of these ancient plants and animals into fossil fuels. Fossil fuels are a very concentrated form of chemical energy that easily transforms into other forms of energy. However, when fossil fuels burn, they release harmful wastes such as sulfur dioxide, nitrogen oxide, and carbon dioxide. Sulfur dioxide and nitrogen oxide contribute to acid rain. Carbon dioxide is suspected of contributing to global climate change.

Nuclear Energy In nuclear energy plants, uranium atoms are split apart in a process called nuclear fission. Nuclear fission produces thermal energy, which heats water, producing steam. The steam turns turbines that produce electric energy. While nuclear energy plant emissions are not harmful, the waste from these plants is radioactive. The safe disposal of radioactive waste is a major challenge associated with nuclear energy.

Key Concept Check What are renewable and nonrenewable energy resources?

✓ Online Quiz

Virtual Lab

Visual Summary

Energy can be transferred and transformed, but it cannot be created or destroyed.

Systems are classified as open systems or closed systems based on their interactions with their environment.

Energy resources are classified as renewable or nonrenewable based on their abundance and availability.

FOLDABLES

Use your lesson Foldable to review the lesson. Save your Foldable for the project at the end of the chapter.

What do you think NOW?

You first read the statements below at the beginning of the chapter.

3. In most systems, no energy is transferred to the environment.

4. Some forms of energy are replenished naturally.

Did you change your mind about whether you agree or disagree with the statements? Rewrite any false statements to make them true.

Use Vocabulary

1. **Define** *energy transformation.*

Understand Key Concepts

2. **Paraphrase** the law of conservation of energy.

3. Which of the following is NOT an example of energy transformations?
   A. A bicyclist pedals to school.
   B. A car's engine moves a car.
   C. A sound wave travels across a hall.
   D. The Sun shines on a tree, and it produces more cells.

4. **Describe** a kind of renewable energy that you could use in your home, and explain why it is a good choice.

Interpret Graphics

5. **Explain** why the object shown here is an open system.

6. **Summarize** Copy and fill in the following graphic organizer to show four possible renewable resources of electric energy.

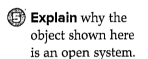

Critical Thinking

7. **Consider** A car company wants to build a wind-powered car that converts 100 percent of the mechanical energy in the wind to the mechanical energy of the moving car. Explain why the company will fail.

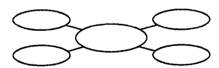 ✓ **Math Practice**

8. A child pushes a toy truck with a force of 5.6 N a distance of 3.5 m. How much work is done on the truck?

Biomass

Fresh Ideas About Not-So-Fresh Sources of Fuel

Grass clippings can be broken down to produce methane gas. The device used to convert grass clippings to methane gas is called a digester. The methane gas produced can be used in place of natural gas in appliances. It also can be used to power turbines that produce electricity.

Many people consider grass clippings, dog waste, and used cooking oil garbage. But instead of seeing these materials as garbage, some innovative thinkers see them as sources of biomass energy.

For centuries, humans have used biomass, such as wood, for energy. New technology is expanding the ways biomass can be used. Now biomass can be converted into fuel used to power automobiles, heat homes, and generate electricity.

The use of these fuel sources has several benefits. First, any fuel produced using biomass decreases dependence on nonrenewable resources such as fossil fuels. Also, use of these materials for fuel decreases the amount of waste going to landfills. Technologies to generate fuel from biomass continue to be developed and improved. Who knows what will be used for fuel in the future!

▲ Dog waste can be converted to fuel in a methane digester. Dog waste contains a lot of energy because of the healthy, energy-rich foods fed to most dogs in the United States.

▲ Used cooking oil is an expensive disposal problem for restaurants. Instead, it can be collected and used on its own or combined with diesel fuel to power specially equipped vehicles.

Your Thinking

Technology has been developed that uses waste from slaughterhouses to make oil. Find out more about this process. Prepare an oral presentation to share what you have learned with other students in your class.

Particles in Motion

Reading Guide

Key Concepts 🔑
ESSENTIAL QUESTIONS

- What is the kinetic molecular theory?

- In what three ways is thermal energy transferred?

- How are thermal conductors and insulators different?

Vocabulary

temperature p. 71

heat p. 72

conduction p. 73

radiation p. 73

convection p. 73

vaporization p. 75

thermal conductor p. 76

thermal insulator p. 76

 Multilingual eGlossary

 BrainPOP®

 7.PS.2, 7.PS.9, SEPS.2, 6-8.LST.4.1

 Go to the resource tab in ConnectED to find the PBL *It's Moving.*

(inquiry) Catchin' Some Waves?

This Agama lizard regulates its body temperature by absorbing thermal energy from its environment. Some lizards raise their body temperature well above the air temperature by absorbing radiant energy transferred by waves from the Sun.

Where is it the hottest? ⚠ Tie back hair and roll up sleeves.

Would your hands get just as warm if you held them at the sides of a campfire instead of directly over a campfire?

① Read and complete a lab safety form. Copy the table into your Science Journal.

② Use **modeling clay** to hold a **birthday candle** upright. Use a **ring stand and clamp** to mount a **thermometer** horizontally above the candle. The thermometer bulb should be 10 cm above the top of the candle. Record the temperature on the thermometer in your table. Use a **match** to light the candle. Record the temperature every 30 seconds until the temperature reaches 70°C. Add more time columns to the table if needed. Blow out the candle.

⚠ *Do not put thermometer within 10 cm of the flame.*

③ Repeat steps 3–5 with a new candle. This time mount the thermometer 10 cm to the side of the candle flame.

Thermometer Above Flame			
Time (sec)	0	30	60	90
Temp. (·C)				

Thermometer to the Side of Flame			
Time (sec)	0	30	60	90
Temp. (·C)				

Think About This

🔑 **Key Concept** How do you think the energy from the flame traveled to the thermometer in each trial? Explain.

▷ **Animation**

Figure 18 Particles that make up all matter, including carbonated beverages, are in constant motion. On average, solid particles move slowest, liquid particles move faster, and gas particles move the fastest.

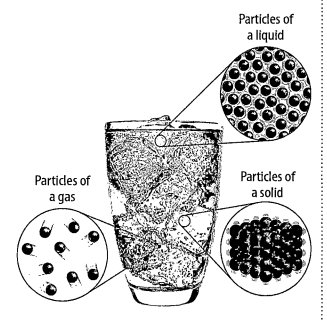

Particles of a liquid

Particles of a gas

Particles of a solid

Kinetic Molecular Theory

You read in Lesson 2 that in every energy transformation some of the energy is transformed into thermal energy. Some of this thermal energy transfers to other materials. The transfer of thermal energy between materials depends on the movement of particles in the materials. The kinetic molecular theory explains how particles move. It has three major points:

- All matter is made of particles.
- Particles are in constant, random motion.
- Particles constantly collide with each other and with the walls of their container.

The kinetic molecular theory explains that the carbonated beverage in **Figure 18** is made of particles. The particles move in different directions and at different speeds. They collide with each other and with the particles that make up the ice and the glass.

 Key Concept Check What are the three points of the kinetic molecular theory?

Foodfolio/age fotostock

Temperature

When you pick up a glass of ice cold soda, the glass feels cold. Could you estimate its temperature? The temperature of something depends on how much kinetic energy the particles that make up the material have. *The measure of the average kinetic energy of the particles in a material is* **temperature.** If most of the drink particles have little kinetic energy, the drink has a low temperature and the glass feels cold. The SI unit for temperature is the kelvin (K). However, scientists often use the Celsius temperature scale (°C) to measure temperature.

Thermal Expansion

Suppose your teacher told everyone in your classroom to run around. There probably would not be enough space in your classroom for everyone to run as fast as they could. But, if you were in a large gymnasium, then everyone could run very quickly. When the particles that make up a material move slowly, they occupy less volume than they do at a higher temperature. As the temperature of a material increases, particles begin to move faster. They collide with each other more often and push each other farther apart. Thermal expansion is the increase in volume of a material due to a temperature increase, as shown in Figure 19. When the temperature of a material decreases, its volume decreases, This is thermal contraction.

Most materials contract as their temperature decreases, but water is an exception. When water is cooled to near its freezing point, interactions between water molecules push the molecules apart. Water expands as it freezes because of these molecular interactions, as shown in Figure 20.

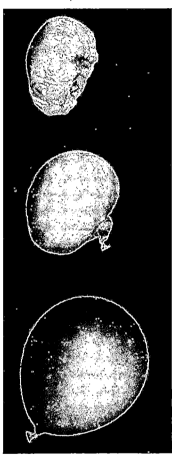

Figure 19 The balloon on the top was cooled to −198°C using liquid nitrogen. As the balloon warms to room temperature, the molecules move faster and expand. The balloon undergoes thermal expansion. ▽

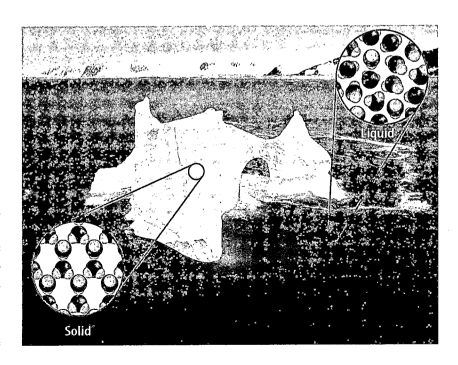

◁ Figure 20 Because of the structure of a water molecule, as water freezes, the molecules attract in a way that creates empty spaces between them. This makes ice less dense than water. Because ice is less dense than water, ice floats on water.

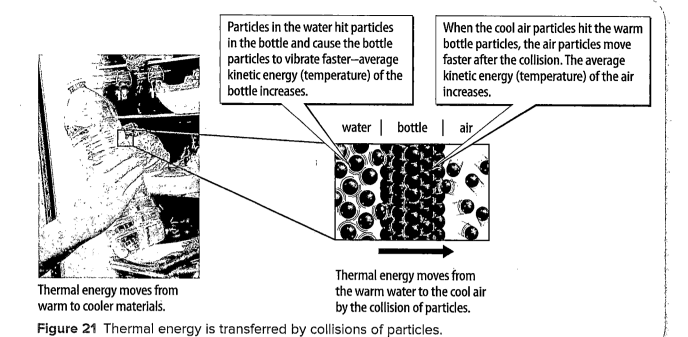

Particles in the water hit particles in the bottle and cause the bottle particles to vibrate faster—average kinetic energy (temperature) of the bottle increases.

When the cool air particles hit the warm bottle particles, the air particles move faster after the collision. The average kinetic energy (temperature) of the air increases.

water | bottle | air

Thermal energy moves from warm to cooler materials.

Thermal energy moves from the warm water to the cool air by the collision of particles.

Figure 21 Thermal energy is transferred by collisions of particles.

Transferring Thermal Energy

Suppose you put a warm bottle of water in the refrigerator. As shown in **Figure 21**, moving water molecules collide with the particles that make up the bottle. These collisions transfer kinetic energy to the particles that make up the bottle, and they vibrate faster. As the particles move faster, their average kinetic energy, or temperature, increases. The particles that make up the bottle then collide with particles that make up the air in the refrigerator.

The average kinetic energy of the particles that make up the air in the refrigerator increases. In other words, the temperature of the air in the refrigerator increases. The average kinetic energy of the particles of water decreases as thermal energy moves from the water to the bottle. Therefore, the temperature of the water decreases.

As the kinetic energy of the particles that make up a material increases, the thermal energy of the particles increases. As the kinetic energy of the particles that make up a material decreases, the thermal energy of the particles decreases. So, when particles transfer kinetic energy, they transfer thermal energy.

Thermal Energy and Heat

Thermal energy moves from warmer materials, such as the warm water in the bottle, to cooler materials, such as the cool air in the refrigerator. *The movement of thermal energy from a region of higher temperature to a region of lower temperature is called* **heat.** Because your hand is warmer than the water bottle, thermal energy moves from your hand to the bottle. When you place the warm bottle in the refrigerator, thermal energy moves from the warm bottle to the cool air in the refrigerator.

Thermal Equilibrium

What happens if you leave the water in the refrigerator for several hours? The temperature of the water, the bottle, and the air in the refrigerator become the same. When the temperatures of materials that are in contact are the same, the materials are said to be in thermal equilibrium. After the materials reach thermal equilibrium, the particles that make up the water, the bottle, and the air continue to collide with each other. The particles transfer kinetic energy back and forth, but the average kinetic energy of all the particles remains the same.

Heat Transfer

Suppose you want to heat water to cook pasta, as shown in Figure 22. You put a pan of water on the stove and turn the stove on. How is thermal energy transferred to the water?

① **Conduction** Fast-moving particles of the gases in the flame collide with the particles that make up the pan. This transfers thermal energy to the pan. Then, the particles that make up the pan collide with particles of water, transferring thermal energy to the water. **Conduction** *is the transfer of thermal energy by collisions between particles in matter.*

② **Radiation** If you put your hands near the side of the pan, you feel warmth. The thermal energy you feel is from **radiation**—*the transfer of thermal energy by electromagnetic waves.* All objects emit radiation, but warmer materials, such as hot water, emit more radiation than cooler ones.

③ **Convection** The flame, or hot gases, heats water at the bottom of the pan. The water at the bottom of the pan undergoes thermal expansion and is now less dense than the water above it. The denser water sinks and forces the less dense, warmer water upward. The water continues this cycle of warming, rising, cooling, and sinking, as thermal energy moves throughout the water. *The transfer of thermal energy by the movement of the particles from one part of a material to another is* **convection.** Convection also occurs in the atmosphere. Warm, less-dense air is forced upward by cooler, more-dense falling air. Thermal energy is transferred as the air rises and sinks.

Key Concept Check In what three ways is thermal energy transferred?

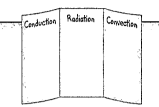
Project-Based Learning Activity

It's Moving! Go online to develop demonstrations that compare and contrast the three types of heat transfer—radiation, convection, and conduction.

WORD ORIGIN

equilibrium
from Latin *aequus*, means "equal"; and *libra*, means "a balance or scale"

Personal Tutor

Figure 22
Conduction, radiation, and convection are ways in which thermal energy is transferred.

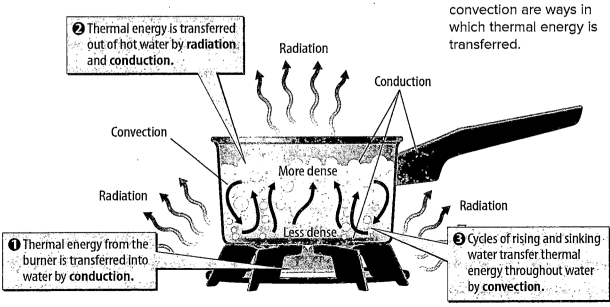

❷ Thermal energy is transferred out of hot water by **radiation** and **conduction.**

Radiation

Conduction

Convection

More dense

Radiation

Less dense

❶ Thermal energy from the burner is transferred into water by **conduction.**

Radiation

❸ Cycles of rising and sinking water transfer thermal energy throughout water by **convection.**

Figure 23 If enough thermal energy is added to a material, it will change state.

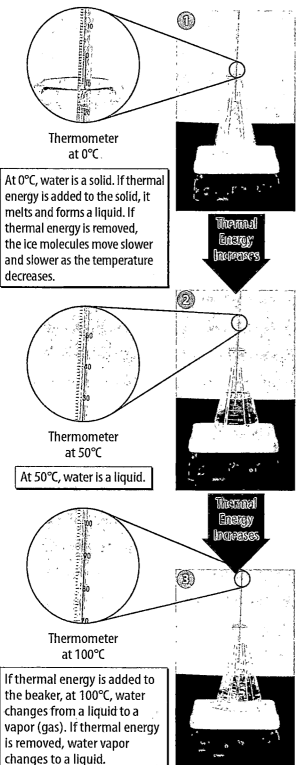

Thermometer at 0°C.

At 0°C, water is a solid. If thermal energy is added to the solid, it melts and forms a liquid. If thermal energy is removed, the ice molecules move slower and slower as the temperature decreases.

Thermometer at 50°C

At 50°C, water is a liquid.

Thermometer at 100°C

If thermal energy is added to the beaker, at 100°C, water changes from a liquid to a vapor (gas). If thermal energy is removed, water vapor changes to a liquid.

Heat and Changes of State

When thermal energy is added or removed from a substance, sometimes only the temperature changes. At other times, a more dramatic change occurs—a change of state.

Changes Between Solids and Liquids

What happens if you place a flask of ice on a hot plate, as shown in **Figure 23?** Thermal energy moves from the hot plate to the flask then to the ice. The temperature of the ice increases. When the temperature of the ice reaches the melting point of ice, 0°C, the ice begins to melt. Melting is the change of state from a solid to a liquid. Although ice melts at 0°C, other materials have different melting points. For example, helium melts at −272°C, silver melts at 962°C, and diamonds melt at a temperature over 3,550°C.

As thermal energy transfers to the melting ice, the temperature (average kinetic energy) of the ice does not change. However, the potential energy of the ice increases. As the water molecules move farther apart, the potential energy between the molecules increases.

The reverse process occurs when thermal energy is removed from water. When water is placed in a freezer, thermal energy moves from the water to the colder air in the freezer. The average kinetic energy (temperature) of the water decreases. When the temperature of the water reaches 0°C, the water begins to freeze. Freezing is the change of state from a liquid to a solid. Notice that the freezing point of water is the same as the melting point of ice. Freezing is the opposite of melting.

While water is freezing, the temperature remains at 0°C until all the water is frozen. Once all the water freezes, the temperature of the ice begins to decrease. As the temperature decreases, the water molecules vibrate in place at a slower and slower rate.

 Reading Check What is a change of state?

Changes Between Liquids and Gases

What happens when ice melts? As thermal energy transfers to the ice, the particles move faster and faster. The average kinetic energy of the water particles that make up ice increases and the ice melts. The temperature of the water continues to increase until it reaches 100°C. At 100°C, water begins to vaporize. **Vaporization** *is the change of state from a liquid to a gas.* While the water is changing state–from a liquid to a gas–the kinetic energy of the particles remains constant.

Liquids vaporize in two ways–boiling and evaporation. Vaporization that occurs within a liquid is called boiling. Vaporization that occurs at the surface of a liquid is called evaporation. Have you heard the term *water vapor?* The gaseous state of a substance that is normally a liquid or a solid at room temperature is called vapor. Because water is liquid at room temperature, its gaseous state is referred to as water vapor.

The reverse process also can occur. Removing thermal energy from a gas changes it to a liquid. The change of state from a gas to a liquid is condensation. The condensation of water vapor that forms on grass overnight is called dew.

Changes Between Solids and Gases

Usually, water transforms from a solid to a liquid and then to a gas as it absorbs thermal energy. However, this is not always the case. On cold winter days, ice often changes directly to water vapor without passing through the liquid state. Sublimation is the change of state that occurs when a solid changes to a gas without passing through the liquid state. Dry ice, or solid carbon dioxide, sublimes as shown in Figure 24. Dry ice is used to keep foods frozen when they are shipped.

When thermal energy is removed from some materials, they undergo deposition. Deposition is the change of state from a gas directly to a solid without passing through the liquid state. Water vapor undergoes deposition when it freezes and forms frost, as shown in Figure 24.

(l)Charles D. Winters/Science Source; (r)Ingram Publishing

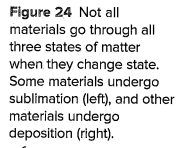

Figure 24 Not all materials go through all three states of matter when they change state. Some materials undergo sublimation (left), and other materials undergo deposition (right).

Visual Check How are sublimation and deposition related?

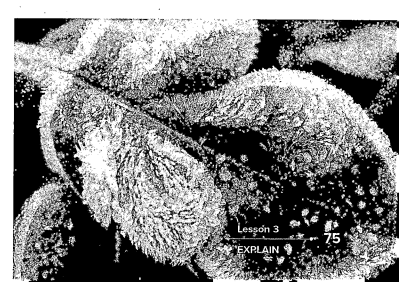

Figure 25 The color variations of this thermogram show the temperature variations in the pan and stove burner. The temperature scale is from white (warmest) through red, yellow, green, cyan, blue, and black (coolest).

Visual Check Why are the handles black?

Conductors and Insulators

When you put a metal pan on a burner, the pan gets very hot. If the pan has a handle made of wood or plastic, such as the one in **Figure 25**, the handle stays cool. Why doesn't the handle get hot like the pan as a result of thermal conduction?

The metal that makes up the pan is a **thermal conductor**, *a material in which thermal energy moves quickly.* The atoms that make up thermal conductors have electrons that are free to move, transferring thermal energy easily. The material that makes up the pan's handles is a **thermal insulator**, *a material in which thermal energy moves slowly.* The electrons in thermal insulators are held tightly in place and do not transfer thermal energy easily.

Key Concept Check How do thermal conductors differ from thermal insulators?

MiniLab

25 minutes

What affects the transfer of thermal energy?

Ice-cold water stays cold longer in a foam cup than in a glass beaker. What other materials keep liquids cold?

① Read and complete a lab safety form.

② Place 75 mL of very warm water in each of three **100-mL beakers.**

③ Place a piece of **aluminum foil** over the first beaker and a piece of **cotton batting** over the second beaker. Leave the third beaker open.

④ Place **ice cubes** of equal sizes in three **petri dishes.** Place one dish on top of each beaker. Use a **stopwatch** to measure the time it takes for each ice cube to melt.

⑤ Make a table in your Science Journal. Label the first column of the rows *Beaker 1, Beaker 2,* and *Beaker 3.* In the second column, record the time it takes each ice cube to melt.

Analyze and Conclude

1. **Identify Cause and Effect** What caused the ice cubes over each beaker to melt? Use the kinetic molecular theory in your explanation.

2. **Identify Relationships** What role did thermal conductors and thermal insulators play in the rate at which the ice cubes melted?

3. **Key Concept** Describe the ways thermal energy transferred from the beakers to the ice.

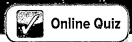
Visual Summary

The kinetic molecular theory explains how particles move in matter.

Thermal energy is transferred in various ways by particles and waves.

Materials vary in how well they conduct thermal energy.

FOLDABLES

Use your lesson Foldable to review the lesson. Save your Foldable for the project at the end of the chapter.

What do you think NOW?

You first read the statements below at the beginning of the chapter.

5. Only particles that make up moving objects are in motion.

6. Thermal energy can be transferred in several ways.

Did you change your mind about whether you agree or disagree with the statements? Rewrite any false statements to make them true.

Use Vocabulary

1 **Define** *temperature* in your own words.

2 **Explain** how heat is related to thermal energy.

Understand Key Concepts

3 **Summarize** the kinetic molecular theory.

4 Which of the following is NOT a way in which thermal energy is transferred?
- **A.** conduction
- **C.** radiation
- **B.** convection
- **D.** sublimation

5 **Differentiate** between a cloth safety belt and a metal buckle in terms of thermal conductors and insulators.

Interpret Graphics

6 **Explain** how the polar bear below can gain thermal energy if the temperature of the air is below freezing.

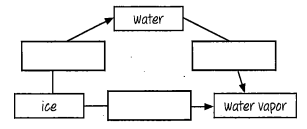

7 **Summarize** Copy and fill in the graphic organizer below showing the state-of-matter changes as thermal energy is added to ice.

Critical Thinking

8 **Compare** You hold a 65°C cup of cocoa. Your hand is 37°C and the outside air is 6°C. Describe the flow of thermal energy.

(tc)EcoPic/iStock/360/Getty Images; (b)Ted Kinsman/Science Source; (r)Ingram Publishing/age fotostock

Lab

Power a Device with a Potato

In this chapter, you have learned about many types of energy and how energy can be transformed and transferred. Can a common potato transfer energy? Think about the inside of a potato. Is there anything in it that can carry an electric current?

Question
Can potatoes conduct electricity and light a bulb?

Procedure
1. Read and complete a lab safety form.
2. With your teammates, discuss what you know about electric circuits. How can you build an electric circuit using a potato as a battery? Write your ideas in your Science Journal. Draw a diagram of your circuit.
3. Use the materials provided to build the circuit shown in the picture.
4. Place half a potato on a paper plate. Push a galvanized, or zinc-coated, nail and a penny into the potato half.
5. Using two alligator clip wires, attach one end of each wire to the nail and to the penny.
6. Attach the positive probe from the multimeter to the alligator clip wire coming from the penny. Attach the negative probe to the alligator clip wire coming from the nail. Does your battery produce an electric current?
7. Push another galvanized nail and a penny into another potato half. Connect the second potato half to the first, as shown in the diagram, connecting the penny on one potato to the nail on the other. Use the meter to test your battery. Record your data in your Science Journal.

Materials

galvanized nails

pennies

LED bulb

Also needed:
potato, alligator clip wires, paper plate, multimeter

Safety

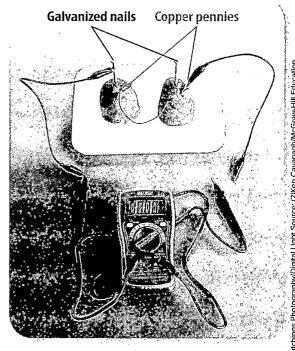

Galvanized nails **Copper pennies**

⑧ Replace the meter with an LED bulb. Hook one end of the potato battery circuit to each wire coming from the bulb. Does the bulb light?

⑨ If necessary, redesign your battery circuit until you get the bulb to light. Review all ideas with your teacher before testing your circuit.

Analyze and Conclude

⑩ **Predict** What sort of devices do you think your potato battery will operate? Explain your answer.

⑪ **Explain** In this battery, electrons moved from the nails to the pennies. Why did this process light the bulb?

⑫ 🔵 **The Big Idea** Describe, in order, all the energy transfers and transformations in your potato battery.

Communicate Your Results

In small groups, discuss how your battery worked and how you might improve its design. Discuss how changing the distance between the penny and the nail might affect your results.

Try other types of food, such as a lemon or an apple. Which type of food produces the most electricity? Try other types of nails, such as a steel nail. Replace the penny with a strip of copper or aluminum. What works? What doesn't?

Hutchings Photography/Digital Light Source

Lab Tips

☑ Check the wires in your circuit frequently to make sure they are in tight contact with the nail and the penny.

☑ Set the meter to the lowest range of DC voltage. Some meters require electricity to operate, so the voltage meter might register a lower voltage than is actually in the potato. Use a battery-operated meter, if possible, to avoid this problem.

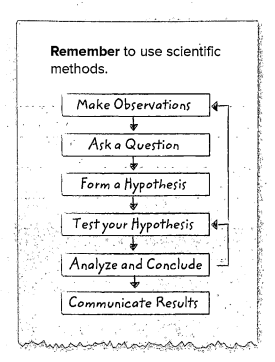

Remember to use scientific methods.

Make Observations →

Ask a Question →

Form a Hypothesis →

Test your Hypothesis →

Analyze and Conclude →

Communicate Results

Energy is transferred from object to object when it does not change form; energy is transformed when it changes form.

Key Concepts Summary

Vocabulary

Lesson 1: Forms of Energy

- **Potential energy** is stored energy, and **kinetic energy** is energy of motion.
- Both **mechanical energy** and **thermal energy** involve kinetic energy and potential energy. Mechanical energy is the sum of the kinetic energy and the potential energy in a system of objects. Thermal energy is the sum of the kinetic energy and the potential energy in a system of particles.
- **Sound energy** and **radiant energy** are carried by waves.

energy p. 51
potential energy p. 51
chemical energy p. 52
nuclear energy p. 52
kinetic energy p. 53
electric energy p. 53
mechanical energy p. 54
thermal energy p. 54
wave p. 55
sound energy p. 55
radiant energy p. 56

Lesson 2: Energy Transfers and Transformations

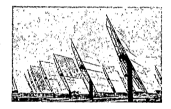

- The **law of conservation of energy** says that energy can be transformed from one form to another, but it cannot be created or destroyed.
- Energy is transformed when it is converted from one form to another. It is transferred when it moves from one object to another.
- **Renewable energy resources** are resources that are replaced as fast as, or faster than they are used. **Nonrenewable energy resources** are resources that are available in limited quantities or are used faster than they can be replaced.

law of conservation of energy p. 60
energy transfer p. 61
energy transformation p. 61
work p. 61
open system p. 63
closed system p. 63
renewable energy resource p. 64
nonrenewable energy resource p. 66

Lesson 3: Particles in Motion

- The kinetic molecular theory says that all objects are made of particles; all particles are in constant, random motion; and the particles collide with each other and with the walls of their container.
- Thermal energy is transferred by **conduction, radiation,** and **convection.**
- A **thermal conductor** transfers thermal energy easily and a **thermal insulator** does not transfer thermal energy easily.

temperature p. 71
heat p. 72
conduction p. 73
radiation p. 73
convection p. 73
vaporization p. 75
thermal conductor p. 76
thermal insulator p. 76

FOLDABLES® Chapter Project

Assemble your lesson Foldables as shown to make a Chapter Project. Use the project to review what you have learned in this chapter.

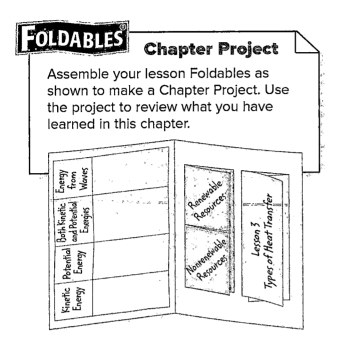

Use Vocabulary

① Compare and contrast sound energy and radiant energy.

② Explain why chemical energy and nuclear energy are both considered potential energy.

③ Describe how an open system differs from a closed system.

④ The energy of moving electrons is _____.

⑤ The energy carried by electromagnetic waves is _____.

⑥ Define *work* in your own words.

⑦ Define *conduction* in your own words.

Link Vocabulary and Key Concepts

 Interactive Concept Map

Copy this concept map, and then use vocabulary terms from the previous page to complete the concept map.

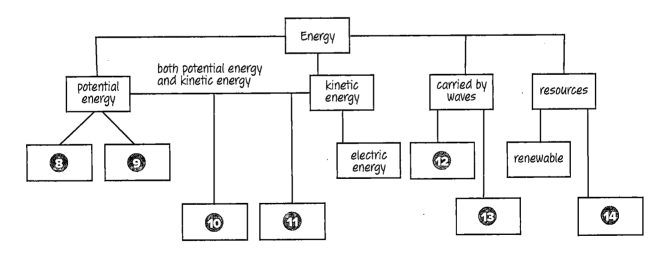

Understand Key Concepts 🔑

1 What type of energy does the statue have?

A. electric energy
B. mechanical energy
C. sound energy
D. thermal energy

2 Which is a form of energy that cannot be stored?

A. chemical energy
B. gravitational potential energy
C. nuclear energy
D. sound energy

3 Waves can transfer energy, but they

A. cannot carry sounds.
B. do not move matter.
C. always have the same wavelength.
D. are unable to move through empty space.

4 Which involves ONLY an energy transfer?

A. A boy turns on an electric toaster to warm a piece of bread.
B. A can of juice cools off in a cooler on a hot summer day.
C. A cat jumps down from a tree branch.
D. A truck burns gasoline and moves 20 km.

5 Which could occur in a closed system?

A. Chemical energy is transformed to electric energy in the system.
B. During a transformation of chemical energy to mechanical energy, thermal energy is released to the environment.
C. Electric energy from the environment is transferred to the system.
D. Radiant energy is transferred to the environment.

6 Which form of energy relies on gravitational potential energy?

A. fossil fuels
B. geothermal
C. hydroelectric
D. nuclear

7 In the picture below, how does the thermal energy definitely flow?

A. from the air to the dog
B. from the dog to the snow
C. from the snow to the air
D. from the snow to the dog

8 Which decreases the thermal energy of a can of soup you just took out of your pantry?

A. letting the can sit on the counter for an hour
B. opening the lid of the can of soup with a can opener
C. placing the can of soup under a bright light
D. putting the can of soup in the refrigerator

Critical Thinking

9 **Identify** all the different forms of energy and all the energy transformations that you see in the picture below.

10 **Compare** the energy transformations that take place in the human body to the energy transformations that take place in a gasoline-powered car.

11 **Compare and contrast** each of the following terms: melting and freezing, boiling and evaporation, and sublimation and deposition.

12 **Judge** Determine whether the following statement is correct and explain your reasoning: *The amount of chemical energy in a flashlight's battery is equal to the radiant energy transferred to the environment.*

13 **Evaluate** Using what you read about thermal energy, explain why sidewalks are built as panels with space between them.

14 **Explain** Convection space heaters are small appliances that sit on the floor. Explain how they can heat an entire room.

Writing in Science

15 **Write** a short explanation to a friend explaining the following scenario: Most air-conditioned rooms are set to a temperature of about 22°C. Human body temperature is 37°C. Why don't people in an air-conditioned room come to thermal equilibrium with the room?

REVIEW THE BIG IDEA

16 Describe at least four energy transfers or energy transformations that occur in your body.

17 The photo below shows an electrical power plant that uses coal to generate electricity. What type of energy resource is coal? What are the advantages and disadvantages of using coal to generate electricity?

Math Skills ✕÷+ Math Practice

Use a Formula

18 A child pulls a toy wagon with a force of 25.0 N for a distance of 8.5 m. How much work did the child do on the wagon?

19 A man pushes a box with a force of 75.0 N across a 12.0 m loading dock. How much work did he do on the box?

Record your answers on the answer sheet provided by your teacher or on a separate sheet of paper.

Multiple Choice

Use the figure to answer questions 1 and 2.

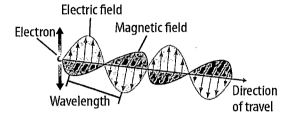

1 Which kind of energy is carried by the wave model shown?

A chemical energy

B electric energy

C radiant energy

D sound energy

2 Which property does this type of wave have that other kinds of waves do not?

A It can travel through air.

B It can travel through water.

C It can travel through a vacuum.

D It can travel through metal wires.

3 Which accurately describes potential energy and kinetic energy?

A A moving soccer ball has potential energy, while a rolling bowling ball has kinetic energy.

B A rock at the top of a cliff has potential energy, while a moving stream has kinetic energy.

C The energy stored in chemical bonds is potential energy, while the energy stored in an atom's nucleus is kinetic energy.

D The energy stored in an atom's nucleus is potential energy, while the energy stored in chemical bonds is kinetic energy.

4 Which describes the sum of potential energy and kinetic energy of objects or systems?

A nuclear energy and electric energy

B nuclear energy and mechanical energy

C thermal energy and electric energy

D thermal energy and mechanical energy

Use the figure to answer questions 5 and 6.

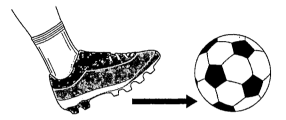

5 The figure above shows someone kicking a soccer ball. Which energy transformation occurs to make the foot move?

A chemical energy to mechanical energy

B mechanical energy to chemical energy

C mechanical energy to mechanical energy

D thermal energy to mechanical energy

6 Which energy transfer occurs to make the ball move?

A chemical energy from ball to foot

B chemical energy from foot to ball

C mechanical energy from ball to foot

D mechanical energy from foot to ball

7 Which is a renewable energy resource that is used to produce electricity?

A biomass

B coal

C natural gas

D petroleum

8 A portable radio transforms chemical energy in batteries into electric energy and then into sound energy. However, not all of the energy from the batteries is converted to sound energy. Which describes how a portable radio still upholds the law of conservation of energy?

A Some energy is destroyed due to inefficiency.

B Some energy goes back into the batteries to be used later.

C Some energy is lost to the surroundings as thermal energy.

D Some energy is lost to the surroundings as chemical energy.

Use the figure to answer question 9.

9 The figure above shows a pan of water being heated on a stove. Which statement is true?

A The pan and the flame are a closed system.

B The natural gas is undergoing an energy transfer.

C Thermal energy is not transferred, and the temperature remains constant.

D This process results in a temperature change and possibly a change of state.

Constructed Response

Use the figure to answer question 10.

water | bottle | air

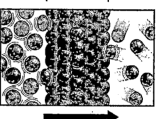

10 Imagine putting a warm bottle of water into a refrigerator. The figure models the particles that make up the water, the bottle, and the air. Explain the energy transfer between the cold refrigerator air outside the bottle and the warm water inside the bottle.

11 How does an open system differ from a closed system?

12 How does the relationship between temperature and volume of water differ from most other materials?

NEED EXTRA HELP?												
If You Missed Question...	1	2	3	4	5	6	7	8	9	10	11	12
Go to Lesson...	1	1	1	1	2	2	2	2	2	3	2	3

Unit 2
Understanding Matter

Sent to her room, Molly Cool dreams of escaping.

If only she could change state and become a liquid, she could flow under the bedroom door and down the stairs...

...then flow to the fireplace where the heat would turn her into vapor and she could escape up the chimney.

I'm free!

Hello birds!

1000 B.C.   **1700**   **1800**

350 B.C.
Greek philosopher Aristotle defines an element as "one of those bodies into which other bodies can decompose, and that itself is not capable of being divided into another."

1704
Isaac Newton proposes that atoms attach to each other by some type of force.

1869
Dmitri Mendeleev publishes the first version of the periodic table.

1874
G. Johnstone Stoney proposes the existence of the electron, a subatomic particle that carries a negative electric charge, after experiments in electrochemistry.

1897
J.J. Thompson demonstrates the existence of the electron, proving Stoney's claim.

Visit ConnectED for this unit's STEM activity.

1907
Physicists Hans Geiger and Ernest Marsden, under the direction of Ernest Rutherford, conduct the famous gold foil experiment. Rutherford concludes that the atom is mostly empty space and that most of the mass is concentrated in the atomic nucleus.

1918
Ernest Rutherford reports that the hydrogen nucleus has a positive charge, and he names it the proton.

1932
James Chadwick discovers the neutron, a subatomic particle with no electric charge and a mass slightly larger than a proton.

Health and Science

Have an upset stomach? Chew on some charcoal. Have a headache? Rub a little peppermint oil on your temples. As shown in **Figure 1**, people have used chemicals to fix physical ailments for thousands of years, long before the development of the first medicines. Many cures were discovered by accident. People did not understand why the cures worked, only that they did work.

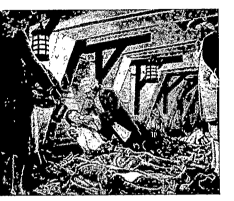

△ **Figure 1** Thousands of years ago, people believed that evil spirits caused illness. Herbs or other natural materials treated symptoms.

Asking Questions About Health

Over time, people asked questions about which cures worked and which cures did not work. They made observations, recorded their findings, and had discussions about cures with other people. This process was the start of the scientific investigation of health. **Health** is the overall condition of an organism or group of organisms at any given time. Early studies focused on treating the physical parts of the body. The study of how chemicals interact in organisms did not come until much later. Recognizing that chemicals can affect health opened a whole new field of study known as biochemistry. The time line in **Figure 2** shows some of the medical and chemical discoveries people made that led to the development of medicines that save lives.

Figure 2 The time line shows several significant discoveries and developments in the history of medicine. ▽

4,200 years ago Clay tablets describe using sesame oil on wounds to treat infection.

3,500 years ago An ancient papyrus described how Egyptians applied moldy bread to wounds to prevent infection.

2,500 years ago Hippocrates, known as the "Father of Medicine," is the first physician known to separate medical knowledge from myth and superstition.

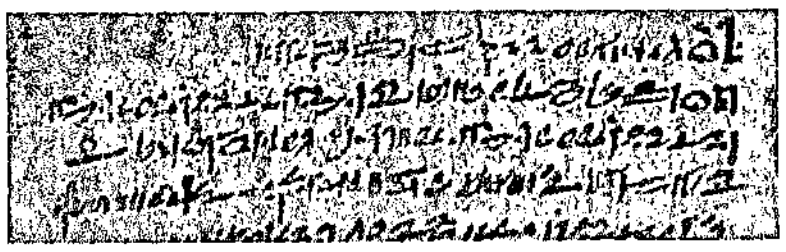

Year 900 The first pharmacy opened in Persia, which is now Iraq.

More than 3,300 years later, scientists found that a chemical in mold broke down the cell membranes of bacteria, killing them. Similar discoveries led to the development of antibiotics.

1740s A doctor found that the disease called scurvy was caused by a lack of Vitamin C.

Early explorers on long sea voyages often lost their teeth or developed deadly sores. Ships could not carry many fruits and vegetables, which contain Vitamin C, because they spoil quickly. Scientists suspect that many early explorers might have died because their diets did not include the proper vitamins.

(t) PARIS PIERCE/Alamy, (bl) DEA/G. DAGLI ORTI/De Agostini Picture Library/Getty Images, (br) MARIA TOUTOUDAKI/Getty Images

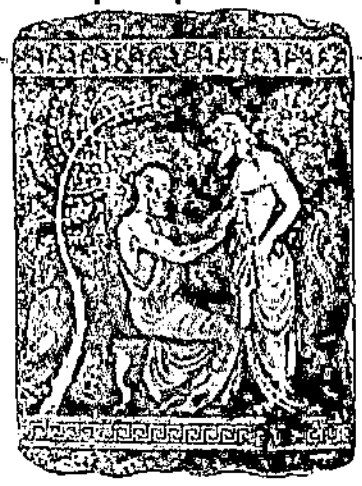

Benefits and Risks of Medicines

Scientists might recognize that a person's body is missing a necessary chemical, but that does not mean they can always fix the problem. For example, people used to get necessary vitamins and minerals by eating natural, whole foods. Today, food processing destroys many nutrients. Foods last longer, but they do not provide all the nutrients the body needs.

Researchers still do not understand the role of many chemicals in the body. Taking a medicine to fix one problem sometimes causes others, called side effects. Some side effects can be worse than the original problem. For example, antibiotics kill some disease-causing bacteria. However, widespread use of antibiotics has resulted in "super bugs"—bacteria that are resistant to treatment.

Histamines are chemicals that have many functions in the body, including regulating sleep and decreasing sensitivity to allergens. However, low levels of histamines have been linked to some serious illnesses. Many medicines have long-term effects on health. Before you take a medicine, you should recognize that you are adding a chemical to your body. You should be as informed as possible about any possible side effects.

Scientists studying digestion in dogs noticed that ants were attracted to the urine of a dog whose pancreas had been removed. They determined the dog's urine contained sugar, which attracted ants. Eventually, scientists discovered that diabetes resulted from a lack of insulin, a chemical produced in the pancreas that regulates blood sugar. Today, some people with diabetes wear an insulin pump that monitors their blood sugar and delivers insulin to their bodies.

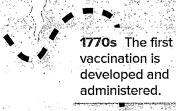

1770s The first vaccination is developed and administered.

1800s Nitrous oxide is first used as an anesthetic by dentists.

1920s Insulin is identified as the missing hormone in people with diabetes.

1920s Penicillin is discovered, but not developed for treatment of disease until the mid-1940s.

2000s First vaccine to target a cause of cancer

Ace Stock Limited/Alamy

MiniLab

15 minutes

Is everyone's chemistry the same?

Each person's body is a unique "chemical factory." Why might using the same medicine to treat illness not work exactly the same way in everyone?

1. Read and complete a lab safety form.

2. Place a strip of **pH paper** on your tongue. Immediately place the paper in a **self-sealing plastic bag.**

3. Compare the color of your paper to the **color guide.** Record the pH in your Science Journal.

4. Record your pH on a class chart for comparison.

Analyze and Conclude

1. **Organize Data** What was the range of pH values among your classmates?

2. **Predict** How might differences in pH affect how well a medicine works in different people?

Chapter 3

SEPS.2, SEPS.3, SEPS.4, SEPS.5

Matter: Properties and Changes

THE BIG IDEA

What gives a substance its unique identity?

Inquiry What properties does it have?

When designing a safe airplane, choosing materials with specific properties is important. Notice how the metal used in the outer shell of this airplane is curved, yet it is strong enough to hold its shape. Think about how properties of the airplane's materials are important to the conditions in which it flies.

- What properties would be important to consider when constructing the outer shell of an airplane?

- Why is metal used for electrical wiring and plastic used for interior walls of an airplane?

- Why do different substances have different properties?

Get Ready to Read

What do you think?

Before you read, decide if you agree or disagree with each of these statements. As you read this chapter, see if you change your mind about any of the statements.

1. The particles in a solid object do not move.

2. Your weight depends on your location.

3. The particles in ice are the same as the particles in liquid water.

4. Mixing powdered drink mix with water causes a new substance to form.

5. If you combine two substances, bubbling is a sign that a new type of substance might be forming.

6. If you stir salt into water, the total amount of matter decreases.

connectED

Your one-stop online resource
connectED.mcgraw-hill.com

LearnSmart®

Chapter Resources Files, Reading Essentials, Get Ready to Read, Quick Vocabulary

Animations, Videos, Interactive Tables

Self-checks, Quizzes, Tests

Project-Based Learning Activities

Lab Manuals, Safety Videos, Virtual Labs & Other Tools

Vocabulary, Multilingual eGlossary, Vocab eGames, Vocab eFlashcards

Personal Tutors

Lesson 1

Reading Guide

Key Concepts 🔑
ESSENTIAL QUESTIONS

- How do particles move in solids, liquids, and gases?

- How are physical properties different from chemical properties?

- How are properties used to identify a substance?

Vocabulary

volume p. 94

solid p. 94

liquid p. 94

gas p. 94

physical property p. 96

mass p. 96

density p. 97

solubility p. 98

chemical property p. 99

 Multilingual eGlossary

 BrainPOP®

 SEPS.2, SEPS.5

Matter and Its Properties

Inquiry What makes this possible?

White-water rafting is a lot of fun, but you have to be prepared. The ride down the rapids can be dangerous, and you need good equipment. What properties must the helmets, the raft, the oars, and the life vests have to make a safe white-water ride possible?

Pixtal/age fotostock

How can you describe a substance?

Think about the different ways you can describe a type of matter. Is it hard? Can you pour it? What color is it? Answering questions like these can help you describe the properties of a substance. In this lab, you will observe how the properties of a mixture can be very different from the properties of the substances it is made from.

1. Read and complete a lab safety form.

2. Using a **small plastic spoon,** measure two spoonfuls of **cornstarch** into a **clear plastic cup.** What does the cornstarch look like? What does it feel like?

3. Slowly stir one spoonful of **water** into the cup containing the cornstarch. Gently roll the new substance around in the cup with your finger.

Think About This

1. What were some properties of the cornstarch and water before they were mixed?

2. 🔑 **Key Concept** How were the properties of the mixture different from the original properties of the cornstarch and water?

What is matter?

Imagine the excitement of white-water rafting through a mountain pass. As your raft plunges up and down through the rushing water, you grip your oar. You hope that the powerful current will lead you safely past the massive boulders. Only after you reach a quiet pool of water can you finally take a breath and enjoy the beautiful surroundings.

Imagine looking around and asking yourself, "What is matter?" Trees, rocks, water, and all the things you might see on a rafting trip are matter because they have mass and take up space. Air, even though you can't see it, is also matter because it has mass and takes up space. Light from the Sun is not matter because it does not have mass and does not take up space. Sounds, forces, and energy also are not matter.

Think about the properties of matter you would see on your white-water rafting trip. The helmet you wear is hard and shiny. The rubber raft is soft and flexible. The water is cool and clear. Matter has many different properties. You will learn about some physical properties and chemical properties of matter in this chapter. You will also read about how these properties help to identify many types of matter.

REVIEW VOCABULARY ·····
matter
anything that has mass and takes up space

Hutchings Photography/Digital Light Source

States of Matter

One property that is useful when you are describing different materials is the state of matter. Three familiar states of matter are solids, liquids, and gases. You can determine a material's state of matter by answering the following questions:

• Does it have a definite shape?

• Does it have a definite volume?

Volume *is the amount of space a sample of matter occupies.* As shown in **Table 1**, a material's state of matter determines whether its shape and its volume change when it is moved from one container to another.

Solids, Liquids, and Gases

Notice in **Table 1** that *a* **solid** *is a state of matter with a definite shape and volume.* The shape and volume of a solid do not change regardless of whether it is inside or outside a container. *A* **liquid** *is a state of matter with a definite volume but not a definite shape.* A liquid changes shape if it is moved to another container, but its volume does not change. *A state of matter without a definite shape or a definite volume is a* **gas.** A gas changes both shape and volume depending on the size and shape of its container.

 Reading Check Which state of matter has a definite shape and a definite volume?

Table 1 Solids, Liquids, and Gases	
Solid Solids, such as rocks, do not change shape or volume regardless of whether they are inside or outside a container.	
Liquid A liquid, such as fruit juice, changes shape if it is moved from one container to another. Its volume does not change.	
Gas A gas, such as nitrogen dioxide, changes both shape and volume if it is moved from one container to another. If the container is not closed, the gas spreads out of the container.	

Hutchings Photography/Digital Light Source

Gas
- no definite shape
- no definite volume
- particles very far apart
- very weak attractive forces between particles
- particles move freely

Solid
- a definite shape
- a definite volume
- particles close together
- strong attractive forces between particles
- particles vibrate in all directions

Liquid
- no definite shape; takes the shape of its container
- definite volume
- particles close together
- weaker attractive forces between particles than in solids
- particles free to move past neighboring particles

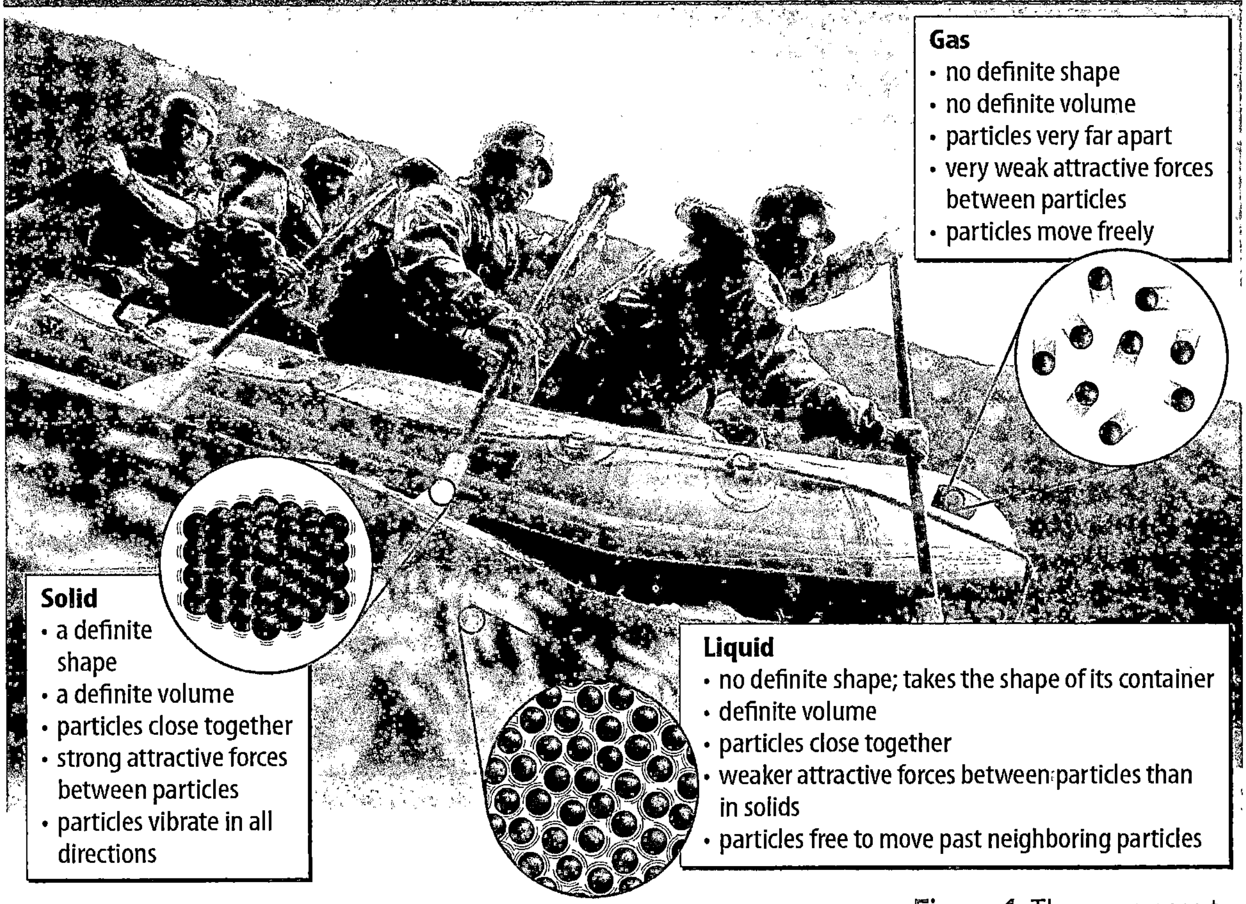

Figure 1 The movement and attraction between particles are different in solids, liquids, and gases.

Visual Check How does the force between particles differ in a solid, a liquid, and a gas?

 **Animation**

Moving Particles

All matter is made of tiny particles that are constantly moving. Notice in **Figure 1** how the movement of particles is different in each state of matter. In solids, particles vibrate back and forth in all directions. However, particles in a solid cannot move from place to place. In liquids, the distance between particles is greater. Particles in liquids can slide past one another, similar to the way marbles in a box slide around. In a gas, particles move freely rather than staying close together.

Key Concept Check How do particles move in solids, liquids, and gases?

Attraction Between Particles

Particles of matter that are close together exert an attractive force, or pull, on each other. The strength of the attraction depends on the distance between particles. Think about how this attraction affects the properties of the objects in **Figure 1**. A strong attraction holds particles of a solid close together in the same position. Liquids can flow because forces between the particles are weaker. Particles of a gas are so spread apart that they are not held together by attractive forces.

©David Madison/Corbis

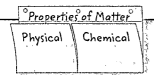

Fold and cut a sheet of paper to make a two-tab book. Label it as shown. Use it to organize your notes about properties of matter.

Properties of Matter

Physical | Chemical

Figure 2 You can measure a material's mass and volume and then calculate its density.

What are physical properties?

Think again about the properties of matter you might observe on a rafting trip. The water feels cold. The raft is heavy. The helmets are hard. The properties of all materials, or types of matter, depend on the substances that make them up. Recall that a substance is a type of matter with a composition that is always the same. *Any characteristic of matter that you can observe without changing the identity of the substances that make it up is a* **physical property.** State of matter, temperature, and the size of an object are all examples of physical properties.

Mass and Weight

Some physical properties of matter, such as mass and weight, depend on the size of the sample. **Mass** *is the amount of matter in an object.* Weight is the gravitational pull on the mass of an object. To measure the mass of a rock, you can use a balance, as shown in **Figure 2.** If more particles were added to the rock, its mass would increase, and the reading on the balance would increase. The weight of the rock would also increase.

Weight depends on the location of an object, but its mass does not. For example, the mass of an object is the same on Earth as it is on the Moon. The object's weight, however, is greater on Earth because the gravitational pull on the object is greater on Earth than on the Moon.

Reading Check How do mass and weight differ?

Mass, Volume, and Density **Personal Tutor**

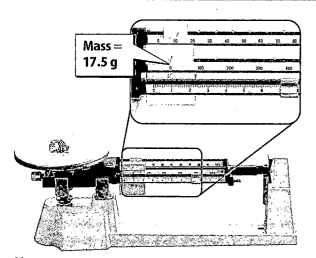

Mass =
17.5 g

Mass
A balance measures an object's mass by comparing it to the known mass of the slides on the balance. Common units for measuring mass are the kilogram (kg) and the gram (g).

Volume = length × width × height

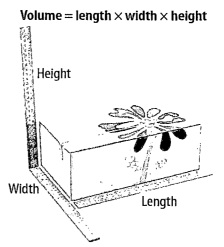

Height

Width

Length

Volume of a Rectangular-Shaped Solid
If a solid has a rectangular shape, you can find its volume by multiplying its length, its width, and its height together. A common unit of volume for a solid is the cubic centimeter (cm³).

Hutchings Photography/Digital Light Source

Volume

Another physical property of matter that depends on the amount or size of the sample is volume. You can measure the volume of a liquid by pouring it into a graduated cylinder or a measuring cup and reading the volume mark. Two ways to measure the volume of a solid are shown in **Figure 2.** If a solid has a regular geometric shape, you can calculate its volume by using the correct formula. If a solid has an irregular shape, you can use the displacement method to measure its volume.

Density

Density is a physical property of matter that does not depend on the size or amount of the sample. **Density** *is the mass per unit volume of a substance.* Density is useful when identifying unknown substances because it is constant for a given substance, regardless of the size of the sample. For example, imagine hiking in the mountains and finding a shiny yellow rock. Is it gold? Suppose you calculate that the density of the rock is 5.0 g/cm^3. This rock cannot be gold because the density of gold is 19.3 g/cm^3. A sample of pure gold, regardless of the size, will always have a density of 19.3 g/cm^3.

 **MiniLab** — 10 minutes

How can you find an object's mass and volume?

1. Read and complete a lab safety form.
2. Obtain a small sample of **modeling clay.**
3. Using a **balance,** find the mass of the sample. Record it in your Science Journal.
4. Add exactly 25 mL of **tap water** to a **50-mL graduated cylinder.**
5. Shape the clay so that it can be placed into the graduated cylinder.
6. Slide the clay into the graduated cylinder. Record the new volume of the water.

Analyze and Conclude

1. **Compare** the volume of the water with the total volume of the water and the clay. What is the volume of the clay?
2. 🔑 **Key Concept** Why are mass and volume considered physical properties?

Initial Volume = 70.0 mL

Final Volume = 73.5 mL

Pyrite

Volume of an Irregular-Shaped Solid
The volume of an irregular-shaped object can be measured by displacement. The volume of the object is the difference between the water level before and after placing the object in the water. The common unit for liquid volume is the milliliter (mL).

Density Equation
$$\text{Density (in g/mL)} = \frac{\text{mass (in g)}}{\text{volume (in mL)}}$$

$$D = \frac{m}{V}$$

To find the density of the rock, first determine the mass and the volume of the rock:

mass: $m = \textbf{17.5 g}$
volume: $V = 73.5 \text{ mL} - 70.0 \text{ mL} = \textbf{3.5 mL}$

Then, divide the mass by the volume:

$$D = \frac{\textbf{17.5 g}}{\textbf{3.5 mL}} = 5.0 \text{ g/mL}$$

Density Calculation
Density can be calculated using the density equation. The common units of density are grams per milliliter (g/mL) or grams per cubic centimeter (g/cm^3). 1 mL = 1 cm^3.

| Drink Mix | Sand |

Figure 3 The drink mix is soluble in water. The sand is not soluble in water.

WORD ORIGIN · · · · · · · · · · · ·

solubility
from Latin *solubilis*, means
"capable of being dissolved"
· · · · · · · · · · · · · · ·

Solubility

You can observe another physical property of matter if you stir a powdered drink mix into water. The powder dissolves, or mixes evenly, in the water. **Solubility** *is the ability of one material to dissolve in another.* You cannot see the drink mix powder in the left glass in **Figure 3** because the powder is soluble in water. The liquid is red because of the food coloring in the powder. The sand settles in the glass because it is not soluble in water.

Melting and Boiling Point

Melting point and boiling point also are physical properties. The melting point is the temperature at which a solid changes to a liquid. Ice cream, for example, melts when it warms enough to reach its melting point. The boiling point is the temperature at which a liquid changes to a gas. If you heat a pan of water, the water will boil, or change to a gas, at its boiling point. Different materials have different melting and boiling points. These temperatures do not depend on the size or amount of the material.

Reading Check How does a substance change at its melting point and at its boiling point?

Additional Physical Properties

Several other physical properties–magnetism, malleability, and electrical conductivity–are shown in **Figure 4**. Notice how the physical properties of each material make it useful. Can you think of other examples of materials chosen for certain uses because of their physical properties?

Physical Properties

Figure 4 Physical properties include magnetism, malleability, and electrical conductivity.

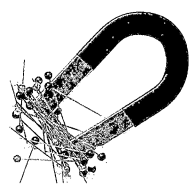

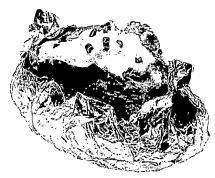

Magnetism is a physical property that allows some materials to attract certain metals.

A malleable material, such as aluminum foil used in cooking, is useful because it can be hammered or rolled into thin sheets.

Some metals, such as copper, are used in electrical wire because of their high electrical conductivity.

Figure 5 Flammability and the ability to rust are examples of chemical properties.

Flammability
In 1937 the airship *Hindenburg* caught fire and crashed. It was filled with hydrogen, a highly flammable gas.

Ability to rust
The metal parts of an old car soon rust because the metal contains iron. The ability to rust is a chemical property of iron.

What are chemical properties?

Have you ever seen an apple turn brown? When you bite into or cut open apples or other fruits, substances that make up the fruit react with oxygen in the air. When substances react with each other, their particles combine to form a new, different substance. The ability of substances in fruit to react with oxygen is a chemical property of the substances. A **chemical property** *is the ability or inability of a substance to combine with or change into one or more new substances.* A chemical property is a characteristic of matter that you observe as it reacts with or changes into a different substance. For example, copper on the roof of a building turns green as it reacts with oxygen in the air. The ability to react with oxygen is a chemical property of copper. Two other chemical properties—flammability and the ability to rust—are shown in **Figure 5.**

 Key Concept Check How do chemical properties and physical properties differ?

Flammability

Flammability is the ability of a type of matter to burn easily. Suppose you are on a camping trip and want to light a campfire. You see rocks, sand, and wood. Which would you choose for your fire? Wood is a good choice because it is flammable. Rocks and sand are not flammable.

Materials are often chosen for certain uses based on flammability. For example, gasoline is used in cars because it burns easily in engines. Materials that are used for cooking pans must not be flammable. The tragedy shown in **Figure 5** resulted when hydrogen, a highly flammable gas, was used in the airship *Hindenburg.* Today, airships are filled with helium, a nonflammable gas.

Ability to Rust

You have probably seen old cars that have begun to rust like the one in **Figure 5.** You might also have seen rust on bicycles or tools left outside. Rust is a substance that forms when iron reacts with water and oxygen in the air. The ability to rust is a chemical property of iron or metals that contain iron.

Table 2 Identifying an Unknown Material by its Physical Properties

Substance	Color	Mass (g)	Melting Point (°C)	Density (g/cm³)
Table salt	white	14.5	801	2.17
Sugar	white	11.5	148	1.53
Baking soda	white	16.0	50	2.16
Unknown	white	16.0	801	2.17

Math Skills

Solve a One-Step Equation

A statement that two expressions are equal is an equation. For example, examine the density equation:

$$D = \frac{m}{V}$$

This equation shows that density, D, is equal to mass, m, divided by volume, V. To solve a one-step equation, place the variables you know into the equation. Then solve for the unknown variable. For example, if an object has a mass of **52 g** and a volume of **4 cm³**, calculate the density as follows:

$$D = \frac{52 \text{ g}}{4 \text{ cm}^3} = 13 \text{ g/cm}^3$$

Practice

A cube of metal measures 3 cm on each side. It has a mass of 216 g. What is the density of the metal?

 Math Practice

 Personal Tutor

Identifying Matter Using Physical Properties

Physical properties are useful for describing types of matter, but they are also useful for identifying unknown substances. For example, look at the substances in **Table 2.** Notice how their physical properties are alike and how they are different. How can you use these properties to identify the unknown substance?

You cannot identify the unknown substance by its color. All of the substances are white. You also cannot identify the unknown substance by its mass or volume. Mass and volume are properties of matter that change with the amount of the sample present. However, recall that melting point and density are properties of matter that do not depend on the size or the amount of the sample. They are more reliable for identifying an unknown substance. Notice that both the melting point and the density of the unknown substance match those of table salt. The unknown substance must be table salt.

When you identify matter using physical properties, consider how the properties are alike and how they are different from known types of matter. It is important that the physical properties you use to identify an unknown type of matter are properties that do not change for any sample size. A cup of salt and a spoonful of salt will have the same melting point and density even though the mass and volume for each will be different. Therefore, melting point and density are physical properties that are reliable when identifying an unknown substance.

 Key Concept Check How are properties used to identify a substance?

Sorting Materials Using Properties

Both physical properties and chemical properties are useful for sorting materials. The beads in Figure 6 are sorted by color and shape—two physical properties. When you bring groceries home from the store, you might put crackers in a cupboard, but you probably put milk and yogurt in the refrigerator to keep them from spoiling. The tendency to spoil is a chemical property of the milk and yogurt. You probably often sort other types of matter by physical or chemical properties without realizing it.

Separating Mixtures Using Physical Properties

Physical properties are useful for separating different types of matter that are mixed. For example, suppose you have a frozen juice pop on a stick. How could you separate the frozen juice from the stick? If you set the freezer pop on a counter, the frozen juice will melt and separate from the stick. The melting point of the juice is much lower than the melting point of the stick. Melting point is a physical property you can use to separate mixtures. Other ways that you can use physical properties to separate mixtures are shown in Figure 7.

Reading Check How could you separate a mixture of sand and small pebbles?

△ **Figure 6** These beads are sorted by color and shape.

Figure 7 Physical properties, such as state of matter, boiling point, and magnetism, can be used to separate mixtures. ▽

Separating Mixtures

Separation by State of Matter	Separation by Boiling Point	Separation by Magnetism

△ Water can flow through the holes in the strainer because it is a liquid. The pasta cannot flow through because the pieces are solid and too large.	△ If you boil a mixture of salt and water, the liquid water changes to a gas when it reaches its boiling point. The salt is left behind.	△ Iron filings, which have the property of magnetism, can be separated from the sand using a magnet. The magnet attracts the iron filings but not the sand.

Visual Check How could you separate a mixture of salt, sand, and iron filings?

(bl) Studio Blond/Getty Images, (others)Hutchings Photography/Digital Light Source

Visual Summary

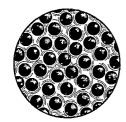 The movement of particles is different in a solid, a liquid, and a gas.

 Physical properties and chemical properties are used to describe types of matter.

 Physical properties such as magnetism can be used to separate mixtures.

FOLDABLES

Use your lesson Foldable to review the lesson. Save your Foldable for the project at the end of the chapter.

What do you think NOW?

You first read the statements below at the beginning of the chapter.

1. The particles in a solid object do not move.

2. Your weight depends on your location.

3. The particles in ice are the same as the particles in liquid water.

Did you change your mind about whether you agree or disagree with the statements? Rewrite any false statements to make them true.

Use Vocabulary

1 A state of matter that has a definite volume but not a definite shape is a _____.

2 **Distinguish** between a physical property and a chemical property.

Understand Key Concepts

3 **Analyze** Which can be used to identify an unknown substance: mass, melting point, density, volume, state of matter?

4 **Contrast** the movement of particles in a solid, a liquid, and a gas.

5 Which of these is a chemical property?
   A. boiling point   C. flammability
   B. density   D. solubility

Interpret Graphics

6 **Explain** Use the drawing to explain why a gas has no definite shape or volume.

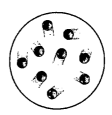

7 **Calculate** Copy the table below and calculate the density of each object.

Object	Mass	Volume	Density
1	6.50 g	1.25 cm³	
2	8.65 g	2.50 mL	

Critical Thinking

8 **Design** an investigation you could use to find the density of a penny.

Math Skills   Math Practice

9 The mass of a mineral is 9.6 g. The mineral is placed in a graduated cylinder containing 8.0 mL of water. The water level rises to 16.0 mL. What is the mineral's density?

(l)John A. Rizzo/Getty Images, (b)Hutchings Photography/Digital Light Source

How can you calculate density?

Density is the mass per unit volume of a substance. In this lab, you will measure the mass of a solid block. Next you will measure the volume in two different ways. Then you will calculate the density of the block for each volume measurement.

Materials

metal block

100-mL graduated cylinder

metric ruler

triple-beam balance

Safety

Learn It

Scientists take measurements when collecting data. In this lab, you will **measure** mass and volume, then use these data to calculate density.

Try It

① Read and complete a lab safety form.

② Copy the data table in your Science Journal. Use a triple beam balance to measure the mass of the metal block. Record your measurements.

③ Use a ruler to measure the length, width, and height of the block. Record your measurements.

④ Pour 30 mL of water into a 100-mL graduated cylinder. Record the volume of the water.

⑤ Carefully slide the metal block into the graduated cylinder. Record the total volume.

⑥ Using the measurements from step 3, determine the volume of the block using this equation:

volume = length × width × height

⑦ Calculate the volume of the block using displacement. Subtract the volume of the water in step 4 from the volume of the water and block in step 5.

Apply It

⑧ **Calculate** Using the mass and each volume measurement of the block, calculate the density of the block.

⑨ **Compare** the density of the block calculated by the two different volumes. *Hint:* 1 mL = 1 cm³. Are they the same? Why or why not?

⑩ 🔑 **Key Concept** Why is density a physical property of the block?

Measurements	
Mass (g)	
Length (cm)	
Width (cm)	
Height (cm)	
Volume of Water (mL)	
Volume of Water and block (mL)	

Hutchings Photography/Digital Light Source

Reading Guide

Key Concepts

ESSENTIAL QUESTIONS

- How are physical changes different from chemical changes?
- How do physical and chemical changes affect mass?

Vocabulary

physical change p. 106

chemical change p. 108

law of conservation of mass p. 111

 Multilingual eGlossary

 BrainPOP®

SEPS.2, SEPS.3, SEPS.4, SEPS.5

Matter and Its Changes

Inquiry Why is it orange?

Streams are usually filled with clear freshwater. What happened to this water? Chemicals from a nearby mine seeped through rocks before flowing into the stream. These chemicals combined with metals in the rocks, causing orange rust to form in the water.

What does a change in the color of matter show?

Matter has many different properties. Chemical properties can only be observed if the matter changes from one type to another. How can you tell if a chemical property has changed? Sometimes a change in the color of matter shows that its chemical properties have changed.

1. Read and complete a lab safety form.
2. Obtain the **red indicator sponge** and the **red acid solution** from your teacher. Predict what will happen if the red acid solution touches the red sponge.
3. Use a **dropper** to remove a few drops of acid solution from the **beaker.** Place the drops on the sponge. ⚠ *Be careful not to splash the liquid onto yourself or your clothing.*
4. Record your observations in your Science Journal.

Think About This

1. Compare the properties of the sponge before and after you placed the acid solution onto the sponge. Was your prediction correct?

2. 🔑 **Key Concept** How do you know that physical properties and chemical properties changed?

Changes of Matter

Imagine going to a park in the spring and then going back to the same spot in the fall. What changes do you think you might see? The changes would depend on where you live. An example of what a park in the fall might look like in many places is shown in **Figure 8.** Leaves that are green in the spring might turn red, yellow, or brown in the fall. The air that was warm in the spring might be cooler in the fall. If you visit the park early on a fall morning, you might notice a thin layer of frost on the leaves. Matter, such as the things you see at a park, can change in many ways. These changes can be either physical or chemical.

✓ **Reading Check** What are some examples of matter changing in winter?

Figure 8 The physical and chemical properties of matter change in a park throughout the year.

(l)Hutchings Photography/Digital Light Source, (b)Brand X Pictures/PunchStock

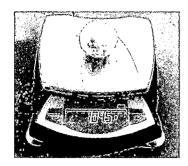

Figure 9 Changing the shape of the modeling clay does not change its mass.

What are physical changes?

A change in the size, shape, form, or state of matter that does not change the matter's identity is a **physical change**. You can see an example of a physical change in **Figure 9**. Recall that mass is an example of a physical property. Notice that the mass of the modeling clay is the same before and after its shape was changed. When a physical change occurs, the chemical properties of the matter stay the same. The substances that make up matter are exactly the same both before and after a physical change.

Dissolving

One of the physical properties you read about in Lesson 1 was solubility—the ability of one material to dissolve, or mix evenly, in another. Dissolving is a physical change because the identities of the substances do not change when they are mixed. As shown in **Figure 10**, the identities of the water molecules and the sugar molecules do not change when sugar crystals dissolve in water.

Reading Check Explain why dissolving is classified as a physical change.

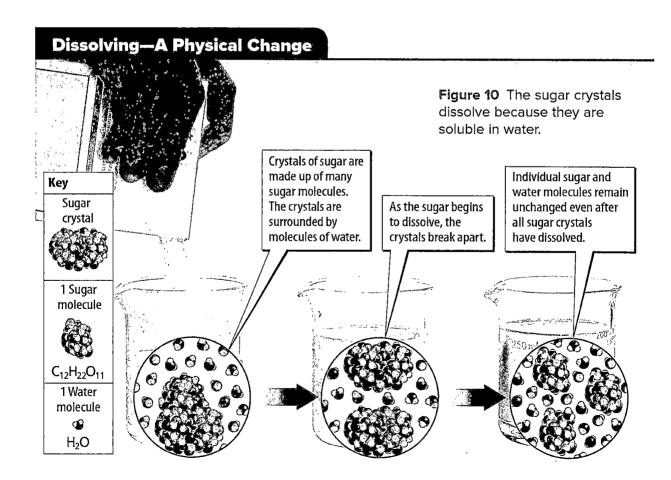

Dissolving—A Physical Change

Figure 10 The sugar crystals dissolve because they are soluble in water.

Crystals of sugar are made up of many sugar molecules. The crystals are surrounded by molecules of water.

As the sugar begins to dissolve, the crystals break apart.

Individual sugar and water molecules remain unchanged even after all sugar crystals have dissolved.

Key

| Sugar crystal |
| 1 Sugar molecule $C_{12}H_{22}O_{11}$ |
| 1 Water molecule H_2O |

Changing State

In Lesson 1 you read about three states of matter—solid, liquid, and gas. Can you think of examples of matter changing from one state to another? A layer of ice might form on a lake in the winter. A glassblower melts glass into a liquid so that it can be formed into shapes. Changes in the state of matter are physical changes.

Melting and Boiling If you heat ice cubes in a pot on the stove, the ice will melt, forming water that soon begins to boil. When a material melts, it changes from a solid to a liquid. When it boils, it changes from a liquid to a gas. The substances that make up the material do not change during a change in the state of matter, as shown in Figure 11. The particles that make up ice (solid water) are the same as the particles that make up water as a liquid or as a gas.

Energy and Change in State The energy of the particles and the distances between the particles are different for a solid, a liquid, and a gas. Changes in energy cause changes in the state of matter. For example, energy must be added to a substance to change it from a solid to a liquid or from a liquid to a gas. Adding energy to a substance can increase its temperature. When the temperature reaches the substance's melting point, the solid changes to a liquid. At the boiling point, the liquid changes to a gas.

What would happen if you changed the rate at which you add energy to a substance? For example, what would happen if you heated an ice cube in your hand instead of in a pot on the stove? The ice would reach its melting point more slowly in your hand. The rate at which one state of matter changes to another depends on the rate at which energy is added to or taken away from the substance.

Changing State

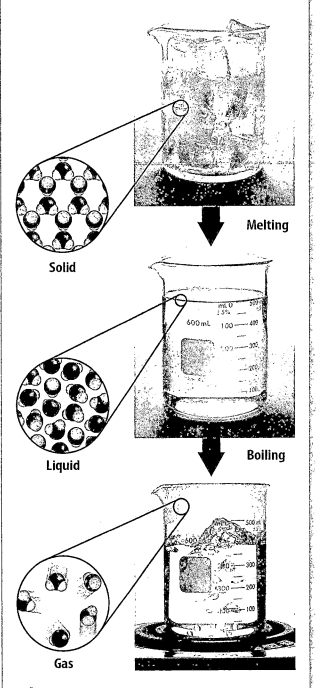

Figure 11 The particles that make up ice (solid water), liquid water, and water vapor (water in the gaseous state) are the same. Changing from one state to another changes only the amount of energy of the particles and the distances between the particles.

Solid

Melting

Liquid

Boiling

Gas

⊘ **Visual Check** Describe the change in the energy and motion of particles of a substance if the substance changes from a gas to a liquid.

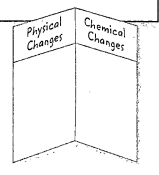
What are chemical changes?

Some changes in matter involve more than just changing physical properties. *A* **chemical change** *is a change in matter in which the substances that make up the matter change into other substances with different chemical and physical properties.* Recall that a chemical property is the ability or inability of a substance to combine with or change into one or more new substances. During a physical change, only the physical properties of matter change. However, the new substance produced during a chemical change has different chemical and physical properties. Another name for a chemical change is a chemical reaction. The particles that make up two or more substances react, or combine, with each other and form a new substance.

Key Concept Check How are chemical changes different from physical changes?

Signs of a Chemical Change

How can you tell that the burning of the trees in Figure 12 is a chemical change? The reaction produces two gases—carbon dioxide and water vapor—even though you cannot see them. After the fire, you can see that any part of the trees that remains is black, and you can see ash—another new substance. But with some changes, the only new substance formed is a gas you cannot see. As trees burn in a forest fire, light and heat are signs of a chemical change. For many reactions, changes in physical properties, such as color or state of matter, are signs that a chemical change has occurred. However, the only sure sign of a chemical change is the formation of a new substance.

Figure 12 A forest fire causes a chemical change in the trees, producing new substances.

Chemical Change

 Animation

Light and heat during a forest fire are signs that a chemical change is occurring.

After the fire, the formation of new substances shows that a chemical change has taken place.

Visual Check Why is the smoke produced during a forest fire a sign of a chemical change?

Formation of Gas Bubbles of gas can form during both a physical change and a chemical change. When you heat a substance to its boiling point, the bubbles show that a liquid is changing to a gas–a physical change. When you combine substances, such as the medicine tablet and the water in Figure 13, gas bubbles show that a chemical change is occurring. Sometimes you cannot see the gas produced, but you might be able to smell it. The aroma of freshly baked bread, for example, is a sign that baking bread causes a chemical reaction that produces a gas.

 Reading Check How can you determine whether the formation of bubbles is the result of a physical change or a chemical change?

Formation of a Precipitate Some chemical reactions result in the formation of a precipitate (prih SIH puh tut). As shown in the middle photo in Figure 13, a precipitate is a solid that sometimes forms when two liquids combine. When a liquid freezes, the solid formed is not a precipitate. A precipitate is not a state change from a liquid to a solid. Instead, the particles that make up two liquids react and form the particles that make up the solid precipitate, a new substance.

Color Change Suppose you want your room to be a different color. You would simply apply paint to the walls. The change in color is a physical change because you have only covered the wall. A new substance does not form. But notice the color of the precipitate in the middle photo of Figure 13. In this case, the change in color is a sign of a chemical change. The photo in the bottom of the figure shows that marshmallows change from white to brown when they are toasted. The change in the color of the marshmallows is also a sign of a chemical change.

 Reading Check What are some signs that a chemical change has occurred?

Figure 13 Formation of a gas, formation of a precipitate, and color change are all signs of a chemical change.

Formation of gas bubbles

Formation of a precipitate

Color change

 Visual Check What is a sign besides color change that indicates that the marshmallow is undergoing a chemical change?

(t) Milton Heilberg/Science Source, (bl) dmilovanovic/Getty Images, (br) Paris L. Gray/AP Images

△ **Figure 14** The flames, the light, and the sound of a fireworks display are signs of a chemical change.

Energy and Chemical Change

Think about a fireworks show. Again and again, you hear loud bangs as the fireworks burst into a display of colors, as in **Figure 14.** The release of thermal energy, light, and sound are signs that the fireworks result from chemical changes. All chemical reactions involve energy changes.

Thermal energy is often needed for a chemical reaction to take place. Suppose you want to bake pretzels, as shown in **Figure 15.** What would happen if you placed one pan of unbaked pretzel dough in the oven and another pan of unbaked pretzel dough on the kitchen counter? Only the dough in the hot oven would become pretzels. Thermal energy is needed for the chemical reactions to occur that bake the pretzels.

Energy in the form of light is needed for other chemical reactions. Photosynthesis is a chemical reaction by which plants and some unicellular organisms produce sugar and oxygen. This process only occurs if the organisms are exposed to light. Many medicines also undergo chemical reactions when exposed to light. You might have seen some medicines stored in orange bottles. If the medicines are not stored in these light-resistant bottles, the ingredients can change into other substances.

Figure 15 Thermal energy is needed for the chemical reactions that take place when baking pretzels. ▷

Can changes be reversed?

Think again about the way matter changes form during a fireworks display. Once the chemicals combine and cause the explosions, you cannot get back the original chemicals. Like most chemical changes, the fireworks display cannot be reversed.

Grating a carrot and cutting an apple are physical changes, but you cannot reverse these changes either. Making a mixture by dissolving salt in a pan of water is also a physical change. You can reverse this change by boiling the mixture. The water will change to a gas, leaving the salt behind in the pan. Some physical changes can be easily reversed, but others cannot.

Reading Check Identify one physical change that can be reversed and one that cannot be reversed.

Conservation of Mass

Physical changes do not affect the mass of substances. When ice melts, for example, the mass of the ice equals the mass of the resulting liquid water. If you cut a piece of paper into strips, the total mass of the paper remains the same. Mass is conserved, or unchanged, during a physical change.

Mass is also conserved during a chemical change. Antoine Lavoisier (AN twon · luh VWAH zee ay) (1743–1794), a French chemist, made this discovery. Lavoisier carefully measured the masses of materials before and after chemical reactions. His discovery is now a scientific law. *The **law of conservation of mass** states that the total mass before a chemical reaction is the same as the total mass after the chemical reaction.* Weight also is the same because it depends on mass. For example, the mass of an unburned match plus the mass of the oxygen it reacts with equals the mass of the ashes plus the masses of all the gases given off when the match burns.

Key Concept Check How do physical and chemical changes affect mass?

Hutchings Photography/Digital Light Source

MiniLab
10 minutes

Is mass conserved during a chemical reaction?

If you have ever seen the glow of a light stick, you have observed a chemical change. How does the chemical reaction affect the mass of the light stick?

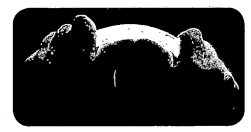

① Read and complete a lab safety form.

② Obtain a **light stick** from your teacher. Carefully remove it from the packaging.

③ Observe the structure of the light stick. Record your observations in your Science Journal.

④ Measure and record the mass of the light stick using a **balance.**

⑤ Grasp the ends of the light stick. Gently bend it to break the inner vial. Shake the stick gently to start the reaction.

⑥ Use a **stopwatch** to time the reaction for 3 minutes. Record your observations.

⑦ Repeat step 4.

Analyze and Conclude

1. **Explain** the purpose of the inner vial in the light stick.

2. **Describe** what occurred when the inner vial was broken.

3. **Key Concept** What effect did the chemical reaction have on the mass? Why?

WORD ORIGIN ·························
conservation
from Latin *conservare*, means "to keep, preserve"

Comparing Physical and Chemical Changes

Suppose you want to explain to a friend the difference between a physical change and a chemical change. What would you say? You could explain that the identity of matter does not change during a physical change, but the identity of matter does change during a chemical change. However, you might not be able to tell just by looking at a substance whether its identity changed. You cannot tell whether the particles that make up the matter are the same or different.

Sometimes deciding if a change is physical or chemical is easy. Often, however, identifying the type of change is like being a detective. You have to look for clues that will help you figure out whether the identity of the substance has changed. For example, look at the summary of physical changes and chemical changes in **Table 3**. A change in color can occur during a chemical change or when substances are mixed (a physical change). Bubbles might indicate the formation of gas (a chemical change) or boiling (a physical change). You must consider many factors when comparing physical and chemical changes.

Table 3 Chemical changes produce a new substance, but physical changes do not.

 Reading Check What are some clues you can use to decide if a change is a physical change or a chemical change?

 Interactive Table

Table 3 Comparing Physical and Chemical Changes		
Type of Change	**Examples**	**Characteristics**
Physical change	• melting • boiling • changing shape • mixing • dissolving • increasing or decreasing in temperature	• Substance is the same before and after the change. • Only physical properties change.
Chemical change	• changing color • burning • rusting • formation of gas • formation of a precipitate • spoiling food • tarnishing silver • digesting food	• Substance is different after the change. • Both physical and chemical properties change.

Physical change

Chemical change

Online Quiz

Virtual Lab

Visual Summary

The identity of a substance does not change during a physical change such as a change in the state of matter.

A new substance is produced during a chemical change.

The law of conservation of mass states that the total mass of the materials does not change during a chemical change.

FOLDABLES

Use your lesson Foldable to review the lesson. Save your Foldable for the project at the end of the chapter.

What do you think NOW?

You first read the statements below at the beginning of the chapter.

4. Mixing powdered drink mix with water causes a new substance to form.

5. If you combine two substances, bubbling is a sign that a new type of substance might be forming.

6. If you stir salt into water, the total amount of mass decreases.

Did you change your mind about whether you agree or disagree with the statements? Rewrite any false statements to make them true.

Use Vocabulary

1 The particles that make up matter do not change during a(n) _____.

Understand Key Concepts

2 **Explain** how physical and chemical changes affect the mass of a material.

3 Which is a physical change?
A. burning wood   C. rusting iron
B. melting ice   D. spoiling food

Interpret Graphics

4 **Analyze** Suppose you mix 12.8 g of one substance with 11.4 g of another. The picture shows the mass you measure for the mixture. Is this reasonable? Explain.

5 **Organize Information** Copy the graphic organizer below, and list an example of each type of change.

Type of Change	Examples
Physical change with formation of bubbles	
Chemical change with formation of bubbles	

Critical Thinking

6 **Consider** Suppose you mix baking soda and white vinegar. What signs might indicate that a chemical change occurs?

7 **Evaluate** You read that a physical change is a change in physical properties, and a chemical change is a change in chemical properties. Do you agree? Explain your answer.

Materials

mineral samples

nail

100-mL graduated cylinder

triple-beam balance

Safety

Identifying Unknown Minerals

Imagine you are a geologist digging for minerals. You find one that you would like to identify. What properties of the mineral would help you? Geologists consider many physical properties of a mineral when determining its identification.

Question

How can you use physical properties to identify unknown minerals?

Procedure

1. Read and complete a lab safety form.
2. Select a mineral sample to observe. Record its color in your Science Journal.
3. Observe the hardness of your mineral.
   a. Scratch your mineral with your fingernail. If it scratches, then your mineral has a low hardness. Go to step 4. If it does not scratch, go to step 3b.
   b. Scratch your mineral with a nail. If it scratches, it has a moderate hardness. If it does not scratch, it has a high hardness.
4. Compare the properties of your mineral with the properties in the chart.

Physical Properties of Minerals			
Mineral	Color	Typical Density (g/cm³)	Hardness
Fluorite	white or light green	3.1	moderate
Gypsum	white or brown	2.3	fairly soft
Hornblende	black or grayish brown	3.2	moderate
Magnetite (iron ore)	dark gray	5.2	moderate
Quartz	white or colorless	2.6	fairly hard
Sphalerite (zinc ore)	black or reddish brown	4.1	fairly soft

⑤ Think about the properties you observed so far. Are you able to determine which mineral you have based on your initial observations? Explain why or why not in your Science Journal.

⑥ Look back through the chapter to review the physical property *density.*

⑦ Design an experiment using mass and volume to determine the density of your mineral.

⑧ Share your procedure with your teacher for approval before conducting your experiment.

⑨ Compare your results with information in the Physical Properties of Minerals table.

Analyze and Conclude

⑩ **Infer** the identity of your mineral sample.

⑪ **The Big Idea** Which physical property was most useful in identifying the mineral? Why?

⑫ **Predict** Suppose you have another sample of the same mineral. What properties would you expect to be the same? What properties would be different?

Communicate Your Results

In a small group, share your experiences and your results. How did you collect and record data? What was successful? Did others use different techniques or get different results? Did anything surprise you?

Choose a different unknown sample to test that looks similar to the one you tested. Which properties might be different? Test your sample in the same way you tested the first one. Were the results the same or different? What can you conclude from this?

Lab Tips

☑ To measure the water in a cylinder accurately, first put your eye at the level of the liquid. Then observe the level at the meniscus (the center or bottom of the curve in the surface of the liquid).

☑ 1 mL = 1 cm³

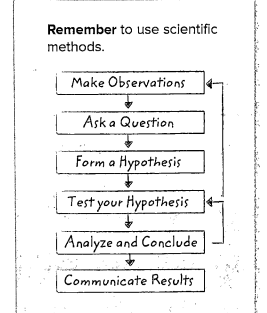

Remember to use scientific methods.

| Make Observations |
| Ask a Question |
| Form a Hypothesis |
| Test your Hypothesis |
| Analyze and Conclude |
| Communicate Results |

Hutchings Photography/Digital Light Source

Physical and chemical properties give a substance its unique identity.

Key Concepts Summary

Lesson 1: Matter and Its Properties

- Particles of a **solid** vibrate about a definite position. Particles of a **liquid** can slide past one another. Particles of a **gas** move freely within their container.
- A **physical property** is a characteristic of matter that you can observe without changing the identity of the substances that make it up. A **chemical property** is the ability or inability of a substance to combine with or change into one or more new substances.
- Some properties of matter do not depend on size or amount of the sample. You can identify a substance by comparing these properties to those of other known substances.

Lesson 2: Matter and Its Changes

- A change in the size, shape, form, or state of matter in which the identity of the matter stays the same is a **physical change.** A change in matter in which the substances that make it up change into other substances with different chemical and physical properties is a **chemical change.**
- The **law of conservation of mass** states that the total mass before a chemical reaction is the same as the total mass after the reaction.

Vocabulary

volume p. 94
solid p. 94
liquid p. 94
gas p. 94
physical property p. 96
mass p. 96
density p. 97
solubility p. 98
chemical property p. 99

physical change p. 106
chemical change p. 108
law of conservation of mass p. 111

(t)Hutchings Photography/Digital Light Source, (b)Milton Heiberg/Science Source

Vocabulary eFlashcards
Vocabulary eGames
Personal Tutor

FOLDABLES Chapter Project

Assemble your lesson Foldables as shown to make a Chapter Project. Use the project to review what you have learned in this chapter.

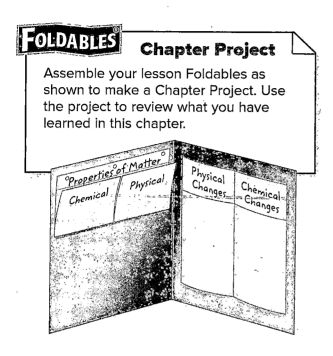

Use Vocabulary

1 A state of matter with a definite volume and a definite shape is a _____.

2 Flammability is an example of a _____ of wood because when wood burns, it changes to different materials.

3 A drink mix dissolves in water because of its _____ in water.

4 The rusting of a metal tool left in the rain is an example of a _____.

5 According to the _____, the mass of an untoasted marshmallow equals its mass after it is toasted plus the mass of any gases produced as it was toasting.

6 Slicing an apple into sections is an example of a _____ that cannot be reversed.

Link Vocabulary and Key Concepts

[▷] **Interactive Concept Map**

Copy this concept map, and then use vocabulary terms from the previous page to complete the concept map.

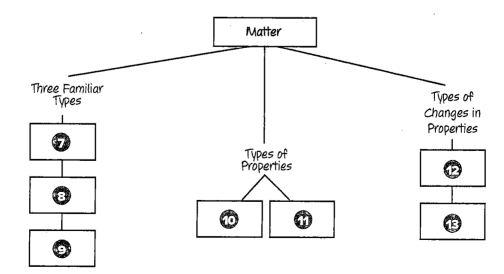

Understand Key Concepts

1 Which is a property of all solids?
- A. Particles are far apart.
- B. Particles vibrate in all directions.
- C. Volume and shape can easily change.
- D. Weak forces exist between particles.

2 Which characteristic is a chemical property?
- A. highly flammable
- B. mass of 15 kg
- C. woolly texture
- D. golden color

3 Which property of an object depends on its location?
- A. density
- B. mass
- C. volume
- D. weight

4 How are the particles of a gas different from the particles of a liquid shown here?

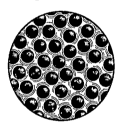

- A. They move more slowly.
- B. They are farther apart.
- C. They have less energy.
- D. They have stronger attractions.

5 Which is a physical change?
- A. burning natural gas
- B. chopping onions
- C. digesting food
- D. exploding dynamite

6 Which stays the same when a substance changes from a liquid to a gas?
- A. density
- B. mass
- C. forces between particles
- D. distance between particles

7 Which is a chemical change?
- A. boiling water
- B. copper turning green in air
- C. freezing fruit juice
- D. slicing a potato

8 Which would be most useful for identifying an unknown liquid?
- A. density
- B. mass
- C. volume
- D. weight

9 What mass is measured on this balance?

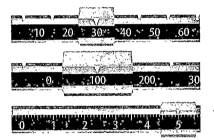

- A. 35 g
- B. 45 g
- C. 135 g
- D. 145 g

10 What causes a chemical reaction when you prepare scrambled eggs?
- A. removing the eggs from the shells
- B. mixing the egg yolks and the egg whites together
- C. heating the eggs in a pan
- D. sprinkling pepper onto the cooked eggs

11 Which describes the formation of a precipitate?
- A. A gas forms when a solid is placed in a liquid.
- B. A liquid forms when a block of metal is heated.
- C. A solid forms when one liquid is poured into another.
- D. Bubbles form when an acid is poured onto a rock.

Critical Thinking

12 Apply Suppose you find a gold-colored ring. Explain why you could use some physical properties but not others to determine whether the ring is actually made of gold.

13 Reason You make lemonade by mixing lemon juice, sugar, and water. Is this a physical change or a chemical change? Explain.

14 Give an example of a physical change you might observe at your school that is reversible and a physical change that is not reversible.

15 Defend A classmate defines a liquid as any substance that can be poured. Use the picture below to explain why this is not an acceptable definition.

16 Suggest a way that you could use displacement to determine the volume of a rock that is too large to fit into a graduated cylinder.

17 Hypothesize A scientist measures the mass of two liquids before and after combining them. The mass after combining the liquids is less than the sum of the masses before. Where is the missing mass?

Writing in Science

18 Write a four-sentence description of an object in your home or classroom. Be sure to identify both physical properties and chemical properties of the object.

REVIEW THE BIG IDEA

19 What gives a substance its unique identity?

20 What are some physical and chemical properties that an airplane manufacturer must consider when choosing materials to be used in constructing the shell of the aircraft shown below?

Math Skills ✕÷ Math Practice

21 Use what you have learned about density to complete the table below. Then, determine the identities of the two unknown metals.

Metal	Mass (g)	Volume (cm³)	Density (g/cm³)
Iron	42.5	5.40	
Lead	28.8	2.55	
Tungsten	69.5	3.60	
Zinc	46.4	6.50	
	61.0	5.40	
	46.4	2.40	

age fotostock/SuperStock

Record your answers on the answer sheet provided by your teacher or on a sheet of paper.

Multiple Choice

1 Which describes the particles in a substance with no definite volume or shape?

   A Particles are close but can move freely.

   B Particles are close but can vibrate in all directions.

   C Particles are far apart and cannot move.

   D Particles are far apart and move freely.

2 Which diagram shows a chemical change?

   A

   B

   C

   D

3 Which is NOT true about firewood that burns completely?

   A Ashes and gases form from the substances in the wood.

   B Oxygen from the air combines with substances in the wood.

   C The total mass of substances in this process decreases.

   D The wood gives off thermal energy and light.

Use the diagram below to answer question 4.

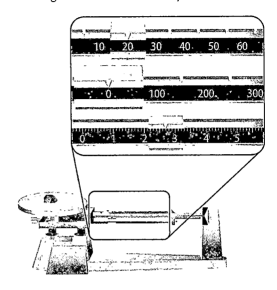

4 What is the mass of the object on the balance scale?

   A 22 g

   B 22.5 g

   C 22.7 g

   D 30 g

5 Which is true when an ice cube melts?

   A Volume and mass increase.

   B Volume and mass do not change.

   C Volume decreases, but mass does not change.

   D Volume increases, but mass decreases.

6 What is the BEST way to separate and save the parts of a sand-and-water mixture?

   A Boil the mixture and collect the steam.

   B Pour the mixture through a filter that only the water can pass through.

   C Lift the sand out of the mix with a spoon.

   D Pour a strong acid into the mixture to dissolve the sand.

Use the table below to answer questions 7 and 8.

Action	Time	Result
Heated	30 minutes	solid
Heated	60 minutes	liquid
Not heated	30 minutes	solid
Not heated	60 minutes	solid

7   Based on the results of this experiment, what can you conclude about heating this unknown substance?

   A   Heating melted it in 30 minutes.

   B   Heating melted it in 60 minutes.

   C   Heating made it solid in 60 minutes.

   D   Heating caused no changes.

8   What can you conclude about the original state of the substance?

   A   It is part solid and part liquid.

   B   It is a liquid.

   C   It is a solid.

   D   It is part liquid and part gas.

9   Which is a sign of a physical change?

   A   Bread gets moldy with age.

   B   Ice forms on a puddle in winter.

   C   The metal on a car starts to rust.

   D   Yeast causes bread dough to rise.

Constructed Response

Use the table below to answer questions 10–13.

Properties	Substance 1	Substance 2	Substance 3
Color	yellow	yellow	yellow
State	solid	solid	solid
Mass	217 g	217 g	75 g
Melting point	505°C	230°C	505°C
Density	3.78 g/cm³	2.76 g/cm³	3.78 g/cm³
Flammable	yes	yes	yes

10   Identify each property of the unknown substances as either chemical or physical. Explain your reasoning.

11   Of the three unknown substances tested, two are the same substance and one is different. Which two substances do you think are the same? Explain your reasoning.

12   Which properties in the table helped you determine your answer in number 11? Which properties were not helpful? Explain your reasoning.

13   What additional physical and chemical properties of substances might the table have included?

NEED EXTRA HELP?													
If You Missed Question...	1	2	3	4	5	6	7	8	9	10	11	12	13
Go to Lesson...	1	2	2	1	1, 2	1	2	2	2	1	1	1	1

Chapter 4

7.PS.2, 7.PS.3, SEPS.2, SEPS.3, SEPS.4, SEPS.5, SEPS.6, SEPS.8, 6-8.LST.4.1, 6-8.LST.5.2

States of Matter

THE BIG IDEA

What physical changes and energy changes occur as matter goes from one state to another?

Inquiry Liquid Glass?

When you look at this blob of molten glass, can you envision it as a beautiful vase? The solid glass was heated in a furnace until it formed a molten liquid. Air is blown through a pipe to make the glass hollow and give it form.

- Can you identify a solid, a liquid, and a gas in the photo?

- What physical changes and energy changes do you think occurred when the glass changed state?

Gregor M. Schmid/Corbis

What do you think?

Before you read, decide if you agree or disagree with each of these statements. As you read this chapter, see if you change your mind about any of the statements.

1. Particles moving at the same speed make up all matter.

2. The particles in a solid do not move.

3. Particles of matter have both potential energy and kinetic energy.

4. When a solid melts, thermal energy is removed from the solid.

5. Changes in temperature and pressure affect gas behavior.

6. If the pressure on a gas increases, the volume of the gas also increases.

Mc Graw Hill Education **connectED**

Your one-stop online resource
connectED.mcgraw-hill.com

 LearnSmart™

 Chapter Resources Files, Reading Essentials, Get Ready to Read, Quick Vocabulary

 Animations, Videos, Interactive Tables

 Self-checks, Quizzes, Tests

 Project-Based Learning Activities

 Lab Manuals, Safety Videos, Virtual Labs & Other Tools

 Vocabulary, Multilingual eGlossary, Vocab eGames, Vocab eFlashcards

 Personal Tutors

Reading Guide

Key Concepts 🗝

ESSENTIAL QUESTIONS

- How do particles move in solids, liquids, and gases?

- How are the forces between particles different in solids, liquids, and gases?

Vocabulary

solid p. 127

liquid p. 128

viscosity p. 128

surface tension p. 129

gas p. 130

vapor p. 130

 Multilingual eGlossary

 7.PS.2, SEPS.2, SEPS.6, SEPS.8, 6-8.LST.4.1

Solids, Liquids, and Gases

Inquiry) Giant Bubbles?

Giant bubbles can be made from a solution of water, soap, and a syrupy liquid called glycerine. These liquids change the properties of water. Soap changes water's surface tension. Glycerine changes the evaporation rate. How do surface tension and evaporation work?

How can you see particles in matter?

It's sometimes difficult to picture how tiny objects, such as the particles that make up matter, move. However, you can use other objects to model the movement of these particles.

1. Read and complete a lab safety form.

2. Place about 50 **copper pellets** into a **plastic petri dish.** Place the cover on the dish, and secure it with **tape.**

3. Hold the dish by the edges. Gently vibrate the dish from side to side no more than 1–2 mm. Observe the pellets. Record your observations in your Science Journal.

4. Repeat step 3, vibrating the dish less than 1 cm from side to side.

5. Repeat step 3, vibrating the dish 3–4 cm from side to side.

Think About This

1. If the pellets represent particles in matter, what do you think the shaking represents?

2. In which part of the experiment do you think the pellets were like a liquid? Explain.

3. 🔑 **Key Concept** If the pellets represent molecules of water, what do you think are the main differences among molecules of ice, water, and vapor?

Describing Matter

Take a closer look at the photo on the previous page. Do you see matter? The three most common forms, or states, of matter on Earth are solids, liquids, and gases. The giant bubble contains air, which is a mixture of gases. The ocean water and the soap mixture used to make the bubble are liquids. The sand, sign, and walkway are a few of the solids in the photo.

There is a fourth state of matter, plasma, that is not shown in this photo. Plasma is high-energy matter consisting of positively and negatively charged particles. Plasma is the most common state of matter in space. It also is in lightning flashes, fluorescent lighting, and stars, such as the Sun.

There are many ways to describe matter. You can describe the state, the color, the texture, and the odor of matter using your senses. You also can describe matter using measurements, such as mass, volume, and density. Mass is the amount of matter in an object. The units for mass are often grams (g) or kilograms (kg). Volume is the amount of space that a sample of matter occupies. The units for liquid volume are usually liters (L) or milliliters (mL). The units for solid volume are usually cubic centimeters (cm^3) or cubic meters (m^3). Density is the mass per unit volume of a substance. The units are usually g/cm^3 or g/mL. Density of a given substance remains constant, regardless of the size of the sample.

Hutchings Photography/Digital Light Source

Particles in Motion

Have you ever wondered what makes something a solid, a liquid, or a gas? Two main factors that determine the state of matter are particle motion and particle forces.

Particles, such as atoms, ions, or molecules, moving in different ways make up all matter. The particles that make up some matter are close together and vibrate back and forth. In other types of matter, the particles are farther apart, move freely, and can spread out. Regardless of how close particles are to each other, they all move in random motion—movement in all directions and at different speeds. However, particles will move in straight lines until they collide with something. Collisions change the speed and direction of the particles' movements.

Forces Between Particles

Recall that atoms that make up matter contain positively charged protons and negatively charged electrons. There is a force of attractions between these oppositely charged particles, as shown in Figure 1.

You just read that the particles that make up matter move at all speeds and in all directions. If the motion of particles slows, the particles move closer together. This is because the attraction between them pulls them toward each other. Strong attractive forces hold particles close together. As the motion of particles increases, particles move farther apart. The attractive forces between particles get weaker. The spaces between them increase and the particles can slip past one another. As the motion of particles continues to increase, they move even farther apart. Eventually, the distance between particles is so great that there are little or no attractive forces between the particles. The particles move randomly and spread out. As you continue to read, you will learn how particle motion and particle forces determine whether matter is a solid, a liquid, or a gas.

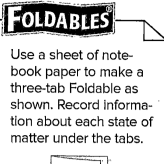

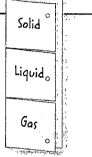

Solid

Liquid

Gas

Figure 1 The forces between particles of matter and the movement of particles determine the physical state of matter.

 Animation

Particles move slowly and can only vibrate in place. Therefore, the attractive forces between particles are strong.

Particles move faster and slip past each other. The distance between particles increases. Therefore, the attractive forces between particles are weaker.

Particles move fast. The distance between the particles is great, and therefore, the attractive forces between particles are very weak.

Solids

If you had to describe a solid, what would you say? You might say, a **solid** *is matter that has a definite shape and a definite volume.* For example, if the skateboard in Figure 2 moves from one location to another, the shape and volume of it do not change.

Particles in a Solid

Why doesn't a solid change its shape and volume? Notice in Figure 2 how the particles in a solid are close together. The particles are very close to their neighboring particles. That's because the attractive forces between the particles are strong and hold them close together. The strong attractive forces and slow motion of the particles keep them tightly held in their positions. The particles simply vibrate back and forth in place. This arrangement gives solids a definite shape and volume.

 Key Concept Check Describe the movement of particles in a solid and the forces between them.

Types of Solids

All solids are not the same. For example, a diamond and a piece of charcoal don't look alike. However, they are both solids made of only carbon atoms. A diamond and a lump of charcoal both contain particles that strongly attract each other and vibrate in place. What makes them different is the arrangement of their particles. Notice in Figure 3 that the arrangement of particles in a diamond is different from that in charcoal. A diamond is a crystalline solid. It has particles arranged in a specific, repeating order. Charcoal is an amorphous solid. It has particles arranged randomly. Different particle arrangements give these materials different properties. For example, a diamond is a hard material, and charcoal is a brittle material.

 Reading Check What is the difference between crystalline and amorphous solids?

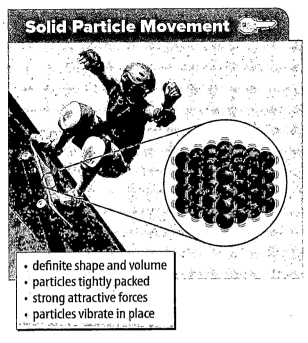

Solid Particle Movement

- definite shape and volume
- particles tightly packed
- strong attractive forces
- particles vibrate in place

△ **Figure 2** The particles in a solid have strong attractive forces and vibrate in place.

Figure 3 Carbon is a solid that can have different particle arrangements. ▽

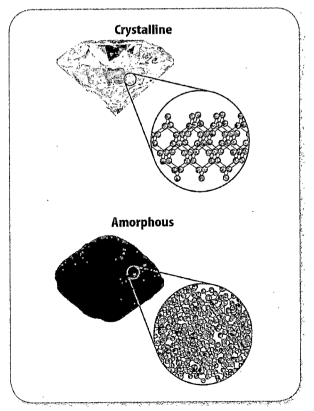

Crystalline

Amorphous

Figure 4 The motion of particles in a liquid causes the particles to move slightly farther apart. ▷

@ **Visual Check** How does the spacing among these particles compare to the particle spacing in **Figure 2**?

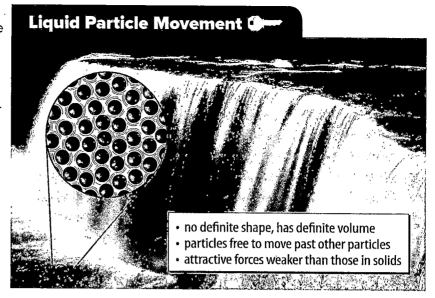

Liquid Particle Movement 0—

• no definite shape, has definite volume
• particles free to move past other particles
• attractive forces weaker than those in solids

Liquids

You have probably seen a waterfall, such as the one in Figure 4. Water is a liquid. *A* **liquid** *is matter with a definite volume but no definite shape.* Liquids flow and can take the shape of their containers. The container for this water is the riverbed.

Particles in a Liquid

How can liquids change their shape? The particle motion in the liquid state of a material is faster than the particle motion in the solid state. This increased particle motion causes the particles to move slightly farther apart. As the particles move farther apart, the attractive forces between the particles decrease. The weaker attractive forces allow particles to slip past one another. The weather forces also enable liquids to flow and take the shape of their containers.

Viscosity

WORD ORIGIN ···········

viscosity
from Latin *viscum,* means "sticky"

If you have ever poured or dipped honey, as shown in Figure 5, you have experienced a liquid with a high viscosity. **Viscosity** (vihs KAW sih tee) *is a measurement of a liquid's resistance to flow.* Honey has high viscosity, while water has low viscosity. Viscosity is due to particle mass, particle shape, and the strength of the attraction between the particles of a liquid. In general, the stronger the attractive forces between particles, the higher the viscosity. For many liquids, viscosity decreases as the liquid becomes warmer. As a liquid becomes warmer, particles begin to move faster and the attractive forces between them get weaker. This allows particles to more easily slip past one another. The mass and shape of particles that make up a liquid also affect viscosity. Large particles or particles with complex shapes tend to move more slowly and have difficulty slipping past one another.

Figure 5 Honey has a high viscosity. ▽

Figure 6 The surface tension of water enables this spider to walk on the surface of a lake.

Surface Tension

How can the nursery web spider in **Figure 6** walk on water? Believe it or not, it is because of the interactions between molecules.

The blowout in **Figure 6** shows the attractive forces between water molecules. Water molecules below the surface are surrounded on all sides by other water molecules. Therefore, they have attractive forces, or pulls, in all directions. The attraction between similar molecules, such as water molecules, is called cohesion.

Water molecules at the surface of a liquid do not have liquid water molecules above them. As a result, they experience a greater downward pull, and the surface particles become tightly stretched like the head of a drum. Molecules at the surface of a liquid have **surface tension,** *the uneven forces acting on the particles on the surface of a liquid.* Surface tension allows a spider to walk on water. In general, the stronger the attractive forces between particles, the greater the surface tension of the liquid.

Recall the giant bubbles at the beginning of the chapter. The thin water-soap film surrounding the bubbles forms because of surface tension between the particles.

 Key Concept Check Describe the movement of particles in a liquid and the forces between them.

(l)Alasdair Thomson/Getty Images; (r)Hutchings Photography/Digital Light Source

MiniLab 20 minutes

How can you make bubble films?

Have you ever observed surface tension? Which liquids have greater surface tension?

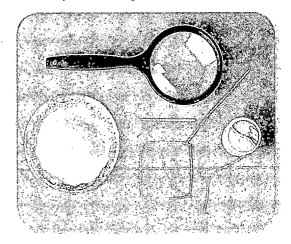

1. Read and complete a lab safety form.
2. Place about 100 mL of cool water in a **small bowl.** Lower a **wire bubble frame** into the bowl, and gently lift it. Use a **magnifying lens** to observe the edges of the frame. Write your observations in your Science Journal.
3. Add a full **dropper** of **liquid dishwashing soap** to the water. Stir with a **toothpick** until mixed. Lower the frame into the mixture and lift it out. Record your observations.
4. Use a toothpick to break the bubble film on one side of the thread. Observe.

Analyze and Conclude

1. **Recognize Cause and Effect** Explain what caused the thread to form an arc when half the bubble film broke.

2. **Key Concept** Explain why pure water doesn't form bubbles. What happens to the forces between water molecules when you add soap?

- no definite shape or volume
- particles far apart and move freely
- slight or weak attractive forces between particles

Figure 7 The particles in a gas are far apart, and there are little or no attractive forces between particles.

Visual Check What are gas particles likely to hit as they move?

Gases

Look at the photograph in **Figure 7**. Where is the gas? *A gas is matter that has no definite volume and no definite shape.* It is not easy to identify the gas because you cannot see it. However, gas particles are inside and outside the inflatable balls. Air is a mixture of gases, including nitrogen, oxygen, argon, and carbon dioxide.

Reading Check What is a gas, and what is another object that contains a gas?

Particles in a Gas

Why don't gases have definite volumes or definite shapes like solids and liquids? Compare the particles in **Figures 2, 4,** and **7**. Notice how the distance between particles differs. As the particles move faster, such as when matter goes from the solid state to the liquid state, the particles move farther apart. When the particles in matter move even faster, such as when matter goes from the liquid state to the gas state, the particles move even farther apart. When the distances between particles change, the attractive forces between the particles also change.

Forces Between Particles

As a type of matter goes from the solid state to the liquid state, the distance between the particles increases and the attractive forces between the particles decrease. When the same matter goes from the liquid state to the gas state, the particles are even farther apart and the attractive forces between the particles are weak or absent. As a result, the particles spread out to fill their container. Because gas particles lack attractive forces between particles, they have no definite shape or definite volume.

Vapor

Have you ever heard the term *vapor?* *The gas state of a substance that is normally a solid or a liquid at room temperature is called* **vapor.** For example, water is normally a liquid at room temperature. When it is in a gas state, such as in air, it is called water vapor. Other substances that can form a vapor are rubbing alcohol, iodine, mercury, and gasoline.

Key Concept Check How do particles move and interact in a gas?

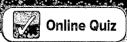
Visual Summary

The particles that make up a solid can only vibrate in place. The particles are close together, and there are strong forces among them.

The particles that make up a liquid are far enough apart that particles can flow past other particles. The forces among these particles are weaker than those in a solid.

The particles that make up a gas are far apart. There is little or no attraction between the particles.

FOLDABLES

Use your lesson Foldable to review the lesson. Save your Foldable for the project at the end of the chapter.

What do you think NOW?

You first read the statements below at the beginning of the chapter.

1. Particles moving at the same speed make up all matter.

2. The particles in a solid do not move.

Did you change your mind about whether you agree or disagree with the statements? Rewrite any false statements to make them true.

Use Vocabulary

1. A measurement of how strongly particles attract one another at the surface of a liquid is _____.

2. **Define** *solid, liquid,* and *gas* in your own words.

3. A measurement of a liquid's resistance to flow is known as _____.

Understand Key Concepts

4. Which state of matter rarely is found on Earth?
   A. gas
   B. liquid
   C. plasma
   D. solid

5. **Compare** particle movement in solids, liquids, and gases.

6. **Compare** the forces between particles in a liquid and in a gas.

Interpret Graphics

7. **Explain** why the particles at the surface in the image below have surface tension while the particles below the surface do not.

8. **Summarize** Copy and fill in the graphic organizer to compare two types of solids.

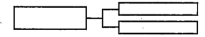

Critical Thinking

9. **Hypothesize** how you could change the viscosity of a cold liquid, and explain why your idea would work.

10. **Summarize** the relationship between the motion of particles and attractive forces between particles.

Freeze-Drying Foods

Have you noticed that the berries you find in some breakfast cereals are lightweight and dry—much different from the berries you get from the market or the garden?

Fresh fruit would spoil quickly if it were packaged in breakfast cereal, so fruits in cereals are often freeze-dried. When liquid is returned to the freeze-dried fruit, its physical properties more closely resemble fresh fruit. Freeze-drying, or lyophilization (lie ah fuh luh ZAY shun), is the process in which a solvent (usually water) is removed from a solid. During this process, a frozen solvent changes to a gas without going through the liquid state. Freeze-dried foods are lightweight and long-lasting. Astronauts have been using freeze-dried food during space travel since the 1960s.

How Freeze-Drying Works

1 Machines called freeze-dryers are used to freeze-dry foods and other products. Fresh or cooked food is flash-frozen, changing moisture in the food to a solid.

2 The frozen food is placed in a large vacuum chamber, where moisture is removed. Heat is applied to accelerate moisture removal. Condenser plates remove vaporized solvent from the chamber and convert the frozen food to a freeze-dried solid.

3 Freeze-dried food is sealed in oxygen- and moisture-proof packages to ensure stability and freshness. When the food is rehydrated, it returns to its near-normal state of weight, color, and texture.

It's Your Turn

PREDICT/DISCOVER What kinds of products besides food are freeze-dried? Use library or internet resources to learn about other products that undergo the freeze-drying process. Discuss the benefits or drawbacks of freeze-drying.

Lesson 2

Reading Guide

Key Concepts 🗝

ESSENTIAL QUESTIONS

- How is temperature related to particle motion?
- How are temperature and thermal energy different?
- What happens to thermal energy when matter changes from one state to another?

Vocabulary

kinetic energy p. 134

temperature p. 134

thermal energy p. 135

vaporization p. 137

evaporation p. 138

condensation p. 138

sublimation p. 138

deposition p. 138

 Multilingual eGlossary

 BrainPOP®
What's Science Got to do With It?"

 7.PS.2, 7.PS.3, SEPS.2

 Go to the resource tab in ConnectED to find the PBL *Particles in Motion.*

Changes in State

Inquiry Spring Thaw?

When you look at a snowman, you probably don't think about states of matter. However, water is one of the few substances that you frequently observe in three states of matter at Earth's temperatures. What energy changes are involved when matter changes state?

Do liquid particles move?

If you look at a glass of milk sitting on a table, it appears to have no motion. But appearances can be deceiving!

1. Read and complete a lab safety form.

2. Use a **dropper,** and place one drop of **2 percent milk** on a **glass slide.** Add a **cover slip.**

3. Place the slide on a **microscope** stage, and focus on low power. Focus on a single globule of fat in the milk. Observe the motion of the globule for several minutes. Record your observations in your Science Journal.

Think About This

1. Describe the motion of the fat globule.

2. What do you think caused the motion of the globule?

3. 🔑 **Key Concept** What do you think would happen to the motion of the fat globule if you warmed the milk? Explain.

Kinetic and Potential Energy

When snow begins to melt after a snowstorm, all three states of water are present. The snow is a solid, the melted snow is a liquid, and the air above the snow and ice contains water vapor, a gas. What causes particles to change state?

Kinetic Energy

Recall that the particles that make up matter are in constant motion. These particles have **kinetic energy,** *the energy an object has due to its motion.* The faster particles move, the more kinetic energy they have. Within a given substance, such as water, particles in the solid state have the least amount of kinetic energy. This is because they only vibrate in place. Particles in the liquid state move faster than particles in the solid state. Therefore, they have more kinetic energy. Particles in the gaseous state move very quickly and have the most kinetic energy of particles of a given substance.

Temperature *is a measure of the average kinetic energy of all the particles in an object.* Within a given substance, a temperature increase means that the particles, on average, are moving at greater speeds, or have a greater average kinetic energy. For example, water molecules at 25°C are generally moving faster and have more kinetic energy than water molecules at 10°C.

☑️ **Key Concept Check** How is temperature related to particle motion?

Potential Energy

In addition to kinetic energy, particles have potential energy. Potential energy is stored energy due to the interactions between particles or objects. For example, when you pick up a ball and then let it go, the gravitational force between the ball and Earth causes the ball to fall toward Earth. Before you let the ball go, it has potential energy.

Potential energy typically increases when objects get farther apart and decreases when they get closer together. The basketball in the top part of Figure 8 is farther off the ground than it is in the bottom part of the figure. The farther an object is from Earth's surface, the greater the gravitational potential energy. As the ball gets closer to the ground, the potential energy decreases.

You can think of the potential energy of particles in a similar way. The chemical potential energy is due to the position of the particles relative to other particles. The chemical potential energy of particles increases and decreases as the distances between particles increase or decrease. The particles in the top part of Figure 8 are farther apart than the particles in the bottom part. The particles that are farther apart have greater chemical potential energy.

Thermal Energy

Thermal energy *is the total potential and kinetic energies of an object.* You can change an object's state of matter by adding or removing thermal energy. When you add thermal energy to an object, the particles either move faster (increased kinetic energy) or get farther apart (increased potential energy) or both. The opposite is true when you remove thermal energy from an object. If enough thermal energy is added or removed, a change of state can occur.

 Key Concept Check How do thermal energy and temperature differ?

Figure 8 The potential energy of the ball depends on the distance between the ball and Earth. The potential energy of particles in matter depends on the distances between the particles.

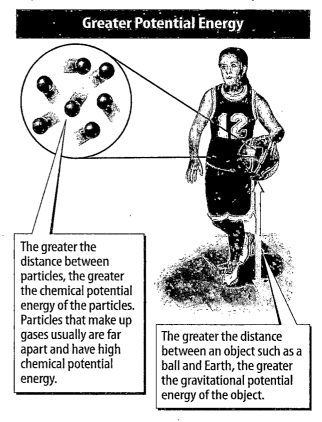

Greater Potential Energy

The greater the distance between particles, the greater the chemical potential energy of the particles. Particles that make up gases usually are far apart and have high chemical potential energy.

The greater the distance between an object such as a ball and Earth, the greater the gravitational potential energy of the object.

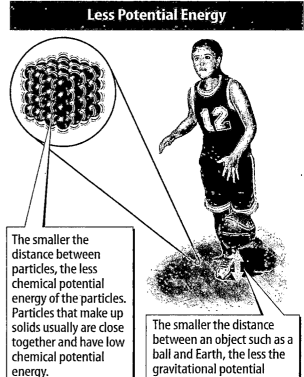

Less Potential Energy

The smaller the distance between particles, the less chemical potential energy of the particles. Particles that make up solids usually are close together and have low chemical potential energy.

The smaller the distance between an object such as a ball and Earth, the less the gravitational potential energy of the object.

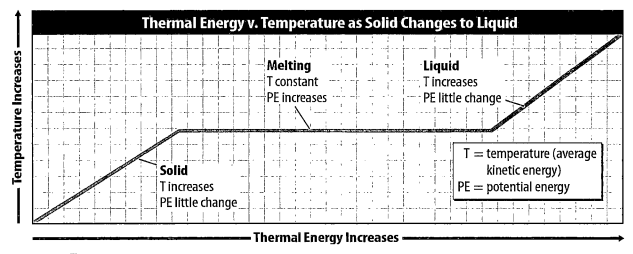

Thermal Energy v. Temperature as Solid Changes to Liquid

Melting
T constant
PE increases

Liquid
T increases
PE little change

Solid
T increases
PE little change

T = temperature (average kinetic energy)
PE = potential energy

Temperature Increases →

Thermal Energy Increases →

Figure 9 Adding thermal energy to matter causes the particles that make up the matter to increase in kinetic energy, potential energy, or both.

Visual Check During melting, which factor remains constant?

Solid to Liquid or Liquid to Solid

When you drink a beverage from an aluminum can, do you recycle the can? Aluminum recycling is one example of a process that involves changing matter from one state to another by adding or removing thermal energy.

Melting

The recycling process involves melting clean, shredded aluminum cans. To change matter from a solid to a liquid, thermal energy must be added. The graph in **Figure 9** shows the relationship between increasing temperature and increasing thermal energy (potential energy + kinetic energy).

At first, both the thermal energy and the temperature increase. The temperature stops increasing when it reaches the melting point of the matter, the temperature at which the solid state changes to the liquid state. As aluminum changes from solid to liquid, the temperature does not change. However, energy changes still occur.

Reading Check What is added to matter to change it from a solid to a liquid?

Energy Changes

What happens when a solid reaches its melting point? Notice the line on the graph is horizontal. This means that the temperature, or average kinetic energy, stops increasing. However, the amount of thermal energy continues to increase. How is this possible?

Once a solid reaches its melting point, the average speed of particles does not change, but the distance between the particles does change. The particles move farther apart and potential energy increases. Once a solid completely melts, the addition of thermal energy will cause the kinetic energy of the particles to increase again, as shown by a temperature increase.

Freezing

After the aluminum melts, it is poured into molds to cool. As the aluminum cools, thermal energy leaves it. Freezing is a process that is the reverse of melting. The temperature at which matter changes from the liquid state to the solid state is its freezing point. To observe the temperature and thermal energy changes that occur to hot aluminum blocks, move from right to left on the graph in **Figure 9.**

During evaporation, a liquid vaporizes only at its surface.

During boiling, a liquid vaporizes at its surface and within the liquid.

Bubbles, or vaporized particles, rise to the top of the liquid and escape from the container.

Liquid to Gas or Gas to Liquid

When you heat water, do you ever notice how bubbles begin to form at the bottom and rise to the surface? The bubbles contain water vapor, a gas. *The change in state of a liquid into a gas is* **vaporization.** Figure 10 shows two types of vaporization—evaporation and boiling.

Boiling

Vaporization that occurs within a liquid is called boiling. The temperature at which boiling occurs in a liquid is called its boiling point. In Figure 11, notice the energy changes that occur during this process. The kinetic energy of particles increases until the liquid reaches its boiling point.

At the boiling point, the potential energy of particles begins increasing. The particles move farther apart until the attractive forces no longer hold them together. At this point, the liquid changes to a gas. When boiling ends, if thermal energy continues to be added, the kinetic energy of the gas particles begins to increase again. Therefore, the temperature begins to increase again as shown on the graph.

△ **Figure 10** ☞ Boiling and evaporation are two kinds of vaporization.

🔍**Visual Check** Why doesn't the evaporation flask have bubbles below the surface?

Personal Tutor

Applying Practices
State Changed, Mass Conserved? Go online to investigate the law of conservation of mass by measuring and comparing the mass of a substance before and after a change of state.

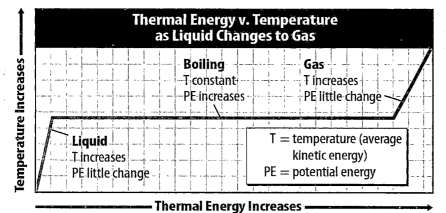

Thermal Energy v. Temperature as Liquid Changes to Gas

Boiling
T constant
PE increases

Gas
T increases
PE little change

Liquid
T increases
PE little change

T = temperature (average kinetic energy)
PE = potential energy

Temperature Increases →

Thermal Energy Increases →

◁ **Figure 11** ☞ When thermal energy is added to a liquid, kinetic energy and potential energy changes occur.

WORD ORIGIN
evaporation
from Latin *evaporare*, means
"disperse in steam or vapor"

Evaporation

Unlike boiling, **evaporation** *is vaporization that occurs only at the surface of a liquid.* Liquid in an open container will vaporize, or change to a gas, over time due to evaporation.

Condensation

Boiling and evaporation are processes that change a liquid to a gas. A reverse process also occurs. When a gas loses enough thermal energy, the gas changes to a liquid, or condenses. *The change of state from a gas to a liquid is called* **condensation.** Overnight, water vapor often condenses on blades of grass, forming dew.

Solid to Gas or Gas to Solid

Is it possible for a solid to become a gas without turning to a liquid first? Yes, in fact, dry ice does. Dry ice, as shown in **Figure 12,** is solid carbon dioxide. It turns immediately into a gas when thermal energy is added to it. The process is called sublimation. **Sublimation** *is the change of state from a solid to a gas without going through the liquid state.* As dry ice sublimes, it cools and condenses the water vapor in the surrounding air, creating a thick fog.

The opposite of sublimation is deposition. **Deposition** *is the change of state of a gas to a solid without going through the liquid state.* For deposition to occur, thermal energy has to be removed from the gas. You might see deposition in autumn when you wake up and there is frost on the grass. As water vapor loses thermal energy, it changes into a solid known as frost.

Reading Check Why are sublimation and deposition unusual changes of state?

Figure 12 Dry ice sublimes—goes directly from the solid state to the gas state—when thermal energy is added. Frost is an example of the opposite process—deposition.

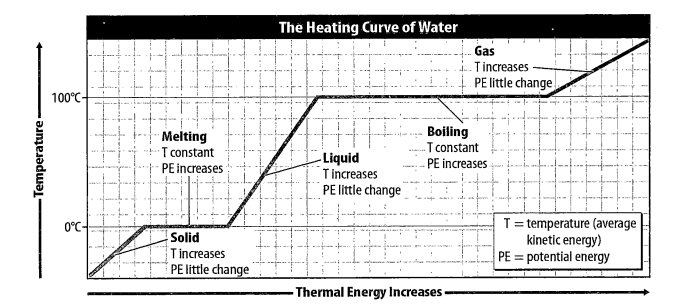

The Heating Curve of Water

Temperature

100°C

0°C

Melting
T constant
PE increases

Solid
T increases
PE little change

Liquid
T increases
PE little change

Gas
T increases
PE little change

Boiling
T constant
PE increases

T = temperature (average kinetic energy)
PE = potential energy

Thermal Energy Increases →

States of Water

Water is the only substance that exists naturally as a solid, a liquid, and a gas within Earth's temperature range. To better understand the energy changes during a change in state, it is helpful to study the heating curve of water, as shown in **Figure 13.**

Adding Thermal Energy

Suppose you place a beaker of ice on a hot plate. The hot plate transfers thermal energy to the beaker and then to the ice. The temperature of the ice increases. Recall that this means the average kinetic energy of the water molecules increases.

At 0°C, the melting point of water, the water molecules vibrate so rapidly that they begin to move out of their places. At this point, added thermal energy only increases the distance between particles and decreases attractive forces–melting occurs. Once melting is complete, the average kinetic energy of the particles (temperature) begins to increase again as more thermal energy is added.

When water reaches 100°C, the boiling point, liquid water begins to change to water vapor. Again, kinetic energy is constant as vaporization occurs. When the change of state is complete, the kinetic energy of molecules increases once more, and so does the temperature.

 Key Concept Check Describe the changes in thermal energy as water goes from a solid to a liquid.

Removing Thermal Energy

The removal of thermal energy is the reverse of the process shown in **Figure 13.** Cooling water vapor changes the gas to a liquid. Cooling the water further changes it to ice.

Figure 13  Water undergoes energy changes and state changes as thermal energy is added and removed.

▷ **Animation**

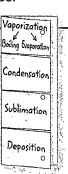

FOLDABLES

Fold a sheet of notebook paper to make a four-tab Foldable as shown. Label the tabs, define the terms, and record what you learn about each term under the tabs.

Vaporization
Boiling Evaporation

Condensation

Sublimation

Deposition

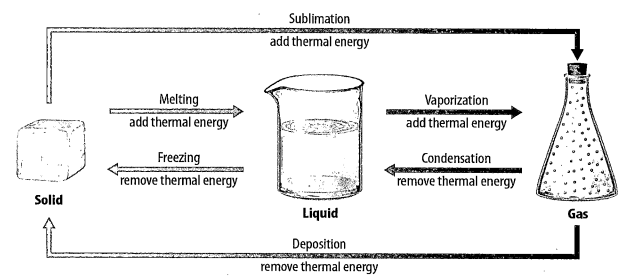

Figure 14 For a change of state to occur, thermal energy must move into or out of matter.

Conservation of Mass and Energy

The diagram in **Figure 14** illustrates the energy changes that occur as thermal energy is added or removed from matter. Notice that opposite processes, melting and freezing and vaporization and condensation, are shown. When matter changes state, matter and energy are always conserved.

When water vaporizes, it appears to disappear. If the invisible gas is captured and its mass added to the remaining mass of the liquid, you would see that matter is conserved. This is also true for energy. Surrounding matter, such as air, often absorbs thermal energy. If you measured all the thermal energy, you would find that energy is conserved.

🔖 MiniLab   20 minutes

How can you make a water thermometer?

What causes liquid in a thermometer to rise and fall?

① Read and complete a lab safety form.

② Place one drop of **food coloring** in a **flask.** Fill the flask to the top with room temperature tap water. Over a **sink or pan,** insert a **one-holed stopper fitted with a glass tube** into the flask. Press down gently. The liquid should rise partway into the tube. Mark the level of the water with a **grease pencil.**

③ Holding the flask by its neck, lower the flask into a pan of hot water. Observe the water level for 3 min. Record your observations in your Science Journal.

④ Remove the flask from the hot water, and lower it into a pan of **ice water.** Observe the water level for 3 min, and record your observations.

Analyze and Conclude

Key Concept Explain what happens to the column of water and the water particles as they are heated and cooled.

Hutchings Photography/Digital Light Source

Visual Summary

All matter has thermal energy. Thermal energy is the sum of potential and kinetic energy.

When thermal energy is added to a liquid, vaporization can occur.

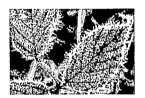

When enough thermal energy is removed from matter, a change of state can occur.

FOLDABLES

Use your lesson Foldable to review the lesson. Save your Foldable for the project at the end of the chapter.

What do you think NOW?

You first read the statements below at the beginning of the chapter.

3. Particles of matter have both potential energy and kinetic energy.

4. When a solid melts, thermal energy is removed from the solid.

Did you change your mind about whether you agree or disagree with the statements? Rewrite any false statements to make them true.

Use Vocabulary

1. The measure of average kinetic energy of the particles in a material is _____.

2. **Define** *kinetic energy* and *thermal energy* in your own words.

3. The change of a liquid into a gas is known as _____.

Understand Key Concepts

4. The process that is opposite of condensation is known as
   A. deposition.   C. melting.
   B. freezing.   D. vaporization.

5. **Explain** how temperature and particle motion are related.

6. **Describe** the relationship between temperature and thermal energy.

7. **Generalize** the changes in thermal energy when matter increases in temperature and then changes state.

Interpret Graphics

8. **Describe** what is occurring below.

9. **Summarize** Copy and fill in the graphic organizer below to identify the two types of vaporization that can occur in matter.

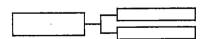

Critical Thinking

10. **Summarize** the energy and state changes that occur when freezing rain falls and solidifies on a wire fence.

11. **Compare** the amount of thermal energy needed to melt a solid and the amount of thermal energy needed to freeze the same liquid.

(t)©DP RM/Alamy; (c)Hutchings Photography/Digital Light Source; (b)Jean du Boisberranger/Getty Images; (br)Charles D. Winters/Science Source

How does dissolving substances in water change its freezing point?

Materials

triple-beam balance

beaker

foam cup

50-mL graduated cylinder

distilled water

Also needed:
ice-salt slush,
test tubes,
thermometers

Safety

You know that when thermal energy is removed from a liquid, the particles move more slowly. At the freezing point, the particles move so slowly that the attractive forces pull them together to form a solid. What happens if the water contains particles of another substance, such as salt? You will form a hypothesis and test the hypothesis to find out.

Learn It

To **form a hypothesis** is to propose a possible explanation for an observation that is testable by a scientific investigation. You **test the hypothesis** by conducting a scientific investigation to see whether the hypothesis is supported.

Try It

1. Read and complete a lab safety form.

2. Form a hypothesis that answers the question in the title of the lab. Write your hypothesis in your Science Journal.

3. Copy the data table into your Science Journal.

4. Use a triple-beam balance to measure 5 g of table salt (NaCl). Dissolve the 5 g of table salt in 50 mL of distilled water.

5. Place 40 mL of distilled water in one large test tube. Place 40 mL of the salt-water mixture in a second large test tube.

6. Measure and record the temperature of the liquids in each test tube.

7. Place both test tubes into a large foam cup filled with crushed ice-salt slush. Gently rotate the thermometers in the test tubes. Record the temperature in each test tube every minute until the temperature remains the same for several minutes.

Apply It

8. How does the data tell you when the freezing point of the liquid has been reached?

9. Do your results support your hypothesis? Why or why not?

10. **Key Concept** Explain your observations in terms of how temperature affects particle motion and how a liquid changes to a solid.

Water	Time (min)	0	1	2	3	4	5	6	7	8
	Temperature (°C)									
Salt water	Time (min)	0	1	2	3	4	5	6	7	8
	Temperature (°C)									

Lesson 3

The Behavior of Gases

Reading Guide

Key Concepts

ESSENTIAL QUESTIONS

- How does the kinetic molecular theory describe the behavior of a gas?

- How are temperature, pressure, and volume related in Boyle's law?

- How is Boyle's law different from Charles's law?

Vocabulary

kinetic molecular theory p. 144

pressure p. 145

Boyle's law p. 146

Charles's law p. 147

 Multilingual eGlossary

 What's Science Got to do With It?

SEPS.3, SEPS.4, SEPS.5, 6-8.LST.4.1, 6-8.LST.5.2

Inquiry Survival Gear?

Why do some pilots wear oxygen masks? Planes fly at high altitudes where the atmosphere has a lower pressure and gas molecules are less concentrated. If the pressure is not adjusted inside the airplane, a pilot must wear an oxygen mask to inhale enough oxygen to keep the body functioning.

Are volume and pressure of a gas related?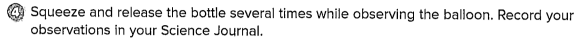

Pressure affects gases differently than it affects solids and liquids. How do pressure changes affect the volume of a gas?

1. Read and complete a lab safety form.

2. Stretch and blow up a **small balloon** several times.

3. Finally, blow up the balloon to a diameter of about 5 cm. Twist the neck, and stretch the mouth of the balloon over the opening of a **plastic bottle. Tape** the neck of the balloon to the bottle.

4. Squeeze and release the bottle several times while observing the balloon. Record your observations in your Science Journal.

Think About This

1. Why doesn't the balloon deflate when you attach it to the bottle?

2. What caused the balloon to inflate when you squeezed the bottle?

3. **Key Concept** Using this lab as a reference, do you think pressure and volume of a gas are related? Explain.

Hutchings Photography/Digital Light Source

Understanding Gas Behavior

Pilots do not worry as much about solids and liquids at high altitudes as they do gases. That is because gases behave differently than solids and liquids. Changes in temperature, pressure, and volume affect the behavior of gases more than they affect solids and liquids.

The explanation of particle behavior in solids, liquids, and gases is based on the kinetic molecular theory. The **kinetic molecular theory** *is an explanation of how particles in matter behave.* Some basic ideas in this theory are

- small particles make up all matter;

- these particles are in constant, random motion;

- the particles collide with other particles, other objects, and the walls of their container;

- when particles collide, no energy is lost.

You have read about most of these, but the last two statements are very important in explaining how gases behave.

Key Concept Check How does the kinetic molecular theory describe the behavior of a gas?

ACADEMIC VOCABULARY

theory
(noun) an explanation of things or events that is based on knowledge gained from many observations and investigations

Greatest volume, least pressure

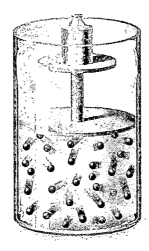

Less volume, more pressure

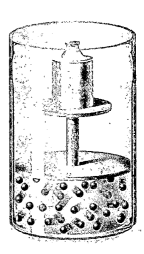

Least volume, most pressure

Figure 15 ☞ As pressure increases, the volume of the gas decreases.

What is pressure?

Particles in gases move constantly. As a result of this movement, gas particles constantly collide with other particles and their container. When particles collide with their container, pressure results. **Pressure** *is the amount of force applied per unit of area.* For example, gas in a cylinder, as shown in **Figure 15**, might contain trillions of gas particles. These particles exert forces on the cylinder each time they strike it. When a weight is added to the plunger, the plunger moves down, compressing the gas in the cylinder. With less space to move around, the particles that make up the gas collide with each other more frequently, causing an increase in pressure. The more the particles are compressed, the more often they collide, increasing the pressure.

Pressure and Volume

Figure 15 also shows the relationship between pressure and volume of gas at a constant temperature. What happens to pressure if the volume of a container changes? Notice that when the volume is greater, the particles have more room to move. This additional space results in fewer collisions within the cylinder, and pressure is less. The gas particles in the middle cylinder have even less volume and more pressure. In the cylinder on the right, the pressure is greater because the volume is less. The particles collide with the container more frequently. Because of the greater number of collisions within the container, pressure is greater.

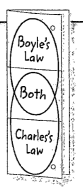

FOLDABLES

Fold a sheet of notebook paper to make a three-tab Foldable and label as shown. Use your Foldable to compare two important gas laws.

Boyle's Law

Both

Charles's Law

Solve Equations

Boyle's law can be stated by the equation

$$V_2 = \frac{P_1 V_1}{P_2}$$

P_1 and V_1 represent the pressure and volume before a change. P_2 and V_2 are the pressure and volume after a change. Pressure is often measured in kilopascals (kPa). For example, what is the final volume of a gas with an initial volume of **50.0 mL** if the pressure increases from **600.0 kPa** to **900.0 kPa**?

1. Replace the terms in the equation with the actual values.

$$V_2 = \frac{(600.0 \text{ kPa})(50.0 \text{ mL})}{(900.0 \text{ kPa})}$$

2. Cancel units, multiply, and then divide.

$$V_2 = \frac{(600.0 \text{ kPa})(50.0 \text{ mL})}{(900.0 \text{ kPa})}$$

$$V_2 = 33.3 \text{ mL}$$

Practice

What is the final volume of a gas with an initial volume of 100.0 mL if the pressure decreases from 500.0 kPa to 250.0 kPa?

 Math Practice

 Personal Tutor

Boyle's Law

You read that the pressure and volume of a gas are related. Robert Boyle (1627–1691), a British scientist, was the first to describe this property of gases. **Boyle's law** *states that pressure of a gas increases if the volume decreases and pressure of a gas decreases if the volume increases, when temperature is constant.* This law can be expressed mathematically as shown to the left.

 Key Concept Check What is the relationship between pressure and volume of a gas if temperature is constant?

Boyle's Law in Action

You have probably felt Boyle's law in action if you have ever traveled in an airplane. While on the ground, the air pressure inside your middle ear and the pressure of the air surrounding you are equal. As the airplane takes off and begins to increase in altitude, the air pressure of the surrounding air decreases. However, the air pressure inside your middle ear does not decrease. The trapped air in your middle ear increases in volume, which can cause pain. These pressure changes also occur when the plane is landing. You can equalize this pressure difference by yawning or chewing gum.

Graphing Boyle's Law

This relationship is shown in the graph in **Figure 16.** Pressure is on the *x*-axis, and volume is on the *y*-axis. Notice that the line decreases in value from left to right. This shows that as the pressure of a gas increases, the volume of the gas decreases.

Figure 16 The graph shows that as pressure increases, volume decreases. This is true only if the temperature of the gas is constant.

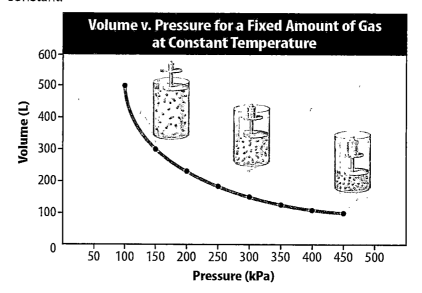

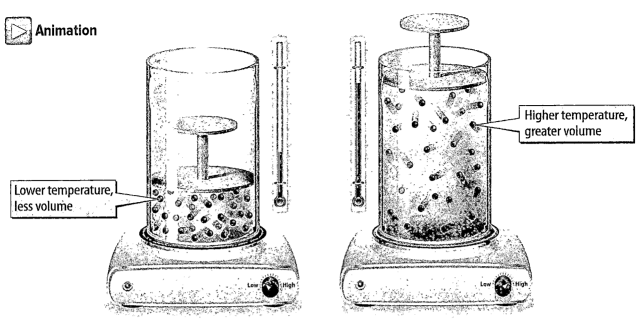

Lower temperature, less volume

Higher temperature, greater volume

Figure 17 🔑 As the temperature of a gas increases, the kinetic energy of the particles increases. The particles move farther apart, and volume increases.

Temperature and Volume

Pressure and volume changes are not the only factors that affect gas behavior. Changing the temperature of a gas also affects its behavior, as shown in Figure 17. The gas in the cylinder on the left has a low temperature. The average kinetic energy of the particles is low, and they move closer together. The volume of the gas is less. When thermal energy is added to the cylinder, the gas particles move faster and spread farther apart. This increases the pressure from gas particles, which push up the plunger. This increases the volume of the container.

Charles's Law

Jacque Charles (1746–1823) was a French scientist who described the relationship between temperature and volume of a gas. **Charles's law** *states that the volume of a gas increases with increasing temperature, if the pressure is constant.* Charles's practical experience with gases was most likely the result of his interest in balloons. Charles and his colleague were the first to pilot and fly a hydrogen-filled balloon in 1783.

🔑 **Key Concept Check** How is Boyle's law different from Charles's law?

🔖 MiniLab   20 minutes

How does temperature affect the volume? 🖐️ 🧴 🗒️ 📖

You can observe Charles's law in action using a few lab supplies.

1. Read and complete a lab safety form.
2. Stretch and blow up a **small balloon** several times.
3. Finally, blow up the balloon to a diameter of about 5 cm. Twist the neck and stretch the mouth of the balloon over the opening of an **ovenproof flask.**
4. Place the flask on a cold **hot plate.** Turn on the hot plate to low, and gradually heat the flask. Record your observations in your Science Journal.
5. ⚠️ *Use **tongs** to remove the flask from the hot plate.* Allow the flask to cool for 5 min. Record your observations.
6. Place the flask in a **bowl of ice water.** Record your observations.

Analyze and Conclude
🔑 **Key Concept** What is the effect of temperature changes on the volume of a gas?

Charles's Law in Action

You have probably seen Charles's law in action if you have ever taken a balloon outside on a cold winter day. Why does a balloon appear slightly deflated when you take it from a warm place to a cold place? When the balloon is in cold air, the temperature of the gas inside the balloon decreases. Recall that a decrease in temperature is a decrease in the average kinetic energy of particles. As a result, the gas particles slow down and begin to get closer together. Fewer particles hit the inside of the balloon. The balloon appears partially deflated. If the balloon is returned to a warm place, the kinetic energy of the particles increases. More particles hit the inside of the balloon and push it out. The volume increases.

 Reading Check What happens when you warm a balloon?

Graphing Charles's Law

The relationship described in Charles's law is shown in the graph of several gases in **Figure 18**. Temperature is on the x-axis and volume is on the y-axis. Notice that the lines are straight and represent increasing values. Each line in the graph is extrapolated to −273°C. *Extrapolated* means the graph is extended beyond the observed data points. This temperature also is referred to as 0 K (kelvin), or absolute zero. This temperature is theoretically the lowest possible temperature of matter. At absolute zero, all particles are at the lowest possible energy state and do not move. The particles contain a minimal amount of thermal energy (potential energy + kinetic energy).

Figure 18 🔑 The volume of a gas increases when the temperature increases at constant pressure.

🔑 **Visual Check** What do the dashed lines mean?

🔑 **Key Concept Check** Which factors must be constant in Boyle's law and in Charles's law?

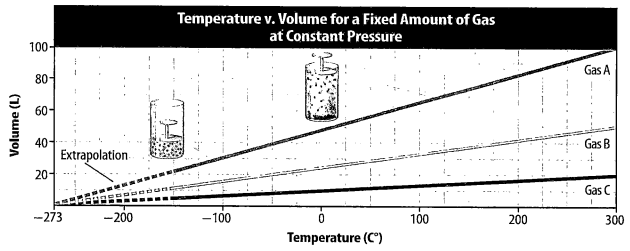
Temperature v. Volume for a Fixed Amount of Gas at Constant Pressure

Online Quiz
Virtual Lab

Visual Summary

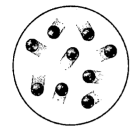

The explanation of particle behavior in solids, liquids, and gases is based on the kinetic molecular theory.

As volume of a gas decreases, the pressure increases when at constant temperature.

At constant pressure, as the temperature of a gas increases, the volume also increases.

FOLDABLES

Use your lesson Foldable to review the lesson. Save your Foldable for the project at the end of the chapter.

What do you think NOW?

You first read the statements below at the beginning of the chapter.

5. Changes in temperature and pressure affect gas behavior.

6. If the pressure on a gas increases, the volume of the gas also increases.

Did you change your mind about whether you agree or disagree with the statements? Rewrite any false statements to make them true.

Use Vocabulary

1 **List** the basic ideas of the kinetic molecular theory.

2 _____ is force applied per unit area.

Understand Key Concepts

3 Which is held constant when a gas obeys Boyle's law?
A. motion
B. pressure
C. temperature
D. volume

4 **Describe** how the kinetic molecular theory explains the behavior of a gas.

5 **Contrast** Charles's law with Boyle's law.

6 **Explain** how temperature, pressure, and volume are related in Boyle's law.

Interpret Graphics

7 **Explain** what happens to the particles to the right when more weights are added.

8 **Identify** Copy and fill in the graphic organizer below to list three factors that affect gas behavior.

Critical Thinking

9 **Describe** what would happen to the pressure of a gas if the volume of the gas doubles while at a constant temperature.

Math Skills 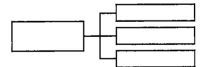 Math Practice

10 **Calculate** The pressure on 400 mL of a gas is raised from 20.5 kPa to 80.5 kPa. What is the final volume of the gas?

Materials

triple-beam
balance

50-mL
graduated
cylinders

beakers

test tubes

thermometers

distilled water

Also needed:
ice, salt

Safety

Design an Experiment to Collect Data

In this chapter, you have learned about the relationship between the motion of particles in matter and change of state. How might you use your knowledge of particles in real life? Suppose that you work for a state highway department in a cold climate. Your job is to test three products. You must determine which is the most effective in melting existing ice, the best at keeping melted ice from refreezing, and the best product to buy.

Question

How can you compare the products? What might make one product better than another? Consider how you can describe and compare the effect of each product on both existing ice and the freezing point of water. Think about controls, variables, and the equipment you have available.

Procedure

(1) Read and complete a lab safety form.

(2) In your Science Journal, write a set of procedures you will use to answer your questions. Include the materials and steps you will use to test the effect of each product on existing ice and on the freezing point of water. How will you record your data? Draw any data tables, such as the example below, that you might need. Have your teacher approve your procedures.

Distilled Water	Time (min)	0	1	2	3	4	5	6	7	8
	Temperature (°C)									
Product A	Time (min)	0	1	2	3	4	5	6	7	8
	Temperature (°C)									
Product B	Time (min)	0	1	2	3	4	5	6	7	8
	Temperature (°C)									
Product C	Time (min)	0	1	2	3	4	5	6	7	8
	Temperature (°C)									

(3) Begin by observing and recording your observations on how each product affects ice. Does it make ice melt or melt faster?

(4) Test the effect of each product on the freezing point of water. Think about how you will ensure that each product is tested in the same way.

(5) Add any additional tests you think you might need to make your recommendation.

Hutchings Photography/Digital Light Source

③

Analyze and Conclude

⑥ **Analyze the data** you have collected. Which product was most effective in melting existing ice? How do you know?

⑦ **Determine** which product was most effective in lowering the freezing point of water.

⑧ **Draw or make a model** to show the effect of dissolved solids on water molecules.

⑨ **Recognize Cause and Effect** In terms of particles, what causes dissolved solids to lower the freezing point of water?

⑩ **Draw Conclusions** In terms of particles, why are some substances more effective than others in lowering the freezing point of water?

⑪ **The Big Idea** Why is the kinetic molecular theory important in understanding how and why matter changes state?

Communicate Your Results

You are to present your recommendations to the road commissioners. Create a graphic presentation that clearly displays your results and justifies your recommendations about which product to buy.

In some states, road crews spray liquid deicer on the roads. If your teacher approves, you may enjoy testing liquids, such as alcohol, corn syrup, or salad oil.

Lab Tips

☑ To ensure fair testing, add the same mass of each product to the ice cubes at the same time.

☑ Be sure to add the same mass of each solid to the same volume of water. About 1 g of solid in 10 mL of water is a good ratio.

☑ Keep adding crushed ice/salt slush to the cup so that the liquid in the test tubes remains below the surface.

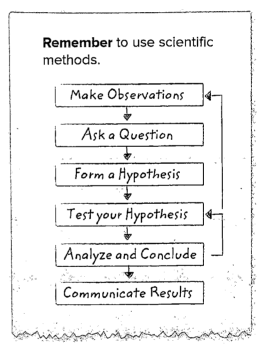

Remember to use scientific methods.

Make Observations

↓

Ask a Question

↓

Form a Hypothesis

↓

Test your Hypothesis

↓

Analyze and Conclude

↓

Communicate Results

As matter changes from one state to another, the distances and the forces between the particles change, and the amount of thermal energy in the matter changes.

Key Concepts Summary

Vocabulary

Lesson 1: Solids, Liquids, and Gases

- Particles vibrate in **solids.** They move faster in **liquids** and even faster in **gases.**
- The force of attraction among particles decreases as matter goes from a solid, to a liquid, and finally to a gas.

| Solid | Liquid | Gas |

solid p. 127
liquid p. 128
viscosity p. 128
surface tension p. 129
gas p. 130
vapor p. 130

Lesson 2: Changes in State

- Because **temperature** is defined as the average **kinetic energy** of particles and kinetic energy depends on particle motion, temperature is directly related to particle motion.
- **Thermal energy** includes both the kinetic energy and the potential energy of particles in matter. However, temperature is only the average kinetic energy of particles in matter.
- Thermal energy must be added or removed from matter for a change of state to occur.

kinetic energy p. 134
temperature p. 134
thermal energy p. 135
vaporization p. 137
evaporation p. 138
condensation p. 138
sublimation p. 138
deposition p. 138

Lesson 3: The Behavior of Gases

- The **kinetic molecular theory** states basic assumptions that are used to describe particles and their interactions in gases and other states of matter.
- **Pressure** of a gas increases if the volume decreases, and pressure of a gas decreases if the volume increases, when temperature is constant.
- **Boyle's law** describes the behavior of a gas when pressure and volume change at constant temperature.
  Charles's law describes the behavior of a gas when temperature and volume change, and pressure is constant.

kinetic molecular theory p. 144
pressure p. 145
Boyle's law p. 146
Charles's law p. 147

FOLDABLES®

Chapter Project

Assemble your lesson Foldables as shown to make a Chapter Project. Use the project to review what you have learned in this chapter.

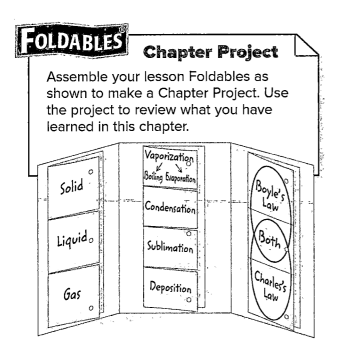

Use Vocabulary

Replace the underlined word with the correct term.

1 Matter with a definite shape and a definite volume is known as a <u>gas</u>.

2 <u>Surface tension</u> is a measure of a liquid's resistance to flow.

3 The gas state of a substance that is normally a solid or a liquid at room temperature is a <u>pressure</u>.

4 <u>Boiling</u> is vaporization that occurs at the surface of a liquid.

5 <u>Boyle's law</u> is an explanation of how particles in matter behave.

6 When graphing a gas obeying <u>Boyle's law</u>, the line will be a straight line with a positive slope.

Link Vocabulary and Key Concepts

▷ **Interactive Concept Map**

Copy this concept map, and then use vocabulary terms from the previous page to complete the concept map.

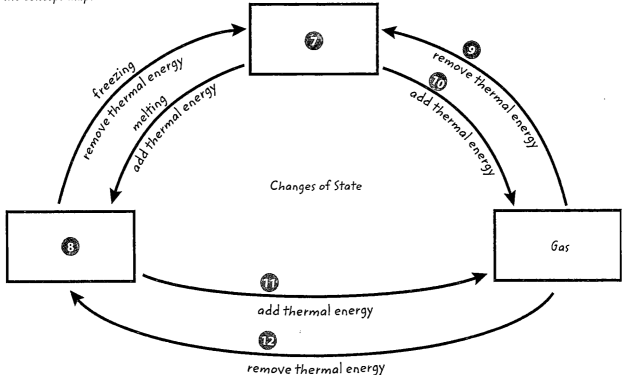

Understand Key Concepts

1 What would happen if you tried to squeeze a gas into a smaller container?
A. The attractive forces between the particles would increase.
B. The force of the particles would prevent you from doing it.
C. The particles would have fewer collisions with the container.
D. The repulsive forces of the particles would pull on the container.

2 Which type of motion in the figure below best represents the movement of gas particles?

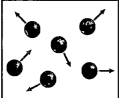 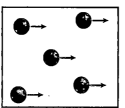

Motion 1   Motion 2

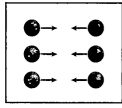 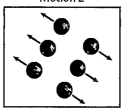

Motion 3   Motion 4

A. motion 1
B. motion 2
C. motion 3
D. motion 4

3 A pile of snow slowly disappears into the air, even though the temperature remains below freezing. Which process explains this?
A. condensation
B. deposition
C. evaporation
D. sublimation

4 Which unit is a density unit?
A. cm^3
B. cm^3/g
C. g
D. g/cm^3

5 Which is a form of vaporization?
A. condensation
B. evaporation
C. freezing
D. melting

6 When a needle is placed on the surface of water, it floats. Which idea best explains why this happens?
A. Boyle's law
B. kinetic molecular theory
C. surface tension
D. viscosity

7 In which material would the particles be most closely spaced?
A. air
B. brick
C. syrup
D. water

Use the graph below to answer questions 8 and 9.

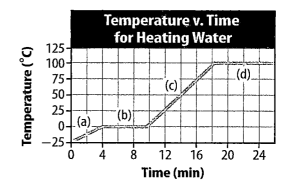

8 Which area of the graph above shows melting of a solid?
A. a
B. b
C. c
D. d

9 Which area or areas of the graph above shows a change in the potential energy of the particles?
A. a
B. a and c
C. b and d
D. c

Critical Thinking

10 Explain how the distances between particles in a solid, a liquid, and a gas help determine the densities of each.

11 Describe what would happen to the volume of a balloon if it were submerged in hot water.

12 Assess The particles of an unknown liquid have very weak attractions for other particles in the liquid. Would you expect the liquid to have a high or low viscosity? Explain your answer.

13 Rank these liquids from highest to lowest viscosity: honey, rubbing alcohol, and ketchup.

14 Evaluate Each beaker below contains the same amount of water. The thermometers show the temperature in each beaker. Explain the kinetic energy differences in each beaker.

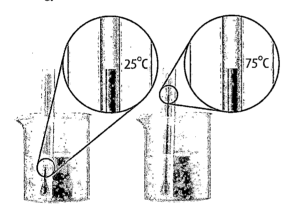

15 Summarize A glass with a few milliliters of water is placed on a counter. No one touches the glass. Explain what happens to the water after a few days.

Writing in Science

16 Write a paragraph that describes how you could determine the melting point of a substance from its heating or cooling curve.

REVIEW THE BIG IDEA

17 During springtime in Alaska, frozen rivers thaw and boats can navigate the rivers again. What physical changes and energy changes occur to the ice molecules when ice changes to water? Explain the process in which water in the river changes to water vapor.

18 In the photo below, explain how the average kinetic energy of the particles changes as the molten glass cools. What instrument could you use to verify the change in the average kinetic energy of the particles?

Math Skills ✕÷ ☑ Math Practice

Solve Equations

19 The pressure on 1 L of a gas is lowered to 200 kPa from a pressure of 600 kPa. What is the final volume of the gas?

20 A gas has a volume of 30 mL at a pressure of 5000 kPa. What is the volume of the gas if the pressure is lowered to 1,250 kPa?

Record your answers on the answer sheet provided by your teacher or on a separate sheet of paper.

Multiple Choice

1 Which property applies to matter that consists of particles vibrating in place?

  A has a definite shape

  B takes the shape of the container

  C flows easily at room temperature

  D particles far apart

Use the figure below to answer questions 2 and 3.

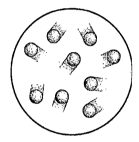

2 Which state of matter is represented above?

  A amorphous solid

  B crystalline solid

  C gas

  D liquid

3 Which best describes the attractive forces between particles shown in the figure?

  A The attractive forces keep the particles vibrating in place.

  B The particles hardly are affected by the attractive forces.

  C The attractive forces keep the particles close together but still allow movement.

  D The particles are locked in their positions because of the attractive forces between them.

4 What happens to matter as its temperature increases?

  A The average kinetic energy of its particles decreases.

  B The average thermal energy of its particles decreases.

  C The particles gain kinetic energy.

  D The particles lose potential energy.

Use the figure to answer question 5.

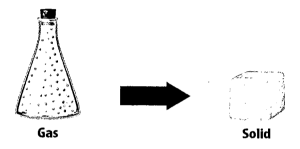

Gas   **Solid**

5 Which process is represented in the figure?

  A deposition

  B freezing

  C sublimation

  D vaporization

6 Which is a fundamental assumption of the kinetic molecular theory?

  A All atoms are composed of subatomic particles.

  B The particles of matter move in predictable paths.

  C No energy is lost when particles collide with one another.

  D Particles of matter never come into contact with one another.

7 Which is true of the thermal energy of particles?

A Thermal energy includes the potential and the kinetic energy of the particles.

B Thermal energy is the same as the average kinetic energy of the particles.

C Thermal energy is the same as the potential energy of particles.

D Thermal energy is the same as the temperature of the particles.

Use the graph below to answer question 8.

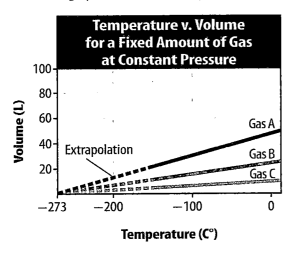

8 Which relationship is shown in the graph?

A Boyle's law

B Charles's law

C kinetic molecular theory

D definition of thermal energy

Constructed Response

9 Some people say that something that does not move very quickly is "as slow as molasses in winter." What property of molasses is described by the saying? Based on the saying, how do you think this property changes with temperature?

Use the graph to answer questions 10 and 11.

A scientist measured the temperature of a sample of frozen mercury as thermal energy is added to the sample. The graph below shows the results.

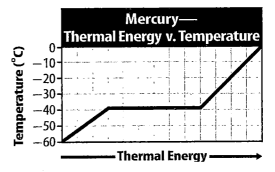

10 At what temperature does mercury melt? How do you know?

11 Describe the motion and arrangement of mercury atoms while the temperature is constant.

12 Atmospheric pressure is greater at the base of a mountain than at its peak. A hiker drinks from a water bottle at the top of a mountain. The bottle is capped tightly. At the base of the mountain, the water bottle has collapsed slightly. What happened to the gas inside the bottle? Assume constant temperature. Explain.

NEED EXTRA HELP?												
If You Missed Question...	1	2	3	4	5	6	7	8	9	10	11	12
Go to Lesson...	1	1	1	2	2	3	2	3	1	1	2	3

Chapter 5

Matter and Atoms

7.PS.1, SEPS.2, SEPS.5, SEPS.8, 6-8.LST.4.1, 6-8.LST.5.2

THE BIG IDEA

How does the classification of matter depend on atoms?

Inquiry Tiny Parts?

From a distance, you might think this looks like a normal picture, but what happens when you look closely? Tiny photographs arranged in a specific way make a new image that looks very different from the individual pictures. The new image depends on the parts and the way they are arranged. Similarly, all the matter around you depends on its parts and the way they are arranged.

- How would the image be different if the individual pictures were arranged in another way?

- How does the image depend on the individual parts?

Scott Camazine/AndreaMosaic/Science Source

Get Ready to Read

What do you think?

Before you read, decide if you agree or disagree with each of these statements. As you read this chapter, see if you change your mind about any of the statements.

1. Things that have no mass are not matter.

2. The arrangement of particles is the same throughout a mixture.

3. An atom that makes up gold is exactly the same as an atom that makes up aluminum.

4. An atom is mostly empty space.

5. If an atom gains electrons, the atom will have a positive charge.

6. Each electron is a cloud of charge that surrounds the center of an atom.

Your one-stop online resource
connectED.mcgraw-hill.com

 LearnSmart℠

 Chapter Resources Files, Reading Essentials, Get Ready to Read, Quick Vocabulary

 Animations, Videos, Interactive Tables

 Self-checks, Quizzes, Tests

 Project-Based Learning Activities

 Lab Manuals, Safety Videos, Virtual Labs & Other Tools

 Vocabulary, Multilingual eGlossary, Vocab eGames, Vocab eFlashcards

 Personal Tutors

Lesson 1

Reading Guide

Key Concepts

ESSENTIAL QUESTIONS

* What is the relationship among atoms, elements, and compounds?

* How are some mixtures different from solutions?

* How do mixtures and compounds differ?

Vocabulary

matter p. 161

atom p. 161

substance p. 162

element p. 163

molecule p. 163

compound p. 164

mixture p. 166

heterogeneous mixture p. 167

homogeneous mixture p. 168

 Multilingual eGlossary

 BrainPOP®
What's Science Got to do With It?

7.PS.1, SEPS.8, 6-8.LST.4.1

Substances and Mixtures

Inquiry Is it pure?

This worker is making a trophy by pouring hot, liquid metal into a mold. The molten metal is bronze, which is a mixture of several metals blended to make the trophy stronger. Why do you think a bronze trophy would be stronger than a pure metal trophy?

David McNew/Getty Images

Can you always see the parts of materials?

If you eat a pizza, you can see the cheese, the pepperoni, and the other parts it is made from. Can you always see the individual parts when you mix materials?

① Read and complete a lab safety form.

② Observe the **materials** at the eight stations your teacher has set up.

③ Record in your Science Journal the name and a short description of each material.

Think About This

1. **Classify** Which materials have easily identifiable parts?

2. 🔑 **Key Concept** Is it always easy to see the parts of materials that are mixed? Explain.

What is matter?

Imagine how much fun it would be to go windsurfing! As the force of the wind pushes the sail, you lean back to balance the board. You feel the heat of the Sun and the spray of water against your face. Whether you are windsurfing on a lake or sitting at your desk in a classroom, everything around you is made of matter. **Matter** *is anything that has mass and takes up space.* Matter is everything you can see, such as water and trees. It is also some things you cannot see, such as air. You know that air is matter because you can feel its mass when it blows against your skin. You can see that it takes up space when it inflates a sail or a balloon.

Anything that does not have mass or volume is not matter. Types of energy, such as heat, sound, and electricity, are not matter. Forces, such as magnetism and gravity, also are not forms of matter.

What is matter made of?

The matter around you, including all solids, liquids, and gases, is made of atoms. *An **atom** is a small particle that is the building block of matter.* In this chapter, you will read that an atom is made of even smaller particles. There are many types of atoms. Each type of atom has a different number of smaller particles. You also will read that atoms can combine with each other in many ways. It is the many kinds of atoms and the ways they combine that form the different types of matter.

✓ **Reading Check** Why are there so many types of matter?

Hutchings Photography/Digital Light Source

WORD ORIGIN ···········

atom
from Greek *atomos*, means "uncut"

Matter
- Anything that has mass and takes up space
- Matter is made up of atoms.

Substances
- Matter with a composition that is always the same

Mixtures
- Matter that can vary in composition

Classifying Matter

Because all the different types of matter around you are made of atoms, they must have characteristics in common. But why do all types of matter look and feel different? How is the matter that makes up a pure gold ring similar to the matter that makes up your favorite soda or even the matter that makes up your body? How are these types of matter different?

As the chart in **Figure 1** shows, scientists place matter into one of two groups—substances or mixtures. Pure gold is in one group. Soda and your body are in the other. What determines whether a type of matter is a substance or a mixture? The difference is in the composition.

What is a substance?

What is the difference between a gold ring and a can of soda? What is the difference between table salt and trail mix? Pure gold is always made up of the same type of atom, but soda is not. Similarly, table salt, or sodium chloride, is always made up of the same types of atoms, but trail mix is not. This is because sodium chloride and gold are substances. A **substance** *is matter with a composition that is always the same.* A certain substance always contains the same kinds of atoms in the same combination. Soda and trail mix are another type of matter that you will read about later in this lesson.

Because gold is a substance, anything that is pure gold will have the same composition. Bars of gold are made of the same atoms as those in a pure gold ring, as shown in **Figure 2.** And, since sodium chloride is a substance, if you are salting your food in Alaska or in Ohio, the atoms that make up the salt will be the same. If the composition of a given substance changes, you will have a new substance.

Reading Check Why is gold classified as a substance?

Figure 2 A substance always contains the same kinds of atoms bonded in the same way. ▼

Substances

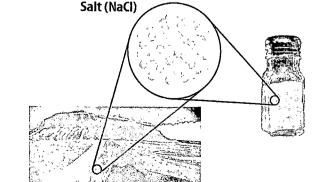

Salt (NaCl)

Gold (Au)

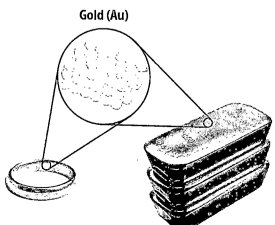

Elements

Some substances, such as gold, are made of only one kind of atom. Others, such as sodium chloride, are made of more than one kind. *An* **element** *is a substance made of only one kind of atom.* All atoms of an element are alike, but atoms of one element are different from atoms of other elements. For example, the element gold is made of only gold atoms, and all gold atoms are alike. But gold atoms are different from silver atoms, oxygen atoms, and atoms of every other element.

Key Concept Check How are atoms and elements related?

What is the smallest part of an element? If you could break down an element into its smallest part, that part would be one atom. Most elements, such as carbon and silver, consist of a large group of individual atoms. Some elements, such as hydrogen and bromine, consist of molecules. *A* **molecule** (MAH lih kyewl) *is two or more atoms that are held together by chemical bonds and act as a unit.* Examples of elements made of individual atoms and molecules are shown in Figure 3.

Elements on the Periodic Table You probably can name many elements, such as carbon, gold, and oxygen. Did you know that there are about 118 known elements? As shown in Figure 4, each element has a symbol, such as C for carbon, Au for gold, and O for oxygen. The periodic table printed in the back of this book gives other information about each element. You will learn more about elements in the next lesson.

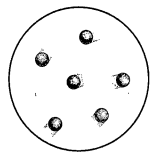

Individual atoms

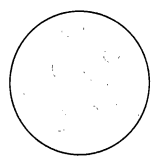

Molecules

Figure 3 The smallest part of all elements is an atom. In some elements, the atoms are grouped into molecules.

| Elements |  Animation |

Figure 4 Element symbols have either one or two letters. Temporary symbols have three letters.

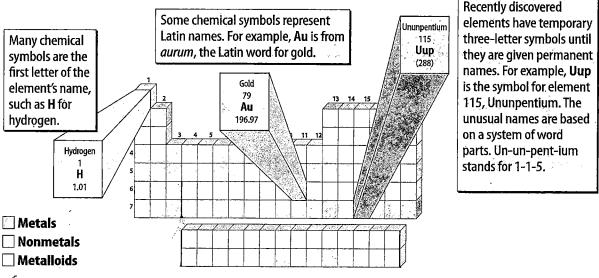

Many chemical symbols are the first letter of the element's name, such as **H** for hydrogen.

Some chemical symbols represent Latin names. For example, **Au** is from *aurum*, the Latin word for gold.

Recently discovered elements have temporary three-letter symbols until they are given permanent names. For example, **Uup** is the symbol for element 115, Ununpentium. The unusual names are based on a system of word parts. Un-un-pent-ium stands for 1-1-5.

Gold
79
Au
196.97

Ununpentium
115
Uup
(288)

Hydrogen
1
H
1.01

☐ **Metals**
☐ **Nonmetals**
☐ **Metalloids**

Visual Check What color are the blocks used for elements that have not yet been verified?

Compounds

Does it surprise you to learn that there are only about 118 different elements? After all, if you think about all the different things you see each day, you could probably name many more types of matter than this. Why are there so many kinds of matter when there are only about 118 elements? Most matter is made of atoms of different types of elements bonded together.

A **compound** *is a substance made of two or more elements that are chemically joined in a specific combination.* Because each compound is made of atoms in a specific combination, a compound is a substance. Pure water (H_2O) is a compound because every sample of pure water contains atoms of hydrogen and oxygen in the same combination—two hydrogen atoms to every oxygen atom. There are many types of matter because elements can join to form compounds.

Molecules Recall that a molecule is two or more atoms that are held together by chemical bonds and that act as a unit. Is a molecule the smallest part of a compound? For many compounds, this is true. Many compounds exist as molecules. An example is water. In water, two hydrogen atoms and one oxygen atom always exist together and act as a unit. Carbon dioxide (CO_2) and table sugar ($C_6H_{12}O_6$) are also examples of compounds that are made of molecules.

However, as shown in Figure 5, some compounds are not made of molecules. In some compounds, such as table salt, or sodium chloride, no specific atoms travel together as a unit. However, table salt (NaCl) is still a substance because it always contains only sodium (Na) and chlorine (Cl) atoms.

 Key Concept Check How do elements and compounds differ?

Figure 5 Sugar particles are molecules because they always travel together as a unit. Salt particles do not travel together as a unit.

Sugar

Salt

Visual Check What happens to the salt particles when the boy mixes the salt in the water? What do you think would happen if the water evaporated?

Properties of Compounds How would you describe sodium chloride, or table salt? The properties of a compound, such as table salt, are usually different from the properties of the elements from which it is made. Table salt, for example, is made of the elements sodium and chlorine. Sodium is a soft metal, and chlorine is a poisonous, green gas. These properties are much different from the table salt you sprinkle on food!

Chemical Formulas Just as elements have chemical symbols, compounds have chemical formulas. A formula includes the symbols of each element in the compound. It also includes numbers, called subscripts, that show the ratio of the elements in the compound. You can see the formulas for some compounds in Table 1.

Different Combinations of Atoms Sometimes the same elements combine to form different compounds. For example, nitrogen and oxygen can form six different compounds. The chemical formulas are N_2O, NO, N_2O_3, NO_2, N_2O_4, and N_2O_5. They contain the same elements, but because the combinations of atoms are different, each compound has different properties, as shown in Table 1.

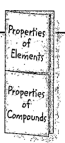

FOLDABLES

Make a vertical two-tab book, and label it as shown. Use it to review properties of elements and compounds.

Properties of Elements

Properties of Compounds

Table 1 Atoms can combine in different ways and form different compounds.

 Personal Tutor

Table 1	
Formula and Molecular Structure	**Properties/Functions**
N_2O Nitrous oxide	colorless gas used as an anesthetic
NO_2 Nitrogen dioxide	brown gas, toxic, air pollutant
N_2O_3 Dinitrogen trioxide	blue liquid

Figure 6 It's hard to tell which is in the glass— pure water (a substance) or lemon-lime soda (a mixture).

What is a mixture?

By looking at the glass of clear liquid in Figure 6, can you tell whether it is lemon-lime soda or water? Lemon-lime soda is almost clear, and someone might confuse it with water, which is a substance. Recall that a substance is matter with a composition that is always the same. However, sodas are a combination of substances such as water, carbon dioxide, sugar, and other compounds. In fact, most solids, liquids, and gases you experience each day are mixtures. A **mixture** is *matter that can vary in composition*. It is made of two or more substances that are blended but are not chemically bonded.

What would happen if you added more sugar to a glass of soda? You would still have soda, but it would be sweeter. Changing the amount of one substance in a mixture does not change the identity of the mixture or its individual substances.

Air and tap water are also mixtures. Air is a mixture of nitrogen, oxygen, and other substances. However, the composition of air can vary. Air in a scuba tank usually contains more oxygen and less of the other substances. Tap water might look like pure water, but it is a mixture of pure water (H_2O) and small amounts of other substances. Since the substances that make up tap water are not bonded together, the composition of tap water can vary. This is true for all mixtures.

MiniLab

20 minutes

How do elements, compounds, and mixtures differ?

The elements in a compound cannot be separated easily. However, you often can use the properties of the substances in a mixture to separate them.

① Read and complete a lab safety form.

② Observe samples of **sand** and **iron filings** with a **magnifying lens.** Record your observations in your Science Journal.

③ Combine the sand and iron filings in a **clear cup.** Stir with a **toothpick.** Observe the mixture with the magnifying lens. Record your observations.

④ Cover one end of a **magnet** with **plastic wrap.** Stir the mixture with the covered magnet. Record your observations.

Analyze and Conclude

1. **Classify** The formula for sand is SiO_2. The symbol for iron is Fe. Use this to classify each as an element, a compound, or a mixture.

2. **Key Concept** What are two ways you could tell from your observations that the combination of sand and iron filings is a mixture and not a substance?

Types of Mixtures

How do trail mix, soda, and air differ? One difference is that trail mix is a solid, soda is a liquid, and air is a gas. This tells you that a mixture can be any state of matter. Another difference is that you can see the individual parts that make up trail mix, but you cannot see the parts that make up soda or air. This is because trail mix is a different type of mixture than soda and air. There are two types of mixtures—heterogeneous (he tuh roh JEE nee us) and homogeneous (hoh muh JEE nee us). The prefix *hetero-* means "different," and the prefix *homo-* means "the same." Heterogeneous and homogeneous mixtures differ in how evenly the substances that compose them are mixed.

ACADEMIC VOCABULARY
individual
(adjective) single; separate

Heterogeneous Mixtures

Suppose you take a bag of trail mix and pour it into two identical bowls. What might you notice? At first glance, each bowl appears the same. However, if you look closely, you might notice that one bowl has more nuts and another bowl has more raisins. The contents of the bowls differ because trail mix is a heterogeneous mixture. A **heterogeneous mixture** *is a mixture in which the substances are not evenly mixed.* Therefore, if you take two samples from the same mixture, such as trail mix, the samples might have different amounts of the individual substances. The mixtures shown in **Figure 7** are examples of heterogeneous mixtures.

Reading Check Explain why vegetable soup is classified as a heterogeneous mixture.

Figure 7 The different parts of a heterogeneous mixture are not evenly mixed.

Heterogeneous Mixtures

The numbers of peanuts, pretzels, raisins, and other types of food in trail mix could change, and it still would be trail mix.

You know that granite is a heterogeneous mixture because you can see the different minerals from which it is made.

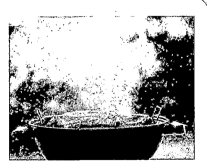

With a microscope, you would be able to see that smoke is a heterogeneous mixture of gas and solid particles.

▲ **Figure 8** Salt is soluble in water. Pepper is insoluble in water. The pepper and water is a mixture, but not a solution.

Homogeneous Mixtures

If you pour soda into two glasses, the amounts of water, carbon dioxide, sugar, and other substances in the mixture would be the same in both glasses. Soda is an example of a **homogeneous mixture**—*a mixture in which two or more substances are evenly mixed, but not bonded together.*

Evenly Mixed Parts In a homogeneous mixture, the substances are so small and evenly mixed that you cannot see the boundaries between substances in the mixture. Brass, a mixture of copper and zinc, is a homogeneous mixture because the copper atoms and the zinc atoms are evenly mixed. You cannot see the boundaries between the different types of substances, even under most microscopes. Lemonade and air are also examples of homogeneous mixtures for the same reason.

Solution Another name for a homogeneous mixture is a solution. A solution is made of two parts—a solvent and one or more solutes. The solvent is the substance that is present in the largest amount. The solutes dissolve, or break apart, and mix evenly in the solvent. In **Figure 8,** water is the solvent, and salt is the solute. Salt is soluble in water. Notice also in the figure that pepper does not dissolve in water. No solution forms between pepper and water. Pepper is insoluble in water.

Other examples of solutions are described in **Figure 9.** Note that all three states of matter—solid, liquid, and gas—can be a solvent or a solute in a solution.

Figure 9 Solids, liquids, and gases can combine to make solutions. ▼

 Key Concept Check How are some mixtures different from solutions?

Homogeneous Mixtures

A trumpet is made of brass, a solution of solid copper and solid zinc.

The natural gas used in a gas stove is a solution of methane, ethane, and other gases.

Ammonia Cleaner

This ammonia cleaner is a solution of water and ammonia gas.

(t) Hutchings Photography/Digital Light Source, (bl) C Squared Studios/Getty Images, (bc) Steve Allen/Brand X Pictures/Alamy, (br) McGraw-Hill Education

168 Chapter 5 EXPLAIN

Compounds v. Mixtures

Think again about putting trail mix into two bowls. If you put more peanuts in one of the bowls, you still have trail mix in both bowls. Since the substances that make up a mixture are not bonded, adding more of one substance does not change the identity or the properties of the mixture. It also does not change the identity or the properties of each individual substance. In a heterogeneous mixture of peanuts, raisins, and pretzels, the properties of the individual parts don't change if you add more peanuts. The peanuts and the raisins don't bond together and become something new.

Similarly, in a solution such as soda or air, the substances do not bond together and form something new. Carbon dioxide, water, sugar, and other substances in soda are mixed together. Nitrogen, oxygen, and other substances in air also keep their separate properties because air is a mixture. If it were a compound, the parts would be bonded and would not keep their separate properties.

 Key Concept Check How do mixtures and compounds differ?

Compounds and Solutions Differ

Compounds and solutions are alike in that they both look like pure substances. Look back at the lemon-lime soda and the water in **Figure 6.** The soda is a solution. A solution might look like a substance because the elements and the compounds that make up a solution are evenly mixed. However, compounds and solutions differ in one important way. The atoms that make up a given compound are bonded together. Therefore, the composition of a given compound is always the same. Changing the composition results in a new compound.

However, the substances that make up a solution, or any other mixture, are not bonded together. Therefore, adding more of one substance will not change the composition of the solution. It will just change the ratio of the substances in the solution. These differences are described in **Table 2.**

Table 2 Differences Between Solutions and Compounds

	Solutions	Compound
Composition	Made up of substances (elements and compounds) evenly mixed together; the composition can vary in a given mixture.	Made up of atoms bonded together; the combination of atoms is always the same in a given compound.
Changing the composition	The solution is still the same with similar properties. However, the relative amounts of substances might be different.	Changing the composition of a compound changes it into a new compound with new properties.
Properties of parts	The substances keep their own properties when they are mixed.	The properties of the compound are different from the properties of the atoms that make it up.

Separating Mixtures

Have you ever picked something you did not like off a slice of pizza? If you have, you have separated a mixture. Because the parts of a mixture are not combined chemically, you can use a physical process, such as removing them by hand, to separate the mixture. The identity of the parts does not change. Separating the parts of a compound is more difficult. The elements that make up a compound are combined chemically. Only a chemical change can separate them.

Separating Heterogeneous Mixtures Separating the parts of a pizza is easy because the pizza has large, solid parts. Two other ways to separate heterogeneous mixtures are shown in **Figure 10.** The strainer in the figure filters larger rocks from the mixture of rocks and dirt. The oil and vinegar is also a heterogeneous mixture because the oil floats on the vinegar. You can separate this mixture by carefully removing the floating oil.

Other properties also might be useful for separating the parts. For example, if one of the parts is magnetic, you could use a magnet to remove it. In a mixture of solid powders, you might dissolve one part in water and then pour it out, leaving the other part behind. In each case, to separate a heterogeneous mixture, you use differences in the physical properties of the parts.

Reading Check Name three methods of separating heterogeneous mixtures.

REVIEW VOCABULARY ·····

chemical change
a change in matter in which the substances that make up the matter change into other substances with different chemical and physical properties

Figure 10 You can separate heterogeneous and homogeneous mixtures.

⊘ **Visual Check** How could you separate the small rocks and dirt that passed through the strainer on the left?

Separating Mixtures

A strainer removes large parts of the heterogeneous mixture of rocks and sediment. Only small rocks and dirt fall through.

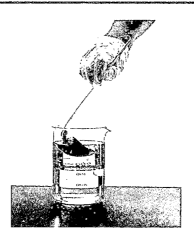

In this heterogeneous mixture of oil and vinegar, the oil floats on the vinegar. You can separate them by lifting off the oil.

Making rock candy is a way of separating a solution. Solid sugar crystals form as a mixture of hot water and sugar cools.

(l)(c)Hutchings Photography/Digital Light Source, (r)Andy Crawford and Tim Ridley/Getty Images

Separating Homogeneous Mixtures Imagine trying to separate soda into water, carbon dioxide, sugar, and other substances it is made from. Because the parts are so small and evenly mixed, separating a homogeneous mixture such as soda can be difficult. However, you can separate some homogeneous mixtures by boiling or evaporation. For example, if you leave a bowl of sugar water outside on a hot day, the water will evaporate, leaving the sugar behind. An example of separating a homogeneous mixture by making rock candy is shown in **Figure 10.**

Visualizing Classification of Matter

Think about all the types of matter you have read about in this lesson. As shown in **Figure 11,** matter can be classified as either a substance or a mixture. Substances are either elements or compounds. The two kinds of mixtures are homogeneous mixtures and heterogeneous mixtures. Notice that all substances and mixtures are made of atoms. Matter is classified according to the types of atoms and the arrangement of atoms in matter. In the next lesson, you will study the structure of atoms.

Figure 11 You can classify matter based on its characteristics.

Classifying Matter

Matter
- Anything that has mass and takes up space
- Matter on Earth is made up of atoms.
- Two classifications of matter: substances and mixtures

Substances
- Matter with a composition that is always the same
- Two types of substances: elements and compounds

Element
- Consists of just one type of atom
- Organized on the periodic table
- Each element has a chemical symbol.

Compound
- Two or more types of atoms bonded together
- Properties are different from the properties of the elements that make it up
- Each compound has a chemical formula.

Substances physically combine to form mixtures.

Mixtures can be separated into substances by physical methods.

Mixtures
- Matter that can vary in composition
- Substances are not bonded together.
- Two types of mixtures: heterogeneous and homogeneous

Heterogeneous Mixture
- Two or more substances unevenly mixed
- Different substances are visible by an unaided eye or a microscope.

Homogeneous Mixture—Solution
- Two or more substances evenly mixed
- Different substances cannot be seen even by a microscope.

Visual Summary

An element is a substance made of only one kind of atom.

The substances that make up a mixture are blended but not chemically bonded.

Homogeneous mixtures have the same makeup of substances throughout a given sample.

FOLDABLES

Use your lesson Foldable to review the lesson. Save your Foldable for the project at the end of the chapter.

What do you think NOW?

You first read the statements below at the beginning of the chapter.

1. Things that have no mass are not matter.

2. The arrangement of particles is the same throughout a mixture.

3. An atom that makes up gold is exactly the same as an atom that makes up aluminum.

Did you change your mind about whether you agree or disagree with the statements? Rewrite any false statements to make them true.

Use Vocabulary

1 A small particle that is the building block of matter is a(n) _____.

2 **Use the term** *substance* in a sentence.

3 **Define** *molecule* in your own words.

Understand Key Concepts

4 **Describe** the relationship among atoms, elements, and compounds.

5 **Explain** how some mixtures are different from solutions.

6 How does changing the amount of one substance affect a mixture's identity and a compound's identity.

Interpret Graphics

7 **Observe** Does the model at the right represent a mixture or a substance? How do you know?

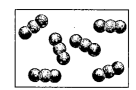

8 **Organize Information** Copy and fill in the graphic organizer below with details about substances and mixtures.

Substances	Mixtures

Critical Thinking

9 **Design** a method to separate a mixture of sugar, sand, and bits of iron.

10 **Decide** During a science investigation, a sample of matter breaks down into two kinds of atoms. Was the original sample an element or a compound? Explain.

Crude Oil

Separating Out Gasoline

Have you ever wondered where the gasoline used in automobiles comes from? Gasoline is part of a mixture of fuels called crude oil. How can workers separate gasoline from this mixture?

One way to separate a mixture is by boiling it. Crude oil is separated by a process called fractional distillation. First, the oil is boiled and allowed to cool. As the crude oil cools, each part changes from a gas to a liquid at a different temperature. Workers catch each fuel just as it changes back to a liquid. Eventually the crude oil is refined into all its useful parts.

1 Crude oil often is taken from liquid deposits deep underground. It might also be taken from rocks or deposits mixed in sand. The crude oil is then sent to a furnace.

Crude oil

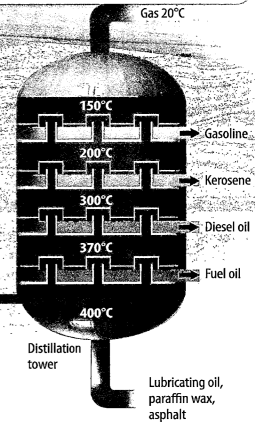

Gas 20°C

150°C → Gasoline

200°C → Kerosene

300°C → Diesel oil

370°C → Fuel oil

400°C

Distillation tower

Lubricating oil, paraffin wax, asphalt

2 A furnace heats the oil inside a pipe until it begins to change from a liquid to a gas. The gas mixture then moves into the distillation tower.

Furnace

3 The distillation tower is hot at the bottom and cooler higher up. As the gas mixture rises to fill the tower, it cools. It also passes over trays at different levels. Each fuel in the mixture changes to a liquid when it cools to a temperature that matches its boiling point. Gasoline changes to a liquid at the level in the tower at 150°C. A tray then catches the gasoline and moves it away.

It's Your Turn

CREATE A POSTER: Blood is a mixture, too. Donated blood often is refined in laboratories to separate it into parts. What are those parts? What are they used for? How are they separated? Find the answers, and create a poster based on your findings.

(inset)sciencephotos/Alamy, (bkgd)Charles Smith/Corbis

Lesson 2

Reading Guide

Key Concepts 🔑
ESSENTIAL QUESTIONS

- Where are protons, neutrons, and electrons located in an atom?

- How is the atomic number related to the number of protons in an atom?

- What effect does changing the number of particles in an atom have on the atom's identity?

Vocabulary

nucleus p. 176

proton p. 176

neutron p. 176

electron p. 176

electron cloud p. 177

atomic number p. 178

isotope p. 179

ion p. 179

 Multilingual eGlossary

 BrainPOP®

 7.PS.1, SEPS.2, SEPS.5, 6-8. LST.4.1, 6-8.LST.5.2

The Structure of Atoms

Inquiry) What makes them different?

This ring is made of two of the most beautiful materials in the world—diamond and gold. Diamond is a clear, sparkling crystal made of only carbon atoms. Gold is a shiny, yellow metal made of only gold atoms. How can they be so different if each is made of just one type of atom? The structure of atoms makes significant differences in materials.

©Bryan F. Peterson/Corbis

How can you make different things from the same parts?

Atoms are all made of the same parts. Atoms can be different from each other because they have different numbers of these parts. In this lab, you will investigate how you can make things that are different from each other even though you use the same parts to make them.

1. Read and complete a lab safety form.

2. Think about how you can join **paper clips, toothpicks,** and **string** to make different types of objects. You must use at least one of each item, but not more than five of any kind.

3. Make the object. Use **tape** to connect the items.

4. Plan and make two more objects using the same three items, varying the numbers of each item.

5. In your Science Journal, describe how each of the objects you made are alike and different.

Think About This

1. **Observe** What do the objects you made have in common? In what ways are they different?

2. 🔑 **Key Concept** What effect do you think increasing or decreasing the number of items you used would have on the objects you made?

The Parts of an Atom

Now that you have read about ways to classify matter, you can probably recognize the different types you see each day. You might see pure elements, such as copper and iron, and you probably see many compounds, such as table salt. Table salt is a compound because it contains the atoms of two different elements—sodium and chlorine—in a specific combination. You also probably see many mixtures. The silver often used in jewelry is a homogeneous mixture of metals that are evenly mixed, but not bonded together.

As you read in Lesson 1, the many types of matter are possible because there are about 118 different elements. Each element is made up of a different type of atom. Atoms can combine in many different ways. They are the basic parts of matter.

What makes the atoms of each element different? Atoms are made of several types of particles. The number of each of these particles in an atom is what makes atoms different from each other. It is what makes so many types of matter possible.

🔎 **Reading Check** What makes the atoms of different elements different from each other?

FOLDABLES

Make a vertical two-column chart book. Label it as shown. Use it to organize information about the particles in an atom.

Particles INSIDE the Nucleus	Particles OUTSIDE the Nucleus

Hutchings Photography/Digital Light Source

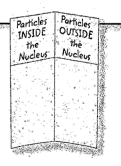

SCIENCE USE V. COMMON USE

charge
Science Use an electrical property of some objects that determines whether the object is positive, negative, or neutral

Common Use buying something with a credit card

WORD ORIGIN

proton
from Greek *protos,* means "first"

The Nucleus—Protons and Neutrons

The basic structure of all atoms is the same. As shown in Figure 12, an atom has a center region with a positive charge. One or more negatively charged particles move around this center region. *The **nucleus** is the region at the center of an atom that contains most of the mass of the atom.* Two kinds of particles make up the nucleus. *A **proton** is a positively charged particle in the nucleus of an atom. A **neutron** is an uncharged particle in the nucleus of an atom.*

 Reading Check Why does a nucleus always have a positive charge?

Electrons

Atoms have no electric charge unless they change in some way. Therefore, there must be a negative charge that balances the positive charge of the nucleus. *An **electron** is a negatively charged particle that occupies the space in an atom outside the nucleus.* Electrons are so small and move so quickly that scientists are unable to tell exactly where a given electron is located at any specific time. Therefore, scientists describe their positions around the nucleus as a cloud rather than specific points. A model of an atom and its parts is shown in Figure 12.

Key Concept Check Where are protons, neutrons, and electrons located in an atom?

Figure 12 All atoms have a positively charged nucleus surrounded by one or more electrons.

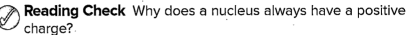

Parts of an Atom Animation

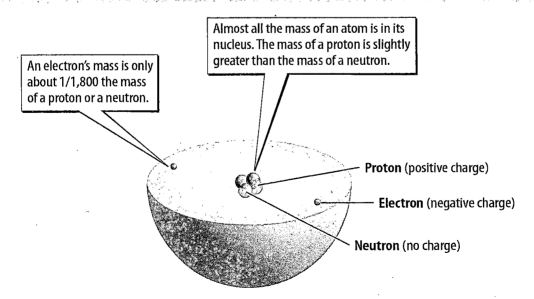

Almost all the mass of an atom is in its nucleus. The mass of a proton is slightly greater than the mass of a neutron.

An electron's mass is only about 1/1,800 the mass of a proton or a neutron.

Proton (positive charge)

Electron (negative charge)

Neutron (no charge)

Visual Check How many protons and how many electrons does this atom have?

An Electron Cloud Drawings of an atom, such as the one in Figure 13, often show electrons circling the nucleus like planets orbiting the Sun. Scientists have conducted experiments that show the movement of electrons is more complex than this. The modern idea of an atom is called the electron-cloud model. *An electron cloud is the region surrounding an atom's nucleus where one or more electrons are most likely to be found.* It is important to understand that an electron is not a cloud of charge. An electron is one tiny particle. An electron cloud is mostly empty space. At any moment in time, electrons are located at specific points within that area.

Electron Energy You have read that electrons are constantly moving around the nucleus in a region called the electron cloud. However, some electrons are closer to the nucleus than others. Electrons occupy certain areas around the nucleus according to their energy, as shown in Figure 13. Electrons close to the nucleus are strongly attracted to it and have less energy. Electrons farther from the nucleus are less attracted to it and have more energy.

The Size of Atoms

It might be difficult to visualize an atom, but every solid, liquid, and gas is made of millions and millions of atoms. Your body, your desk, and the air you breathe are all made of tiny atoms. To understand how small an atom is, look at Figure 14. Suppose you could increase the size of everything around you. If you could multiply the width of an atom by 100 million, or 1×10^8, it would be the size of an orange. An orange would then increase to the size of Earth!

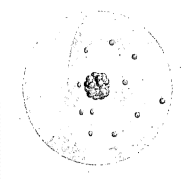

△ **Figure 13** Electrons farther from the nucleus have more energy.

Math Skills

Use Scientific Notation

Scientists write very large and very small values using scientific notation. A gram of carbon has about 50,000,000,000,000,000,000 atoms. Express this in scientific notation.

1. Move the decimal until one nonzero digit remains on the left:

    5.0000000000000000000

2. Count the places you moved. Here it is 19 left.

3. Show that number as a power of 10. The exponent is negative if the decimal moves right and positive if it moves left. Answer: 5×10^{19}

4. Reverse the process to change scientific notation back to a whole number.

Practice
The diameter of a carbon atom is 2.2×10^{-8} cm. Write this as a whole number.

 Math Practice

 Personal Tutor

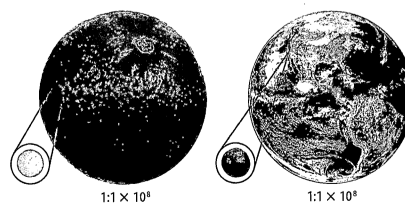

1:1 × 10⁸   1:1 × 10⁸

△ **Figure 14** If an orange were the size of Earth, then an atom would be the size of an orange.

MiniLab

20 minutes

How can you model atoms?

You can use models to study parts of atoms.

Element	Protons	Neutrons	Electrons
Boron	5	6	
		5	4
Carbon		6	6
	2	2	
Nitrogen	7	6	

① Read and complete a lab safety form.

② Copy the table above into your Science Journal. Fill in the blanks in the table.

③ Use pieces of **toothpicks** and **colored marshmallows** to model the nucleus of an atom of each element. Use pink for protons and green for neutrons.

⚠ *Do not eat any food you use for a lab.*

④ On a desk, use yellow marshmallows to surround each nucleus with electrons.

Analyze and Conclude

1. **Decide** Which model element's atomic number is greatest? How do you know?

2. **Key Concept** What would change if the last model element had eight protons?

Differences in Atoms

In some ways atoms are alike. Each has a positively charged nucleus surrounded by a negatively charged electron cloud. But atoms can differ from each other in several ways. Atoms can have different numbers of protons, neutrons, or electrons.

Protons and Atomic Number

Look at the periodic table in the back of this book. In each block, the number under the element name shows how many protons each atom of the element has. For example, each oxygen atom has eight protons. *The* **atomic number** *is the number of protons in the nucleus of an atom of an element.* If there are 12 protons in the nucleus of an atom, that element's atomic number is 12. Examine **Figure 15**. Notice that the atomic number of magnesium is the whole number above its symbol. The atomic number of carbon is 6. This means that each carbon atom has 6 protons.

Every element in the periodic table has a different atomic number. You can identify an element if you know either its atomic number or the number of protons its atoms have. If an atom has a different number of protons, it is a different element.

Key Concept Check How is the atomic number related to the number of protons in an atom?

Figure 15 🔑 An atomic number is the number of protons in each atom of the element.

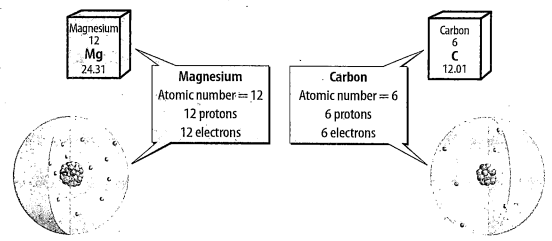

Neutrons and Isotopes

Each atom of an element contains the same number of protons, but the number of neutrons can vary. *An* **isotope** (I suh tohp) *is one of two or more atoms of an element having the same number of protons, but a different number of neutrons.* Boron-10 and boron-11 are isotopes of boron, as shown in **Figure 16.** Notice that boron-10 has ten particles in its nucleus. Boron-11 has 11 particles in its nucleus.

 Reading Check How do fluorine-19 and fluorine-20 differ?

Electrons and Ions

You read that atoms can differ by the number of protons or neutrons they have. **Figure 17** illustrates a third way atoms can differ—by the number of electrons. A neutral, or uncharged, atom has the same number of positively charged protons and negatively charged electrons. As atoms bond, their numbers of electrons can change. Because electrons are negatively charged, a neutral atom that has lost an electron has a positive charge. A neutral atom that has gained an electron has a negative charge. *An* **ion** (I ahn) *is an atom that has a charge because it has gained or lost electrons.* Because the number of protons is unchanged, an ion is the same element it was before.

In the previous lesson, you read that each particle of a compound is two or more atoms of different elements bonded together. One of the ways compounds form is when one or more electrons move from an atom of an element to an atom of a different element. This results in a positive ion for one element and a negative ion for the other element.

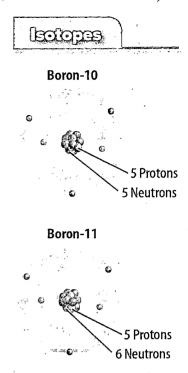

▲ **Figure 16** Boron-10 and boron-11 are isotopes. The number of protons is the same, but the number of neutrons is different.

Figure 17 A positive ion has fewer electrons than protons. A negative ion has more electrons than protons. ▼

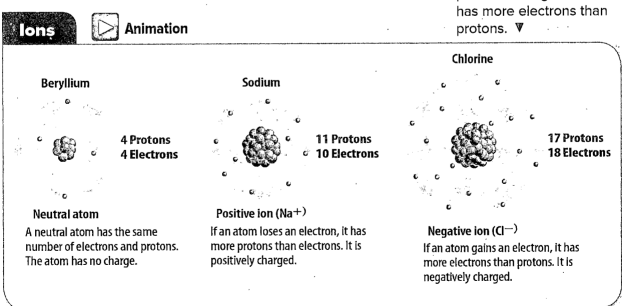

| Ions | Animation |

Beryllium

4 Protons
4 Electrons

Neutral atom

A neutral atom has the same number of electrons and protons. The atom has no charge.

Sodium

11 Protons
10 Electrons

Positive ion (Na+)

If an atom loses an electron, it has more protons than electrons. It is positively charged.

Chlorine

17 Protons
18 Electrons

Negative ion (Cl−)

If an atom gains an electron, it has more electrons than protons. It is negatively charged.

Visual Check Would a nitrogen atom be a positive or a negative ion if it had 10 electrons? Why?

Table 3 Possible Changes in Atoms

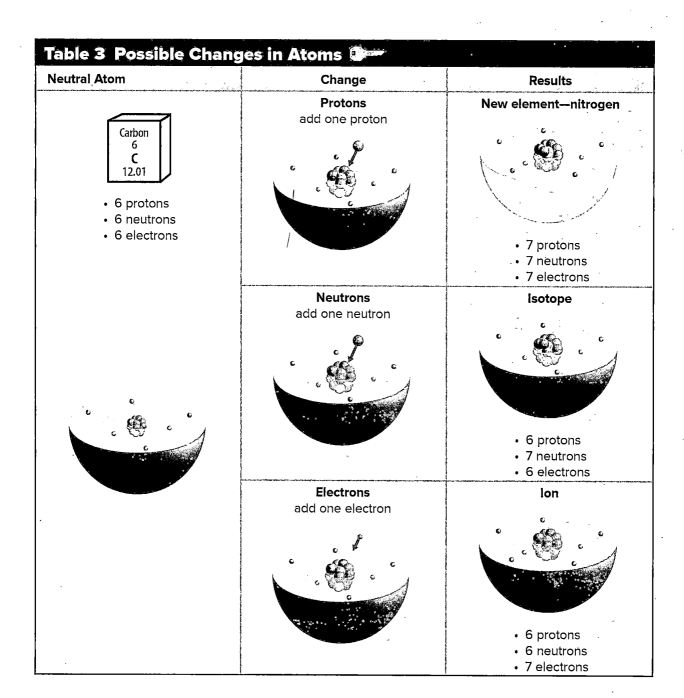

Neutral Atom	Change	Results
Carbon 6 **C** 12.01 • 6 protons • 6 neutrons • 6 electrons	**Protons** add one proton	**New element—nitrogen** • 7 protons • 7 neutrons • 7 electrons
	Neutrons add one neutron	**Isotope** • 6 protons • 7 neutrons • 6 electrons
	Electrons add one electron	**Ion** • 6 protons • 6 neutrons • 7 electrons

Atoms and Matter

You have now read that matter can be either a substance or a mixture. A substance has a composition that is always the same, but the composition of a mixture can vary. All types of matter are made of atoms. The atoms of a certain element always have the same number of protons, but the number of neutrons can vary. When elements combine to form compounds, the number of electrons in the atoms can change. The different ways in which atoms can change are summarized in Table 3.

Look back at the diamond and gold ring on the first page of this lesson. Now can you answer the question of how they can be so different if each is made of just one type of atom? Each carbon atom in diamond has six protons. Each gold atom has 79 protons. The parts of an atom give an element its identity. The ways in which the atoms combine result in the many different kinds of matter.

Key Concept Check What effect does changing the number of particles in an atom have on the atom's identity?

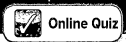

Lesson 2 Review

Visual Summary

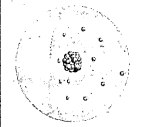

All matter is made of atoms. Atoms are made of protons, electrons, and neutrons.

An orange is about 100 million times wider than an atom.

Atoms of the same element can have different numbers of neutrons.

FOLDABLES

Use your lesson Foldable to review the lesson. Save your Foldable for the project at the end of the chapter.

What do you think

You first read the statements below at the beginning of the chapter.

4. An atom is mostly empty space.

5. If an atom gains electrons, the atom will have a positive charge.

6. Each electron is a cloud of charge that surrounds the center of an atom.

Did you change your mind about whether you agree or disagree with the statements? Rewrite any false statements to make them true.

Use Vocabulary

1 **Distinguish** between a proton and a neutron.

2 An atom that has lost one or more electrons is a(n) _____.

3 **Use the term** *isotope* in a complete sentence.

Understand Key Concepts

4 Which is located outside the nucleus of an atom?
A. electron   C. neutron
B. ion   D. proton

5 **Identify** the element that has nine protons.

6 **Explain** how atomic number relates to the number of particles in an atom's nucleus.

Interpret Graphics

7 **Organize** Copy and fill in the graphic organizer below to summarize what you have learned about the parts, the sizes, and the differences of atoms.

Properties of Atoms	
Parts	
Sizes	
Differences	

Critical Thinking

8 **Decide** Can you tell which element an atom is if you know its charge and the number of electrons it has? Explain.

Math Skills Math Practice

9 The diameter of an atomic nucleus is about 0.0000000000000016 cm. Express this number in scientific notation.

10 The mass of a hydrogen atom is about 1.67×10^{-27} kg. Express this as a whole number.

Balloon Molecules

Knowing how atoms join to form the smallest parts of a compound can be useful. It can sometimes help you predict properties of compounds. It also can help you understand how compounds combine to form mixtures. In this lab, you will connect small balloons to make models of molecules.

Question

How do atoms combine to make molecules?

Procedure

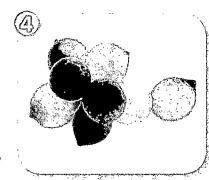

① Read and complete a lab safety form.

② Look at the molecule models in the table below. Each molecule is made of two or more atoms. Each type of atom is drawn in a different color.

③ Notice that a water molecule—H_2O—consists of two hydrogen atoms and one oxygen atom.

④ Inflate three balloons as models of the three atoms that make up a water molecule. Choose one color for the two hydrogen atoms and a different color for the oxygen atom. Inflate each balloon until it is about 4 cm wide.

⑤ Look at the shape of the water molecule in the table. Use tape to connect your model atoms in that shape.

⑥ Use a black marker to write H on each hydrogen balloon and O on the oxygen balloon.

⑦ Write *Water H_2O* on an index card, and place the card next to your model.

Materials

balloons

tape

black marker

index cards

Safety

Water H_2O	Carbon dioxide CO_2	Bromine Br_2	Dinitrogen tetraoxide N_2O_4
Chloroform $CHCl_3$	Ammonia NH_3	Hydrogen peroxide H_2O_2	Ozone O_3

⑧ Look at the molecules in the table. Choose three molecules that you would like to model. Notice the types of atoms that make up the molecules you have chosen to model.

⑨ Choose a different color balloon for each type of atom. If possible, use the same colors for hydrogen and oxygen that you used for your water molecule.

⑩ Use tape to connect the atoms in the same arrangements shown in the table. Then use a marker to write the chemical symbol of each element on the balloon for that type of atom.

⑪ Label an index card for each molecule, just as you did for the water molecule. Display each of your models together.

Analyze and Conclude

⑫ **Analyze** Which, if any, of the molecules you modeled represent the smallest particles of a substance? Which, if any, represent the smallest particles of an element? Explain.

⑬ 🆘 **The Big Idea** How do the molecules you modeled depend on atoms?

Communicate Your Results

Use a digital camera to take photographs of each model you made. Then, use the photos to make a computer presentation explaining the atoms that join to make each molecule you modeled.

Make models for the other compounds shown in this chapter, including any that you did not previously make in the table on the previous page. Remember that the smallest parts of some compounds, such as NaCl, are not molecules because the same atoms do not always travel together. You can still model these particles as long as you keep in mind that they are not called molecules.

⑩

Lab Tips

☑ When making your models, it is best to have all the balloons inflated to the same size, but keep in mind that real atoms have different diameters.

☑ Press down lightly when writing the chemical symbols on the model atoms to avoid popping the balloons.

Remember to use scientific methods.

Make Observations
↓
Ask a Question
↓
Form a Hypothesis
↓
Test your Hypothesis
↓
Analyze and Conclude
↓
Communicate Results

 Matter is classified according to the type and arrangement of atoms from which it is made.

Key Concepts Summary

Lesson 1: Substances and Mixtures

- An **atom** is a building block of **matter**. An **element** is matter made of only one type of atom. A **compound** is a **substance** that contains two or more elements.

- A **heterogeneous mixture** is not a solution because the substances that make up a heterogeneous mixture are not evenly mixed. The substances that make up a solution, or a **homogeneous mixture,** are evenly mixed.

- **Mixtures** differ from compounds in their composition, whether their parts join, and the properties of their parts.

Lesson 2: The Structure of Atoms

- The center of an atom is the **nucleus.** The nucleus contains **protons** and **neutrons. Electrons** occupy the space in an atom outside the nucleus.

- The identity of an atom is determined by its **atomic number.** The atomic number is the number of protons in the atom.

- The identity of an atom stays the same if the number of neutrons or electrons changes.

Vocabulary

matter p. 161

atom p. 161

substance p. 162

element p. 163

molecule p. 163

compound p. 164

mixture p. 166

heterogeneous mixture p. 167

homogeneous mixture p. 168

nucleus p. 176

proton p. 176

neutron p. 176

electron p. 176

electron cloud p. 177

atomic number p. 178

isotope p. 179

ion p. 179

Vocabulary eFlashcards
Vocabulary eGames
Personal Tutor

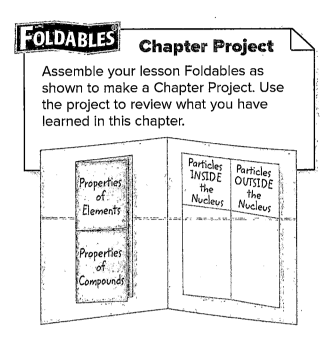

FOLDABLES **Chapter Project**

Assemble your lesson Foldables as shown to make a Chapter Project. Use the project to review what you have learned in this chapter.

Use Vocabulary

1 A particle that consists of two or more atoms bonded together is a(n) _____.

2 A salad is an example of a(n) _____ because it is a mixture in which you can easily remove the individual parts.

3 Matter is classified as a(n) _____ if it is made of two or more substances that are physically blended but are not chemically bonded.

4 A positively charged particle in the nucleus of an atom is a(n) _____.

5 Almost all of the mass of an atom is found in the _____ of an atom.

6 If a chlorine atom gains an electron, it becomes a(n) _____ of chlorine.

Link Vocabulary and Key Concepts

Interactive Concept Map

Copy this concept map, and then use vocabulary terms from the previous page to complete the concept map.

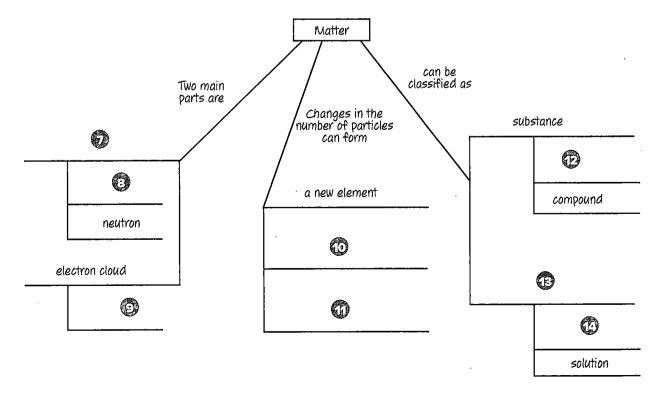

Understand Key Concepts

1 Which is a substance?
  A. fruit salad
  B. granola cereal
  C. spaghetti
  D. table salt

2 Which is the best model for a homogeneous mixture?
  A.
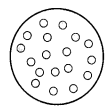

  B.
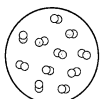

  C.
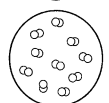

  D.
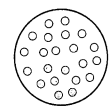

3 Which is a property of all atoms?
  A. more electrons than protons
  B. a nucleus with a positive charge
  C. a positively charged electron cloud
  D. same number of protons as neutrons

4 Which is another name for a solution?
  A. element
  B. compound
  C. heterogeneous mixture
  D. homogeneous mixture

5 Which would you most likely be able to separate into its parts by filtering?
  A. heterogeneous mixture of two liquids
  B. heterogeneous mixture of two solids
  C. homogeneous mixture of two liquids
  D. homogeneous mixture of two solids

6 Where is almost all the mass of an atom located?
  A. in the electrons
  B. in the neutrons
  C. in the nucleus
  D. in the protons

7 Which best describes an electron cloud?
  A. an area of charged particles with a fixed boundary
  B. electrons on a fixed path around the nucleus
  C. mostly empty space with tiny charged particles in it
  D. a solid mass of charge around the nucleus

8 Which is true about carbon-12 compared with carbon-13?
  A. Carbon-12 has more neutrons.
  B. Carbon-12 has more protons.
  C. Carbon-13 has more neutrons.
  D. Carbon-13 has more protons.

9 Look at the periodic table block below for potassium. How many electrons does an uncharged atom of potassium have?

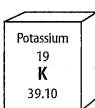

  A. 19
  B. 20
  C. 39
  D. 40

Critical Thinking

10 Classify Look at the illustration below. Is this a model of a substance or a mixture? How do you know?

11 Deduce Each atom of protium has one proton, no neutrons, and one electron. Each atom of deuterium has one proton, two neutrons, and one electron. Are these the same or different elements? Why?

12 Decide Suppose you mix several liquids in a jar. After a few minutes, the liquids form layers. Is this a homogeneous mixture or a heterogeneous mixture? Why?

13 Describe a method for separating a mixture of salt water.

14 Generalize Consider the substances N_2O_5, H_2, CH_4, H_2O, KCl, and O_2. Is it possible to tell just from the symbols and the numbers which are elements and which are compounds? Explain.

15 Suggest how you can define an electron cloud differently from the chapter.

16 Analyze A substance has an atomic number of 80. How many protons and electrons do atoms of the substance have? What is the substance?

Writing in Science

17 Write a paragraph in which you explain the modern atomic model to an adult who has never heard of it before. Include two questions he or she might ask, and write answers to the questions.

 REVIEW BIG IDEA

18 Explain how compounds, elements, heterogeneous mixtures, homogeneous mixtures, matter, and substances are related.

19 The photograph below depends on its parts. This is similar to the relationship of matter and atoms. How does the classification of matter depend on atoms?

Math Skills ✕➗ ✓ Math Practice

Use Scientific Notation

20 The mass of one carbon atom is 0.0000000000000000000000001994 g. Express this number in scientific notation.

21 The mass of an electron is about 9.11×10^{-31} kg. Write this as a whole number.

22 In 1 L of hydrogen gas, there are about 54,000,000,000,000,000,000,000 hydrogen atoms. Express the number of atoms using scientific notation.

23 Particles in chemistry are often described by the unit mole. One mole is defined as about 6.022×10^{23} particles. Write this as a whole number.

24 The mass of hydrogen-3, tritium, is about 5.01×10^{-27} kg. Write this as a whole number.

Record your answers on the answer sheet provided by your teacher or on a sheet of paper.

Multiple Choice

Use the figure below to answer questions 1 and 2.

1 How many atoms are in the particle?

A 1

B 2

C 3

D 5

2 Which kind of matter might contain only this type of particle?

A a compound

B an element

C a heterogeneous mixture

D a homogeneous mixture

3 Which class of matter is the least evenly mixed?

A compounds

B heterogeneous mixtures

C homogeneous mixtures

D solutions

4 Which correctly describes a compound but not a mixture?

A All the atoms are of the same element.

B All the molecules have at least two atoms.

C The combination of substances never changes.

D The substances can be separated without breaking bonds.

5 A girl pours a spoonful of sugar into a glass of warm water. She stirs the water until the sugar disappears. When she tastes the water, she notices that it is now sweet. Which describes the kind of matter in the glass?

A a compound

B an element

C a solution

D a substance

6 How could you separate a mixture of stone and wooden beads that are all the same size?

A Add water to the mixture and skim off the wooden beads, which float.

B Heat the mixture until the stone beads melt.

C Strain the mixture to separate out the stone beads.

D Use a magnet to pull out the wooden beads.

Use the figure below to answer question 7.

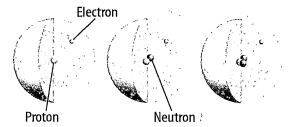

7 The figure shows models of three different atoms. What can you conclude about the three models shown in the figure?

A They all show positive ions.

B They all show negative ions.

C They all show the same element.

D They all show the same isotope.

8 What is the atomic number of an atom that has 2 electrons, 3 protons, and 4 neutrons?

A 2

B 3

C 4

D 7

Use the table below to answer questions 9 and 10.

	Number of Protons	Number of Neutrons	Number of Electrons
A	8	8	8
B	8	8	10
C	8	9	8
D	9	10	9

9 The table shows the numbers of protons, neutrons, and electrons for four atoms. Which atom has a negative charge?

A A

B B

C C

D D

10 Which of the atoms is a different element than the others?

A A

B B

C C

D D

Constructed Response

11 How do protons, electrons, and neutrons differ in charge and location in the atom?

Use the figures below to answer questions 12 and 13.

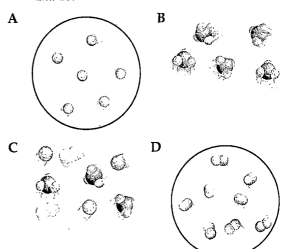

12 Classify each model A–D as either an element, a compound, or a mixture. Explain your reasoning for each answer.

13 Imagine that samples A and D were reacted and formed a compound. Then imagine that the same samples were combined to form a mixture. How would the two combinations differ?

14 Suppose a neutral atom has 5 protons, 5 neutrons, and 5 electrons. List the number of protons, electrons, and neutrons for the following:

a. a positive ion of the same element

b. a negative ion of the same element

c. a neutral isotope of the same element

NEED EXTRA HELP?														
If You Missed Question...	1	2	3	4	5	6	7	8	9	10	11	12	13	14
Go to Lesson...	1	1	1	1	1	1	2	2	2	2	1	1	2	2

EXPLORING EARTH

12000 B.C.
A map scratched into a mammoth jawbone, the oldest surviving map, depicts a group of settlements and the surrounding countryside in what is now Mehirich, Ukraine.

2300 B.C.
The oldest surviving city map, a map of the Mesopotamian city of Lagash that includes the layout of the city, is created.

150 A.D.
Ptolemy illustrates a world map with Earth as a sphere from 60°N to 30°S latitudes.

1506
Francesco Rosselli produces the first map to show the "New World."

1930s
Maps become increasingly accurate and factual due to the widespread use of aerial photography after World War I.

1960s
Geographic Information
Systems (GIS) are
developed. GIS displays
large amounts of
information and includes
computer software and
hardware as well as digital
data and storage.

1993
The space-based
Global
Positioning
System achieves
initial operational
capability.

2005
An internet
mapping tool
displays satellite
images of Earth's
surface.

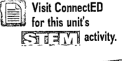 Visit ConnectED
for this unit's
STEM activity.

Nature of SCIENCE

Science and History

About 500,000 years ago, early humans used stone to make tools, weapons, and small decorative items. Then, about 8,000 years ago, someone might have spied a shiny object among the rocks. It was gold–thought to be the first metal discovered by humans. Gold was very different from stone. It did not break when it was struck. It could easily be shaped into useful and beautiful objects. Over time, other metals were discovered. Each metal helped advance human civilization. Metals from Earth's crust have helped humans progress from the Stone Age to the Moon, to Mars, and beyond.

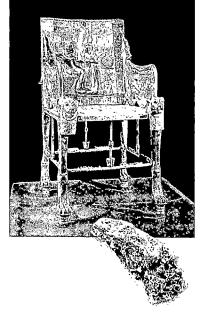

Gold

Since the time of its discovery, gold has been a symbol of wealth and power. It is used mainly in jewelry, coins, and other valuable objects. King Tut's coffin was made of pure gold. Tut's body was surrounded by the largest collection of gold objects ever discovered–chariots, statues, jewelry, and a golden throne. Because gold is so valuable, much of it is recycled. If you own a piece of gold jewelry, it might contain gold that was mined thousands of years ago!

Lead

Ancient Egyptians used the mineral lead sulfide, also called galena, as eye paint. About 5,500 years ago, metalworkers found that galena melts at a low temperature, forming puddles of the lead. Lead bends easily, and the Romans shaped it into pipes for carrying water. Over the years, the Romans realized that lead was entering the water and was toxic to humans. Despite possible danger, lead water pipes were common in modern homes for decades. Finally, however, in 2004 the use of lead pipes in home construction was banned.

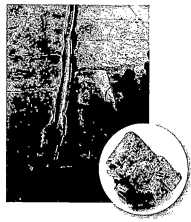

Copper

The first metal commonly traded was copper. About 5,000 years ago, Native Americans mined more than half a million tons of copper from the area that is now Michigan. Copper is stronger than gold. Back then, it was shaped into saws, axes, and other tools. Stronger saws made it easier to cut down trees. The wood from trees then could be used to build boats, which allowed trade routes to expand. Many cultures today still use methods to shape copper that are similar to those used by ancient peoples.

Tin and Bronze

Around 4,500 years ago, the Sumerians noticed differences in the copper they used. Some flowed more easily when it melted and was stronger after it hardened. They discovered that this harder copper contained another metal–tin. Metalworkers began combining tin and copper to produce a metal called bronze. Bronze eventually replaced copper as the most important metal to society. Bronze was strong and cheap enough to make everyday tools. It could easily be shaped into arrowheads, armor, axes, and sword blades. People admired the appearance of bronze. It continues to be used in sculptures. Bronze, along with gold and silver, is used in Olympic medals as a symbol of excellence.

Iron and Steel

Although iron-containing rock was known centuries ago, people couldn't build fires hot enough to melt the rock and separate out the iron. As fire-building methods improved, iron use became more common. It replaced bronze for all uses except art. Iron farm tools revolutionized agriculture. Iron weapons became the choice for war. Like metals used by earlier civilizations, iron increased trade and wealth, and improved people's lives.

In the 17th century, metalworkers developed a way to mix iron with carbon. This process formed steel. Steel quickly became valued for its strength, resistance to rusting, and ease of use in welding. Besides being used in the construction of skyscrapers, bridges, and highways, steel is used to make tools, ships, vehicles, machines, and appliances.

Try to imagine your world without metals. Throughout history, metals changed society as people learned to use them.

MiniLab
20 minutes

How do a metal's properties affect its uses?

Why are different common objects made of a variety of different metals?

① Read and complete a lab safety form.

② Examine a **lead fishing weight,** a piece of **copper tubing,** and an **iron bolt.**

③ Create a table comparing characteristics of the objects in your Science Journal.

④ Use a **hammer** to tap on each item. Record your observations in your table.

Analyze and Conclude

1. **Infer** Why was lead, not copper or iron, used to make the fishing weight?

2. **Compare** What similarities do all three objects share?

3. **Infer** Why do you think ancient peoples used lead for pipes and iron for weapons?

Earth's Structure

How is Earth structured?

Inquiry What is in the sky?

These dancing lights in the night sky are called an aurora. Interactions between Earth's atmosphere and charged particles from the Sun cause an aurora. Conditions deep in Earth's interior structure create a magnetic field that attracts the charged particles to Earth's North Pole and South Pole.

• How is Earth structured?

• How does Earth's core create Earth's magnetic field?

Robert Postma/age fotostock

What do you think?

Before you read, decide if you agree or disagree with each of these statements. As you read this chapter, see if you change your mind about any of the statements.

1. People have always known that Earth is round.

2. Earth's hydrosphere is made of hydrogen gas.

3. Earth's interior is made of distinct layers.

4. Scientists discovered that Earth's outer core is liquid by drilling deep wells.

5. All ocean floors are flat.

6. Most of Earth's surface is covered by water.

Your one-stop online resource
connectED.mcgraw-hill.com

 LearnSmart®

 Chapter Resources Files, Reading Essentials, Get Ready to Read, Quick Vocabulary

 Animations, Videos, Interactive Tables

 Self-checks, Quizzes, Tests

 Project-Based Learning Activities

 Lab Manuals, Safety Videos, Virtual Labs & Other Tools

 Vocabulary, Multilingual eGlossary, Vocab eGames, Vocab eFlashcards

 Personal Tutors

Spherical Earth

Reading Guide

Key Concepts

ESSENTIAL QUESTIONS

- What are Earth's major systems and how do they interact?

- Why does Earth have a spherical shape?

Vocabulary

sphere p. 197

geosphere p. 198

gravity p. 199

density p. 201

 Multilingual eGlossary

▷ **Science Video**

 7.ESS.5, SEPS.2, SEPS.5, SEPS.8, 6-8.LST.4.1, 6-8. LST.7.1, 6-8.LST.7.3

Inquiry Why is Earth spherical?

This image of Earth was taken from space. Notice Earth's shape and the wispy clouds that surround part of the planet. What else do you notice about Earth?

How can you model Earth's systems?

Earth has different systems made of water, solid materials, air, and life. Each system has unique characteristics.

1. Read and complete a lab safety form.
2. Set a **clear plastic container** on your table, and add **gravel** to a depth of about 2 cm.
3. Pour equal volumes of **corn syrup** and **colored water** into the container.
4. Observe the container for 2 minutes. Record your observations in your Science Journal.

Think About This

1. What happened to the materials?

2. 🔑 **Key Concept** Which Earth system did each material represent?

Describing Earth

Imagine standing on a mountaintop. You can probably see that the land stretches out beneath you for miles. But you cannot see all of Earth—it is far too large. People have tried to determine the shape and size of Earth for centuries. They have done so by examining the parts they can see.

Many years ago, people believed that Earth was a flat disk with land in the center and water at the edges. Later they used clues to determine Earth's true shape, such as studying Earth's shadow on the Moon during an eclipse.

The Size and Shape of Earth

Now there are better ways to get a view of Earth—the largest of the four rocky planets closest to the Sun. Using satellites and other technology, scientists know that Earth is a sphere. *A* **sphere** *is shaped like a ball, with all points on the surface at an equal distance from the center.* But Earth is not a perfect sphere. As illustrated in **Figure 1**, Earth is somewhat flattened at the poles with a slight bulge around the equator. This means the diameter of Earth is larger around the equator than at the poles. Earth has an average diameter of almost 13,000 km.

Figure 1 The red dashes around the image of Earth illustrate a perfect sphere. The blue dashes represent Earth's axis. Earth is shaped like a sphere that is somewhat flattened.

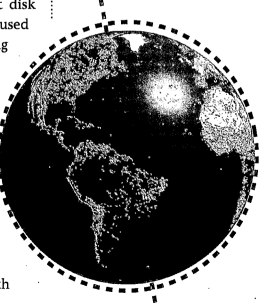

Hutchings Photography/Digital Light Source

Earth Systems

Earth is large and complex. To simplify the task of studying Earth, scientists describe Earth systems, as shown in Figure 2. All of these systems interact by exchanging matter and energy. For example, water from the ocean evaporates and enters the atmosphere. Later, the water precipitates onto land and washes salts into the ocean.

The Atmosphere, the Hydrosphere, and the Cryosphere

The atmosphere is the layer of gases surrounding Earth. It is Earth's outermost system. This layer is hundreds of kilometers thick. It is a mixture of nitrogen, oxygen, carbon dioxide, and traces of other gases. The hydrosphere is water on Earth's surface, water underground, and liquid water in the atmosphere.

Most of the water in the hydrosphere is in salty oceans. Freshwater is in most rivers and lakes and underground. Frozen water, such as glaciers, is part of the cryosphere, also. Water continually moves between the atmosphere and the hydrosphere. This is one example of how Earth systems interact.

The Geosphere and the Biosphere

The geosphere is Earth's entire solid body. It contains the thin layer of soil and sediments on Earth's surface, down to it's rocky center. It is the largest Earth system. The biosphere includes all living things on Earth. Organisms in the biosphere live within and interact with the atmosphere, hydrosphere, and even the geosphere.

 Key Concept Check Identify Earth's major systems.

Earth's Systems

Figure 2 Earth's systems interact. A change in one Earth system affects all other Earth systems. They exchange energy and matter, making Earth suitable for life.

Atmosphere: layer of gases surrounding Earth

Hydrosphere: liquid water on Earth

Geosphere: Earth's entire solid body

Biosphere: all living organisms on Earth

Cryosphere: frozen water on Earth

How did Earth form?

Earth formed about 4.6 billion years ago (bya), along with the Sun and the rest of our solar system. Materials from a large cloud of gas and dust came together, forming the Sun and all the planets. In order to understand how this happened, you first need to know how gravity works.

The Influence of Gravity

Gravity *is the force that every object exerts on all other objects because of their masses.* The force of gravity between two objects depends on the objects' masses and the distance between them. The more mass either object has, or the closer together they are, the stronger the gravitational force. You can see an example of this in **Figure 3.**

Force of Gravity

The two objects in row A are the same distance apart as the two objects in row B. One of the objects in row B has more mass, creating a stronger gravitational force between the two objects in row B.

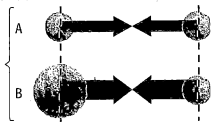

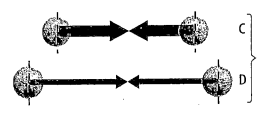

All four objects have the same mass. The two objects in row C are closer to each other than the two objects in row D and, therefore, have a stronger gravitational force between them.

Figure 3 Mass and distance affect the strength of the gravitational force between objects. This strength is represented by the thickness of the arrows. The thicker the arrows, the greater the force between the two objects.

Visual Check Why does Earth exert a greater gravitational force on you than other objects do?

The force of gravity is strongest between the objects in row B. Even though the objects in row A are the same distance apart as those in row B, the force of gravity between them is weaker because they have less mass. The force of gravity is weakest between the objects in row D.

Reading Check What factors affect the strength of the gravitational force between objects?

As illustrated in **Figure 4**, all objects on or near Earth are pulled toward Earth's center by gravity. Earth's gravity holds us on Earth's surface. Since Earth has more mass than any object near you, it exerts a greater gravitational force on you than other objects do. You don't notice the gravitational force between less massive objects.

Figure 4 Earth's gravity pulls objects toward the center of Earth.

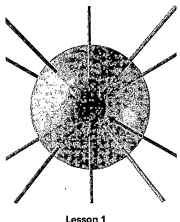

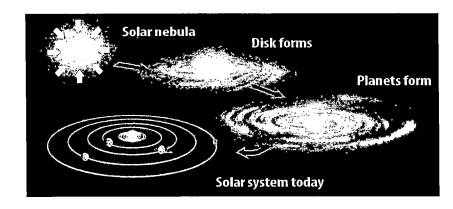

Solar nebula

Disk forms

Planets form

Solar system today

Figure 5 Gravity helped change a cloud of dust, gas, and ice, called a nebula, into our solar system. The Sun formed first, and the planets formed from the swirling disk of particles that remained.

Ø **Visual Check** Our solar system formed from what type of cloud?

MiniLab   15 minutes

Which materials will sink?

You can investigate the density of a material by comparing it to the density of water.

① Read and complete a lab safety form.

② Add water to a **clear, glass bowl** until it is about three-quarters full.

③ Hold a piece of **balsa wood** just under the surface of the water, then release it. Record your observations in your Science Journal. Remove the wood from the bowl.

④ Repeat step 2, using a piece of **granite, pumice,** and then **ironwood.**

Analyze and Conclude

1. **Summarize** Which materials sank? Which materials floated? Hypothesize why this happened.

2. ⌐○══ **Key Concept** Use the concept of density to infer why the hydrosphere is above the geosphere but below the atmosphere.

The Solar Nebula

The force of gravity played a major role in the formation of our solar system. As shown in **Figure 5**, the solar system formed from a cloud of gas, ice, and dust called a nebula. Gravity pulled the materials closer together. The nebula shrank and flattened into a disk. The disk began to rotate. The materials in the center of the disk became denser, forming a star—the Sun.

Next, the planets began to take shape from the remaining bits of material. Earth formed as gravity pulled these small particles together. As they collided, they stuck to each other and formed larger, unevenly shaped objects. These larger objects had more mass and attracted more particles. Eventually enough matter collected and formed Earth. But how did the unevenly shaped, young planet become spherical?

Early Earth

Eventually the newly formed Earth grew massive and generated thermal energy, commonly called heat, in its interior. The rocks of the planet softened and began to flow.

Gravity pulled in the irregular bumps on the surface of the newly formed planet. As a result, Earth developed a relatively even spherical surface.

⌐○══ **Key Concept Check** How did Earth develop its spherical shape?

The Formation of Earth's Layers

Thermal energy from Earth's interior affected Earth in other ways, as well. Before heating up, Earth was a mixture of solid particles. The thermal energy melted some of this material and it began to flow. As it flowed, Earth developed distinct layers of different materials.

The different materials formed layers according to their densities. **Density** *is the amount of mass in a material per unit volume.* Density can be described mathematically as

$$D = m/V$$

where D is the density of the material, m is the material's mass, and V is its volume. If two materials have the same volume, the denser material will have more mass.

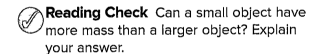 **Reading Check** Can a small object have more mass than a larger object? Explain your answer.

There is a stronger gravitational force between Earth and a denser object than there is between Earth and a less dense object. You can see this if you put an iron block and a pinewood block with the same volumes in a pan of water. The wooden block, which is less dense than water, will float on the water's surface. The iron block, which is denser than water, will be pulled through the water to the bottom of the pan.

When ancient Earth started melting, something much like this happened. The densest materials sank and formed the innermost layer of Earth. The least dense materials stayed at the surface, and formed a separate layer. The materials with intermediate densities formed layers in between the top layer and the bottom layer. Earth's three major layers are shown in Figure 6.

Figure 6 Earth's geosphere is divided into three major layers.

Math Skills

Solve One-Step Equations

Comparing the masses of substances is useful only if the same volume of each substance is used. To calculate density, divide the mass by the volume. The unit for density is a unit of mass, such as g, divided by a unit of volume, such as cm^3. For example, an aluminum cube has a mass of 27 g and a volume of 10 cm^3. The density of aluminum is 27 g / 10 cm^3 = 2.7 g/cm^3.

Practice

A chunk of gold with a volume of 5.00 cm^3 has a mass of 96.5 g. What is the density of gold?

 Math Practice

 Personal Tutor

WORD ORIGIN

density
from Latin *densus,* means "thick, crowded"

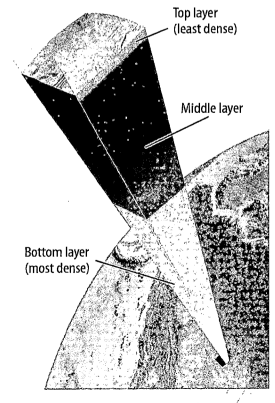

Top layer
(least dense)

Middle layer

Bottom layer
(most dense)

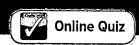
Visual Summary

 Earth's systems, including the atmosphere, hydrosphere, cryosphere, biosphere, and geosphere, interact with one another.

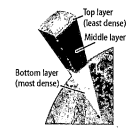 The geosphere is the solid body of Earth.

Top layer (least dense)
Middle layer
Bottom layer (most dense)

 The solar system, including Earth, formed about 4.6 bya. Gravity caused particles to come together and formed a spherical Earth.

FOLDABLES

Use your lesson Foldable to review the lesson. Save your Foldable for the project at the end of the chapter.

What do you think NOW?

You first read the statements below at the beginning of the chapter.

1. People have always known that Earth is round.

2. Earth's hydrosphere is made of hydrogen gas.

Did you change your mind about whether you agree or disagree with the statements? Rewrite any false statements to make them true.

Use Vocabulary

1 The Earth system made mainly of surface water is called the _____.

2 Use the term *density* in a sentence.

Understand Key Concepts

3 Which is part of the atmosphere?
A. a rock
B. a tree
C. oxygen gas
D. the ocean

4 **Describe** how gravity affected Earth's shape during Earth's formation.

Interpret Graphics

5 **Organize** Copy and complete the graphic organizer below to show each of Earth's systems.

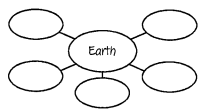

Earth

Critical Thinking

6 **Combine** your understanding of how Earth became spherical and observations of the Moon. Then form a hypothesis about the formation of the Moon.

7 **Explain** As the newly formed Earth became spherical, did it grow larger or become smaller? Explain your answer.

Math Skills 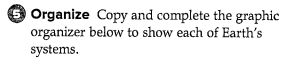 Math Practice

8 At a given temperature, 3.00 m³ of carbon dioxide has a mass of 5.94 kg. What is the density of carbon dioxide at this temperature?

◄ George Harlow studies diamonds to learn more about Earth's interior.

Time capsules

Formed billions of years ago in Earth's mantle, diamonds hold important clues about our planet's mysterious interior.

George Harlow is fascinated by diamonds. Not because of their dazzling shine or their value, but because of what they can reveal about Earth. He considers diamonds to be tiny time capsules that capture a picture of the ancient mantle, where they became crystals.

Most diamonds we find today formed billions of years ago deep within Earth's mantle, over 161 km below Earth's surface. Tiny bits of mantle, called inclusions, were trapped inside these extremely hard crystals as they formed. Millions of years later, the inclusions' diamond cases still protect them.

Harlow collects these diamonds from places such as Australia, Africa, and Thailand. Back in the lab, Harlow and his colleagues remove inclusions from diamonds. First, they break open a diamond with a tool similar to a nutcracker. Then they use a microscope and a pinlike tool to sift through the diamond rubble. They look for an inclusion, which is about the size of a grain of sand. When they find one, they use an electron microprobe and a laser to analyze the inclusion's composition, or chemical makeup. The sample might be tiny, but it's enough for scientists to learn the temperature, pressure, and composition of the mantle in which the diamond formed.

Next time you see a diamond, you might wonder if it too has a tiny bit of ancient mantle from deep inside Earth.

Going Up?

Diamond crystals form deep within the mantle under intense pressures and temperatures. They come to Earth's surface in molten rock, or magma. The magma pulls diamonds from rock deep underground and rapidly carries them to the surface. The magma erupts onto Earth's surface in small, explosive volcanoes. Diamonds and other crystals and rocks from the mantle are in deep, carrot-shaped cones called kimberlite pipes that are part of these rare volcanoes.

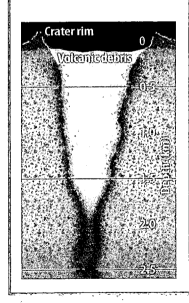

Crater rim
Volcanic debris

It's Your Turn

RESEARCH Diamonds are the world's most popular gemstone. What other uses do diamonds have? Research the properties of diamonds and how they are used in industry. Report your findings to your class.

Earth's Interior

Inquiry What is inside Earth?

Earth is thousands of kilometers thick. The deepest caves, mines, and wells in the world barely scratch Earth's surface. How do you think scientists learn about Earth's interior?

Launch Lab

10 minutes

How can you model Earth's layers?

Earth is made of three main layers: the thin outer crust, the thick mantle, and the central core. You can use different objects to model these layers.

1. Read and complete a lab safety form.

2. Place a **hard-cooked egg** on a **paper towel**. Use a **magnifying lens** to closely examine the surface of the egg. Is its shell smooth or rough? Record your observations in your Science Journal.

3. Carefully peel away the shell from the egg.

4. Use the **plastic knife** to cut the egg in half. Observe the characteristics of the shell, the egg white, and the yolk.

5. Make a drawing of the egg's layers in your Science Journal. Which layers could represent layers of Earth? Label the layers as *crust, mantle,* or *core*.

Think About This

1. What other objects could be used to model Earth's layers?

2. **Key Concept** Explain why a hard-cooked egg is a good model for Earth's layers.

Clues to Earth's Interior

Were you ever given a gift and had to wait to open it? Maybe you tried to figure out what was inside by tapping on it or shaking it. Using methods such as these, you might have been able to determine the gift's contents. Scientists can't see what is inside Earth, either. But they can use indirect methods to discover what Earth's interior is like.

What's below Earth's surface?

Deep mines and wells give scientists hints about Earth's interior. The deepest mine ever constructed is a gold mine in South Africa. It is nearly 4 km deep. People can go down the mine to explore the geosphere.

Drilled wells are even deeper. The deepest well is on the Kola Peninsula in Russia. It is more than 12 km deep. Drilling to such great depths is extremely difficult—it took more than 20 years to drill the Kola well. Even though people cannot go down in the well, they can send instruments down to make observations and bring samples to the surface. What have scientists learned about Earth's interior by studying mines and wells like the two mentioned above?

REVIEW VOCABULARY
observation
an act of recognizing and noting a fact or an occurrence

Hutchings Photography/Digital Light Source

Lesson 2
EXPLORE
205

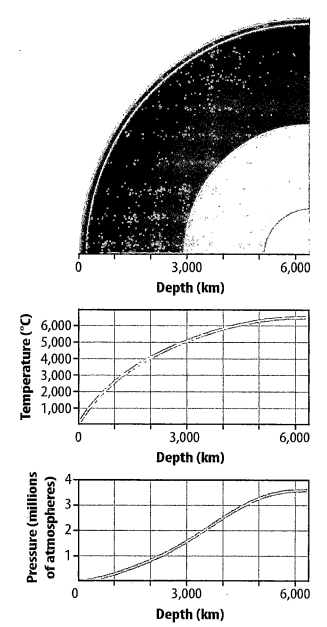

Figure 7 Temperature and pressure increase with depth in the geosphere.

Temperature and Pressure Increase with Depth

One thing that workers notice in deep mines or wells is that it is hot inside Earth. In the South African gold mines, 3.9 km below Earth's surface, the temperature is about 53°C (127°F). The temperature at the bottom of the Kola well is 190°C (374°F). That's hot enough to bake cookies! No one has ever recorded the temperature of Earth's center, but it is estimated to be about 6,000°C (10,832°F). As shown in Figure 7, temperature within Earth increases with increasing depth.

Not only does temperature increase, but pressure also increases as depth increases inside Earth. This is due to the weight of the overlying rocks. The high pressure squeezes the rocks and makes them much denser than surface rocks.

Reading Check Describe how pressure changes with depth within Earth.

High temperatures and pressures make it difficult to drill deep wells. The depth of the Kola well is less than 1 percent of the distance to Earth's center. Therefore, only a small part of the geosphere has been sampled. How can scientists learn about what is below the deepest wells?

Using Earthquake Waves

As you read earlier, scientists use indirect methods to study Earth's interior. They get most of their evidence by analyzing earthquake waves. Earthquakes release energy in the form of three types of waves. As these waves move through Earth, they are affected by the different materials they travel through. Some waves cannot travel through certain materials. Other waves change direction when they reach certain materials. By studying how the waves move, scientists are able to infer the density and composition of materials within Earth.

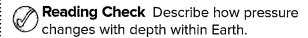

FOLDABLES

Make a layered book from two sheets of paper. Use your book to organize information about Earth's crust, mantle, outer core, and inner core.

Crust
Mantle
Outer core
Inner core

Earth's Layers

Recall that differences in density resulted in materials within Earth forming layers. Each layer has a different composition, with the densest materials in the center of Earth and the least dense materials at the surface.

Crust

The brittle, rocky outer layer of Earth is called the **crust.** It is much thinner than the other layers, like the shell on a hard-cooked egg. It is the least dense layer of the geosphere. It is made mostly of elements of low mass, such as silicon and oxygen.

Crustal rocks are under oceans and on land. The crust under oceans is called oceanic crust. It is made of dense rocks that contain iron and magnesium. The crust on land is called continental crust. It is less dense and about four times thicker than oceanic crust. Continental crust is thickest under tall mountains. Figure 8 shows a comparison of the two types of crust.

There is a distinct boundary between the crust and the layer beneath it. When earthquake waves cross this boundary, they speed up. This indicates that the layer beneath the crust, called the mantle, is denser than the crust.

Reading Check How does oceanic crust differ from continental crust?

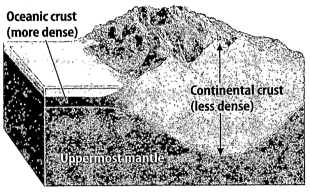

Oceanic crust (more dense)

Continental crust (less dense)

Uppermost mantle

Personal Tutor

Figure 8 Oceanic crust is thin and dense compared to continental crust.

MiniLab

Which liquid is densest? 🥽 🧤 ⚗️

Earth's layers were determined by density. The iron in the inner core makes up Earth's densest layer. The silicon and oxygen in Earth's crust are much less dense.

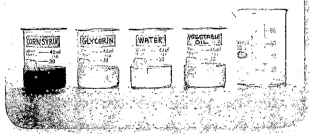

① Read and complete a lab safety form.

② Pour 50 mL of **corn syrup** into a **100-mL beaker.** Label the beaker.

③ Fill the remaining three beakers with 50 mL of **glycerin, water,** and **vegetable oil,** respectively. Label them.

④ Stir a few drops of **blue food coloring** into the water using a **spoon.**

⑤ Rinse the spoon. Then stir a few drops of **red food coloring** into the corn syrup.

⑥ Pour the corn syrup into a **250-mL beaker.**

⑦ Use a **funnel** to gently pour the glycerin on top of the corn syrup. Hold the funnel along the side of the beaker.

⑧ Repeat step 7 using the vegetable oil, then the water.

Analyze and Conclude

1. **Describe** what happened to the liquids. Why did this occur?

2. **Key Concept** How are the layers of liquid in the beaker similar to Earth's layers?

Mantle

Earth's mantle is immediately below the crust. *The **mantle** is the thick middle layer in the solid part of Earth.* It contains more iron and magnesium than oceanic crust does. This makes it denser than either type of crust. Like the crust, the mantle is made of rock. Scientists group the mantle into layers according to the way rocks react when forces push or pull on them. Figure 9 shows the mantle and the other layers of Earth.

Uppermost Mantle The rocks in the uppermost layer of the mantle are brittle and rigid, like the rocks in the crust. Because of this, *scientists group the crust and the uppermost mantle into a rigid layer called the **lithosphere*** (LIH thuh sfihr).

Asthenosphere Below the lithosphere, rocks in the upper mantle are so hot that, while they are solid, the rocks are no longer brittle. Instead, they begin to flow. Scientists use the term *plastic* to describe rocks that flow in this way. *This plastic layer within the mantle is called the **asthenosphere*** (as THEN uh sfihr).

Reading Check Compare the lithosphere and the asthenosphere.

The asthenosphere does not resemble the plastics used to make everyday products. The word *plastic* refers to materials that are soft enough to flow. The asthenosphere flows very slowly. Even if it were possible to visit the mantle, you could never see this flow. Rocks in the asthenosphere move about as slowly as your fingernails grow.

Upper Mantle and Lower Mantle The rock in the upper and lower mantle below the asthenosphere is hotter than the rock in the asthenosphere, yet it does not flow. How can this be? The pressure at this depth is so great that no melting occurs. While increased temperature tends to melt rock, high pressure tends to prevent melting. High pressure squeezes the rock into a solid. The solid rock of the upper mantle and the lower mantle forms the largest layer of Earth.

WORD ORIGIN
asthenosphere
from Greek *asthenes*, means "weak"; and *spharia*, means "sphere"

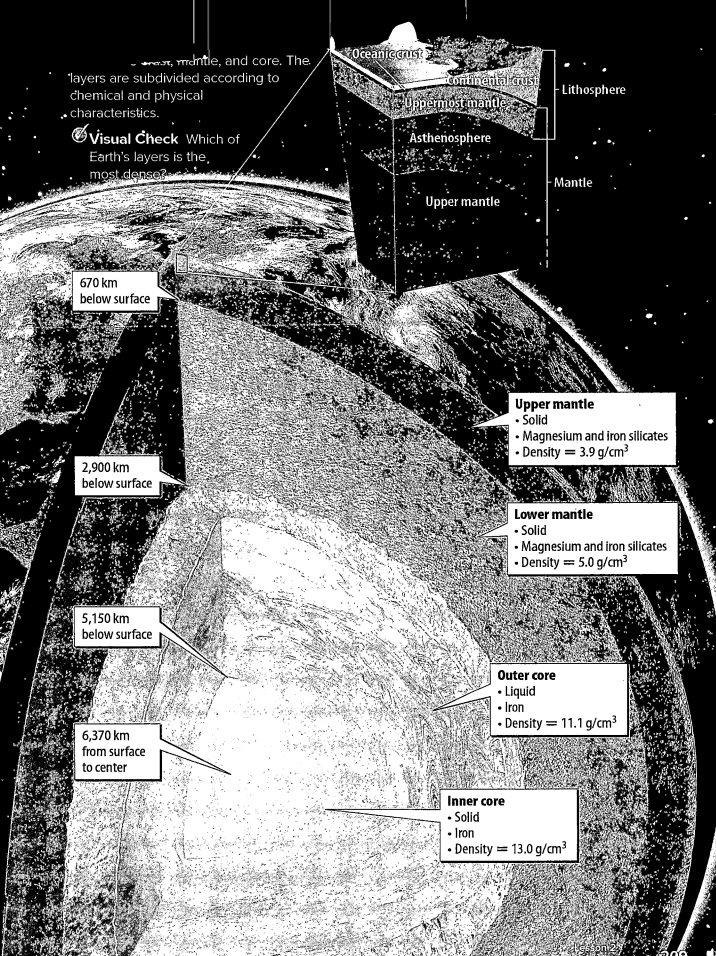

..., mantle, and core. The layers are subdivided according to chemical and physical characteristics.

✅Visual Check Which of Earth's layers is the most dense?

Oceanic crust

Continental crust

Uppermost mantle

Lithosphere

Asthenosphere

Upper mantle

Mantle

670 km below surface

2,900 km below surface

5,150 km below surface

6,370 km from surface to center

Upper mantle
- Solid
- Magnesium and iron silicates
- Density = 3.9 g/cm^3

Lower mantle
- Solid
- Magnesium and iron silicates
- Density = 5.0 g/cm^3

Outer core
- Liquid
- Iron
- Density = 11.1 g/cm^3

Inner core
- Solid
- Iron
- Density = 13.0 g/cm^3

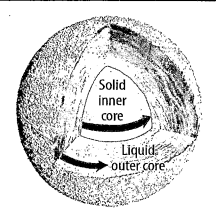

Figure 10 Earth's core has a liquid outer layer surrounding a solid inner layer of iron. The inner core spins a little faster than the outer core.

Visual Check How do the arrows in this figure indicate that the inner core spins faster than the outer core?

SCIENCE USE V.
COMMON USE

nickel
Science Use a specific type of metal

Common Use a coin worth five cents

 Applying Practices

How do Earth's layers compare?
Go online to identify and compare the chemical and physical layers of Earth's interior.

Core

The dense metallic center of Earth is the **core,** as shown in Figure 10. If you imagine Earth as a hard-cooked egg, the core is the yolk. Earth's crust and mantle are made of rock. Why is the core made of metal? Recall that in Earth's early history, the planet was much hotter than it is now. Earth materials flowed, like they do in the asthenosphere today. Scientists don't know how much of Earth melted. But they do know that it was soft enough for gravity to pull the densest material down to the center. This dense material is metal. It is mostly iron with small amounts of nickel and other elements. The core has a liquid outer core and a solid inner core.

Key Concept Check What are the interior layers of Earth?

Outer Core If pressure is great enough to keep the lower mantle in a solid state, how can the outer core be liquid? The mantle and core are made of different materials, and have different melting temperatures. Just like in the asthenosphere, the effects of temperature outweigh the effects of pressure in the outer core. Scientists used the indirect method of analyzing earthquake waves and learned that Earth's outer core is liquid.

Key Concept Check What evidence indicates that the outer core is liquid?

Inner Core The inner core is a dense ball of solid iron crystals. The pressure in the center of Earth is so high that even at temperatures of about 6,000°C, the iron is in a solid state. Because the outer core is liquid, it is not rigidly attached to the inner core. The inner core spins a little faster than the rest of Earth.

Earth's Core and Geomagnetism

Why does a compass needle point north? The metallic compass needle lines up with the magnetic field surrounding Earth. Earth's spinning core creates the magnetic field.

Earth's Magnetic Field

Recall that Earth's inner core spins faster than the outer core. This produces streams of flowing, molten iron in the outer core. Earth's magnetic field is a region of magnetism produced in part by the flow of molten materials in the outer core. The magnetic field acts much like a giant bar magnet. It has opposite poles, as shown in **Figure 11.**

For centuries, people have used compasses and Earth's magnetic field to navigate. But, the magnetic field is not completely stable. Over geologic time, its strength and direction vary. At several times in Earth's history, the direction has even reversed.

Magnetosphere

Earth's magnetic field protects Earth from cosmic rays and charged particles coming from the Sun. It pushes away some charged particles and traps others. *The outer part of the magnetic field that interacts with these particles is called the* **magnetosphere.** Examine **Figure 12** to see how the shape of the magnetosphere is produced by the flow of these charged particles.

Figure 11 Earth's magnetic field is produced by the movement of molten materials in the outer core.

WORD ORIGIN
magnetosphere
from Latin *magnes*, means "lodestone"; and *spharia*, means "sphere"

The Magnetosphere

Figure 12 Trapped particles and Earth's magnetic field form a shield around Earth.

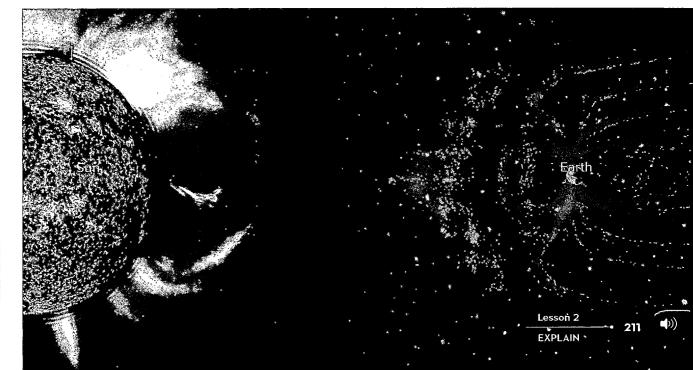

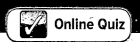
Visual Summary

Earth's layers include the crust, mantle, and core. Oceanic crust is under oceans. The continents are made of continental crust.

The mantle is Earth's thickest layer. It includes part of the lithosphere and the asthenosphere.

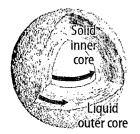

Earth's core has a liquid outer core and a solid inner core.

FOLDABLES

Use your lesson Foldable to review the lesson. Save your Foldable for the project at the end of the chapter.

What do you think NOW?

You first read the statements below at the beginning of the chapter.

3. Earth's interior is made of distinct layers.

4. Scientists discovered that Earth's outer core is liquid by drilling deep wells.

Did you change your mind about whether you agree or disagree with the statements? Rewrite any false statements to make them true.

Use Vocabulary

1 The layer of Earth made of metal is the _____.

2 **Distinguish** between the crust and the lithosphere.

3 **Use the terms** *core* and *mantle* in a complete sentence.

Understand Key Concepts

4 Which of Earth's layers is made of melted materials?
  A. the crust   C. the lithosphere
  B. the inner core   D. the outer core

5 **Design** a model of Earth's layers. List the materials needed to make your model.

6 **Classify** Earth's layers based on their physical properties.

Interpret Graphics

7 **Identify** and compare the two types of crust shown below.

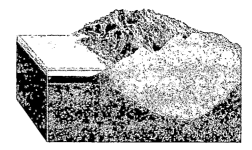

8 **Determine Cause and Effect** Draw a graphic organizer like the one below and list two facts about Earth's magnetic field.

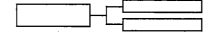

Critical Thinking

9 **Evaluate** Earthquakes produce waves that help scientists study Earth's interior, but earthquake waves can also cause damage. Discuss whether earthquake waves are good or bad.

How can you find the density of a liquid?

Earth's interior is made of solids and liquids that have different densities. You can measure volume and mass and then calculate density using the equation:

$$\text{Density} = \frac{\text{Mass}}{\text{Volume}}$$

Materials

beaker

balance

graduated cylinder

vegetable oil

corn syrup

isopropyl alcohol

Safety

Learn It

Scientists **measure** to learn how much they have of a particular type of matter. Recall that matter is anything that has mass and volume. You can measure mass using a triple-beam balance. The unit of mass you will use most often is the gram (g). You can measure liquid volume using a graduated cylinder. Milliliter (mL) is the unit of volume you will use most often.

Try It

1. Read and complete a lab safety form.
2. Measure the mass of a 50-mL graduated cylinder. Record the mass in your Science Journal.
3. Pour about 15 mL of alcohol into a clean beaker.
4. Slowly pour the alcohol into the graduated cylinder until the alcohol measures 10 mL.

5. Measure and record the mass of the alcohol and the graduated cylinder.
6. In your Science Journal, subtract the mass recorded in step 2 from the mass recorded in step 5.
7. Empty and clean the graduated cylinder as instructed by your teacher.
8. Repeat steps 3–7 using the corn syrup and then the vegetable oil.

Apply It

9. Calculate and record the density of each liquid using your mass and volume measurements and the equation shown above.
10. Which fluid has the greatest density? Which has the least? Explain your answer.
11. **Key Concept** Based on what you have learned, describe the relative density of Earth's layers.

Lesson 3

Reading Guide

Key Concepts

ESSENTIAL QUESTIONS

- What are Earth's major landforms and how do they compare?
- What are the major landform regions of the United States?

Vocabulary

landform p. 216

plain p. 218

plateau p. 219

mountain p. 219

 Multilingual eGlossary

 BrainPOP®

7.ESS.5, SEPS.2, SEPS.3, SEPS.4, SEPS.6, SEPS.8, 6-8. LST.4.1

Earth's Surface

Inquiry **What do you see?**

Some features on Earth's surface are flat and low. Other features are steep and high. What else is different about these features?

How can you measure topographic relief?

Relief describes differences in elevation for a given area. The area might have tall mountains or deep valleys. In this lab, you will use simple materials to measure relief on a model landscape.

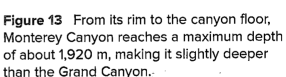

1. Read and complete a lab safety form.
2. Form some **salt dough** into a thick disk slightly larger than your hand.
3. With your fingers spread apart, press your hand firmly into the dough so that some of the dough squeezes up between your fingers.
4. Stretch **dental floss** across the finger impressions in the dough. Slice off a section of the dough model by pressing the dental floss down through the dough.
5. Also make a slice through the palm section of your dough model.
6. Observe the profiles of your two cross sections. Use a **ruler** to measure the difference between the highest and lowest points within the palm section.
7. Measure the difference between the highest and lowest points within the fingers section.

Think About This

1. What is the difference in elevation between the highest and lowest points of your hand print?

2. **Key Concept** Compare and contrast your model features. How are they similar to features on Earth?

Oceans and Continents

Earth's surface is made of oceans and continents. Oceans cover more than 70 percent of Earth's surface. The surface of the ocean is relatively smooth. But what is below the water's surface? Imagine that you can explore the ocean floor as easily as you travel on dry land. What do you think you would see there?

Many of the features that appear on dry land, such as mountains, valleys, and canyons, also appear on the ocean floor. For example, the longest mountain ranges on Earth are near the centers of the oceans. Monterey Canyon, illustrated in Figure 13, is a submarine canyon which is comparable in size to the Grand Canyon on land.

Figure 13 From its rim to the canyon floor, Monterey Canyon reaches a maximum depth of about 1,920 m, making it slightly deeper than the Grand Canyon.

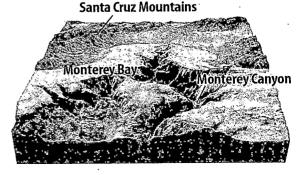

Figure 14 Earth's common landforms are characterized by size, shape, slope, elevation, and relief.

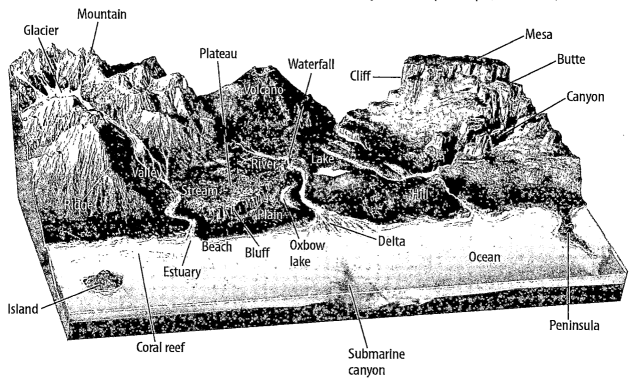

Glacier · Mountain · Plateau · Waterfall · Cliff · Mesa · Butte · Canyon · Volcano · Lake · River · Valley · Ridge · Stream · Hill · Plain · Beach · Bluff · Oxbow lake · Delta · Ocean · Estuary · Island · Coral reef · Submarine canyon · Peninsula

✍ **Visual Check** Which landforms are most familiar to you?

Landforms

ACADEMIC VOCABULARY

feature
(noun) the structure, form, or appearance of something

Mountains, plains, plateaus, canyons, and other features are called landforms. Some examples of Earth's landforms are shown in **Figure 14**. **Landforms** *are topographic features formed by processes that shape Earth's surface.* They can be as big as mountains or as small as ant hills. Characteristics such as size, shape, slope, elevation, relief, and orientation to the surrounding landscape are often used to describe landforms. A landform is usually identified by its form and location.

🔑 **Key Concept Check** What are landforms?

Landforms are not permanent. Their characteristics change over time. Many factors such as erosion or uplift of Earth's surface can create and affect landforms.

Elevation

Scientists use the term *elevation* to describe the height above sea level of a particular feature. Some landforms have high elevation. Other landforms have low elevation. For example, elevation is one of the major characteristics that is used to distinguish a plain from a plateau.

Relief

Do you recall how you measured relief in the Launch Lab at the beginning of this lesson? *Relief* is a term that scientists use to describe differences in elevation. Some landforms or geographic areas are described as having low relief. This means that there is a relatively small difference between the lowest elevation and the highest elevation in an area. Landforms or areas with high relief have a relatively large difference between the lowest elevation and the highest elevation. For example, if you were to climb out of the Grand Canyon, you would say it has high relief.

Topography

Scientists use the term *topography* to describe the shape of a geographic area. You can describe the topography of a small location or you can think about the general topography of a large region. Relief and topography can be used to describe features on continents and on the ocean floor. Next, you will read how relief and elevation are used to describe the most common landforms on Earth—plains, plateaus, and mountains.

MiniLab

20 minutes

How do landforms compare?

The terms *gully, ravine,* and *canyon* all describe an elongated depression formed by erosion from water. But how do these landforms differ?

① Read and complete a lab safety form.

② Working with a partner, use a **dictionary** to find the definition of the landforms in one of the lists below.

List 1	List 2	List 3	List 4
butte	hill	bay	channel
mesa	knoll	cove	strait
plateau	mountain	gulf	sound

③ Use **modeling clay** to represent the landforms in the list you chose.

④ Use **scissors** to cut different colors of **construction paper** and make scenes with your landforms.

⑤ Label each part of the scene.

Analyze and Conclude

Key Concept Compare and contrast the model landforms.

Figure 15 🔑 Plains, plateaus, and mountains differ in terms of elevation and relief. ▷

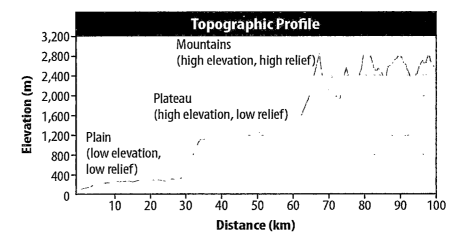

Topographic Profile

Mountains (high elevation, high relief)

Plateau (high elevation, low relief)

Plain (low elevation, low relief)

Elevation (m): 3,200, 2,800, 2,400, 2,000, 1,600, 1,200, 800, 400, 0

Distance (km): 10 20 30 40 50 60 70 80 90 100

WORD ORIGIN

plain
from Latin *planus*, means "flat, level"

Plains

The features that cover most of Earth's surface are plains. **Plains** *are landforms with low relief and low elevation,* as illustrated in **Figure 15.** The broad, flat area in the center of North America is called the interior plains, as shown in **Figure 16.**

Plains can form when sediments are deposited by water or wind. Their soil is often rich. For this reason, many plains are used for growing crops or grazing animals.

Major Landform Regions

Figure 16 This map shows the major landform regions on Earth—plains, plateaus, and mountains.

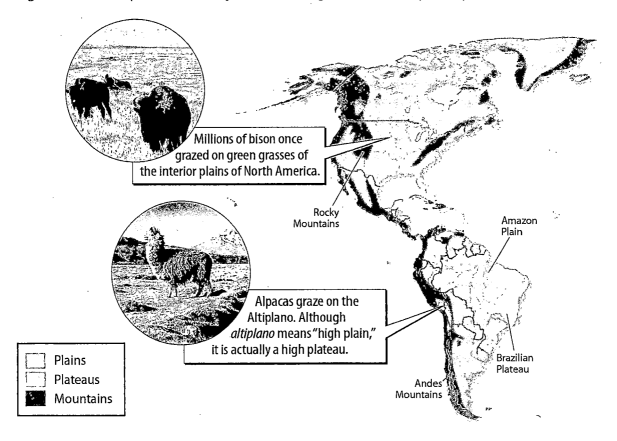

Millions of bison once grazed on green grasses of the interior plains of North America.

Alpacas graze on the Altiplano. Although *altiplano* means "high plain," it is actually a high plateau.

Rocky Mountains

Amazon Plain

Brazilian Plateau

Andes Mountains

☐ Plains
☐ Plateaus
■ Mountains

(t)Medioimages/Photodisc/PunchStock; (b)©Jonathan Andrew/Corbis

Plateaus

As you just read, plains are relatively flat and low. In contrast, plateaus are flat and high. **Plateaus** *are areas with low relief and high elevation.* Look again at **Figure 15** to see how a plateau differs from a plain.

Plateaus are much higher than the surrounding land and often have steep, rugged sides. They are less common than plains, but they are on every continent. Find some plateaus in different parts of the world in **Figure 16**.

(✓) **Reading Check** Describe a plateau.

Plateaus can form when forces within Earth uplift rock layers or cause collisions between sections of Earth's crust. For example, the highest plateau in the world is the Tibetan Plateau, called the "roof of the world." It is still being formed by collisions between India and Asia.

Plateaus also can be formed by volcanic activity. For example, the Columbia Plateau in the western United States is the result of the buildup of many successive lava flows.

Mountains

The tallest landforms of all are mountains. **Mountains** *are landforms with high relief and high elevation.* Look again at the world map in **Figure 16.** How many of Earth's well-known mountains can you find?

Mountains can form in several different ways. Some mountains form from the buildup of lava on the ocean floor. Eventually, the mountain grows tall enough to rise above the ocean's surface. The Hawaiian Islands are mountains that formed this way. Other mountains form when forces inside Earth fold, push, or uplift huge blocks of rocks. The Himalayas, the Rocky Mountains, and the Appalachian Mountains all formed from tremendous forces within Earth.

(✓) **Visual Check** Which of Earth's three major types of landforms—plains, plateaus, or mountains—covers most of Earth's land surface?

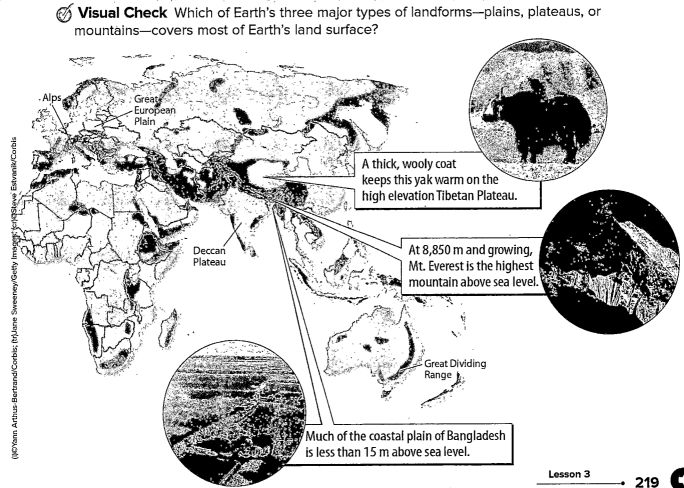

Alps

Great European Plain

Deccan Plateau

A thick, wooly coat keeps this yak warm on the high elevation Tibetan Plateau.

At 8,850 m and growing, Mt. Everest is the highest mountain above sea level.

Great Dividing Range

Much of the coastal plain of Bangladesh is less than 15 m above sea level.

(l)©Yann Arthus-Bertrand/Corbis; (tr)©Steve Estvanik/Corbis; (cr)©Jane Sweeney/Getty Images

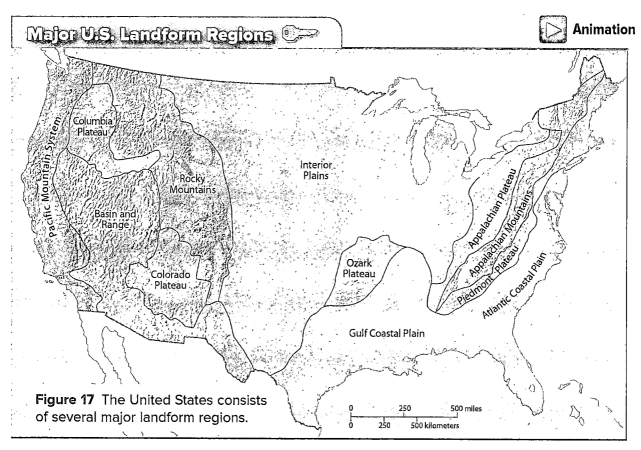

Figure 17 The United States consists of several major landform regions.

⬮ **Visual Check** Which landform region do you live in?

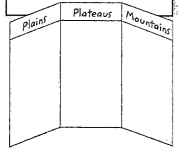

FOLDABLES

Make a tri-fold book from a sheet of paper. Label it as shown. Use it to organize your notes about Earth's major landforms.

Plains | Plateaus | Mountains

Major Landform Regions in the United States

From flat plains to towering mountains, the United States has a variety of landforms. The major landform regions in the United States are shown in **Figure 17.**

Coastal plains are along much of the East Coast and the Gulf Coast. These plains formed millions of years ago when sediments were deposited on the ocean floor.

The interior plains make up much of the central part of the United States. This flat, grassy area has thick soils and is well suited for growing crops and grazing animals.

The Appalachian Mountains, in the eastern United States, began forming about 480 million years ago (mya). They were once much taller than they are today. Erosion has reduced their average elevation to about 2,000 m. The Rocky Mountains are in the western United States and western Canada. They are younger, taller, and more rugged than the Appalachians.

The Colorado Plateau is also a rugged region. It formed when forces within Earth lifted up huge sections of Earth's crust. Over time, the Colorado River cut through the plateau, forming the Grand Canyon.

📝 **Key Concept Check** Describe at least three major landform regions in the United States.

Visual Summary

Landforms are topographic features formed by processes that shape Earth's surface.

Major landforms include flat plains, high plateaus, and rugged mountains.

Major landform regions in the United States include the Appalachian Mountains, the Great Plains, the Colorado Plateau, and the Rocky Mountains.

FOLDABLES

Use your lesson Foldable to review the lesson. Save your Foldable for the project at the end of the chapter.

What do you think NOW?

You first read the statements below at the beginning of the chapter.

5. All ocean floors are flat.

6. Most of Earth's surface is covered by water.

Did you change your mind about whether you agree or disagree with the statements? Rewrite any false statements to make them true.

Use Vocabulary

1 Plains and mountains are examples of _____ formed by processes that shape Earth's surface.

2 A(n) _____ is a landform with high relief and high elevation.

3 **Distinguish** between a plain and a plateau.

Understand Key Concepts

4 A landform with low relief and high elevation is a
   A. mountain.　　**C.** plateau.
   B. plain.　　　　**D.** topography.

5 **Describe** any landforms that are near your school.

Interpret Graphics

6 **Compare** Study the illustration below. How do plains compare to plateaus in terms of relief?

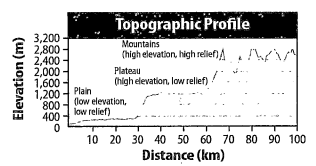

Topographic Profile

Mountains (high elevation, high relief)
Plateau (high elevation, low relief)
Plain (low elevation, low relief)

Elevation (m): 3,200 2,800 2,400 2,000 1,600 1,200 800 400 0

Distance (km): 10 20 30 40 50 60 70 80 90 100

7 **Summarize** Copy and fill in the graphic organizer below to identify the major types of landforms.

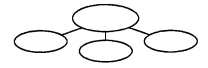

Critical Thinking

8 **Suggest** a way to model plains, plateaus, and mountains by using sheets of cardboard.

9 **Evaluate** the drawbacks and benefits of living in the mountains.

Materials

salt dough

food coloring

waxed paper

centimeter ruler

plastic knife

rolling pin
or can

Safety

Modeling Earth and Its Layers

Earth has distinct layers. Each layer has a specific relative volume. You can use those volumes to build a model of Earth with each of the layers in proportion.

Question

Knowing the relative volume of Earth's inner core, outer core, mantle, and crust, how can you build an accurate scale model of these layers?

Procedure

① Read and complete a lab safety form.

② Obtain a piece of salt dough from your teacher. Study the chart below showing the relative volume of each layer of Earth. How can you use that data to turn your lump of dough into a model of Earth's layers?

The Relative Volumes of Each Layer of Earth	
Layer	Relative Volume (%)
Inner core	0.7
Outer core	15.7
Mantle	82.0
Crust	1.6

③ You might have lots of ideas about how to divide your dough into the correct proportions to build your model. Here is one way you could try:

- Work on a sheet of waxed paper so the dough won't stick. Roll your dough into a cylinder that measures 10 cm long. The cylinder represents 100 percent of the volume.

- Now use your centimeter ruler to measure and mark off each of the percentages listed in the chart.

- Cut off each piece and roll it into a sphere.

④ Use the data from the chart to figure out how you can build an accurate model.

⑤ Make a model of Earth's layers using the spheres that represent the relative volume of each layer. Add some food coloring to make each of the four spheres a different color. Work the salt dough so that the color is evenly distributed. Form each lump of dough into a sphere again. Your spheres should look similar to the ones shown in the photo below.

⑥ Cut in half the sphere representing the outer core.

⑦ Gently make a small depression in the flat side of each half of the outer core. Then place the inner core inside the outer core and seal the sphere.

⑧ Cut in half the sphere representing the mantle.

⑨ Gently make a small depression in the flat side of each half of the mantle. Fit the sphere representing the inner and outer cores into the mantle.

⑩ The last sphere represents Earth's crust. Put it on a piece of waxed paper and use a rolling pin (or a can) to spread out the sphere enough to make it fit onto the outside of the mantle.

⑪ Cut your model in half.

Analyze and Conclude

⑫ **The Big Idea** Describe how each layer of Earth is represented on your model.

⑬ **Think Critically** Do you think your model accurately shows the volumes of the different layers? Why or why not?

⑭ **Draw a Conclusion** What can you conclude about the relative volumes of the different layers? Why couldn't you stretch the crust out far enough to cover the mantle? Why couldn't you just add more dough to the crust?

Communicate Your Results

Draw and label Earth's layers. Display the drawing next to your model and use both to explain what you have discovered about Earth's layers.

How could you make an edible model of Earth's layers? Hint: Think about using ice cream or gelatin molds.

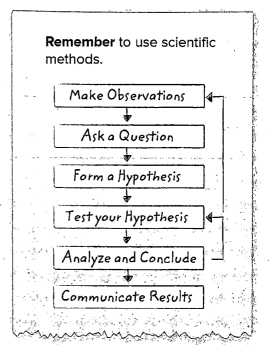

Remember to use scientific methods.

Make Observations

Ask a Question

Form a Hypothesis

Test your Hypothesis

Analyze and Conclude

Communicate Results

Earth's three major layers are the crust, the mantle, and the core.

Key Concepts Summary

Vocabulary

Lesson 1: Spherical Earth

- Earth's major systems include the atmosphere, hydrosphere, cryosphere, biosphere, and **geosphere.**

- All major Earth systems interact by exchanging matter and energy. A change in one Earth system affects all other Earth systems.

- **Gravity** caused particles to come together to form a spherical Earth.

sphere p. 197
geosphere p. 198
gravity p. 199
density p. 210

Lesson 2: Earth's Interior

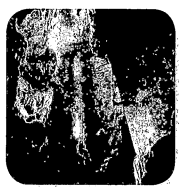

- Earth's interior layers include the **crust, mantle,** and **core.**

- By analyzing earthquake waves, scientists have determined that the outer core is liquid and the inner core is solid.

crust p. 207
mantle p. 208
lithosphere p. 208
asthenosphere p. 208
core p. 210
magnetosphere p. 211

Lesson 3: Earth's Surface

- Earth's major **landforms** include **plains, plateaus,** and **mountains.** Plains have low relief and low elevation. Plateaus have low relief and high elevation. Mountains have high relief and high elevation.

- Plains, plateaus, and mountains are all found in the United States.

landform p. 216
plain p. 218
plateau p. 219
mountain p. 219

(t)©Bloomimage/Corbis; (c)Stephen Alvarez/Getty Images; (b)David Gralian/Alamy

Personal Tutor

Vocabulary eFlashcards

Vocabulary eGames

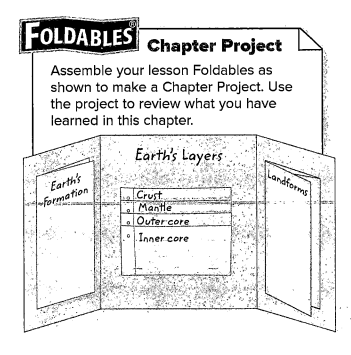

FOLDABLES **Chapter Project**

Assemble your lesson Foldables as shown to make a Chapter Project. Use the project to review what you have learned in this chapter.

Use Vocabulary

1 Earth formed when _____ pulled together gas and dust that was spinning around the Sun.

2 The gravitational force is greater between similar-sized objects that have a higher _____.

3 The _____ is the largest of Earth's systems.

4 Small amounts of melted material in the _____ produce flow in the mantle.

5 The least dense rocks on Earth are in the _____.

6 Liquid in the _____ produces Earth's magnetic field.

7 A topographic feature formed by processes that shape Earth's surface is a _____.

8 A(n) _____ has low relief and low elevation.

9 A landform that is high and flat is a(n) _____.

Link Vocabulary and Key Concepts

 Interactive Concept Map

Copy this concept map, and then use vocabulary terms from the previous page to complete the concept map.

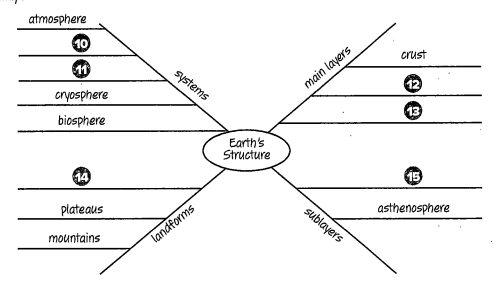

Understand Key Concepts

1. What does the biosphere contain?
   A. air
   B. living things
   C. rocks
   D. water

2. What affects the strength of gravity between two objects?
   A. the density of the objects
   B. the mass of the objects
   C. the distance between the objects
   D. both the mass and the distance between the objects

3. The figure below shows Earth's layers. What does the red layer represent?
   A. asthenosphere
   B. crust
   C. lithosphere
   D. mantle

4. What is the shape of Earth?
   A. disklike
   B. slightly flattened sphere
   C. sphere
   D. sphere that bulges at the poles

5. Which do scientists use to learn about Earth's core?
   A. earthquake waves
   B. mines
   C. temperature measurements
   D. wells

6. What does the magnetosphere protect people from?
   A. asteroids
   B. cosmic rays
   C. global warming
   D. sun spots

7. In the figure below, what feature is the arrow pointing to?
   A. core
   B. mountain
   C. plain
   D. plateau

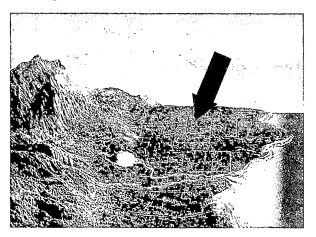

8. What does topography describe?
   A. depth of an ocean feature
   B. height of a landform
   C. shape of a given area
   D. width of an area

9. What is true of landforms?
   A. They are all flat.
   B. They are permanent.
   C. They change over time.
   D. They are only on continents.

10. A box sitting on the floor models what type of landform?
    A. mountain
    B. plain
    C. plateau
    D. relief

Critical Thinking

11 **Explain** how gravity would affect you differently on a planet with less mass than Earth, such as Mercury.

12 **Compare** materials in the geosphere to materials in the atmosphere.

13 **Consider** How would Earth's layers be affected if all the materials that make up Earth had the same density?

14 **Relate** How do Earth's systems interact?

15 **Explain** why everything on or near Earth is pulled toward Earth's center.

16 **State** how the crust and the uppermost mantle are similar.

17 **Summarize** Earth's crust, mantle, and core on the basis of relative position, density, and composition.

18 **Create** a model of Earth's magnetosphere.

19 **Explain** how a plateau differs from a plain.

20 **Summarize** the characteristics of the landform regions labeled in the map below.

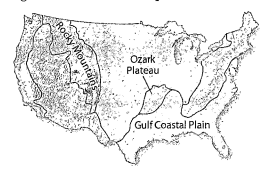

Rocky Mountains
Ozark Plateau
Gulf Coastal Plain

21 **Evaluate** which type of landform is best suited for agriculture.

Writing in Science

22 A song includes lyrics that usually rhyme. Write the lyrics to a song about the elevation of landforms.

REVIEW **THE BIG IDEA**

23 Identify and describe the different layers of Earth.

24 How does Earth's core create Earth's magnetic field?

25 Hypothesize what might happen to life on Earth if Earth did not have a magnetosphere.

Math Skills ✓ Math Practice

Solve One-Step Equations

26 A large weather balloon holds 3.00 m³ of air. The air in the balloon has a mass of 3.75 kg. What is the density of the air in the balloon?

27 A pine board has a volume of 18 cm³. The mass of the board is 9.0 g. What is the density of the pine board?

28 100 cm³ of water has a mass of 100 g. Will the pine board in the previous question float or sink in the water?

Robert Postma/age fotostock

Record your answers on the answer sheet provided by your teacher or on a sheet of paper.

Multiple Choice

1 Density equals

A mass divided by volume.

B mass times volume.

C volume divided by mass.

D volume times mass.

2 Which force gave Earth its spherical shape?

A electricity

B friction

C gravity

D magnetism

Use the diagram below to answer question 3.

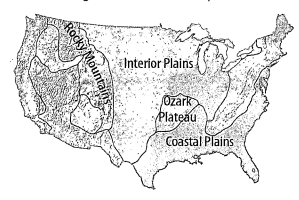

3 Which landform covers the largest area of the central United States?

A Coastal Plains

B Interior Plains

C Ozark Plateau

D Rocky Mountains

4 Which describes Earth's asthenosphere?

A brittle

B fast-moving

C freeze-dried

D plastic

Use the diagram and the graphs below to answer question 5.

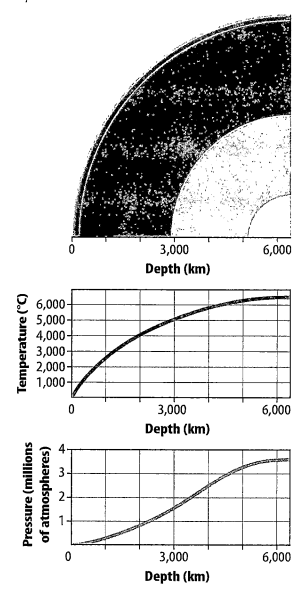

5 Which describes temperature and pressure at Earth's center?

A high pressure and high temperature

B high pressure and low temperature

C low pressure and high temperature

D low pressure and low temperature

6 Which explains the term *topography*?

   A the geological ages of features

   B the heights and locations of features

   C the seasonal variations of features

   D the travel routes between features

7 Which is the correct order of Earth's layers from the surface to the center?

   A crust, core, mantle

   B crust, mantle, core

   C mantle, core, crust

   D mantle, crust, core

Use the diagram below to answer question 8.

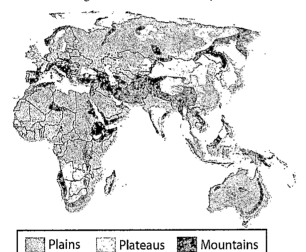

   ▨ Plains   ⬚ Plateaus   ▩ Mountains

8 Which continent has the greatest area of plateaus?

   A Africa

   B Asia

   C Australia

   D Europe

Constructed Response

9 Compare and contrast plateaus and plains.

Use the diagrams below to answer questions 10–12.

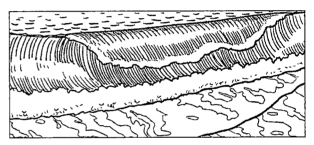

10 Three Earth systems are highlighted above. Name each system and describe its features.

11 Describe how these three systems interact.

12 Draw a diagram of the fourth major Earth system. Describe its features.

NEED EXTRA HELP?												
If You Missed Question...	1	2	3	4	5	6	7	8	9	10	11	12
Go to Lesson...	1	1	3	2	2	3	2	3	3	1	1	1

Chapter 7

7.ESS.1, SEPS.1, SEPS.2, SEPS.3, SEPS.4, SEPS.6, SEPS.8

Minerals and Rocks

THE BIG IDEA How are minerals and rocks formed, identified, classified, and used?

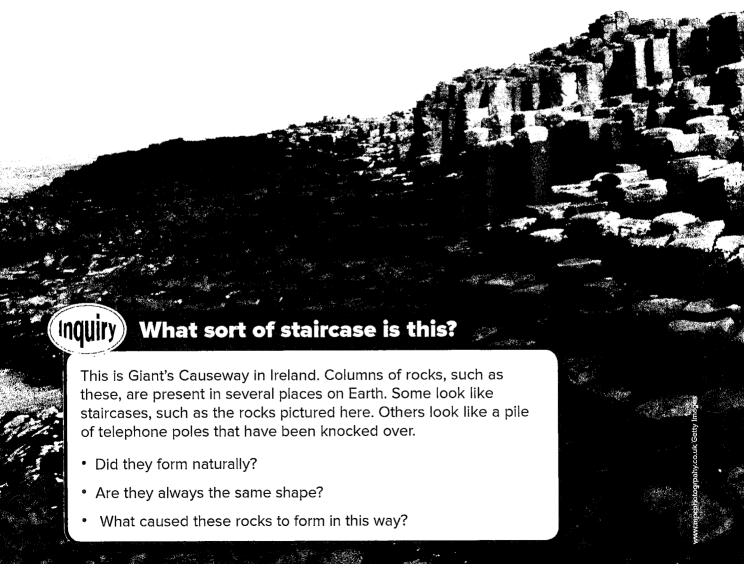

Inquiry What sort of staircase is this?

This is Giant's Causeway in Ireland. Columns of rocks, such as these, are present in several places on Earth. Some look like staircases, such as the rocks pictured here. Others look like a pile of telephone poles that have been knocked over.

- Did they form naturally?
- Are they always the same shape?
- What caused these rocks to form in this way?

www.mpcphotography.co.uk/Getty Images

Lesson 1

Reading Guide

Key Concepts

ESSENTIAL QUESTIONS

° How do minerals form?

° What properties can be used to identify minerals?

° What are some uses of minerals in everyday life?

Vocabulary

mineral p. 233

crystal structure p. 234

crystallization p. 235

streak p. 237

luster p. 237

cleavage p. 237

fracture p. 237

ore p. 239

 Multilingual eGlossary

 BrainPOP®
Science Video

7.ESS.1

Minerals

(Inquiry) Where on Earth are minerals?

Minerals are all around you every day. Sometimes you can even pick up a mineral right from the ground! But most minerals need to mined from beneath Earth's surface, which requires large equipment and areas of land. What is a mineral? Where can you find minerals? What can you use them for?

Is everything crystal clear?

Do you have several shirts that are nearly the same color or style? If so, you probably know the subtle differences that make each unique. The same is true for the thousands of minerals on Earth. To most people, many of these minerals look exactly the same. In this lab, you'll examine four transparent minerals and demonstrate that not everything is crystal clear.

1. Read and complete a lab safety form.

2. In your Science Journal, draw a data table in which to record your observations. Record your observations after each step.

3. Use a **magnifying lens** to examine each **mineral.**

4. Place each mineral over this sentence, and observe the words.

5. Place the minerals in a **small bowl** of warm water for 2–3 minutes. Take the minerals out of the water and dry them with **paper towels.** Examine each mineral.

6. Carefully place one drop of **dilute hydrochloric acid** on each mineral. Record your observations. Use the paper towels to wipe the minerals dry.

Think About This

1. How are the minerals the same? How are they different?

2. 🗝️ **Key Concept** How do you think each mineral might be used in everyday life?

What is a mineral?

Do you ever drink mineral water? Maybe you take vitamins and minerals to stay healthy. The word *mineral* has many common meanings, but for geologists, scientists who study Earth and the materials of which it is made, this word has a very specific definition.

A **mineral** *is a solid that is naturally occurring, inorganic, and has a crystal structure, and definite chemical composition.* In order for a substance to be classified as a mineral, it must have all five of the characteristics listed in the definition above. Samples of pyrite and coal are shown in Figure 1. Coal is made of ancient compressed plant material. Pyrite crystals are made of the elements iron and sulfur. One of these is a mineral, but the other is not. By considering each of the five characteristics of minerals, you can determine which sample is the mineral. The information on the next page will help you do this.

Figure 1 Both coal, on the left, and pyrite, on the right, are shiny, hard substances that form deep inside Earth. But only one is a mineral.

✓ **Reading Check** What five characteristics define a mineral?

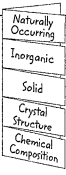
Math Skills

Use Ratios

A ratio compares numbers. For example, in the chemical formula for water, H_2O, the number 2 is called a subscript. The subscript tells you how many atoms of that element are in the formula. A symbol with no subscript means that element has one atom. So, the ratio of hydrogen (H) atoms to oxygen (O) atoms in H_2O is 2:1. This is read *two to one*.

Practice

Quartz has the formula SiO_2. What is the ratio of silicon (Si) atoms to oxygen (O) atoms in quartz?

Math Practice

Personal Tutor

Characteristics of Minerals

To be classified as a mineral, a substance must form naturally. Materials made by people are not considered minerals. Diamonds that form deep beneath Earth's surface are minerals, but diamonds that are made in a laboratory are not. As shown in **Figure 2**, these two types of diamonds can look very similar.

Materials that contain carbon and were once alive are organic. Minerals cannot be organic. This means that a mineral cannot have once been alive, and it cannot contain anything that was once alive, such as plant parts.

A mineral must be solid. Liquids and gases are not considered to be minerals. So, while solid ice is a mineral, water is not.

 Personal Tutor

Figure 2 Natural and artificial diamonds look very much alike, but only the natural diamond on the right is a mineral.

A mineral must have a crystal structure. *The atoms in a crystal are arranged in an orderly, repeating pattern called a* **crystal structure.** This organized structure produces smooth faces and sharp edges on a crystal. The faces and edges of the pyrite crystals shown in **Figure 1** are produced by this internal atomic structure.

A mineral is made of specific amounts of elements. A chemical formula shows how much of each element is present in the mineral. For example, pyrite is made of the elements iron (Fe) and sulfur (S). There always must be one iron atom for every two sulfur atoms. Therefore, the chemical formula for pyrite is FeS_2.

Look again at **Figure 1.** Because the plants that turned into the coal were once alive, coal is not a mineral. The pyrite has all five characteristics of a mineral, so it is a mineral.

Mineral Formation

How do atoms form minerals? Atoms within a liquid join together to form a solid. **Crystallization** *is the process by which atoms form a solid with an orderly, repeating pattern.* Crystallization can happen in two main ways.

Crystallization from Magma When melted rock material—called magma—cools, some of the atoms join together and form solid crystals. As the liquid continues to cool, atoms are added to the surface of the crystals. The longer it takes the magma to cool, the more atoms are added to the crystal. Large crystals grow when the magma cools slowly. If the magma cools quickly, there is only enough time for small crystals to grow.

Crystallization from Water Many substances, such as sugar and salt, dissolve in water, especially if the water is warm. When water cools or evaporates, the particles of the dissolved substances come together again in the solution and crystallize. The gold shown in Figure 3 formed this way. The orderly arrangement of atoms in this mineral is visible using a very powerful microscope.

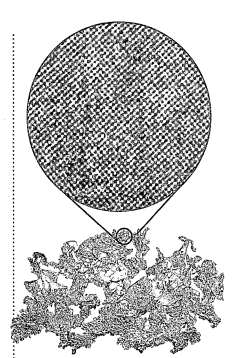

Figure 3 The orderly atomic structure of gold crystals produces these neat rows of atoms.

Key Concept Check How do minerals form?

 MiniLab

20 minutes

How does your garden grow?

Just like plants in a garden, minerals grow, or form, in different ways. Some minerals form when magma or lava cools and hardens. Other minerals form when atoms and molecules dissolved in water join and crystallize. Can you grow a "garden" of mineral crystals?

① Read and complete a lab safety form.

② Pour 500 mL of hot water into a **beaker.** Using a **spoon,** slowly add the **solid** to the water. Stir with a **stirring rod** until no more of the solid dissolves.

③ Use **hot mitts** to pick up the beaker and carefully pour about 100 mL of the solution into each **shallow glass dish.**

④ Put the dishes where they will not be disturbed. Use a **magnifying lens** to observe the crystals that form in your dish over the next couple of days. Record your observations in your Science Journal.

Analyze and Conclude

1. **Observe** What do your crystals look like? Be specific in your description.

2. **Measure** How big are the largest crystals? The smallest ones?

3. **Recognize Cause and Effect** What factors affected the size of the crystals that formed?

4. **Key Concept** How did the minerals form in this activity?

SCIENCE USE V. COMMON USE

property
Science Use a quality or characteristic of an individual or thing

Common Use something owned or possessed

Table 1 🔑 The minerals on the Mohs hardness scale are classified according to their relative hardness. Some common materials that can be used to test mineral samples also are included.

◎ **Visual Check** Which minerals are harder than glass?

Mineral Identification

Every mineral has a unique set of physical properties, or characteristics. These properties are used to identify minerals. Generally, it is necessary to investigate several properties in order to distinguish between similar minerals.

Density

If you pick up two mineral samples that are about the same size, one might feel heavier than the other. The heavier mineral has a higher density. It has more mass in the same volume. The densities of many minerals are quite similar, but a very high or a very low density can be useful for identifying a mineral.

Hardness

The hardness of a mineral is measured by observing how easily it is scratched or how easily it scratches something else. The Mohs hardness scale, shown in **Table 1**, ranks hardness from 1 to 10. On this scale, diamond is the hardest mineral, with a hardness value of 10. The softest mineral is talc, with a hardness of 1.

Table 1 Mohs Hardness Scale

Hardness	Mineral or Ordinary Object		Hardness	Mineral or Ordinary Object	
10	diamond		5	apatite	
9	corundum		4.5	wire nail	
			4	fluorite	
8	topaz		3.5	copper wire or copper coin (penny)	
			3	calcite	
7	quartz		2.5	fingernail	
6.5	streak plate		2	gypsum	
6	feldspar		1	talc	
5.5	glass, steel knife blade				

(l to r, t to b)Smithsonian Institution/Corbis, Andrew Silver/U.S. Geological Survey, Andrew Silver/U.S. Geological Survey, Doug Sherman/Geofile, José Manuel Sanchis Calvete/Corbis, José Manuel Sanchis Calvete/Corbis, José Manuel Sanchis Calvete/Corbis, Harry Taylor/Getty Images, Doug Sherman/Geofile, Dr. Parvinder Sethi

Color and Streak

Some minerals have a unique color that can be used for identification. The mineral malachite always has a distinctive green color. But the colors of most minerals vary. Quartz is a common mineral that has many different colors.

Even though the colors of most minerals vary from specimen to specimen, the color of a mineral's powder does not. *The color of a mineral's powder is called its* **streak.** Streak is observed by scratching the mineral across a tile of unglazed porcelain. Sometimes, the color of a mineral and the color of its streak are different, as illustrated by the hematite shown in Figure 4.

Luster

Minerals reflect light in different ways. **Luster** *describes the way that a mineral's surface reflects light.* Many terms are used to describe mineral luster. Some of these terms are *metallic, glassy, earthy,* or *pearly.* Figure 4 contains an example of the mineral hematite, which can have either a metallic luster or a dull luster. The muscovite mica shown in Figure 4 has a pearly luster, and the quartz has a glassy luster.

Cleavage and Fracture

Two properties are used to describe the ways that minerals break. *If a mineral breaks along smooth, flat surfaces, it displays* **cleavage.** A mineral can break along a single cleavage direction, or it can have more than one direction. As shown in Figure 4, muscovite mica has one cleavage direction and peels off in sheets. Halite has three distinct cleavage directions and breaks into cubes.

A mineral that breaks along rough or irregular surfaces displays **fracture.** The quartz in Figure 4 shows fracture.

Reading Check How does cleavage differ from fracture?

Figure 4 ☞ Minerals can be described in many different ways. The minerals pictured here have a variety of colors, streaks, and luster, and they break in different ways.

Visual Check Which mineral displays cleavage? Which displays fracture?

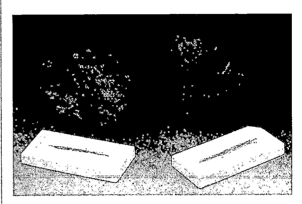

Hematite can have a red, brown, or black color, but its streak is always a dark, rusty red. Hematite's luster can be metallic or dull.

Muscovite displays cleavage in one direction. Parts of the crystals can peel off in flakes or sheets.

Quartz forms in a variety of colors—clear, purple, orange, or pink, such as the quartz pictured above.

ACADEMIC VOCABULARY

exhibit
(verb) to display, to present for
the public to see

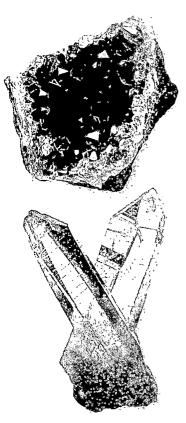

△ **Figure 5** The smaller
amethyst crystals on the
top formed in a small,
crowded space. More
space allowed the quartz
crystals on the bottom to
grow large and distinct.

Crystal Shape

Minerals exhibit many different crystal shapes. A mineral's atomic structure determines its crystal shape. Crystal shapes can vary greatly. The crystals of hematite, shown in **Figure 4**, are relatively shapeless, so they are described as massive. Muscovite mica has diamond-shaped or six-sided crystals, but muscovite commonly occurs in flat, sheetlike layers, as shown in **Figure 4**. Amethyst, a type of quartz, has crystals shaped like pyramids, as shown in **Figure 5**.

Sometimes crystals grow so close to each other that the crystal shape is not visible. If there is room for large crystals to grow, the crystal shape can be useful for identifying the mineral. A comparison of small, crowded amethyst crystals and large, well-formed quartz crystals is shown in **Figure 5**.

 Key Concept Check What are the common properties used to identify minerals?

Unusual Properties

Some minerals have unusual properties that make them easy to identify. For example, halite tastes salty. Magnetite is magnetic and attracts steel objects. Calcite fizzes when acid is dropped on it. A variety of calcite, called Iceland spar, also has a property called double refraction. As shown in **Figure 6**, images viewed through the calcite crystal appear doubled.

Quartz crystals can produce an electric current when compressed. This property makes quartz crystals useful in radios, microphones, and watches.

Several minerals display the property of fluorescence. Quartz and calcite, as shown in **Figure 6**, glow under ultraviolet light.

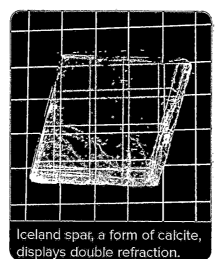

Iceland spar, a form of calcite, displays double refraction.

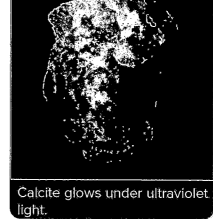

Calcite glows under ultraviolet light.

Figure 6 Some minerals have unique properties.

Figure 7 Minerals have a variety of uses in our daily lives. Toothpaste, cosmetics, and table salt are just a few everyday items that contain minerals.

△ Toothpaste contains calcite or silica.

◁ Common table salt contains the mineral halite.

Some cosmetics contain mica. ▷

Minerals in Everyday Life

You might not be aware of how important minerals are in your life. From the moment you wake in the morning until you fall asleep at night, you use materials made from minerals. A few common examples are shown in **Figure 7.** Some minerals are valuable because we use them every day. We appreciate others simply for their beauty.

Did you know that beverage cans and car batteries are made from minerals? These items are made of metals. Most metals combine with other elements in the formation of a mineral. For example, aluminum can be extracted from the rock bauxite. The minerals must be processed to remove the metals from them. *Deposits of metallic or nonmetallic minerals that can be produced at a profit are called* **ores.**

Some minerals, such as gemstones, are valuable because of their appearance. Specific physical properties make the gemstones valuable. They usually are harder than quartz. Their luster is generally brilliant, and gemstones often have intense colors. The natural crystals are cut and polished, such as the emeralds shown in **Figure 8.**

Key Concept Check How are minerals used in everyday life?

Figure 8 When rough emeralds, such as the one on the left, are cut and polished, they look like the gem to the right. ▽

(l) ©Tom Grill/Corbis, (tr,cr)Getty Images, (b)Luis Veiga/Getty Images

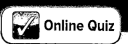

Visual Summary

Hardness varies from mineral to mineral and can be used to help identify certain minerals.

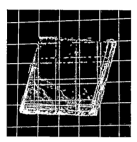

All minerals have specific crystal shapes and properties that can be used to help identify them.

Minerals are present in everyday items such as toothpaste, makeup, and household items.

FOLDABLES

Use your lesson Foldable to review the lesson. Save your Foldable for the project at the end of the chapter.

What do you think NOW?

You first read the statements below at the beginning of the chapter.

1. Minerals generally are identified by observing their color.

2. Minerals are made of crystals.

Did you change your mind about whether you agree or disagree with the statements? Rewrite any false statements to make them true.

Use Vocabulary

1 **Distinguish** between the terms *crystal structure* and *crystallization*.

2 The color of a mineral's powder is called its

_____.

3 **Define** *luster* in your own words.

Understand Key Concepts

4 **Explain** Bones contain elements found in minerals and have a definite structure. Why is bone NOT a mineral?

5 Which mineral property is least reliable in mineral identification?
 A. color **C.** hardness
 B. streak **D.** luster

6 **Give an example** of an object you use daily that is made from a mineral.

Interpret Graphics

7 **Draw** a graphic organizer like the one below, and list the five characteristics of a mineral.

Critical Thinking

8 **Suggest** a plan to investigate and identify unknown mineral samples.

9 **Justify** why natural diamonds are worth much more than manufactured diamonds.

Math Skills   Math Practice

10 Calcite has the formula $CaCO_3$. What is the ratio of calcium (Ca) to carbon (C) to oxygen (O) atoms in calcite?

11 What is the formula for hematite if it's ratio of iron (Fe) to oxygen (O) atoms is 3:4?

Cave of Crystals

An Amazing Sight!

or any rock collector, a geode is a thrilling find. Splitting these hollow rocks in half reveals perfectly formed crystals inside. In 2000, two brothers found themselves inside something like a giant geode. They discovered the Cave of Crystals 300 m under the Chihuahuan Desert in Mexico. The limestone cave is filled with some of the largest crystals ever found—gigantic, shimmering beams the size of trees. Inside the cave, the temperature is about 43°C, and it is very humid. When researchers are in the cave, they wear special suits so they can work in the steaming hot conditions. Scientists are now working to identify and understand the natural conditions that allowed the crystals to become so large.

AMERICAN MUSEUM & NATURAL HISTORY

What are the crystals made of?
The crystals are made of the mineral selenite, a transparent and colorless form of gypsum. Gypsum has a hardness of 2 on the Mohs hardness scale. So even though some of the crystals have edges that are as sharp as blades, the crystals are soft enough to be scratched by your fingernail.

How did the crystals form?
Hundreds of thousands of years ago, a magma chamber below the caves heated groundwater in Earth's crust. The hot water became mineral-rich by dissolving minerals from the surrounding rock. It seeped through cracks in the limestone caves. As the water cooled over time, the dissolved minerals crystallized.

How did the crystals get so big?
The more time crystals have to grow, the bigger they become. The Cave of Crystals was left undisturbed for thousands of years, so the crystals grew very large. The crystals stopped growing only because local miners drained the groundwater, emptying the cave of the mineral-rich water.

◁ These selenite crystals are the same shape as the giants in the Cave of Crystals. They are much smaller, though, because they did not have as much time to grow.

It's Your Turn

Suppose you are in charge of tourism for the Cave of Crystals. Write a tourist brochure describing what visitors can expect to see and experience in the cave. Be sure to include a list of dos and don'ts.

Lesson 2

Rocks

Reading Guide

Key Concepts

ESSENTIAL QUESTIONS

- What characteristics can be used to classify rocks?
- How do the different types of rocks form?
- What are some uses of rocks in everyday life?

Vocabulary

rock p. 243

grain p. 243

magma p. 244

lava p. 244

texture p. 244

sediment p. 245

lithification p. 245

foliation p. 247

 Multilingual eGlossary

 BrainPOP®

 7.ESS.1, SEPS.2, SEPS.3, SEPS.8

Inquiry How did they form?

These rocks are at the bottom of the Grand Canyon and are very old. They have certain characteristics that allow geologists to identify exactly what type of rock they are. All rocks do not look the same. Geologists use the different characteristics of rocks to categorize the different rock types on Earth.

Zach Holmes/Alamy

What does a rock's texture tell you about the rock? 🔲

Do you have a sweater or a shirt that is so soft you want to wear it all the time? Softness is a texture. The word texture is also used to describe rocks. But, it does not refer to the way a rock's surface feels. A rock's texture refers to the sizes of the grains, or particles, in the rock and how they are arranged. What can a rock's texture tell you about how the rock formed?

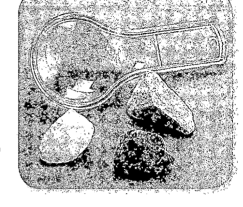

① Read and complete a lab safety form.

② Make a data table in your Science Journal in which to record your observations. Your table should include columns for three different rocks, drawings of their textures, and detailed descriptions of the textures.

③ Use a **magnifying lens** to closely examine sets of **rocks.** Note the sizes of the grains and how the grains in each rock are arranged. Record your observations.

Think About This

1. Which rock might have formed from magma? Which might have formed in water? Which might have formed under pressure?

2. Contrast the three different rock textures.

3. 🗝 **Key Concept** How do you think texture might be used to classify rocks?

What is a rock?

Sometimes you can tell how an object was made simply by looking at the finished product. If someone serves you eggs for breakfast, you can tell whether they were fried or scrambled. In much the same way, a geologist can tell how a rock was formed just by looking at it. The two rocks in **Figure 9** mostly contain quartz, feldspar and biotite mica. But the rocks look different because they formed in different ways.

A **rock** *is a naturally occurring solid mixture composed of minerals, smaller rock fragments, organic matter, or glass. The individual particles in a rock are called* **grains.** Both rocks shown in **Figure 9** are made of mineral grains. The arrangement of the grains give clues to understanding how the rocks formed.

Figure 9 These rocks contain the same minerals, but, because they formed differently, they have different appearances.

✓ **Reading Check** What types of grains make up rocks?

🔎 **Visual Check** How are these two rock samples different?

Classifying Rocks

Most of Earth's surface is made of rocks. The different kinds of rocks are classified based on the way they form. There are three major types of rocks: igneous, metamorphic, and sedimentary.

Igneous Rocks

Igneous rocks are the most abundant rocks on Earth. Most of them form deep below Earth's surface, but some form on Earth's surface. Igneous rocks might form in different places, but they all form in a similar way.

Formation of Igneous Rocks *Molten rock is called* **magma** *when it is inside Earth. Molten rock that erupts onto Earth's surface is called* **lava.** As magma or lava cools, mineral crystals begin to form. These minerals form the grains of a new igneous rock.

Texture and Composition Geologists classify igneous rocks according to texture and mineral composition. For rocks, **texture** *refers to grain size and how the grains are arranged.*

Lava at Earth's surface cools quickly, so crystals do not have much time to increase in size. The crystals are small, like the crystals in the basalt shown in Figure 10. Geologists describe the texture of igneous rocks with small crystals as fine-grained. Deep below Earth's surface, magma cools slowly, and crystals have more time to grow. The crystals are larger, like the crystals in the granite shown in Figure 10. Geologists describe the texture of igneous rocks with large crystals as coarse-grained.

Igneous rocks such as granite and basalt differ in texture. They also differ in composition, or the minerals they contain. Granite contains mostly light-colored minerals such as quartz and potassium feldspar. Basalt is made of dark minerals such as pyroxene [pi RAHK seen] and olivine [AHL ih veen]. Note the differences in color between the two rocks in Figure 10.

 Key Concept Check What characteristics are used to classify igneous rocks?

Environments of Igneous Rock Formation

Figure 10 Igneous rocks form as magma or lava cools. Magma that cools deep beneath Earth's surface cools slowly and forms large crystals, such as the ones in granite. Lava that cools at Earth's surface cools quickly and forms small crystals, such as the crystals in basalt.

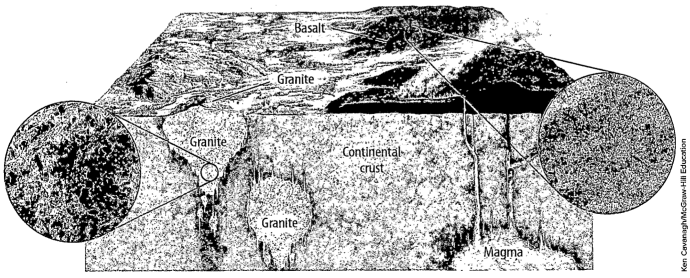

Ken Cavanagh/McGraw-Hill Education

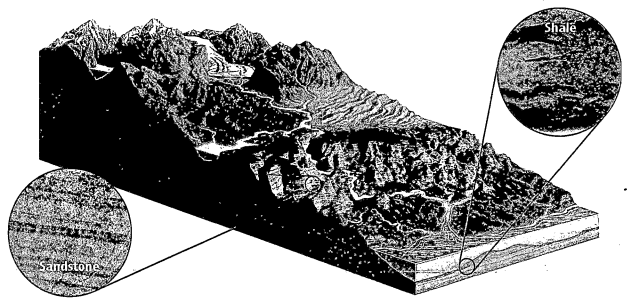

Sedimentary Rocks

Natural processes break down rocks. *Rock and mineral fragments that are loose or suspended in water are called* **sediment**. Just as molten rock is a source material for igneous rocks, sediment is the source material for most sedimentary rocks.

Formation of Sedimentary Rocks **Lithification** *is the process through which sediment turns into rock*. Study **Figure 11**. How can sediment become solid rock? Usually, sediment is formed through weathering by water, ice, or wind. These agents also remove, or erode, the sediment. Sediment eventually is deposited in low areas called basins. Layers of sediment build up, and the weight of the upper layers compacts the lower layers.

Dissolved minerals, usually quartz or calcite in water, cement the grains together and form sedimentary rocks, such as the sandstone and shale in **Figure 11**. Dissolved solids also can crystallize directly from a water solution and form sedimentary rocks such as rock salt.

Texture and Composition Similar to igneous rocks, sedimentary rocks can be described as fine-grained or coarse-grained. The shape of the grains also can be described as rounded or angular. Grains usually are angular when first broken but often become rounded during transport. Rounded grains can help distinguish sedimentary rocks from some igneous rocks.

The composition of a sedimentary rock depends on the minerals in the sediment from which it formed. Sandstone is a sedimentary rock that usually is made of quartz grains. Shale is made from much smaller grains of quartz and clay minerals.

Figure 11 Sediment travels downhill and settles in layers within basins. Eventually, the sediment becomes compacted and cemented together, forming sedimentary rocks.

FOLDABLES

Use a sheet of paper to make a folded table. Label it as shown. Use it to compare types of rocks.

Rocks	Formation	Texture	Composition
Igneous			
Sedimentary			
Metamorphic			

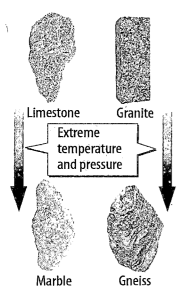

Limestone   Granite

Extreme
temperature
and pressure

Marble   Gneiss

Figure 12 Each metamorphic rock has a parent rock.

 **Visual Check** Which rock does not show the direction of increased pressure?

 Animation

Metamorphic Rocks

Sometimes rocks can change into new and different rocks without erosion or melting. Extreme high temperatures and pressure cause these changes. The original rocks are called parent rocks, and the new rocks are called metamorphic rocks.

Formation of Metamorphic Rocks Metamorphic rocks form when parent rocks are squeezed, heated, or exposed to hot fluids. The rocks do not melt. They remain solid, but the texture and, sometimes, the mineral composition of the parent rock change. This process is metamorphism.

Texture and Composition The textures of most metamorphic rocks result from increases in temperature and pressure. This process is illustrated in **Figure 12**. The mineral composition of metamorphic rocks might be the result of minerals that are present in the parent rock, or they might grow in the new metamorphic rock. You read about gemstones in Lesson 1. Many gemstones are minerals that formed as a result of metamorphism.

Key Concept Check How do metamorphic rocks form?

MiniLab   20 minutes

How do heat and pressure change rocks?

Have you ever discovered a forgotten peanut butter sandwich at the bottom of your backpack? If so, you know well that heat and pressure can change things! When rocks are exposed to heat and pressure, they can become metamorphic rocks. In this lab, you'll model two types of metamorphism.

1. Read and complete a lab safety form.
2. Drop a handful of **uncooked spaghetti noodles** onto your desk. Observe and record how they are arranged relative to each other.
3. In one quick motion, use the edges of your hands to bring the noodles back together. Observe and record how the noodles now are arranged relative to each other.
4. Put an **egg white** in a **shallow glass dish.**
5. Use a **hot plate** to heat a **beaker** half-filled with water. ⚠ Do not touch the hot plate or boil the water.
6. Use **tongs** to place the beaker on the egg white. Observe what happens and record your observations in your Science Journal.

Analyze and Conclude

1. **Recognize Cause and Effect** How did the spaghetti noodles and the egg white change? How are these changes like metamorphism?

2. **Key Concept** How does this activity model how metamorphic rocks form?

(1) McGraw-Hill Education, (2)Brent Turner/BLT Productions, (3,4) Jacques Cornell/McGraw-Hill Education, (5)Hutchings Photography/Digital Light Source

Foliated Metamorphic Rocks Recall that crystals form in a variety of shapes. Minerals with flat shapes, such as mica, produce a foliated texture. **Foliation** [foh lee AY shun] *results when pressures cause flat minerals to line up, giving the rock a layered appearance.* Eventually distinct bands of light and dark minerals form, as shown in the sample of gneiss [NISE] in Figure 12. Foliation is the most obvious characteristic of metamorphic rocks.

Nonfoliated Metamorphic Rocks Marble, another type of metamorphic rock is not foliated. The grains in the marble pictured in Figure 12 are not flattened like the grains in gneiss. The calcite crystals that make up marble became blocklike and square when exposed to high temperatures and pressure. Marble has a nonfoliated texture.

Rocks in Everyday Life

Rocks are abundant natural resources that are used in many ways based on their physical characteristics. Some igneous rocks are hard and durable, such as the granite used to construct the fountain shown in Figure 13. The igneous rock pumice is soft but contains small pieces of hard glass, which makes it useful for polishing and cleaning.

Natural layering makes sedimentary rock a high-quality building stone. Both sandstone and limestone are used in buildings. The building pictured in Figure 14 is made of sandstone. Limestone also is used to make cement, which is then used in construction applications, including building highways.

Foliated metamorphic rocks, such as slate, split into flat pieces. Slate makes durable, fireproof roofing shingles, such as the ones shown in Figure 15. Other metamorphic rocks are used in art. Marble is soft enough to carve and often is used for making detailed sculptures.

 Key Concept Check What are some everyday uses for rocks?

Figure 13 Granite was used to build this fountain. ▷

Figure 14 This building in Jordan was carved and constructed out of sandstone. ▽

Figure 15 Slate sometimes is used on roofs like the ones on this house. ▽

(t)T.Lehne/Lotuseaters/Alamy, (c)R. Strange/PhotoLink/Getty Images, (b)David Williams/Alamy

✓ Online Quiz
Virtual Lab

Visual Summary

Interlocking crystals of different sizes are common in igneous rocks.

The individual grains that form sedimentary rocks can be mineral grains or fragments of other rocks.

Increases in temperature and pressure cause minerals to change in size and shape.

FOLDABLES

Use your lesson Foldable to review the lesson. Save your Foldable for the project at the end of the chapter.

What do you think NOW?

You first read the statements below at the beginning of the chapter.

3. Once a rock forms, it lasts forever.

4. All rocks form when melted rock cools and changes into a solid.

Did you change your mind about whether you agree or disagree with the statements? Rewrite any false statements to make them true.

Use Vocabulary

1. **Distinguish** between lava and magma.

2. Loose grains of rock material are called _____.

3. **Use the term** *lithification* in a sentence.

Understand Key Concepts

4. **Explain** how sedimentary rocks form.

5. Which list shows the correct sequence?
    A. shale, foliation, basalt
    B. gneiss, lithification, shale
    C. granite, metamorphism, gneiss
    D. sandstone, lithification, sediment

6. **Compare** the formation of sandstone to the formation of gneiss.

Interpret Graphics

7. **Analyze** the figure below. Identify the parent rock, the metamorphic rock, and what the red arrow represents.

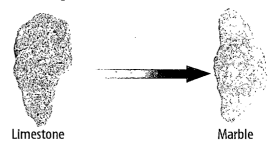

Limestone   Marble

8. **Draw** a graphic organizer like the one below. List the two major textures of metamorphic rocks and why they form.

Texture	Formation

Critical Thinking

9. **Invent** a new way to classify the major rock types.

10. **Classify** the following rock and justify your answer: light brown in color; small, sand-sized pieces of quartz cemented together in layers.

Materials

rock samples

magnifying lens

glass plate

Safety

How are rocks similar and different?

Do you have any collections? If so, you might have the objects in the collections sorted according to how they are the same or how they are different. In this lab, you will use a key to compare and contrast various rock samples in order to identify them.

Learn It

Comparing objects means finding similarities. Contrasting objects means finding differences. How can you **compare and contrast** rock samples to correctly identify different rocks?

Try It

① Read and complete a lab safety form.

② In your Science Journal, draw a table like the one shown below.

③ Use the rock identification key as a guide while you examine your rocks.

④ Study your rock samples. Organize them into groups based on common characteristics. In your Science Journal, record what characteristics you used to group the rocks.

⑤ Use the key and a magnifying lens, as needed, to identify each rock.

⑥ Record each rock type and name in your data table.

Apply It

⑦ **Compare and Contrast** How are the rocks similar? How are they different?

⑧ 🔑 **Key Concept** How can you identify and classify rocks based on characteristics related to their origin?

Data for Ten Different Rock Samples

Sample	Type of Rock	Name of Rock
1.		
2.		
3.		
4.		
5.		
6.		
7.		
8.		
9.		
10.		

The Rock Cycle

Reading Guide

Key Concepts

ESSENTIAL QUESTIONS

- How do surface processes contribute to the rock cycle?

- How is the rock cycle related to plate tectonics?

Vocabulary

rock cycle p. 251

extrusive rock p. 252

intrusive rock p. 252

uplift p. 252

deposition p. 253

 Multilingual eGlossary

7.ESS.1, SEPS.1, SEPS.2, SEPS.3, SEPS.4, SEPS.6, SEPS.8

Inquiry Where did all the rock layers go?

Monument Valley, Utah, is home to these towering rock formations. Over millions of years, processes on Earth's surface have worn away the surrounding rock layers, leaving the more resistant rocks behind. What do you think this landscape will look like in another few million years?

Do you "rock"?

Have you ever walked across a gravel road in your bare feet? If so, you know that rocks are hard. However, even though they are hard, rocks can change. How can you make a model of a rock that allows you to observe some of the changes that can turn it from one type into another?

① Read and complete a lab safety form.

② Break **small candles** in half over a piece of **waxed paper.**

③ Drop the pieces of candle into very warm water.

④ After 10–20 seconds, use **forceps** to remove all the candle pieces and stack them back on the waxed paper.

⑤ Wrap the candles in the waxed paper and squeeze tightly to press the warm pieces.

Think About This

1. What type of rock did you model? Explain.

2. What changed the model rocks in step 2 to those in step 5? What type of rock formed?

3. 🔑 **Key Concept** How might different processes contribute to the rock cycle?

What is the rock cycle?

Do you have a recycling program at school? Or do you recycle at home? When materials such as paper or metal are recycled, they are used over again but not always for the same things. The metal from the beverage can you recycled yesterday might end up in a baseball bat.

Recycling also occurs naturally on Earth. The rock material that formed Earth 4.6 billion years ago is still here, but much of it has changed many times throughout Earth's history. *The series of processes that continually change one rock type into another is called the* **rock cycle.**

As materials move through the rock cycle, they can take the form of igneous rocks, sedimentary rocks, or metamorphic rocks. At times, the material might not be rock at all. It might be sediment, magma, or lava, such as that pictured in **Figure 16.**

📝 **Reading Check** How is the rock cycle similar to recycling?

Figure 16 Earth materials move through the rock cycle, changing both form and their location on Earth.

(t)Hutchings Photography/Digital Light Source, (b)Masterfile

Figure 17 As rocks and rock material move slowly through the rock cycle, they are continually transformed from one rock type to another.

Ⓥ **Visual Check** Describe a path through the rock cycle that would result in the formation of a metamorphic rock.

Processes of the Rock Cycle

Mineral and rock formation are important processes in the rock cycle. The rock cycle is continuous, with no beginning or end. As shown in Figure 17, some processes take place on Earth's surface, and others take place deep beneath Earth's surface.

Cooling and Crystallization

Melted rock material is present both on and below Earth's surface. *When lava cools and crystallizes on Earth's surface, the igneous rock that forms is called* **extrusive rock.** *When magma cools and crystallizes inside Earth, the igneous rock that forms is called* **intrusive rock.**

Uplift

If intrusive rocks form deep within Earth, how are they ever exposed at the surface? **Uplift** *is the process that moves large amounts of rock up to Earth's surface and to higher elevations.* Uplift is driven by Earth's tectonic activity and often is associated with mountain building.

SCIENCE USE V. COMMON USE···

intrusive
Science Use igneous rock that forms as a result of injecting magma into an existing rock body

Common Use the condition of being not welcome or invited
················

Weathering and Erosion

Uplift brings rocks to Earth's surface where they are exposed to the environment. Glaciers, wind, and rain, along with the activities of some organisms, start to break down exposed rocks. The same glaciers, wind, and rain also carry sediment to low-lying areas, called basins, by the process of erosion.

Deposition

Eventually, glaciers, wind, and water slow down enough that they can no longer transport the sediment. *The process of laying down sediment in a new location is called* **deposition**. Deposition forms layers of sediment. As time passes, more and more layers are deposited.

 Key Concept Check How are surface processes involved in the rock cycle?

Compaction and Cementation

The weight of overlying layers of sediment pushes the grains of the bottom layers closer together. This process is called compaction. Sedimentary rocks have tiny spaces, called pores, between the grains. Pores sometimes contain water and dissolved minerals. When these minerals crystallize, they cement the grains together. Figure 17 shows the path of sediment from weathering and erosion to compaction and cementation.

FOLDABLES

Make a horizontal two-column chart book. Label it as shown. Use it to organize your notes on rock formation.

Internal Processes | External Processes

MiniLab
15 minutes

How can you turn one sedimentary rock into another?

The formation of a rock involves many changes. How can you model some of the changes that turn one sedimentary rock into another?

1. Read and complete a lab safety form.
2. Stack some **craft sticks** on the table. Prop up one end of a **baking dish** by laying it on the craft sticks.
3. Rub two **rocks** together over the dish. Observe how the rocks change.
4. Observe what happens to the sediment. Record your observations in your Science Journal.
5. Add some **white glue** to the sediment that collects at the bottom of the dish. Allow the glue to dry. Observe.
6. Predict what will happen to the sediment as the glue dries. Record your prediction.

Analyze and Conclude

1. **Model** What rock cycle process did you model in step 3? In step 4? In step 5?

2. **Explain** Use the rock cycle to explain how rocks are related.

3. **Key Concept** How are surface processes involved in the rock cycle?

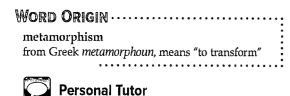

WORD ORIGIN

metamorphism
from Greek *metamorphoun*, means "to transform"

Personal Tutor

Shale

Slate

Phyllite

Schist

Gneiss

Increasing temperature and pressure

Figure 18 Rocks change form under high temperatures and pressure.

Visual Check How do the characteristics of the rocks change with increased pressure and temperature?

Temperature and Pressure

Recall that rocks subjected to high temperature and pressure undergo metamorphism. This usually occurs far below Earth's surface. The progression of metamorphism can be observed in some rocks, as shown in **Figure 18.** As temperature and pressure increase, the sedimentary rock shale, shown at the top of **Figure 18,** changes to the metamorphic rock slate.

The rocks shown in **Figure 18,** slate, phyllite, schist, and gneiss, form from shale with increasing temperature and pressure. If the temperature is high enough, the rock melts and becomes magma. Igneous rocks form as the magma cools, and the material continues through the rock cycle.

Rocks and Plate Tectonics

The theory of plate tectonics states that Earth's surface is broken into rigid plates. The plates move as a result of Earth's internal thermal energy and convection in the mantle. The theory explains the movement of continents. It also explains earthquakes, volcanoes, and the formation of new crust. These events occur at plate boundaries, where tectonic plates interact.

Igneous rock forms where volcanoes occur and where plates move apart. Where plates collide, rocks are subjected to intense pressure and can undergo metamorphism. Colliding plates also can cause uplift or can push rock deep below Earth's surface, where it melts and forms magma. At Earth's surface, uplifted rocks are exposed and weathered. Weathered rock forms sediment, which eventually can form sedimentary rock.

Processes within Earth that move tectonic plates also drive part of the rock cycle. The rock cycle also includes surface processes. As long as these processes exist, the rock cycle will continue.

Key Concept Check How is the rock cycle related to plate tectonics?

Visual Summary

Weathering and erosion are important processes in the rock cycle.

Uplift contributes to rock cycle processes on Earth's surface.

Plate tectonic activity contributes to rock cycle processes beneath Earth's surface.

FOLDABLES

Use your lesson Foldable to review the lesson. Save your Foldable for the project at the end of the chapter.

What do you think NOW?

You first read the statements below at the beginning of the chapter.

5. All rocks are related through the rock cycle.

6. Rocks move at a slow and constant rate through the rock cycle.

Did you change your mind about whether you agree or disagree with the statements? Rewrite any false statements to make them true.

Use Vocabulary

1. **Distinguish** between intrusive igneous rocks and extrusive igneous rocks.

2. **Define** *deposition* in your own words.

3. **Use the term** *rock cycle* in a sentence.

Understand Key Concepts

4. Which term refers to breaking rocks apart?
   A. cementation C. deposition
   B. crystallization D. weathering

5. **Give an example** of a rock cycle process that occurs on Earth's surface and one that occurs below Earth's surface.

6. **Classify** each of the following terms as Earth materials or rock cycle processes: magma, crystallization, sedimentary rocks, sediment, uplift, cementation.

Interpret Graphics

7. **Determine** what process must occur between the magma chamber and the intrusive rock in the figure below.

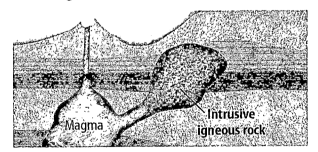

8. **Draw** a graphic organizer like the one below and sequence the following terms: erosion, compaction, sedimentary rock, deposition, uplift, weathering, cementation.

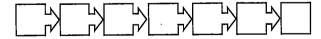

Critical Thinking

9. **Infer** where you would look along a tectonic plate to find the youngest rock.

Materials

bag of "loot"

mineral-testing tools

magnifying lens

paper towels

Safety

Design a Forensic Investigation

The local jewelry store has been robbed! The thief had planned to leave common minerals at the scene to replace the valuable ones. However, she was caught in the act, and both the valuable and the common minerals ended up mixed together on the store's floor. The police have called you in as a forensic geologist to help them sort through the rubble and identify the valuable minerals.

Question

Think about what you learned about minerals in this chapter. Use that information and the paragraph above to formulate a question to help you solve this case.

Procedure

① Read and complete a lab safety form.

② Copy the data table shown below into your Science Journal. Complete the table as you test each mineral. Add columns and rows as needed.

③ Remove the loot from its bag. Use a magnifying lens to examine each mineral. Record any interesting or unique observations about each mineral in your data table.

(1,2) McGraw-Hill Education, (3,4,5)Hutchings Photography/Digital Light Source

Sample #	color	hardness	reaction to HCL	streak	luster	other
1.						
2.						

④ Identify and investigate the properties of the minerals. Use the mineral-testing tools to determine the hardness, the streak, and the reaction to dilute hydrochloric acid of each piece of loot. Record your observations in your data table.

⑤ Use your data table and the Minerals table in the Reference Handbook to identify each of the minerals involved in this imaginary heist.

Analyze and Conclude

⑥ **Compare and Contrast** How are minerals alike and how do they differ?

⑦ **Evaluate** Were any of the samples valuable minerals such as gold, silver, rubies, diamonds, or emeralds? How do you know?

⑧ **Draw Conclusions** What properties of minerals make them useful or desirable for jewelry?

⑨ **The Big Idea** How are minerals and rocks formed, identified, classified, and used?

Communicate Your Results

Choose your favorite piece of loot from the bag. On a small piece of poster board, write the name of this mineral and its properties. Then, with two or more other students, "combine" your minerals to form a rock. Write the name of the rock you made on another piece of poster board. Compose a two-minute skit to demonstrate and explain how the rock formed and how it, and the minerals in it, might be used in everyday life.

Use your observations from this lab to visually examine jewelry worn by your classmates or family members. Try to identify the minerals in each piece if jewelry. Be careful not to damage the jewelry!

Lab Tips

☑ **CAUTION:** Use only one drop of hydrochloric acid to test each mineral. Use paper towels to completely remove any acid from the minerals.

☑ When testing hardness, use the mineral to try to scratch the testing materials. Do not scratch the mineral itself unless instructed to do so.

Remember to use scientific methods.

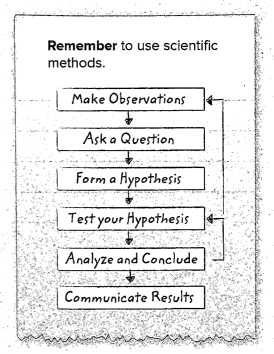

Make Observations
↓
Ask a Question
↓
Form a Hypothesis
↓
Test your Hypothesis
↓
Analyze and Conclude
↓
Communicate Results

Minerals and rocks form through natural processes, have practical uses in everyday life, and are valued for their beauty. Minerals can be identified based on their physical properties. Rocks are classified based on their physical characteristics and how they formed.

Key Concepts Summary

Vocabulary

Lesson 1: Minerals

- **Minerals** form when solids crystallize from molten material or from solutions.
- Properties such as color, **streak**, hardness, and **cleavage** are used to identify minerals. Unique properties such as magnetism, reaction to acid, and fluorescence can also be used to identify certain minerals.
- Minerals are used to make everyday products such as toothpaste and makeup. Metals are used in cars and buildings. Gemstones are valued for their beauty.

mineral p. 233

crystal structure p. 234

crystallization p. 235

streak p. 237

luster p. 237

cleavage p. 237

fracture p. 237

ore p. 239

Lesson 2: Rocks

- Rocks are classified based on their **texture** and composition.

- Igneous rocks form when **magma** or **lava** solidifies. Sedimentary rocks form when **sediments** are **lithified.** Metamorphic rocks form when parent rocks are changed by thermal energy, pressure, or hot fluids.
- Rocks are used in construction, abrasives, and art.

rock p. 243

grain p. 243

magma p. 244

lava p. 244

texture p. 244

sediment p. 245

lithification p. 245

foliation p. 247

Lesson 3: The Rock Cycle

- Surface processes break down existing rocks into sediment. They transport this sediment to locations where it undergoes **deposition** and can be recycled to make more rocks.
- Thermal energy is released at plate boundaries. This thermal energy provides the energy needed for making igneous and metamorphic rocks. It also drives the forces that expose rocks to processes occurring on Earth's surface.

rock cycle p. 251

extrusive rock p. 252

intrusive rock p. 252

uplift p. 252

deposition p. 253

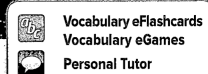

FOLDABLES

Chapter Project

Assemble your lesson Foldables as shown to make a Chapter Project. Use the project to review what you have learned in this chapter.

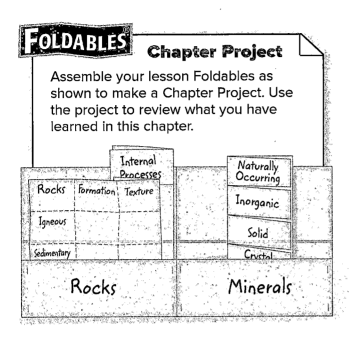

Internal Processes

Rocks | Formation | Texture

Igneous

Sedimentary

Naturally Occurring

Inorganic

Solid

Crystal

Rocks   **Minerals**

Use Vocabulary

1. A mineral deposit that can be mined for a profit is a(n) _____.

2. How does color differ from streak?

3. Loose rock and mineral fragments are called _____.

4. Define the word *rock* in your own words.

5. The process that brings rocks formed deep within Earth to the surface is called _____.

6. Relate the words *deposition* and *lithification*.

▷ **Interactive Concept Map**

Link Vocabulary and Key Concepts

Copy this concept map, and then use vocabulary terms from the previous page to complete the concept map.

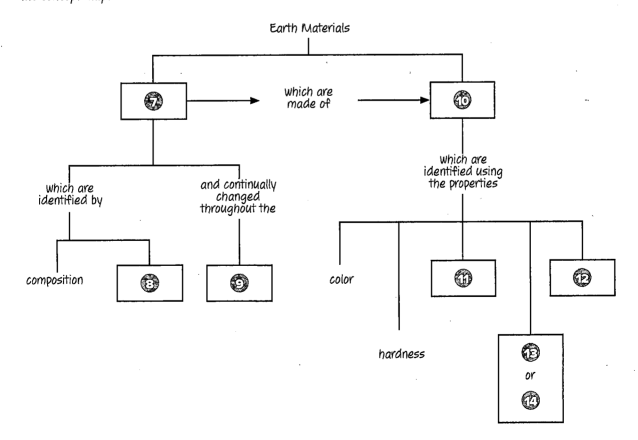

Earth Materials

7

which are made of

10

which are identified by

composition   **8**   **9**

and continually changed throughout the

which are identified using the properties

color   **11**   **12**

hardness   **13** or **14**

Understand Key Concepts

1 Based on what you know about the Mohs hardness scale and mineral hardness, which mineral would make a good sandpaper?

A. fluorite
B. gypsum
C. quartz
D. talc

2 Which describes a way that minerals form?

A. changing from gas to liquid
B. changing from liquid to gas
C. changing from liquid to solid
D. changing from solid to gas

3 Which are mineral resources?

A. gemstones and wood
B. metals and cotton
C. metals and gemstones
D. wood and cotton

4 What can you learn from a mineral's chemical formula?

A. composition
B. crystal structure
C. texture
D. hardness

5 Which type of rock forms from magma and contains large interlocking crystals?

A. extrusive igneous
B. intrusive igneous
C. foliated metamorphic
D. nonfoliated metamorphic

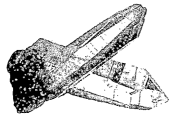

6 What characteristic can be used to identify the mineral pictured above?

A. color
B. crystal structure
C. density
D. hardness

7 Texture of sedimentary rock refers to

A. whether the rock cooled slowly or quickly.
B. whether the rock feels smooth or rough.
C. whether the rock is foliated or nonfoliated.
D. whether the rock has coarse or fine grains.

8 Which process is necessary in order for granite to undergo weathering and erosion?

A. cementation
B. compaction
C. deposition
D. uplift

9 What is the energy source for producing magma?

A. external thermal energy
B. internal thermal energy
C. pressure
D. the Sun

10 What processes are necessary in order to turn the material in the picture below into rock?

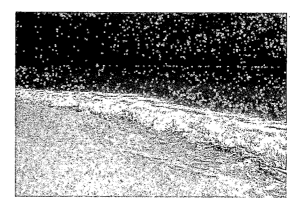

A. compaction and cementation
B. cooling and crystallization
C. uplift and deposition
D. weathering and erosion

Critical Thinking

11 Compare the textures of the three main types of rocks.

12 Infer why there is no longer a rock cycle on the Moon.

13 Evaluate the relative worth of minerals that are valued for their beauty and those that are used for practical purposes.

14 Analyze which rock is more useful for building a roof—slate or granite? Explain your reasoning.

15 Predict what would happen to a sample of gneiss if it were heated enough to melt the mineral grains.

16 Construct a flow chart showing the formation of quartzite starting with a mountain and ending with quartzite. (Quartzite is metamorphosed sandstone.)

17 Critique the rock cycle diagram below. Include one feature of the diagram that you find useful and one feature that could be improved.

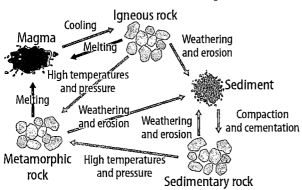

18 Summarize How do geologists identify minerals?

Writing in Science

19 Write an acrostic poem based on the term *rock cycle*. Acrostic poems are written without rhyming. The letters of the given term form the first letter of each line of the poem, which, when read downward, spells out the term.

REVIEW

20 How can you use the rock cycle to explain how rocks are related?

21 What are some minerals and rocks that you use every day?

Math Skills — Math Practice

Use Ratios

22 The ratio of iron (Fe) to chromium (Cr) to oxygen (O) in the mineral chromite is 1:2:4. What is the formula for chromite?

23 One form of the mineral feldspar has the formula $KAlSi_3O_8$. What is the ratio of potassium (K) to aluminum (Al) to silicon (Si) to oxygen (O) atoms in feldspar?

24 The ratio of aluminum (Al) to oxygen (O) atoms in the mineral corundum is 2:3. Write the formula for corundum.

www.mpcphotogrpahy.co.uk/Getty Images

Record your answers on the answer sheet provided by your teacher or on a sheet of paper.

Multiple Choice

1 Which is NOT a characteristic of minerals?

   A They are only solids.

   B They form from decaying materials.

   C They have a crystal structure.

   D They have a definite composition.

2 Which property is NOT used to identify minerals?

   A color

   B fracture

   C streak

   D weight

Use the figure below to answer question 3.

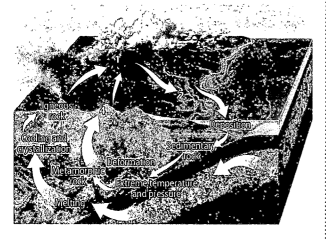

3 Which arrow on the diagram represents uplift?

   A 1

   B 2

   C 3

   D 4

4 Which process produces features that distinguish gneiss from marble?

   A crystallization

   B foliation

   C lithification

   D sedimentation

5 Which characteristic is unique to metamorphic rock?

   A It can form from erosion.

   B It can form from lithification.

   C It can form from parent rocks.

   D It can have a layered appearance.

Use the table below to answer question 6.

10	diamond
9	corundum
8	topaz
7	quartz
6	feldspar
5.5	glass
5	apatite
4.5	nail
4	fluorite
3.5	penny
3	calcite
2.5	fingernail
2	gypsum
1	talc

6 Use the Mohs hardness scale to determine which statement is correct.

   A A fingernail will scratch talc.

   B A nail will scratch apatite.

   C Corundum will scratch diamond.

   D Quartz will not scratch glass.

7 Which is NOT present in sediment?

   A magma

   B minerals

   C rock fragments

   D organic matter

8 Which is the last step in the formation of sedimentary rock?

   A cementation

   B compaction

   C deposition

   D erosion

Use the figure below to answer question 9.

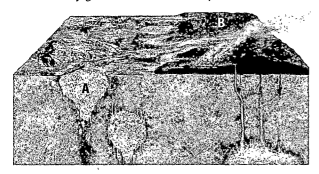

9 Which statement about the igneous rocks in the diagram is correct?

   A Rock A is extrusive.

   B Rock B is intrusive.

   C Rock A cooled slowly and formed small crystals.

   D Rock B cooled quickly and formed small crystals.

Constructed Response

Use the figure below to answer questions 10 and 11.

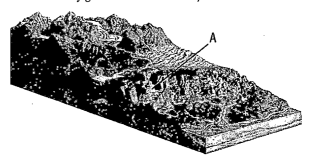

10 Identify the kind of rock that is labeled *A* in the figure. Then describe how it forms.

11 Describe a use for the type of rocks formed by the process in the figure. Give at least two examples of rocks used in this way.

12 Identify three surface processes that are part of the rock cycle. Explain the roles of each process in the cycle.

13 Which properties of a mineral can you observe using a penny, a pocketknife, and a magnifying lens? Explain your answers.

NEED EXTRA HELP?													
If You Missed Question...	1	2	3	4	5	6	7	8	9	10	11	12	13
Go to Lesson...	1	1	3	2	3	1	2	2	2	2	2	2	1

7.ESS.4, SEPS.1, SEPS.2, SEPS.3, SEPS.4, SEPS.5, SEPS.6, SEPS.8, 6-8.LST.4.1, 6-8. LST.5.2, 6-8.LST.7.1, 6-8.LST.7.3

Erosion and Deposition

THE BIG IDEA

How do erosion and deposition shape Earth's surface?

Inquiry Waves of Rock?

The swirling slopes of this ravine look as if heavy machines carved patterns in the rock. But nature formed these patterns.

- What do you think caused the layers of colors in the rock?

- Why do you think the rock has smooth curves instead of sharp edges?

- How do you think erosion and deposition formed waves in the rock?

Johnnya123/iStock/Getty Images

What do you think?

Before you read, decide if you agree or disagree with each of these statements. As you read this chapter, see if you change your mind about any of the statements.

1. Wind, water, ice, and gravity continually shape Earth's surface.

2. Different sizes of sediment tend to mix when being moved along by water.

3. A beach is a landform that does not change over time.

4. Windblown sediment can cut and polish exposed rock surfaces.

5. Landslides are a natural process that cannot be influenced by human activities.

6. A glacier leaves behind very smooth land as it moves through an area.

connectED

Your one-stop online resource
connectED.mcgraw-hill.com

 LearnSmart®

 Chapter Resources Files, Reading Essentials, Get Ready to Read, Quick Vocabulary

 Animations, Videos, Interactive Tables

 Self-checks, Quizzes, Tests

 Project-Based Learning Activities

 Lab Manuals, Safety Videos, Virtual Labs & Other Tools

 Vocabulary, Multilingual eGlossary, Vocab eGames, Vocab eFlashcards

 Personal Tutors

Reading Guide

Key Concepts 🔑
ESSENTIAL QUESTIONS

- How can erosion shape and sort sediment?

- How are erosion and deposition related?

- What features suggest whether erosion or deposition created a landform?

Vocabulary

erosion p. 269

deposition p. 271

 Multilingual eGlossary

 7.ESS.4, 6-8.LST.7.1, 6-8.LST.7.3

The Erosion-Deposition Process

Inquiry Stripes and Cuts?

Long ago, this area was at the bottom of an ocean. Today, it is dry land in Badlands National Park, South Dakota. Why do you think these hills are striped? What do you think caused such deep cuts in the land? What natural processes created landforms such as these?

How do the shape and size of sediment differ?

Sediment forms when rocks break apart. Wind, water, and other factors move the sediment from place to place. As the sediment moves, its shape and size can change. In this activity, you will observe the different shapes and sizes of sediment.

1. Read and complete a lab safety form.

2. Obtain a **bag of sediment** from your teacher. Pour the sediment onto a sheet of **paper.**

3. Use a **magnifying lens** to observe the differences in shape and size of the sediment.

4. Divide the sediment into groups according to its size and whether it has rounded or sharp edges.

Think About This

1. What were the different groups you used to sort the sediment?

2. **Key Concept** How do you think movement by wind and water might affect the shape and size of the sediment?

Reshaping Earth's Surface

Have you ever seen bulldozers, backhoes, and dump trucks at the construction site of a building project? You might have seen a bulldozer smoothing the land and making a flat surface or pushing soil around and forming hills. A backhoe might have been digging deep trenches for water or sewer lines. The dump trucks might have been dumping gravel or other building materials into small piles. The changes that people make to a landscape at a construction site are small examples of those that happen naturally to Earth's surface.

A combination of constructive processes and destructive processes produce landforms. Constructive processes build up features on Earth's surface. For example, lava erupting from a volcano hardens and forms new land on the area where the lava falls. Destructive processes tear down features on Earth's surface. A strong hurricane, for example, can wash part of a shoreline into the sea. Constructive and destructive processes continually shape and reshape Earth's surface.

ACADEMIC VOCABULARY

process
(noun) an ongoing event or a series of related events

Hutchings Photography/Digital Light Source

Personal Tutor

Figure 1 The continual weathering, erosion, and deposition of sediment occurs from the top of a mountain and across Earth's surface to the distant ocean.

Weathering is the breakdown of rock. Chemical weathering changes the mineral composition of rock. Physical weathering breaks rock into smaller pieces without changing its composition.

⊘**Visual Check** How do you think weathering and erosion will affect the mountains over the next thousand years?

Figure 2 Different rates of weathering of rock can produce unusual rock formations.

A Continual Process of Change

Imagine standing on a mountain, such as one shown in Figure 1. In the distance you might see a river or an ocean. What was this area like thousands of years ago? Will the mountains still be here thousands of years from now? Landforms on Earth are constantly changing, but the changes often happen so slowly that you do not notice them. What causes these changes?

Weathering

One destructive process that changes Earth's surface is weathering, the breakdown of rock. Chemical weathering changes the chemical composition of rock. Physical weathering breaks rock into pieces, called sediment, but it does not change the chemical composition of rock. Gravel, sand, silt, and clay are different sizes of sediment.

Weathering Agents Water, wind, and ice are called agents, or causes, of weathering. Water, for example, can dissolve minerals in rock. Wind can grind and polish rocks by blowing particles against them. Also, a rock can break apart as ice expands or as plant roots grow within cracks in the rock.

Different Rates of Weathering The mineral composition of some rocks makes them more resistant to weathering than other rocks. The differences in weathering rates can produce unusual landforms, as shown in Figure 2. Weathering can break away less resistant parts of the rock and leave behind the more resistant parts.

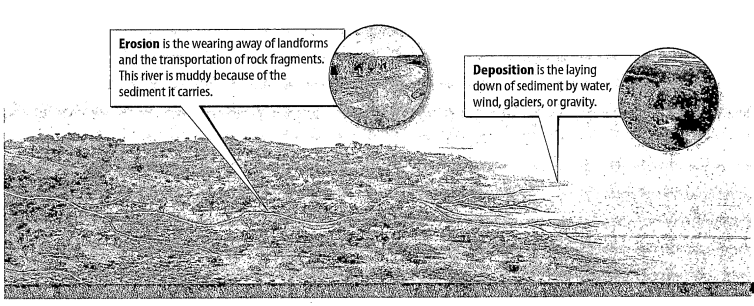

Erosion is the wearing away of landforms and the transportation of rock fragments. This river is muddy because of the sediment it carries.

Deposition is the laying down of sediment by water, wind, glaciers, or gravity.

Erosion

What happens to weathered material? This material is often transported away from its source rock in another destructive process called erosion. **Erosion** *is the removal of weathered material from one location to another.* Agents of erosion include water, wind, glaciers, and gravity. The muddy water shown in **Figure 1**, for example, is evidence of erosion.

The Rate of Erosion Like weathering, erosion occurs at different rates. For example, a rushing stream can erode a large quantity of material quickly. However, a gentle stream might erode a small amount of material slowly. Factors that affect the rate of erosion include weather, climate, topo-graphy, and type of rock. For example, strong wind transports weathered rock more easily than a gentle breeze does. Weathered rock moves faster down a steep hill than across a flat area. The presence of plants and the way humans use the land also affect the rate of erosion. Erosion occurs faster on barren land than on land covered with vegetation.

Reading Check What are some factors that affect the rate of erosion?

(tl)©Medioimages/Punchstock; (tr)Digital Vision/SuperStock; (b)Hutchings Photography/Digital Light Source

---

MiniLab
15 minutes

Can weathering be measured?

You can measure the weathering of rocks.

1. Read and complete a lab safety form.

2. Obtain **pieces of broken rock.** Rinse the rocks and pat completely dry with **paper towels.**

3. Measure the rocks' mass using a **balance.** Record your data in your Science Journal.

4. Place the rocks in a **plastic bottle.** Cover the rocks with water, and seal the bottle. Shake the bottle vigorously for 5 minutes.

5. Rinse the rocks and pat completely dry with paper towels. Record the mass again.

Analyze and Conclude

1. **Compare and contrast** the mass of the rocks before and after shaking.

2. **Key Concept** What evidence suggests that weathering has occurred?

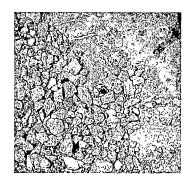

Figure 3 Erosion can change poorly rounded rocks (top) to well-rounded rocks (bottom).

Rate of Erosion and Rock Type The rate of erosion sometimes depends on the type of rock. Weathering can break some types of rock, such as sandstone, into large pieces. Other rock types, such as shale or siltstone, can easily break into smaller pieces. These smaller pieces can be removed and transported faster by agents of erosion. For example, large rocks in streams usually move only short distances every few decades, but silt particles might move a kilometer or more each day.

Rounding Rock fragments bump against each other during erosion. When this happens, the shapes of the fragments can change. Rock fragments can range from poorly rounded to well-rounded. The more spherical and well-rounded a rock is, the more it has been polished during erosion. Rough edges break off as the rock fragments bump against each other. Differences in sediment rounding are shown in Figure 3.

 Key Concept Check How can erosion affect the shape of sediment?

Sorting Erosion also affects the level of sorting of sediment. Sorting is the separating of items into groups according to one or more properties. As sediment is transported, it can become sorted by grain size, as shown in Figure 4. Sediment is often well-sorted when it has been moved a lot by wind or waves. Poorly sorted sediment often results from rapid transportation, perhaps by a storm, a flash flood, or a volcanic eruption. Sediment left at the edges of glaciers is also poorly sorted.

 Key Concept Check How can erosion sort sediment?

Sediment Sorting by Size

Figure 4 Erosion can sort sediment according to its size.

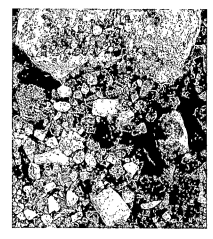

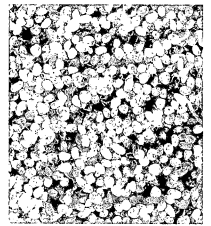

Poorly sorted sediment has a wide range of sizes.

Moderately sorted sediment has a small range of sizes.

Well-sorted sediment is all about the same size.

Deposition

You have read about two destructive processes that shape Earth's surface—weathering and erosion. After material has been eroded, a constructive process takes place. **Deposition** *is the laying down or settling of eroded material.* As water or wind slows down, it has less energy and can hold less sediment. Some of the sediment can then be laid down, or deposited.

 Key Concept Check How are erosion and deposition related?

Depositional Environments Sediment is deposited in locations called depositional environments. These locations are on land, along coasts, or in oceans. Examples include swamps, deltas, beaches, and the ocean floor.

 Reading Check What is a depositional environment?

Environments where sediment is transported and deposited quickly are high-energy environments. Examples include rushing rivers, ocean shores with large waves, and deserts with strong winds. Large grains of sediment tend to be deposited in high-energy environments.

Small grains of sediment are often deposited in low-energy environments. Deep lakes and areas of slow-moving air or water are low-energy environments. The swamp shown in **Figure 5** is an example of a low-energy environment. The material that makes up a fine-grained sedimentary rock, such as shale, was probably deposited in a low-energy environment.

Sediment Layers Sediment deposited in water typically forms layers called beds. Some examples of beds appear as "stripes" in the photo at the beginning of this lesson. Beds often form as layers of sediment at the bottom of rivers, lakes, and oceans. These layers can be preserved in sedimentary rocks.

WORD ORIGIN ············

deposition
from French *deposer,* means "put down"

REVIEW VOCABULARY ····

swamp
a wetland occasionally or partially covered with water

A Low-Energy Depositional Environment

Figure 5 Silt and clay are deposited in low-energy environments such as swamps. Swamp deposits also include dark, organic material from decaying trees and other plants.

DEA/F. BARBAGALLO/Getty Images

Figure 6 The tall, steep, somewhat sharp features shown in these photographs are common in landforms carved by erosion.

The Tepees in the Painted Desert of Arizona

Hoodoos at Bryce Canyon National Park

Glacier National Park in Montana

📝**Visual Check** How did the passage of glaciers through these mountains change the shape of the valleys?

Interpreting Landforms

What do landform characteristics, such as structure, elevation, and rock exposure, suggest about the development of landforms? Examples of landforms include mountains, valleys, plains, sea cliffs, and beaches. These landforms are always changing, although you might not observe these changes in your lifetime. Landform characteristics can be observed to determine whether destructive forces, such as erosion, or constructive forces, such as deposition, produced the landforms.

Landforms Created by Erosion

Landforms can have features that are clearly produced by erosion. These landforms are often tall, jagged structures with cuts in layers of rock, as shown in the photographs in Figure 6.

① Landforms formed by erosion can expose several layers of rock. The Tepees in the Painted Desert of Arizona contain several layers of different materials. Over time, erosion wore away parts of the land, leaving behind multicolored mounds.

② Recall that different rates of erosion can result in unusual landforms when some rocks erode and leave more erosion-resistant rocks behind. For example, tall, protruding landforms called hoodoos are shown in the middle photograph of Figure 6. Over time, water and ice eroded the less-resistant sedimentary rock. The remaining rocks are more resistant. If you would like to examine hoodoos more closely, look back at Figure 2.

③ Glacial erosion and coastal erosion also form unique landforms. Glacial erosion can produce ice-carved features in mountains. The U-shaped valleys of Glacier National Park in Montana, shown in the bottom photograph, formed by glacial erosion. Coastal erosion forms picturesque landforms, such as sea cliffs, caves, and sea arches.

Landforms Created by Deposition

Landforms created by deposition are often flat and low-lying. Wind deposition, for example, can gradually form deserts of sand. Deposition also occurs where mountain streams reach the gentle slopes of wide, flat valleys. An apron of sediment, called an alluvial fan, often forms where a stream flows from a steep, narrow canyon onto a flat plain at the foot of a mountain, as shown in Figure 7.

Reading Check How does an alluvial fan develop?

Water traveling in a river can slow due to friction with the edges and the bottom of the river channel. An increase in channel width or depth also can slow the current and promote deposition. Deposition along a riverbed occurs where the speed of the water slows. This deposition can form a sandbar, as shown in Figure 8. The endpoint for most rivers is where they reach a lake or an ocean and deposit sediment under water. Wave action along shorelines also moves and deposits sediment.

△ **Figure 7** An alluvial fan is a gently sloping mass of sediment that forms where a stream empties onto flat land at the foot of a steep slope.

◁ **Figure 8** A sandbar is a depositional feature in rivers and near ocean shores.

As glaciers melt, they can leave behind piles of sediment and rock. For example, glaciers can create long, narrow deposits called eskers and moraines. In the United States, these features are best preserved in northern states such as Wisconsin and New York. You will read more about glacial deposition in Lesson 3.

Comparing Landforms

Look again at the landforms shown in Figure 6, Figure 7, and Figure 8. Notice how landforms produced by erosion and deposition are different. Erosion produces landforms that are often tall and jagged, but deposition usually produces landforms on flat, low land. By observing the features of a landform, you can infer whether erosion or deposition produced it.

Key Concept Check What features suggest whether erosion or deposition produced a landform?

FOLDABLES

Make a two-tab book and label it as shown. Use your book to describe and identify some landforms created by the processes of erosion and deposition.

Landforms created by

Erosion | Deposition

Visual Summary

 Erosion occurring at different rates can carve rock into interesting landforms.

 Rock fragments with rough edges are rounded during transportation.

 Landforms produced by deposition are often flat and low-lying.

 FOLDABLES

Use your lesson Foldable to review the lesson. Save your Foldable for the project at the end of the chapter.

What do you think NOW?

You first read the statements below at the beginning of the chapter.

1. Wind, water, ice, and gravity continually shape Earth's surface.

2. Different sizes of sediment tend to mix when being moved along by water.

Did you change your mind about whether you agree or disagree with the statements? Rewrite any false statements to make them true.

Use Vocabulary

1. Define *deposition* in your own words.

2. Use the term *erosion* in a complete sentence.

Understand Key Concepts

3. Which would most likely leave behind well-sorted sediment?
A. flash flood   C. ocean waves
B. melting glacier   D. volcanic eruption

4. Describe some features of an alluvial fan that suggest that it was formed by deposition.

5. Explain how erosion and deposition by a stream are related.

Interpret Graphics

6. Examine the illustration of sediment particle sizes shown below.

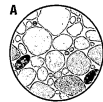 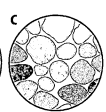

Classify each set of particles as well-sorted, moderately sorted, or poorly sorted. Explain.

7. Sequence Copy and fill in the graphic organizer below to describe a possible history of a grain of the mineral quartz that begins in a boulder at the top of a mountain and ends as a piece of sand on the coast.

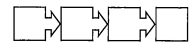

Critical Thinking

8. Decide Imagine a river that deposits only small particles where it flows into a sea. Is the river current most likely fast or slow? Why?

(t)Image Source; (c)©Stephen Reynolds; (b)Digital Vision/SuperStock

Clues from the Canyon

AMERICAN
MUSEUM
NATURAL
HISTORY

isitors to the Grand Canyon in Arizona are awestruck by its magnificent size and depth. But to many scientists, the canyon's walls are even more impressive. The soaring walls hold about 40 layers of colorful rocks in shades of red, yellow, brown, and gray. Each layer is like a page in a history book about Earth's past—and the deeper the layer, the older it is. The different layers reflect the particular types of environments in which they formed.

Weathering The canyon walls continue to weather and erode today. Rockfalls and landslides are common. Harder rock such as sandstone weathers in big chunks that break off, forming steep cliffs. The softer rocks weather and erode more easily. This forms gentle slopes.

Deposition These rock layers formed between 280 million and 260 million years ago. During the early part of this period, the region was covered by sand dunes and wind-deposited layers of sand. Later, shallow seas covered this area and layers of shells settled on the seafloor. Gradually, the sediments were compacted and cemented together and these multicolored layers of sedimentary rock were formed.

Erosion Several million years ago, the movement of tectonic plates pushed up the layers of rock. This formed what is called the Colorado Plateau. As the rocks rose higher, the slope of the Colorado River became steeper and its waters flowed faster and with greater force. The Colorado River cut through the weathered rock and carried away sediment. Over millions of years, this erosion formed the canyon.

It's Your Turn

With a partner, find a photo of a local natural land formation. Research and write short descriptions explaining how parts of the formation were created. Attach your descriptions to the appropriate places on the photo.

Reading Guide

Key Concepts

ESSENTIAL QUESTIONS

- What are the stages of stream development?

- How do water erosion and deposition change Earth's surface?

- How do wind erosion and deposition change Earth's surface?

Vocabulary

meander p. 278

longshore current p. 279

delta p. 280

abrasion p. 282

dune p. 282

loess p. 282

 Multilingual eGlossary

 What's Science Got to do With It?

( ) SEPS.2, SEPS.3, SEPS.6

Landforms Shaped by Water and Wind

Inquiry Twisted River?

As a river flows down a mountain, it usually flows in the same general direction. What causes this river to flow side-to-side? Why doesn't it flow in a straight path?

Theo Allofs/Getty Images

How do water and wind shape Earth?

Imagine a fast-moving river rushing over rocks or a strong wind blowing across a field. What changes on Earth do the water and the wind cause?

1. Form into groups and discuss the pictures below with others in your group.

2. Can you recognize evidence of ways water and wind have changed the land—through both erosion and deposition?

Landforms Shaped by Water and Wind

Think About This

1. What are some examples of erosion and deposition in the pictures?

2. 🔑 **Key Concept** Describe ways you think water might have changed the land in the pictures. What are some ways wind might have changed the land?

Shaping the Land with Water and Wind

Recall that landforms on Earth's surface undergo continual change. Weathering and erosion are destructive processes that shape Earth's surface. These destructive processes often produce tall, jagged landforms. Deposition is a constructive process that also shapes Earth's surface. Constructive processes often produce flat, low-lying landforms.

What causes these processes that continually tear down and build up Earth's surface? In this lesson, you will read that water and wind are two important agents of weathering, erosion, and deposition. The cliffs shown in Figure 9 are an example of how erosion by water and wind can change the shape of landforms. In the next lesson you will read about ways Earth's surface is changed by the downhill movement of rocks and soil and by the movement of glaciers.

Figure 9 Erosion by water and wind formed these cliffs along Lake Superior.

(l to r, t to b)Harald Sund/Photographer's Choice/Getty Images; (2)©Steve Hamblin/Corbis; (3)Image Source/Getty Images; (4)Michael Melford/Getty Images; (5)Robert Glusic/Photodisc/Getty Images; (6)©Royalty-Free/Corbis; (7)Dirk Anschutz/Getty Images

Figure 10 Water erosion carved this V-shaped valley at Lower Falls, Yellowstone National Park, in Wyoming.

FOLDABLES

Make a two-tab book and label it as shown. Use your book to organize information about landforms and features created by erosion and deposition by water and wind.

Erosion and Deposition

| Water | Wind |

Water Erosion and Deposition

Water can shape landforms on and below Earth's surface. The speed of water movement and the depositional environment often affect the shape of landforms.

Water Erosion

If you have ever had a chance to wade into an ocean and feel the waves rushing toward shore, you know that moving water can be incredibly strong. Moving water causes erosion along streams, at beaches, and underground.

Stream Erosion Streams are active systems that erode land and transport sediment. The erosion produced by a stream depends on the stream's energy. This energy is usually greatest in steep, mountainous areas where young streams flow rapidly downhill. The rushing water often carves V-shaped valleys, such as the one shown in Figure 10. Waterfalls and river rapids are common in steep mountain streams.

Water in a young stream slows as it reaches gentler slopes. The stream is then called a mature stream, such as the one shown in Figure 11. Slower moving water erodes the sides of a stream channel more than its bottom, and the stream develops curves. *A* **meander** *is a broad, C-shaped curve in a stream.*

When a stream reaches flat land, it moves even slower and is called an old stream. Over time, meanders change shape. More erosion occurs on the outside of bends where water flows faster. More deposition occurs on the inside of bends where water flows slower. Over time, the meander's size increases.

Key Concept Check Describe the stream development stages.

Stages of Stream Development

 Animation

Figure 11 Streams change as they flow from steep slopes to gentle slopes and finally to flat plains.

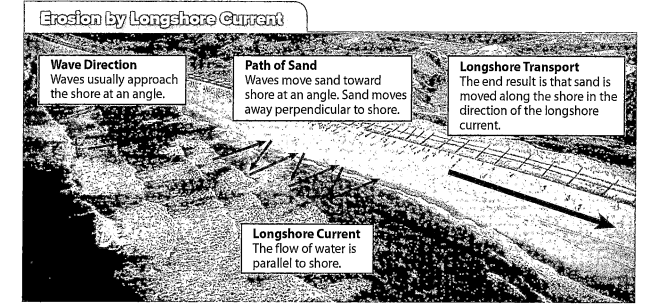

Erosion by Longshore Current

Wave Direction Waves usually approach the shore at an angle.

Path of Sand Waves move sand toward shore at an angle. Sand moves away perpendicular to shore.

Longshore Transport The end result is that sand is moved along the shore in the direction of the longshore current.

Longshore Current The flow of water is parallel to shore.

Coastal Erosion Like streams, coastlines continually change. Waves crashing onto shore erode loose sand, gravel, and rock along coastlines. One type of coastal erosion is shown in Figure 12. *A* **longshore current** *is a current that flows parallel to the shoreline.* This current moves sediment and continually changes the size and shape of beaches. Coastal erosion also occurs when the cutting action of waves along rocky shores forms sea cliffs. Erosional features such as sea caves, sea stacks (tall pillars just offshore), and sea arches (rock bridges extending into the sea) can form when waves erode less resistant rocks along the shore.

 Key Concept Check How does water erosion change Earth's surface?

Groundwater Erosion Water that flows underground can also erode rock. Have you ever wondered how caves form? When carbon dioxide in the air mixes with rainwater, a weak acid forms. Some of this rainwater becomes groundwater. As acidic groundwater seeps through rock and soil, it can pass through layers of limestone. The acidic water dissolves and washes away the limestone, forming a cave, as shown in Figure 13.

Reading Check How does water erosion form a cave?

△ **Figure 12** A longshore current erodes and deposits large amounts of sediment along a shoreline.

Visual Check What causes the sand to move away perpendicular to shore?

△ **Figure 13** Carlsbad Caverns in New Mexico was formed by water erosion.

(t)Karl Johaentges/LOOK-foto/Getty Images; (b)©Steve Hamblin/Corbis

Figure 14 This delta formed by deposition of sediment when water flowed from a river into an ocean.

MiniLab  20 minutes

How do stalactites form?

A stalactite forms when minerals are deposited as crystals. In this lab, you will model the formation of a stalactite.

① Read and complete a lab safety form.

② Use **scissors** to poke a hole in the bottom of a **small paper cup.**

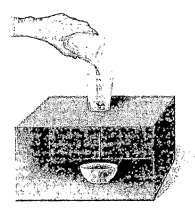

③ Tie a **washer** to one end of a 25-cm length of **yarn.** Thread the other end through the hole in the cup and a hole in the top of a **box.** Place the cup on the box with the holes aligned.

④ Half-fill **another cup** with **Epsom salts.** Add **warm water** until the cup is full. Stir with a **spoon.** Pour the salt water into the cup with yarn so that it drips down the yarn into a **bowl.**

⑤ Record in your Science Journal observations of your model each day for one week.

Analyze and Conclude

1. **Describe** daily changes in your model.

2. **Key Concept** How did this activity model the formation of a stalactite?

Water Deposition

Flowing water deposits sediment as the water slows. A loss of speed reduces the amount of energy that the water has to carry sediment.

Deposition Along Streams Deposition by a stream can occur anywhere along its path where the water's speed decreases. As you read earlier, slower-moving water deposits sediment on the inside curves of meanders. A stream also slows and deposits sediment when it reaches flat land or a large body of water, such as a lake or an ocean. An example is the delta shown in Figure 14. *A delta is a large deposit of sediment that forms where a stream enters a large body of water.*

Deposition Along Coastlines Much of the sand on most ocean beaches was originally deposited by rivers. Longshore currents transport the sand along ocean coasts. Eventually, sand is deposited where currents are slower and have less energy. Sandy beaches often develop at those locations.

Key Concept Check How does water deposition change Earth's surface?

Groundwater Deposition Weathering and erosion produce caves, but deposition forms many structures within caves. Look again at Figure 13. The cave contains landforms that dripping groundwater formed as it deposited minerals. Over time, the deposits developed into stalactites and stalagmites. Stalactites hang from the ceiling. Stalagmites build up on the cave's floor.

©Royalty-Free/Corbis

Land Use Practices

Damage caused by water erosion can be affected by the ways people use land. Two areas of concern are beaches along coasts and surface areas within continental interiors.

Beach Erosion Ocean waves can erode beaches by removing sediment. To reduce this erosion, people sometimes build structures such as retaining walls, or groins, like those shown in Figure 15. A row of groins is constructed at right angles to the shore. They are built to trap sediment and reduce the erosive effects of longshore currents.

Some ways people affect beaches are unintended. For example, people build dams on rivers for purposes of flood control and other reasons. However, dams on rivers prevent river sand from reaching beaches. Beach sand that is washed out to sea by waves is not replaced.

Surface Erosion Reducing the amount of vegetation or removing it from the land increases surface erosion. Agricultural production, construction activities, and cutting trees for lumber and paper production are some reasons that people remove vegetation.

Reading Check What are some ways human activities affect water erosion?

A floodplain is a wide, flat area next to a river. It is usually dry land but can be flooded when the river overflows. Heavy rain or rapid melting of snow can cause a river to flood. Building within a floodplain is risky, as shown in Figure 16. However, floods supply mineral-rich soil that is ideal for farming. One way to decrease flooding on a floodplain is to build a levee. A levee is a long, low ridge of soil along a river. However, decreasing flooding also decreases the renewed supply of mineral-rich soil for farming.

△ **Figure 15** These shoreline groins prevent beach erosion by trapping sediment.

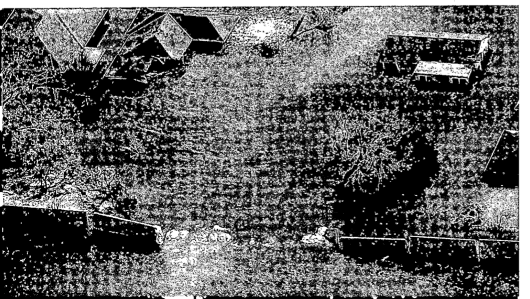

◁ **Figure 16** This 2005 levee break in New Orleans caused extensive flood damage.

▲ **Figure 17** Wind abrasion carved this unusual landform in the red sandstone of Nevada's Valley of Fire region.

WORD ORIGIN ··········

loess
from Swiss German *Lösch,*
means "loose"

Wind Erosion and Deposition

If you think about a gentle wind that blows leaves in the autumn, it seems unlikely that the wind can cause land erosion and deposition. But strong or long-lasting winds can significantly change the land.

Wind Erosion

As wind carries sediment along, the sediment cuts and polishes exposed rock. **Abrasion** *is the grinding away of rock or other surfaces as particles carried by wind, water, or ice scrape against them.* Examples of rock surfaces carved by wind abrasion are shown in **Figure 17** and at the beginning of this chapter.

Wind Deposition

Two common types of wind-blown deposits are dunes and loess (LUHS). *A* **dune** *is a pile of windblown sand.* Over time, entire fields of dunes can travel across the land as wind continues to blow the sand. Some dunes are shown in **Figure 18**. **Loess** *is a crumbly, windblown deposit of silt and clay.* One type of loess forms from rock that was ground up and deposited by glaciers. Wind picks up this fine-grain sediment and redeposits it as thick layers of dust called loess.

 Key Concept Check How do wind erosion and deposition change Earth's surface?

Land Use Practices

People contribute to wind erosion. For example, plowed fields and dry, overgrazed pastures expose soil. Strong winds can remove topsoil that is not held in place by plants. One way to slow the effects of wind erosion is to leave fields unplowed after harvesting crops. Farmers can also plant rows of trees to slow wind and protect the farmland.

Figure 18 Dunes, such as these in Death Valley, California, formed by the deposition of wind-blown sand. ▶

Visual Check What are two effects wind has had on this landscape?

Wind Erosion and Deposition

Online Quiz
Virtual Lab

Visual Summary

Water erosion changes Earth's surface. An example of this is the change in features of a stream over time.

Water transports sediment and deposits it in places where the speed of the water decreases.

Wind erosion can change Earth's surface by moving sediment. A dune and loess are two types of wind deposition.

FOLDABLES

Use your lesson Foldable to review the lesson. Save your Foldable for the project at the end of the chapter.

What do you think NOW?

You first read the statements below at the beginning of the chapter.

3. A beach is a landform that does not change over time.

4. Windblown sediment can cut and polish exposed rock surfaces.

Did you change your mind about whether you agree or disagree with the statements? Rewrite any false statements to make them true.

Use Vocabulary

1 **Distinguish** between loess and a dune.

2 **Use the term** *delta* in a complete sentence.

3 Sediment is transported parallel to the shoreline by a _____.

Understand Key Concepts

4 Which feature would a young river most likely have?
   A. meander   C. waterfall
   B. slow movement   D. wide channel

5 **Explain** how wind erosion might affect exposed rock.

6 **Compare and contrast** the advantages and disadvantages of farming on a floodplain.

Interpret Graphics

7 **Determine Cause and Effect** Copy and fill in the graphic organizer below to identify two ways waves cause seashore erosion.

8 **Examine** the image below.

How have erosion and deposition shaped the stream?

Critical Thinking

9 **Suppose** the amount of sand in front of a large, beachfront hotel is slowly disappearing. Explain the process that is likely causing this problem. Suggest a way to avoid further loss of sand.

10 **Recommend** What are some steps a farmer could take to avoid wind erosion and water erosion of farmland?

How do water erosion and deposition occur along a stream?

Water flowing in a stream erodes the land it flows over. As stream water slows down, it deposits sediments. You can learn about this type of erosion and deposition by analyzing how water shapes land.

Materials

sand

paper cup

craft sticks

tub

stream table

small rock

Also needed:
drain tube

Safety

Learn It

When you **analyze** an event, such as erosion or deposition, you observe the different things that happen. You also consider the effects of changes. In this activity, you will analyze how erosion and deposition occur along a stream.

Try It

① Read and complete a lab safety form.

② Half-fill a stream table with sand. Add water to dampen the sand. Tilt the table slightly, and put the drain tube in a tub.

③ Flatten the sand into a gentle slope. Slowly pour water from a paper cup onto the high end of the sand. Notice the movement of sand along the water's path. Record your observations in your Science Journal.

④ Flatten the sand again. Use a craft stick to make a straight channel for the water. Pour water into the channel slowly and then faster. Analyze the movement of sand along the channel.

Apply It

⑤ Test the effect of having an object, such as a rock, in the water's path. Analyze how this affects the path of the water and the movement of sand.

⑥ Think about how flowing water affects the shape of a meander. Test this with your damp sand and water. Describe your results.

⑦ 🔑 **Key Concept** How did water erosion and deposition occur along the stream?

③

(t to b)Ken Cavanagh/McGraw-Hill Education; (2–5, r)Hutchings Photography/Digital Light Source; (6)Jacques Cornell/McGraw-Hill Education

Lesson 3

Mass Wasting and Glaciers

Reading Guide

Key Concepts 🔑

ESSENTIAL QUESTIONS

- What are some ways gravity shapes Earth's surface?

- How do glaciers erode Earth's surface?

Vocabulary

mass wasting p. 286

landslide p. 287

talus p. 287

glacier p. 289

till p. 290

moraine p. 290

outwash p. 290

 Multilingual eGlossary

 BrainPOP®

 7.ESS.4, SEPS.1, SEPS.2, SEPS.3, SEPS.4, SEPS.5, SEPS.6, SEPS.8, 6-8.LST.4.1, 6-8.LST.5.2, 6-8.LST.7.1, 6-8.LST.7.3

Inquiry River of Mud?

Heavy rains loosened the sediment on this mountain. Eventually the land collapsed and caused a river of mud to flow downhill. Events such as this can seriously damage land as well as homes and businesses.

Michael D. Kennedy/U.S. Navy via Getty Images

How does a moving glacier shape Earth's surface?

A glacier is a huge mass of slow-moving ice. The weight of a glacier is so great that its movement causes significant erosion and deposition along its path. In this lab, you will use a model glacier to observe these effects.

1. Read and complete a lab safety form.

2. Half-fill an **aluminum pan** with **dirt** and **gravel**. Mix enough water so that the dirt holds together easily. Use **two books** to raise one end of the pan.

3. Sprinkle **colored sand** at the top of the dirt hill.

4. Place a **model glacier** at the top of the hill. Slowly move the glacier downhill, pressing down gently.

Think About This

1. What happened to the colored sand as the glacier moved downhill?

2. **Key Concept** What kinds of erosion and deposition did your model glacier cause?

Mass Wasting

Have you ever seen or heard a news report about a large pile of boulders that has fallen down a mountain onto a road? This is an example of a mass wasting event. **Mass wasting** *is the downhill movement of a large mass of rocks or soil because of the pull of gravity.* There are two important parts to this definition:

• material moves in bulk as a large mass

• gravity is the dominant cause of movement. For example, the mass moves all at once, rather than as separate pieces over a long period of time. Also, the mass is not moved by, in, on, or under a transporting agent such as water, ice, or air.

Reading Check Describe two characteristics of a mass wasting event.

Look again at the photo on the previous page. It is a photo of a mass wasting event called a mud flow. Even though water did not transport the mud, it did contribute to this mass wasting event. Mass wasting commonly occurs when soil on a hillside is soaked with rainwater. The water-soaked soil becomes so heavy that it breaks loose and slides down the hillside.

Recall that vegetation on a steep slope reduces the amount of water erosion during a heavy rainfall. The presence of thick vegetation on a slope also reduces the likelihood of a mass wasting event. Root systems of plants help hold sediment in place. Vegetation also reduces the force of falling rain. This minimizes erosion by allowing water to gently soak into the soil.

Hutchings Photography/Digital Light Source

Examples of Mass Wasting 🔑

Rockfall

Slump

Creep

Erosion by Mass Wasting

There are many types of mass wasting events. For example, *a landslide is the rapid downhill movement of soil, loose rocks, and boulders.* Two types of landslides are a rockfall, such as the one shown in **Figure 19**, and a mudslide, shown on the first page of this lesson. Slump is a type of mass wasting where the material moves slowly, in a large mass. If the material moves too slowly to be noticeable, causing trees and other objects to lean over, the event is called creep, also shown in **Figure 19**.

The amount of erosion that occurs during a mass wasting event depends on factors such as the type of rock, the amount of water in the soil, and how strongly the rock and soil are held together. Erosion also tends to be more destructive when the mass wasting occurs on steep slopes. For example, landslides on a steep hillside can cause extensive damage because they transport large amounts of material quickly.

Key Concept Check What are some ways gravity shapes Earth's surface?

Deposition by Mass Wasting

The erosion that occurs during mass wasting continues as long as gravity is greater than other forces holding the rock and soil in place. But when the material reaches a stable location, such as the base of a mountain, the material is deposited. **Talus** *is a pile of angular rocks and sediment from a rockfall,* like the pile of rock at the base of the hill in **Figure 19**.

Figure 19 A rockfall, slump, and creep are examples of mass wasting.

Visual Check What evidence do you see in the figure that mass wasting has occurred?

FOLDABLES

Make a two-tab book and label it as shown. Use your book to organize information about landforms and features created by erosion and deposition by mass wasting and by glaciers.

Erosion and Deposition

| Mass Wasting | Glaciers |

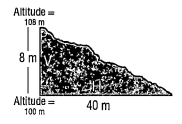

Figure 20 Building on steep slopes can increase the risk of a landslide. Construction or removal of vegetation makes the hillside even less stable.

Land Use Practices

Human activities can affect both the severity of mass wasting and the tendency for it to occur. The homes in **Figure 20** were built on steep and unstable slopes and were damaged during a landslide. Removing vegetation increases soil erosion and can promote mass wasting. The use of heavy machines or blasting can shake the ground and trigger mass wasting. In addition, landscaping can make a slope steeper. A steep slope is more likely to undergo mass wasting.

Reading Check What are some ways human activities can increase or decrease the risk of mass wasting?

MiniLab   20 minutes

How does the slope of a hill affect erosion?

1. Read and complete a lab safety form.
2. Use **scissors** to poke holes in one end of an **aluminum pan.** Prop the other end up with a **book.** Place a **second pan** under the low end. Pile **300 mL of soil** in the high end.
3. Quickly pour **400 mL of water** over the soil. Drain the water from the second pan. Use a **balance** to measure the mass of the soil that was washed into the second pan.
4. Clean the pans. Using fresh soil, repeat steps 2 and 3 with **three books** holding up the pan.

Analyze and Conclude

1. **Predict** what your results would have been if you had sprinkled the water on slowly.

2. **Key Concept** How did the slope of the hill affect the amount of erosion?

(t)Frazer Harrison/Getty Images; (b)Hutchings Photography/Digital Light Source

Glacial Erosion and Deposition

You have read about erosion and deposition caused by mass wasting events. Glaciers can also cause erosion and deposition. *A glacier is a large mass of ice that formed on land and moves slowly across Earth's surface.* Glaciers form on land in areas where the amount of snowfall is greater than the amount of snowmelt. Although glaciers appear to be motionless, they can move several centimeters or more each day.

There are two main types of glaciers—alpine glaciers and ice sheets. Alpine glaciers, like the one shown in Figure 21, form in mountains and flow downhill. More than 100,000 alpine glaciers exist on Earth today. Ice sheets cover large areas of land and move outward from central locations. Continental ice sheets were common in past ice ages but only exist today on Antarctica and Greenland.

Glacial Erosion

Glaciers erode Earth's surface as they slide over it. They act as bulldozers, carving the land as they move. Rocks and grit frozen within the ice create grooves and scratches on underlying rocks. This is similar to the way sandpaper scratches wood. Alpine glaciers produce distinctive erosional features like the ones shown in Figure 22. Notice the U-shaped valleys that glaciers carved through the mountains.

Key Concept Check How do glaciers erode Earth's surface?

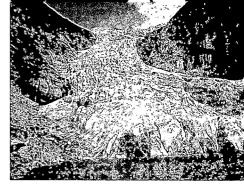

△ **Figure 21** The Mendenhall Glacier in Alaska is an alpine glacier.

Applying Practices

How have large-scale physical processes shaped the land? Go online to construct an explanation for how glaciers and karst topography have shaped Indiana.

Figure 22 Alpine glaciers produce distinctive erosion features.

Visual Check How would the mountains and the valley be different if a glacier had not passed through? ▽

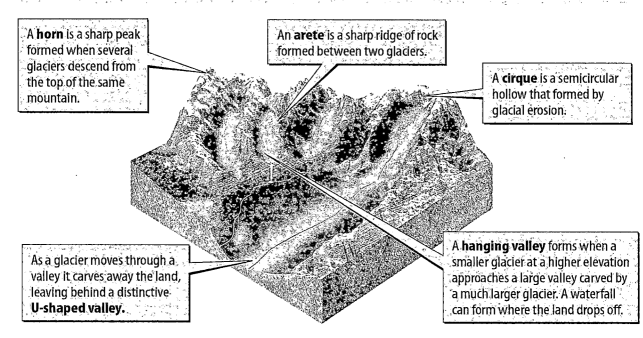

A **horn** is a sharp peak formed when several glaciers descend from the top of the same mountain.

An **arete** is a sharp ridge of rock formed between two glaciers.

A **cirque** is a semicircular hollow that formed by glacial erosion.

As a glacier moves through a valley it carves away the land, leaving behind a distinctive **U-shaped valley.**

A **hanging valley** forms when a smaller glacier at a higher elevation approaches a large valley carved by a much larger glacier. A waterfall can form where the land drops off.

Figure 23 Melting glaciers form various land features as they deposit rock and sediment.

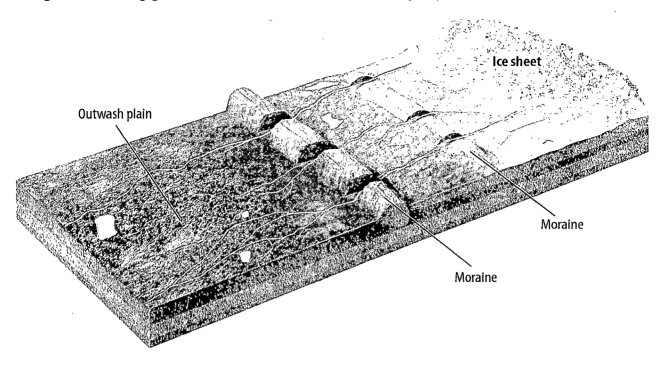

Outwash plain

Ice sheet

Moraine

Moraine

SCIENCE USE V. COMMON USE ···
till
Science Use rock and sediment
deposited by a glacier

Common Use to work by plow-
ing, sowing, and raising crops

WORD ORIGIN ···········
moraine
from French *morena*, means
"mound of earth"

Glacial Deposition

Glaciers slowly melt as they move down from high altitudes or when the climate in the area warms. Sediment that was once frozen in the ice eventually is deposited in various forms, as illustrated in Figure 23. **Till** *is a mixture of various sizes of sediment deposited by a glacier.* Deposits of till are poorly sorted. They commonly contain particles that range in size from boulders to silt. Till often piles up along the sides and fronts of glaciers. It can be shaped and streamlined into many features by the moving ice. For example, *a* **moraine** *is a mound or ridge of unsorted sediment deposited by a glacier.* **Outwash** *is layered sediment deposited by streams of water that flow from a melting glacier.* Outwash consists mostly of well sorted sand and gravel.

 Reading Check How does outwash differ from a moraine?

Land Use Practices

At first, it might not seem that human activities affect glaciers. But in some ways, the effects are more significant than they are for other forms of erosion and deposition. For example, human activities contribute to global warming–the gradual increase in Earth's average temperature. This can cause considerable melting of glaciers. Glaciers contain about two-thirds of all the freshwater on Earth. As glaciers melt, sea level rises around the world and coastal flooding is possible.

Visual Summary

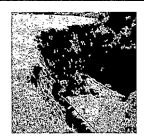

Mass wasting can occur very fast, such as when a landslide occurs, or slowly over many years.

Material moved by a mass wasting event is deposited when it reaches a relatively stable location. An example is talus deposited at the base of this hill.

A glacier erodes Earth's surface as it moves and melts. Glaciers can form U-shaped valleys when they move past mountains.

FOLDABLES

Use your lesson Foldable to review the lesson. Save your Foldable for the project at the end of the chapter.

What do you think NOW?

You first read the statements below at the beginning of the chapter.

5. Landslides are a natural process that cannot be influenced by human activities.

6. A glacier leaves behind very smooth land as it moves through an area.

Did you change your mind about whether you agree or disagree with the statements? Rewrite any false statements to make them true.

Use Vocabulary

1. **Define** *mass wasting* in your own words.

2. **Use the term** *talus* in a complete sentence.

3. Erosion by the movement of a _____ can produce a U-shaped valley.

Understand Key Concepts

4. Which is the slowest mass wasting event?
   A. creep   C. rockfall
   B. landslide   D. slump

5. **Classify** each of the following as features of either erosion or deposition: (a) arete, (b) outwash, (c) cirque, and (d) till.

Interpret Graphics

6. **Examine** the drawing. What feature formed by the glacier is indicated by the arrow?

Glacier

7. **Compare and Contrast** Copy and fill in the table below to compare and contrast moraine and outwash.

Similarities	Differences

Critical Thinking

8. **Compose** a list of evidence for erosion and deposition that you might find in a mountain park that would indicate that glaciers once existed in the area.

Math Skills   Math Practice

9. A mountain's base is 2,500 m high. The peak is 3,500 m high. The horizontal distance covers 4,000 m. What is the percent slope?

Avoiding a Landslide

The damage caused by landslides can be costly to humans. Sometimes landslides are even deadly. Landslides occur most often after a period of heavy rain in regions prone to earthquakes. In this lab, you will analyze ways to protect a house from a landslide.

Ask a Question

What are some ways to reduce the risk of a landslide?

Make Observations

1. Read and complete a lab safety form.
2. In a pan, mix two parts sand to one part water. There should be 2–3 cm of damp sand in the pan.
3. Shape the damp sand into a hill. Place a model house on top of the hill.

4. Using a cup, pour water over the hill, as if it were raining. Record your observations in your Science Journal.
5. Rebuild the hill and the house. This time, gently shake the pan, as if there were an earthquake. Record your observations.

Landslide Test Observations		
Setup	Action	Observations
damp sand hill, no ground cover	pour on water with no shaking	
damp sand hill, no ground cover	pour water and shake the pan	

Form a Hypothesis

⑥ Suppose someone built a house on the top of a hill. What are three ways to reduce the risk of a landslide? For each way, develop a hypothesis to save the house from a landslide.

Test Your Hypothesis

⑦ Develop a plan for testing each hypothesis. Present your plans to your teacher. When they are approved, obtain additional materials from your teacher to implement the plans.

⑧ Test your plans with both rain and an earthquake. Rebuild the hill and replace the house between tests, if necessary.

Analyze and Conclude

⑨ **Describe** the results of your tests. For each test, was your hypothesis correct? What might have worked better?

⑩ **Analyze** What is the relationship between the amount of water in the soil and the likelihood of a landslide? Use specific examples from the lab in your explanation.

⑪ **The Big Idea** What are some ways people can alter Earth's surface to reduce the risk of a landslide?

Communicate Your Results

People who live in areas prone to landslides need to take precautions to protect their homes. Write and perform a 30-second public service announcement that describes your results and how they can help people protect their homes.

Evaluate your home for risk of a landslide. Is it on a slope? Do you get a lot of rain? Do you live in an area prone to earthquakes?

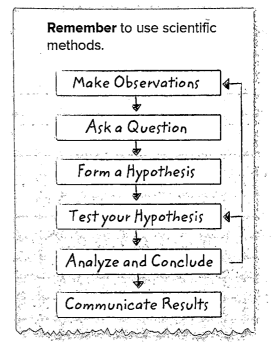

Lab Tips

☑ Mix the sand and water completely, but allow water to drain out to make a strong hill.

☑ Before testing your hypotheses, predict which method will be most effective in reducing the risk of a landslide.

Remember to use scientific methods.

Make Observations →

Ask a Question ↓

Form a Hypothesis ↓

Test your Hypothesis ↓

Analyze and Conclude ↓

Communicate Results

 Erosion and deposition shape Earth's surface by building up and tearing down landforms.

Key Concepts Summary

Vocabulary

Lesson 1: The Erosion-Deposition Process

- **Erosion** is the wearing away and transportation of weathered material. **Deposition** is the laying down of the eroded material.
- Erosion tends to make rocks more rounded. Erosion can sort sediment according to its grain size.
- Landforms produced by deposition are usually on flat, low land. Landforms produced by erosion are often tall and/or jagged.

erosion p. 269
deposition p. 271

Lesson 2: Landforms Shaped by Water and Wind

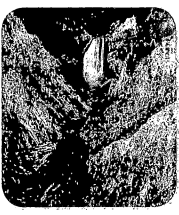

- A young stream moves quickly down steep slopes. A mature stream moves more slowly and develops **meanders.** An old stream is wider and moves slowly.
- Water erosion can form V-shaped valleys. **Longshore currents** reshape beaches. Deposition of sediment from water can form **deltas.**
- Wind **abrasion** can change the shape of rock. Wind deposition can form a **dune** or **loess.**

meander p. 278
longshore current p. 279
delta p. 280
abrasion p. 282
dune p. 282
loess p. 282

Lesson 3: Mass Wasting and Glaciers

- Gravity can shape Earth's surface through **mass wasting.** Creep is an example of mass wasting.
- A **glacier** erodes Earth's surface as it moves by carving grooves and scratches into rock.

mass wasting p. 286
landslide p. 287
talus p. 287
glacier p. 289
till p. 290
moraine p. 290
outwash p. 290

(t)Marc Crumpler/Getty Images; (c)Michael Melford/Getty Images; (b)©paolo gislimberti/Alamy

Personal Tutor

Vocabulary eFlashcards
Vocabulary eGames

FOLDABLES® Chapter Project

Assemble your lesson Foldables as shown to make a Chapter Project. Use the project to review what you have learned in this chapter.

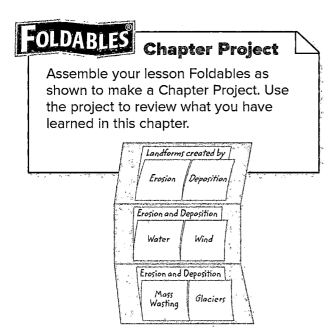

Use Vocabulary

1 Water moving sediment down slopes and a glacier forming a U-shaped valley as it moves past mountains are examples of _____.

2 Wind has less energy as it slows, and _____ of sediment occurs.

3 The grinding of rock as water, wind, or glaciers move sediment is _____.

4 An apron of sediment known as a(n) _____ forms where a stream enters a lake or an ocean.

5 A landslide and creep are types of _____.

6 A large pile of rocks formed from a rockfall is _____.

Link Vocabulary and Key Concepts

 Interactive Concept Map

Copy this concept map, and then use vocabulary terms from the previous page to complete the concept map.

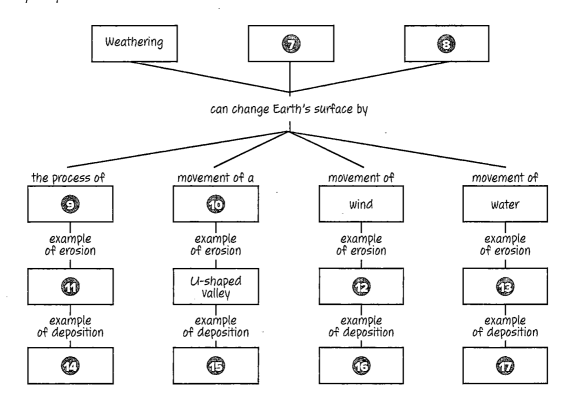

Understand Key Concepts

1. Which is a structure created mostly by deposition?
   A. cirque
   B. hoodoo
   C. sandbar
   D. slump

2. Which shows an example of sediment that is both poorly rounded and well-sorted?

   A.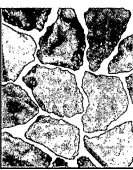

   C.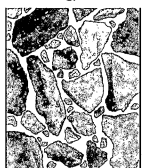

   B.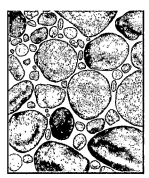

   D.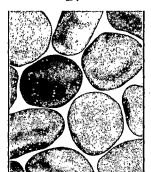

3. Which is typically a low-energy depositional environment?
   A. a fast-moving river
   B. an ocean shore with waves
   C. a stream with meanders
   D. a swamp with decaying trees

4. Which would most likely produce a moraine?
   A. a glacier
   B. an ocean
   C. a river
   D. the wind

5. The illustration below shows a type of mass wasting.

   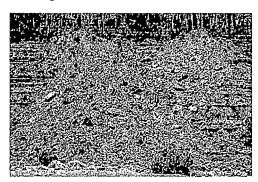

   Which was produced by this event?
   A. cirque
   B. moraine
   C. talus
   D. till

6. What is the main difference between slump and creep?
   A. the type of land that is affected
   B. the place where they occur
   C. the speed at which they occur
   D. the amount of rain that causes them

7. Which best describes the difference between a dune and loess?
   A. They are produced in different places.
   B. One is erosion, and the other is deposition.
   C. They are deposits of different-sized particles.
   D. One is caused by wind, and the other is caused by water.

8. Where would you most likely find a meander?
   A. in a cave
   B. in a mature stream
   C. under a glacier
   D. beside a waterfall

9. Which is built to prevent beach erosion?
   A. delta
   B. groin
   C. levee
   D. sandbar

©Stephen Reynolds

Critical Thinking

10 Describe one erosion feature and one deposition feature you might expect to find (a) in a valley, (b) in a desert, and (c) high in the mountains.

11 Classify these landforms as formed mostly by erosion or deposition: (a) cirque, (b) sand dune, (c) alluvial fan, (d) hoodoo.

12 Construct a chart that lists three careless land uses that result in mass wasting that could be dangerous to humans. Include in your chart details about how each land use could be changed to be safer.

13 Produce a list of at least three hazardous erosion or deposition conditions that would be worse during a particularly stormy, rainy season.

14 Predict several ways the mountains and the valleys shown below might change as the glaciers slide down slopes.

15 Contrast the rounding and sorting of sediment caused by a young stream to that caused by an old stream.

Writing in Science

16 Write Imagine you are planning to build a home on a high cliff overlooking the sea. Write a paragraph that assesses the potential for mass wasting along the cliff. Describe at least four features that would concern you.

REVIEW THE BIG IDEA

17 How do erosion and deposition shape Earth's surface?

18 The photo below shows a landform known as The Wave in the southwestern United States. Explain how erosion and deposition might have produced this landform.

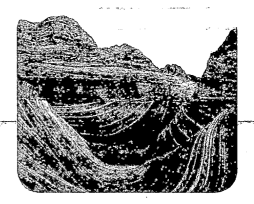

Math Skills ×÷ Math Practice

Use Ratios

19 Calculate the average percent slope of the mountains in parts a and b.

   a. Mountain A rises from 3,200 m to 6,700 m over a horizontal distance of 10,000 m.

   b. Mountain B rises from 1,400 m to 9,400 m over a horizontal distance of 2.5 km.

   c. If mountains A and B are composed of the same materials, which mountain is more likely to experience mass wasting?

20 If the slope of a hill is 10 percent, how many meters does the hill rise for every 10 m of horizontal distance?

Record your answers on the answer sheet provided by your teacher or on a sheet of paper.

Multiple Choice

1 Which landform is created by deposition?

   A alluvial fan

   B glacial valley

   C mountain range

   D river channel

Use the diagram below to answer question 2.

2 Which process formed the features shown in the diagram above?

   A A stream eroded and deposited sediment.

   B Groundwater deposited minerals in a cave.

   C Groundwater dissolved several layers of rock.

   D Wind and ice wore away soft sedimentary rock.

3 Which causes movement in mass wasting?

   A gravity

   B ice

   C magnetism

   D wind

4 Which typically is NOT a depositional environment?

   A delta

   B mountain peak

   C ocean floor

   D swamp

Use the diagram below to answer questions 5 and 6.

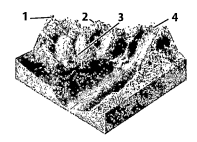

5 Which landform on the diagram above is a cirque?

   A 1

   B 2

   C 3

   D 4

6 How did structure 1 form in the diagram above?

   A A glacier deposited a large amount of land as it moved.

   B A small glacier approached a valley carved by a large glacier.

   C Several glaciers descended from the top of the same mountain.

   D Two glaciers formed on either side of a ridge.

7 Which agent of erosion can create a limestone cave?

   A acidic water

   B freezing and melting ice

   C growing plant roots

   D gusty wind

8 Which deposit does mass wasting create?

   A loess

   B outwash

   C talus

   D till

Use the diagram below to answer question 9.

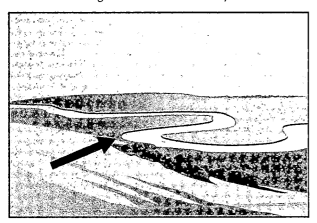

9 Which river feature does the arrow point to in the diagram above?

   A a current

   B a meander

   C a valley

   D an alluvial fan

10 Which is true of a longshore current?

   A It ALWAYS flows perpendicular to the shoreline.

   B It can form large underground caves.

   C It continually changes the size and shape of beaches.

   D It creates stretches of sand dunes along the beach.

11 Which geological process is often caused by the growth of plant roots?

   A deposition

   B erosion

   C sorting

   D weathering

Constructed Response

Use the diagram below to answer questions 12 and 13.

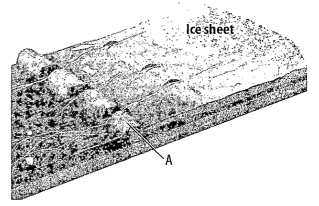

12 Describe the characteristics of deposits found in the feature labeled *A*.

13 How did feature *A* form?

14 A sedimentary rock formation contains alternating layers of fine-grained rock and conglomerate rock, which contains smooth pebble-sized sediments. What is the process that most likely deposited the sediments that make up this rock formation?

15 What factors determine the amount of erosion that occurs during a mass wasting event? How does slope affect the destructive power of this event?

16 What is the typical appearance of a landform formed by erosion?

NEED EXTRA HELP?																
If You Missed Question...	1	2	3	4	5	6	7	8	9	10	11	12	13	14	15	16
Go to Lesson...	1	2	3	1	3	3	2	3	2	2	1	3	3	1, 2	3	1

Unit 4
Dynamic Earth

1900   2000

1899–1900
John Joly releases his findings from calculating the age of Earth using the rate of oceanic salt accumulation. He determines that the oceans are about 80–100 million years old.

1905
Ernest Rutherford and Bertrand Boltwood use radiometric dating to determine the age of rock samples. This technique would later be used to determine the age of Earth.

1956
Today's accepted age of Earth is determined by C.C. Patterson using uranium-lead isotope dating on several meteorites.

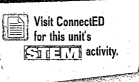

Visit ConnectED for this unit's **STEM** activity.

Graphs

Imagine that 3 seconds are left in the semifinal game of your favorite sporting event. The clock runs out, and the buzzer sounds! You cheer as your team advances to the finals! You grab the bracket that you made and record another win.

A bracket organizes and displays the wins and losses of teams in a tournament, as shown in **Figure 1**. Brackets, like maps, tables, and graphs, are a type of chart. A **chart** is a visual display that organizes information. Charts help you organize data. Charts also help you identify patterns, trends, or errors in your data and communicate data to others.

What are tables?

Suppose you volunteer for a cleanup program at a local beach. The organizers need to know the types of debris found at different times of the year. Each month, you collect debris, separate it into categories, and weigh each category of debris. You record your data in a table. A **table** is a type of chart that organizes related data in columns and rows. Titles are usually placed at the top of each column or at the beginning of each row to help organize the data, as shown in **Table 1**.

What are graphs?

A table contains data but it does not clearly show relationships among data. However, displaying data as a graph does clearly show relationships. A **graph** is a type of chart that shows relationships between variables. The organizers of the cleanup program could make different types of graphs from the information in your table to help them better analyze the data.

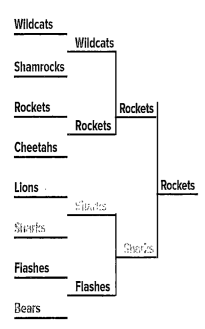

▲ **Figure 1** A sporting bracket is a type of chart that easily enables you to see which team has won the most games in a tournament.

Table 1 This table organizes data on collected debris into rows and columns so measurements can easily be recorded, compared, and used. ▼

Table 1 Types and Amounts of Debris							
Types of Debris	Jan	Mar	May	July	Sept	Nov	Total for Year
Plastic	3.0	3.5	3.8	4.0	3.7	3.0	21.0
Polystyrene	0.5	1.3	3.2	4.0	2.5	1.2	12.7
Glass	0.8	1.2	1.5	2.0	1.5	1.0	8.0
Rubber	1.1	1.0	1.3	1.5	1.2	1.3	7.4
Metal	1.0	1.0	1.1	1.4	1.1	1.0	6.6
Paper	1.3	1.1	1.5	1.5	0.8	0.3	6.5
Total for Month	9.4	10.6	13.1	15.1	12.1	9.5	69.8

Circle Graphs

If the cleanup organizers want to know the most common type of debris, they will probably use a circle graph. A circle graph shows the percentage of the total that each category represents. This circle graph shows that plastic makes up the largest percentage of debris. The cleanup organizers could then place plastic recycling barrels on the beach so people can recycle their plastic trash.

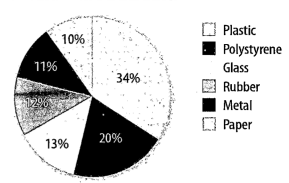

Beach Debris Distribution

- ☐ Plastic
- ■ Polystyrene
- Glass
- ▒ Rubber
- ■ Metal
- ☐ Paper

10% 11% 34% 12% 13% 20%

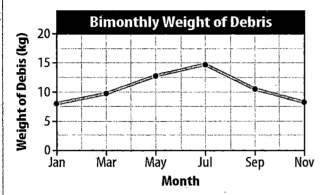

Line Graphs

Suppose the cleanup organizers want to know how the total amount of debris on the beach changes throughout the year. They probably will use a line graph. This line graph shows that volunteers collected more debris in summer than in winter. The cleanup organizers could then create a public service announcement for radio stations that reminds beachgoers to throw trash into trash cans and recycling barrels while visiting the beach.

Bar Graphs

Volunteers collected the most debris in July. The cleanup organizers want to know how much of each type of debris volunteers collected in July. Bar graphs are useful for comparing different categories of measurements. This bar graph shows that 4 kg of both plastic and polystyrene were collected in July. The cleanup organizers could then suggest that beach concession stands use smaller, recyclable food containers.

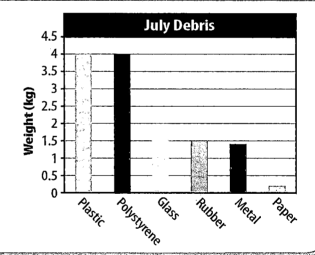

🔖 MiniLab

25 minutes

How can graphs keep the beach clean?

Suppose you work with the cleanup organizers. What information do you need to make recommendations for keeping the beach cleaner?

① Based on the type of information in **Table 1,** write a new question about beach debris.

② Make a graph that allows you to answer your question.

Analyze and Conclude

1. **Distinguish** How did you decide what type of graph to make?

2. **Explain** How did you use your graph to answer your question?

3. **Modify** What recommendations can you make based on your analysis of your graph?

Chapter 9

7.ESS.3, SEPS.2, SEPS.3, SEPS.4,
SEPS.5, SEPS.8, 6-8.LST.1.1, 6-8.LST.1.2,
6-8.LST.2.2, 6-8.LST.3.2, 6-8.LST.5.1,
6-8.LST.5.2, 6-8.LST.7.1, 6-8.LST.7.3

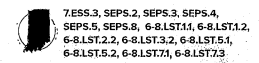

Plate Tectonics

THE BIG IDEA What is the theory of plate tectonics?

 Is this a volcano?

Iceland is home to many active volcanoes like this one. This eruption is called a fissure eruption. This occurs when lava erupts from a long crack, or fissure, in Earth's crust.

- Why is the crust breaking apart here?

- What factors determine where a volcano will form?

- How are volcanoes associated with plate tectonics?

Arctic-Images/Getty Images

Get Ready to Read

What do you think?

Before you read, decide if you agree or disagree with each of these statements. As you read this chapter, see if you change your mind about any of the statements.

1. India has always been north of the equator.

2. All the continents once formed one supercontinent.

3. The seafloor is flat.

4. Volcanic activity occurs only on the seafloor.

5. Continents drift across a molten mantle.

6. Mountain ranges can form when continents collide.

Mc Graw Hill Education | connectED

Your one-stop online resource
connectED.mcgraw-hill.com

 LearnSmart*

 Chapter Resources Files, Reading Essentials, Get Ready to Read, Quick Vocabulary

 Animations, Videos, Interactive Tables

 Self-checks, Quizzes, Tests

 Project-Based Learning Activities

 Lab Manuals, Safety Videos, Virtual Labs & Other Tools

 Vocabulary, Multilingual eGlossary, Vocab eGames, Vocab eFlashcards

 Personal Tutors

Reading Guide

Key Concepts 🔑
ESSENTIAL QUESTIONS

- What evidence supports continental drift?

- Why did scientists question the continental drift hypothesis?

Vocabulary

Pangaea p. 307

continental drift p. 307

 Multilingual eGlossary

 BrainPOP®

 7.ESS.3, 6-8.LST.1.1, 6-8.LST.2.2, 6-8.LST.7.1, 6-8.LST.7.3

The Continental Drift Hypothesis

Inquiry) How did this happen?

In Iceland, elongated cracks called rift zones are easy to find. Why do rift zones occur here? Iceland is above an area of the seafloor where Earth's crust is breaking apart. Earth's crust is constantly on the move. Scientists realized this long ago, but they could not prove how or why this happened.

Bernhard Edmaier/Science Source

Launch Lab

Can you put together a peel puzzle?

Early map makers observed that the coastlines of Africa and South America appeared as if they could fit together like pieces of a puzzle. Scientists eventually discovered that these continents were once part of a large landmass. Can you use an orange peel to illustrate how continents may have fit together?

1. Read and complete a lab safety form.
2. Carefully peel an **orange,** keeping the orange-peel pieces as large as possible.
3. Set the orange aside.
4. Refit the orange-peel pieces back together in the shape of a sphere.
5. After successfully reconstructing the orange peel, disassemble your pieces.
6. Trade the entire orange peel with a classmate and try to reconstruct his or her orange peel.

Think About This

1. Which orange peel was easier for you to reconstruct? Why?

2. Look at a world map. Do the coastlines of any other continents appear to fit together?

3. **Key Concept** What additional evidence would you need to prove that all the continents might have once fit together?

Pangaea

Did you know that Earth's surface is on the move? Can you feel it? Each year, North America moves a few centimeters farther away from Europe and closer to Asia. That is several centimeters, or about the thickness of a textbook. Even though you don't necessarily feel this motion, Earth's surface moves slowly every day.

Nearly 100 years ago Alfred Wegener (VAY guh nuhr), a German scientist, began an important investigation that continues today. Wegener wanted to know whether Earth's continents were fixed in their positions. He proposed that *all the continents were once part of a supercontinent called* **Pangaea** (pan JEE uh). Over time Pangaea began breaking apart, and the continents slowly moved to their present positions. Wegener proposed the hypothesis of **continental drift,** *which suggested that continents are in constant motion on the surface of Earth.*

Alfred Wegener observed the similarities of continental coastlines now separated by oceans. Look at the outlines of Africa and South America in Figure 1. Notice how they could fit together like pieces of a puzzle. Hundreds of years ago mapmakers noticed this jigsaw-puzzle pattern as they made the first maps of the continents.

Figure 1 The eastern coast of South America mirrors the shape of the west coast of Africa.

Continental shelf

Evidence That Continents Move

If you had discovered continental drift, how would you have tested your hypothesis? The most obvious evidence for continental drift is that the continents appear to fit together like pieces of a puzzle. But scientists were skeptical, and Wegener needed additional evidence to help support his hypothesis.

Climate Clues

Wegener used climate clues to support his continental drift hypothesis. He studied the sediments deposited by glaciers in South America and Africa, as well as in India and Australia. Beneath these sediments, Wegener discovered glacial grooves, or deep scratches in rocks made as the glaciers moved across land. Figure 2 shows where these glacial features are found on neighboring continents today. Because these regions are too warm for glaciers to develop today, Wegener proposed that they were once located near the South Pole.

When Wegener pieced Pangaea together, he proposed that South America, Africa, India, and Australia were located closer to Antarctica 280 million years ago. He suggested that the climate of the southern hemisphere was much cooler at the time. Glaciers covered large areas that are now parts of these continents. These glaciers would have been similar to the ice sheet that covers much of Antarctica today.

Climate Clues

 Animation

Figure 2 If the southern hemisphere continents could be reassembled into Pangaea, the presence of an ice sheet would explain the glacial features on these continents today.

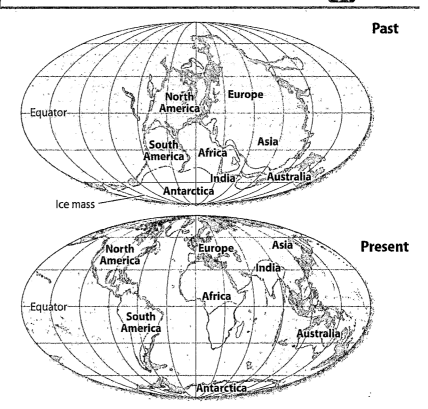

Fossil Clues

Animals and plants that live on different continents can be unique to that continent alone. Lions live in Africa but not in South America. Kangaroos live in Australia but not on any other continent. Because oceans separate continents, these animals cannot travel from one continent to another by natural means. However, fossils of similar organisms have been found on several continents separated by oceans. How did this happen? Wegener argued that these continents must have been connected some time in the past.

Fossils of a plant called *Glossopteris* (glahs AHP tur us) have been discovered in rocks from South America, Africa, India, Australia, and Antarctica. These continents are far apart today. The plant's seeds could not have traveled across the vast oceans that separate them. **Figure 3** shows that when these continents were part of Pangaea 225 million years ago, *Glossopteris* lived in one region. Evidence suggests these plants grew in a swampy environment. Therefore, the climate of this region, including Antarctica, was different than it is today. Antarctica had a warm and wet climate. The climate had changed drastically from what it was 55 million years earlier when glaciers existed.

 Reading Check How did climate in Antarctica change between 280 and 225 million years ago?

Fossil Clues

Figure 3 Fossils of *Glossopteris* have been found on many continents that are now separated by oceans. The orange area in the image on the right represents where *Glossopteris* fossils have been found.

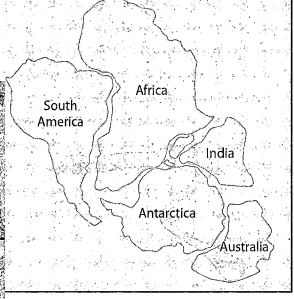

Visual Check Which of the continents would not support *Glossopteris* growth today?

©Walter Geiersperger/Corbis

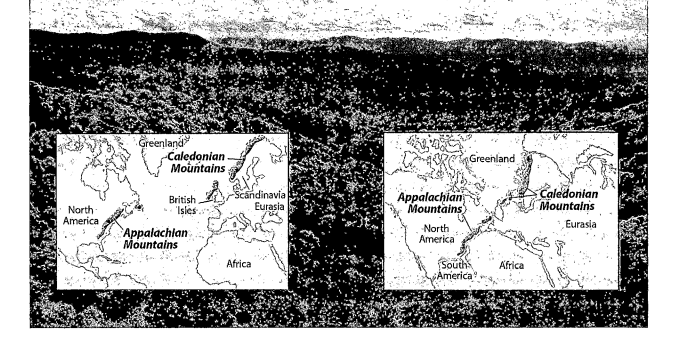

Figure 4 If you could move North America and Europe next to each other, the Appalachian Mountains and the Caledonian mountains would appear to form one continuous mountain range with similar formations.

Make a horizontal half-book and write the title as shown. Use it to organize your notes on the continental drift hypothesis.

Evidence for the Continental Drift Hypothesis

Rock Clues

Wegener realized he needed more evidence to support the continental drift hypothesis. He observed that mountain ranges like the ones shown in **Figure 4** and rock formations on different continents had common origins. Today, geologists can determine when these rocks formed. For example, geologists suggest that large-scale volcanic eruptions occurred on the western coast of Africa and the eastern coast of South America at about the same time hundreds of millions of years ago. The volcanic rocks from the eruptions are identical in both chemistry and age. Refer back to **Figure 1**. If you could superimpose similar rock types onto the maps, these rocks would be in the area where Africa and South America fit together.

The Caledonian mountain range in northern Europe and the Appalachian Mountains in eastern North America are similar in age and structure. They are also composed of the same rock types. If you placed North America and Europe next to each other, these mountains would meet and form one long, continuous mountain belt. **Figure 4** illustrates where this mountain range would be.

✓ **Key Concept Check** How were similar rock types used to support the continental drift hypothesis?

Harold R. Stinnette Photo Stock/Alamy

What was missing?

Wegener continued to support the continental drift hypothesis until his death in 1930. Wegener's ideas were not widely accepted until nearly four decades later. Why were scientists skeptical of Wegener's hypothesis? Although Wegener had evidence to suggest that continents were on the move, he could not explain how they moved.

One reason scientists questioned continental drift was because it is a slow process. It was not possible for Wegener to measure how fast the continents moved. The main objection to the continental drift hypothesis, however, was that Wegener could not explain what forces caused the continents to move. The mantle beneath the continents and the seafloor is made of solid rock. How could continents push their way through solid rock? Wegener needed more scientific evidence to prove his hypothesis. However, this evidence was hidden on the seafloor between the drifting continents. The evidence necessary to prove continental drift was not discovered until long after Wegener's death.

 Key Concept Check Why did scientists argue against Wegener's continental drift hypothesis?

MiniLab

20 minutes

How do you use clues to put puzzle pieces together?

When you put a puzzle together, you use clues to figure out which pieces fit next to each other. How did Wegener use a similar technique to piece together Pangaea?

① Read and complete a lab safety form.

② Using **scissors,** cut a piece of **newspaper** or a page from a **magazine** into an irregular shape with a diameter of about 25 cm.

③ Cut the piece of paper into at least 12 but not more than 20 pieces.

④ Exchange your puzzle with a partner and try to fit the new puzzle pieces together.

⑤ Reclaim your puzzle and remove any three pieces. Exchange your incomplete puzzle with a different partner. Try to put the incomplete puzzles back together.

Analyze and Conclude

1. **Summarize** Make a list of the clues you used to put together your partner's puzzle.

2. **Describe** How was putting together a complete puzzle different from putting together an incomplete puzzle?

3. **Key Concept** What clues did Wegener use to hypothesize the existence of Pangaea? What clues were missing from Wegener's puzzle?

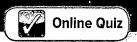
Visual Summary

Past

All continents were once part of a supercontinent called Pangaea.

Present

Evidence found on present-day continents suggests that the continents have moved across Earth's surface.

FOLDABLES

Use your lesson Foldable to review the lesson. Save your Foldable for the project at the end of the chapter.

What do you think NOW?

You first read the statements below at the beginning of the chapter.

1. India has always been north of the equator.

2. All the continents once formed one supercontinent.

Did you change your mind about whether you agree or disagree with the statements? Rewrite any false statements to make them true.

Use Vocabulary

1 **Define** *Pangaea.*

2 **Explain** How can you use models or demonstrations to explain the continental drift hypothesis?

Understand Key Concepts

3 **Identify** the scientist who first proposed that the continents move away from or toward each other.

4 Which can be used as an indicator of past climate?
- **A.** fossils
- **B.** lava flows
- **C.** mountain ranges
- **D.** tides

Interpret Graphics

5 **Interpret** Look at the map of the continents below. What direction has South America moved relative to Africa?

6 **Summarize** Copy and fill in the graphic organizer below to show the evidence Alfred Wegener used to support his continental drift hypothesis.

Continental Drift Hypothesis

Critical Thinking

7 **Recognize** The shape and age of the Appalachian Mountains are similar to the Caledonian mountains in northern Europe. What else could be similar?

8 **Explain** If continents continue to drift, is it possible that a new supercontinent will form? Which continents might be next to each other 200 million years from now?

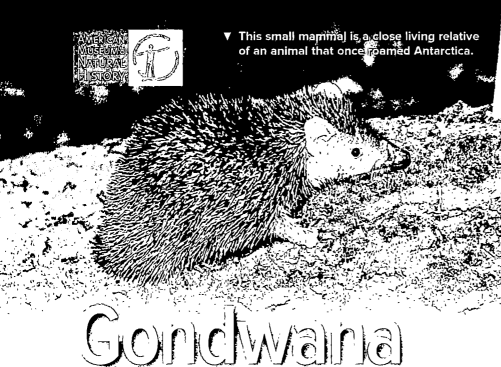

Gondwana

▲ **Ross MacPhee is a paleontologist working for the American Museum of Natural History in New York City. Here, he is searching for fossils in Antarctica.**

A Fossil Clue from the Giant Landmass that Once Dominated the Southern Hemisphere

f you could travel back in time 120 million years, you would probably discover that Earth looked very different than it does today. Scientists believe that instead of seven continents, there were two giant landmasses, or supercontinents, on Earth at that time. Scientists named the landmass in the northern hemisphere *Laurasia*. The landmass in the southern hemisphere is known as *Gondwana*. It included the present-day continents of Antarctica, South America, Australia, and Africa.

How do scientists know that Gondwana existed? Ross MacPhee is a paleontologist—a scientist who studies fossils. MacPhee recently traveled to Antarctica where he discovered the fossilized tooth of a small land mammal. After carefully examining the tooth, he realized that it resembled fossils from ancient land mammals found in Africa and North America. MacPhee believes that these mammals are the ancient relatives of a mammal living today on the African island-nation of Madagascar.

▲ *Gondwana* and *Laurasia* formed as the supercontinent Pangaea broke apart.

How did the fossil remains and their present-day relatives become separated by kilometers of ocean? MacPhee hypothesizes that the mammal migrated across land bridges that once connected parts of Gondwana. Over millions of years, the movement of Earth's tectonic plates broke up this supercontinent. New ocean basins formed between the continents, resulting in the arrangement of landmasses that we see today.

Your Turn

RESEARCH Millions of years ago, the island of Madagascar separated from the continent of Gondwana. In this environment, the animals of Madagascar changed and adapted. Research and report on one animal. Describe some of its unique adaptations.

Lesson 2

Development of a Theory

Reading Guide

Key Concepts
ESSENTIAL QUESTIONS

- What is seafloor spreading?
- What evidence is used to support seafloor spreading?

Vocabulary
mid-ocean ridge p. 315
seafloor spreading p. 316
normal polarity p. 318
magnetic reversal p. 318
reversed polarity p. 318

 Multilingual eGlossary

 7.ESS.3, SEPS.2, SEPS.5, 6-8.LST.2.2

Inquiry) What do the colors represent?

The colors in this satellite image show topography. The warm colors, red, pink, and yellow, represent landforms above sea level. The greens and blues indicate changes in topography below sea level. Deep in the Atlantic Ocean there is a mountain range, shown here as a linear feature in green. Is there a connection between this landform and the continental drift hypothesis?

Can you guess the age of the glue?

The age of the seafloor can be determined by measuring magnetic patterns in rocks from the bottom of the ocean. How can similar patterns in drying glue be used to show age relationships between rocks exposed on the seafloor?

1. Read and complete a lab safety form.
2. Carefully spread a thin layer of **rubber cement** on a sheet of **paper.**
3. Observe for 3 minutes. Record the pattern of how the glue dries in your Science Journal.
4. Repeat step 2. After 1 minute, exchange papers with a classmate.
5. Ask the classmate to observe and tell you which part of the glue dried first.

Think About This

1. What evidence helped you to determine the oldest and youngest glue layers?

2. How is this similar to a geologist trying to estimate the age of rocks on the seafloor?

3. 🗝 **Key Concept** How could magnetic patterns in rock help predict a rock's age?

Mapping the Ocean Floor

During the late 1940s after World War II, scientists began exploring the seafloor in greater detail. They were able to determine the depth of the ocean using a device called an echo sounder, as shown in **Figure 5**. Once ocean depths were determined, scientists used these data to create a topographic map of the seafloor. These new topographic maps of the seafloor revealed that vast mountain ranges stretched for many miles deep below the ocean's surface. *The mountain ranges in the middle of the oceans are called* **mid-ocean ridges.** Mid-ocean ridges, shown in **Figure 5**, are much longer than any mountain range on land.

Figure 5 An echo sounder produces sound waves that travel from a ship to the seafloor and back. The deeper the ocean, the longer the time this takes. Depth can be used to determine seafloor topography.

Hutchings Photography/Digital Light Source

Seafloor Topography

Mid-ocean ridge

Magma

Sediment

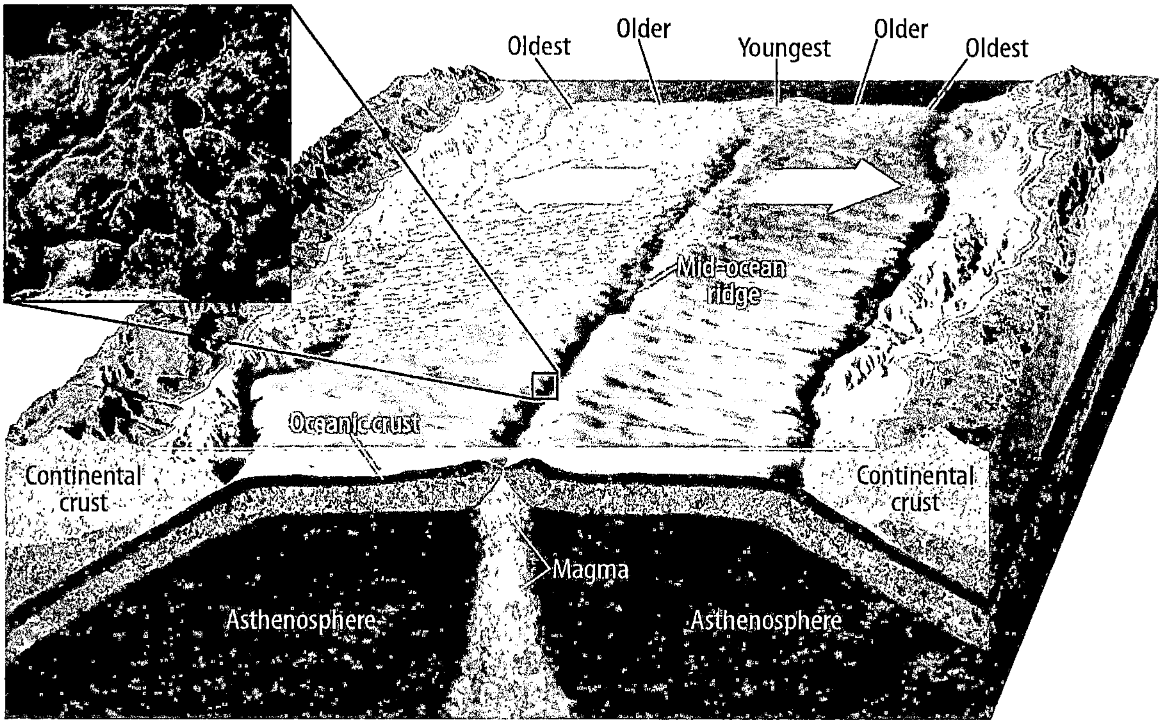

Pillow lava

Oldest Older Youngest Older Oldest

Mid-ocean ridge

Oceanic crust

Continental crust Continental crust

Magma

Asthenosphere Asthenosphere

Figure 6 When lava erupts along a mid-ocean ridge, it cools and crystallizes, forming a type of rock called basalt. Basalt is the dominant rock on the seafloor. The youngest basalt is closest to the ridge. The oldest basalt is farther away from the ridge.

*Ⓥ***Visual Check** Looking at the image above, can you propose a pattern that exists in rocks on either side of the mid-ocean ridge?

Seafloor Spreading

By the 1960s scientists discovered a new process that helped explain continental drift. This process, shown in **Figure 6,** is called seafloor spreading. **Seafloor spreading** *is the process by which new oceanic crust forms along a mid-ocean ridge and older oceanic crust moves away from the ridge.*

When the seafloor spreads, the mantle below melts and forms magma. Because magma is less dense than solid mantle material, it rises through cracks in the crust along the mid-ocean ridge. When magma erupts on Earth's surface, it is called lava. As this lava cools and crystallizes on the seafloor, it forms a type of rock called basalt. Because the lava erupts into water, it cools rapidly and forms rounded structures called pillow lavas. Notice the shape of the pillow lava shown in **Figure 6.**

As the seafloor continues to spread apart, the older oceanic crust moves away from the mid-ocean ridge. The closer the crust is to a mid-ocean ridge, the younger the oceanic crust is. Scientists argued that if the seafloor spreads, the continents must also be moving. A mechanism to explain continental drift was finally discovered long after Wegener proposed his hypothesis.

✓ **Key Concept Check** What is seafloor spreading?

Image courtesy of Submarine Ring of Fire 2002 Exploration, NOAA-OE.

Topography of the Seafloor

The rugged mountains that make up the mid-ocean ridge system can form in two different ways. For example, large amounts of lava can erupt from the center of the ridge, cool and build up around the ridge. Or, as the lava cools and forms new crust, it cracks. The rocks move up or down along these cracks in the seafloor, forming jagged mountain ranges.

Reading Check How do mountains form along the mid-ocean ridge?

Over time, sediment accumulates on top of the oceanic crust. Close to the mid-ocean ridge there is almost no sediment. Far from the mid-ocean ridge, the layer of sediment becomes thick enough to make the seafloor smooth. This part of the seafloor, shown in Figure 7, is called the abyssal (uh BIH sul) plain.

Moving Continents Around

The theory of seafloor spreading provides a way to explain how continents move. Continents do not move through the solid mantle or the seafloor. Instead, continents move as the seafloor spreads along a mid-ocean ridge.

MiniLab 20 minutes

How old is the Atlantic Ocean?

If you measure the width of the Atlantic Ocean and you know the rate of seafloor spreading, you can calculate the age of the Atlantic.

1. Use a **ruler** to measure the horizontal distance between a point on the eastern coast of South America and a point on the western coast of Africa on a **world map.** Repeat three times and calculate the average distance in your Science Journal.

2. Use the map's legend to convert the average distance from centimeters to kilometers.

3. If Africa and South America have been moving away from each other at a rate of 2.5 cm per year, calculate the age of the Atlantic Ocean.

Analyze and Conclude

1. **Measure** Did your measurements vary?

2. **Key Concept** How does the age you calculated compare to the breakup of Pangaea 200 million years ago?

Abyssal Plain

Figure 7 The abyssal plain is flat due to an accumulation of sediments far from the ridge.

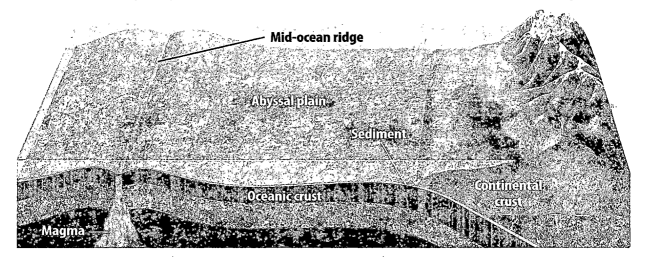

Visual Check Compare and contrast the topography of a mid-ocean ridge to an abyssal plain.

Development of a Theory

The first evidence used to support seafloor spreading was discovered in rocks on the seafloor. Scientists studied the magnetic signature of minerals in these rocks. To understand this, you need to understand the direction and orientation of Earth's magnetic field and how rocks record magnetic information.

Magnetic Reversals

Recall that the iron-rich, liquid outer core is like a giant magnet that creates Earth's magnetic field. The direction of the magnetic field is not constant. Today's magnetic field, shown in Figure 8, is described as having **normal polarity**—*a state in which magnetized objects, such as compass needles, will orient themselves to point north.* Sometimes a **magnetic reversal** *occurs and the magnetic field reverses direction.* The opposite of normal polarity is **reversed polarity**—*a state in which magnetized objects would reverse direction and orient themselves to point south,* as shown in Figure 8. Magnetic reversals occur every few hundred thousand to every few million years.

Reading Check Is Earth's magnetic field currently normal or reversed polarity?

Rocks Reveal Magnetic Signature

Basalt on the seafloor contains iron-rich minerals that are magnetic. Each mineral acts like a small magnet. Figure 9 shows how magnetic minerals align themselves with Earth's magnetic field. When lava erupts along a mid-ocean ridge, it cools and crystallizes. This permanently records the direction and orientation of Earth's magnetic field at the time of the eruption. Scientists have discovered parallel patterns in the magnetic signature of rocks on either side of a mid-ocean ridge.

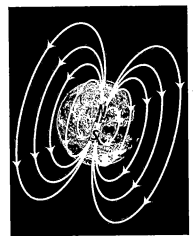
Reversed magnetic field

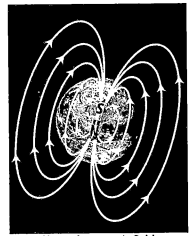
Normal magnetic field

△ **Figure 8** Earth's magnetic field is like a large bar magnet. Therefore, the north end of a compass magnet is drawn to the south pole of Earth's magnetic field.

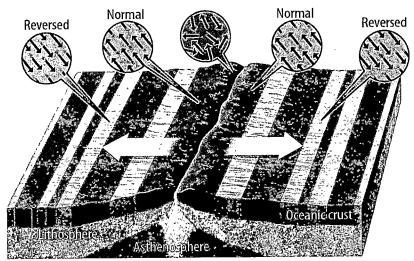
Reversed　Normal　Normal　Reversed

Figure 9 Iron-rich minerals in cooling lava align with Earth's magnetic field. When Earth's magnetic field changes direction, minerals in fresh lava record a new magnetic signature. ▷

Visual Check Describe the pattern in the magnetic stripes shown in the image to the right.

Figure 10 A mirror image in the magnetic stripes on either side of the mid-ocean ridge shows that the crust formed at the ridge is carried away in opposite directions.

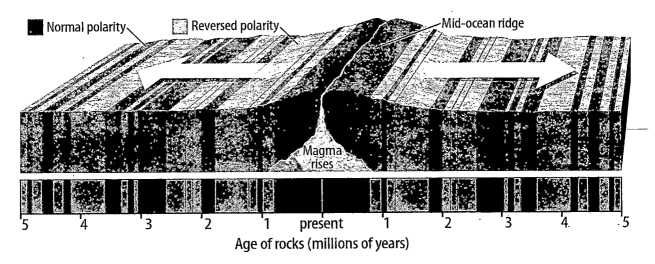

■ Normal polarity ☐ Reversed polarity — Mid-ocean ridge

Magma rises

5   4   3   2   1   present   1   2   3   4   5

Age of rocks (millions of years)

Evidence to Support the Theory

How did scientists prove the theory of seafloor spreading? Scientists studied magnetic minerals in rocks from the seafloor. They used a magnetometer (mag nuh TAH muh tur) to measure and record the magnetic signature of these rocks. These measurements revealed a surprising pattern. Scientists have discovered parallel magnetic stripes on either side of the mid-ocean ridge. Each pair of stripes has a similar composition, age, and magnetic character. Each magnetic stripe in **Figure 10** represents crust that formed and magnetized at a mid-ocean ridge during a period of either normal or reversed polarity. The pairs of magnetic stripes confirm that the ocean crust formed at mid-ocean ridges is carried away from the center of the ridges in opposite directions.

 Reading Check How do magnetic minerals help support the theory of seafloor spreading?

Other measurements made on the seafloor confirm seafloor spreading. By drilling a hole into the seafloor and measuring the temperature beneath the surface, scientists can measure the amount of thermal energy leaving Earth. The measurements show that more thermal energy leaves Earth near mid-ocean ridges than is released from beneath the abyssal plains.

Additionally, sediment collected from the seafloor can be dated. Results show that the sediment closest to the mid-ocean ridge is younger than the sediment farther away from the ridge. Sediment ages as it is carried away. Sediment thickness also increases with distance away from the mid-ocean ridge.

ACADEMIC VOCABULARY
normal
(adjective) conforming to a type, standard, or regular pattern

FOLDABLES

Make a layered book using two sheets of notebook paper. Use the two pages to record your notes and the inside to illustrate seafloor spreading.

Seafloor Spreading

Visual Summary

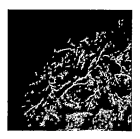

Lava erupts along mid-ocean ridges.

Mid-ocean ridges are large mountain ranges that extend throughout Earth's oceans.

A magnetic reversal occurs when Earth's magnetic field changes direction.

FOLDABLES

Use your lesson Foldable to review the lesson. Save your Foldable for the project at the end of the chapter.

What do you think NOW?

You first read the statements below at the beginning of the chapter.

3. The seafloor is flat.

4. Volcanic activity occurs only on the seafloor.

Did you change your mind about whether you agree or disagree with the statements? Rewrite any false statements to make them true.

Use Vocabulary

1 **Explain** how rocks on the seafloor record magnetic reversals over time.

2 **Diagram** the process of seafloor spreading.

3 **Use the term** *seafloor spreading* to explain how a mid-ocean ridge forms.

Understand Key Concepts

4 Oceanic crust forms
   A. at mid-ocean ridges.
   B. everywhere on the seafloor.
   C. on the abyssal plains.
   D. by magnetic reversals.

5 **Explain** why magnetic stripes on the seafloor are parallel to the mid-ocean ridge.

6 **Describe** how scientists can measure the depth to the seafloor.

Interpret Graphics

7 **Determine** Refer to the image above. Where is the youngest crust? Where is the oldest crust?

8 **Describe** how seafloor spreading helps to explain the continental drift hypothesis.

9 **Sequence Information** Copy and fill in the graphic organizer below to explain the steps in the formation of a mid-ocean ridge.

Critical Thinking

10 **Infer** why magnetic stripes in the Pacific Ocean are wider than in the Atlantic Ocean.

11 **Explain** why the thickness of seafloor sediments increases with increasing distance from the ocean ridge.

Image courtesy of Submarine Ring of Fire 2002 Exploration, NOAA-OE.

How do rocks on the seafloor vary with age away from a mid-ocean ridge?

Scientists discovered that new ocean crust forms at a mid-ocean ridge and spreads away from the ridge slowly over time. This process is called seafloor spreading. The age of the seafloor is one component that supports this theory.

Materials

vanilla yogurt
berry yogurt

foam board
(10 cm × 4 cm)

waxed paper

plastic spoon

Safety

Do not eat anything used in this lab.

Learn It

Scientists use **models** to represent real-world science. By creating a three-dimensional model of volcanic activity along the Mid-Atlantic Ridge, scientists can model the seafloor spreading process. They can then compare this process to the actual age of the seafloor. In this skill lab, you will investigate how the age of rocks on the seafloor changes with distance away from the ridge.

Try It

1. Read and complete a lab safety form.

2. Lay the sheet of waxed paper flat on the lab table. Place two spoonfuls of vanilla yogurt in a straight line near the center of the waxed paper, leaving it lumpy and full.

3. Lay the two pieces of foam board over the yogurt, leaving a small opening in the middle. Push the foam boards together and down, so the yogurt oozes up and over each of the foam boards.

4. Pull the foam boards apart and add a new row of two spoonfuls of berry yogurt down the middle. Lift the boards and place them partly over the new row. Push them together gently. Observe the outer edges of the new yogurt while you are moving the foam boards together.

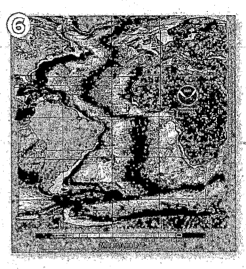

5. Repeat step 4 with one more spoonful of vanilla yogurt. Then repeat again with one more spoonful of berry yogurt.

Apply It

6. Compare the map and the model. Where is the Mid-Atlantic Ridge on the map? Where is it represented in your model?

7. Which of your yogurt strips matches today on this map? And millions of years ago?

8. How do scientists determine the ages of different parts of the ocean floor?

9. **Conclude** What happened to the yogurt when you added more?

10. 🔑 **Key Concept** What happens to the material already on the ocean floor when magma erupts along a mid-ocean ridge?

Reading Guide

Key Concepts 🗝

ESSENTIAL QUESTIONS

- What is the theory of plate tectonics?
- What are the three types of plate boundaries?
- Why do tectonic plates move?

Vocabulary

plate tectonics p. 323

lithosphere p. 324

divergent plate boundary p. 325

transform plate boundary p. 325

convergent plate boundary p. 325

subduction p. 325

convection p. 328

ridge push p. 329

slab pull p. 329

  Multilingual eGlossary

7.ESS.3, SEPS.2, SEPS.3, SEPS.4, SEPS.5, SEPS.8, 6-8. LST.1.1, 6-8.LST.1.2, 6-8.LST.2.2, 6-8.LST.3.2, 6-8.LST.5.1, 6-8.LST.5.2, 6-8.LST.7.3

The Theory of Plate Tectonics

Inquiry) How did these islands form?

The photograph shows a chain of active volcanoes. These volcanoes make up the Aleutian Islands of Alaska. Just south of these volcanic islands is a 6-km deep ocean trench. Why did these volcanic mountains form in a line? Can you predict where volcanoes are? Are they related to plate tectonics?

Launch Lab

Can you determine density by observing buoyancy?

Density is the measure of an object's mass relative to its volume. Buoyancy is the upward force a liquid places on objects that are immersed in it. If you immerse objects with equal densities into liquids that have different densities, the buoyant forces will be different. An object will sink or float depending on the density of the liquid compared to the object. Earth's layers differ in density. These layers float or sink depending on density and buoyant force.

1. Read and complete a lab safety form.

2. Obtain four **test tubes.** Place them in a **test-tube rack.** Add **water** to one test tube until it is ¾ full.

3. Repeat with the other test tubes using **vegetable oil** and **glucose syrup.** One test tube should remain empty.

4. Drop **beads** of equal density into each test tube. Observe what the object does when immersed in each liquid. Record your observations in your Science Journal.

Think About This

1. How did you determine which liquid has the highest density?

2. **Key Concept** What happens when layers of rock with different densities collide?

The Plate Tectonics Theory

When you blow into a balloon, the balloon expands and its surface area also increases. Similarly, if oceanic crust continues to form at mid-ocean ridges and is never destroyed, Earth's surface area should increase. However, this is not the case. The older crust must be destroyed somewhere–but where?

By the late 1960s a more complete theory, called plate tectonics, was proposed. The theory of **plate tectonics** states that *Earth's surface is made of rigid slabs of rock, or plates, that move with respect to each other.* This new theory suggested that Earth's surface is divided into large plates of rigid rock. Each plate moves over Earth's hot and semi-plastic mantle.

Key Concept Check What is plate tectonics?

Geologists use the word *tectonic* to describe the forces that shape Earth's surface and the rock structures that form as a result. Plate tectonics provides an explanation for the occurrence of earthquakes and volcanic eruptions. When plates separate on the seafloor, earthquakes result and a mid-ocean ridge forms. When plates come together, one plate can dive under the other, causing earthquakes and creating a chain of volcanoes. When plates slide past each other, earthquakes can result.

Hutchings Photography/Digital Light Source

North
American
Plate

Juan
de Fuca
Plate

Cocos
Plate

Pacific
Plate

Nazca
Plate

Caribbean
Plate

South
American
Plate

Scotia Plate

Eurasian Plate

Arabian
Plate

African Plate

Antarctic Plate

North
American
Plate

Philippine
Plate

Pacific Plate

Indo-Australian
Plate

← → Divergent
boundary
→← Convergent
boundary
—— Plate
boundary

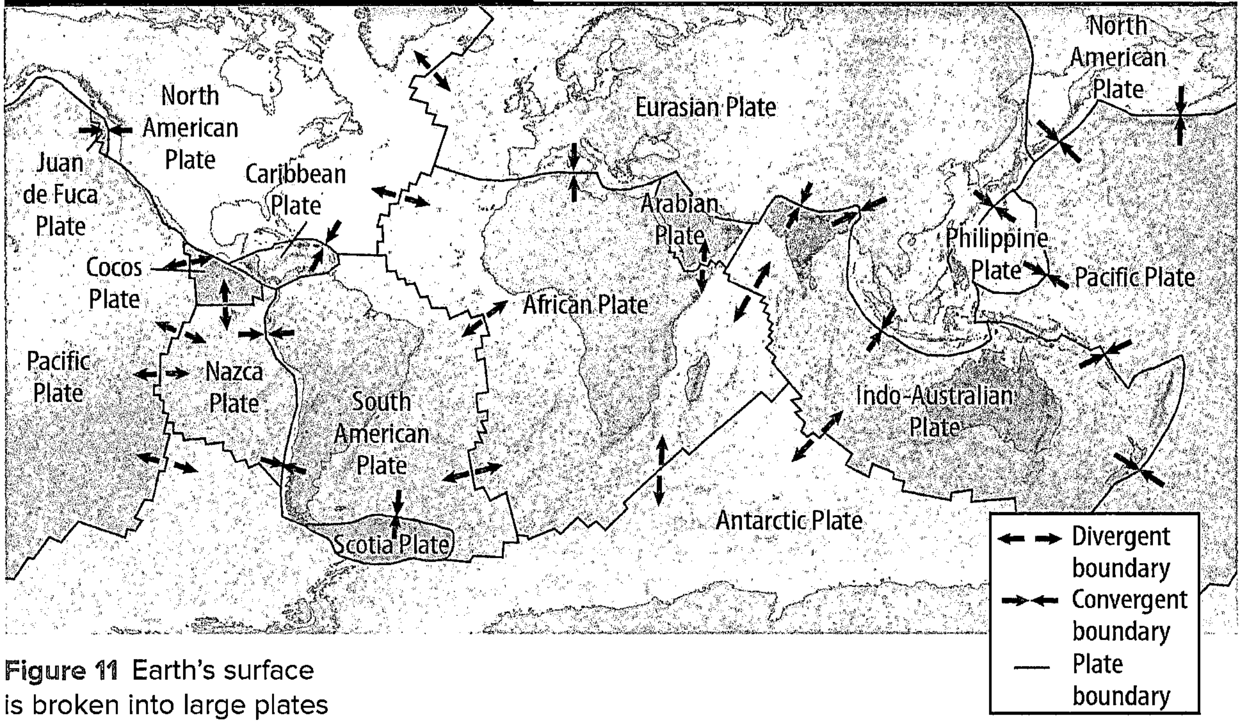

Figure 11 Earth's surface is broken into large plates that fit together like pieces of a giant jigsaw puzzle. The arrows show the general direction of movement of each plate.

Tectonic Plates

You read on the previous page that the theory of plate tectonics states that Earth's surface is divided into rigid plates that move relative to one another. These plates are "floating" on top of a hot and semi-plastic mantle. The map in **Figure 11** illustrates Earth's major plates and the boundaries that define them. The Pacific Plate is the largest plate. The Juan de Fuca Plate is one of the smallest plates. It is between the North American and Pacific Plates. Notice the boundaries that run through the oceans. Many of these boundaries mark the positions of the mid-ocean ridges.

Earth's outermost layers are cold and rigid compared to the layers within Earth's interior. *The cold and rigid outermost rock layer is called the* **lithosphere.** It is made up of the crust and the uppermost mantle. The lithosphere is thin below mid-ocean ridges and thick below continents. Earth's tectonic plates are large pieces of lithosphere. These lithospheric plates fit together like the pieces of a giant jigsaw puzzle.

The layer of Earth below the lithosphere is called the asthenosphere (as THEN uh sfihr). This layer is so hot that although it is solid, it behaves like a plastic material. This enables Earth's plates to move because the hotter, plastic mantle material beneath them can flow. The interactions between lithosphere and asthenosphere help to explain plate tectonics.

✅ **Reading Check** What are Earth's outermost layers called?

SCIENCE USE V. COMMON USE

plastic
Science Use capable of being molded or changing shape without breaking

Common Use any of numerous organic, synthetic, or processed materials made into objects

Plate Boundaries

Place two books side by side and imagine each book represents a tectonic plate. A plate boundary exists where the books meet. How many different ways can you move the books with respect to each other? You can pull the books apart, you can push the books together, and you can slide the books past one another. Earth's tectonic plates move in much the same way.

Divergent Plate Boundaries

Mid-ocean ridges are located along divergent plate boundaries. A **divergent plate boundary** *forms where two plates separate.* When the seafloor spreads at a mid-ocean ridge, lava erupts, cools, and forms new oceanic crust. Divergent plate boundaries can also exist in the middle of a continent. They pull continents apart and form rift valleys. The East African Rift is an example of a continental rift.

Transform Plate Boundaries

The famous San Andreas Fault in California is an example of a transform plate boundary. A **transform plate boundary** *forms where two plates slide past each other.* As they move past each other, the plates can get stuck and stop moving. Stress builds up where the plates are "stuck." Eventually, the stress is too great and the rocks break, suddenly moving apart. This results in a rapid release of energy as earthquakes.

Convergent Plate Boundaries

Convergent plate boundaries *form where two plates collide. The denser plate sinks below the more buoyant plate in a process called* **subduction.** The area where a denser plate descends into Earth along a convergent plate boundary is called a subduction zone.

When two oceanic plates collide, the older and denser oceanic plate will subduct beneath the younger oceanic plate. This creates a deep ocean trench and a line of volcanoes called an island arc. This process can also occur when an oceanic plate and a continental plate collide. The denser oceanic plate subducts under the edge of the continent. This creates a deep ocean trench. A line of volcanoes forms above the subducting plate on the edge of the continent.

Over time, an oceanic plate can be completely subducted, dragging an attached continent behind it. When two continents collide, neither plate is subducted, and mountains such as the Himalayas in southern Asia form from uplifted rock. **Table 1** on the next page summarizes the interactions of Earth's tectonic plates.

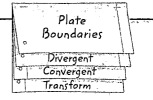

FOLDABLES

Make a layered book using two sheets of notebook paper. Use it to organize information about the different types of plate boundaries and the features that form there.

Plate Boundaries
Divergent
Convergent
Transform

WORD ORIGIN ············

subduction
from Latin *subductus*, means "to lead under, removal"

 Key Concept Check What are the three types of plate boundaries?

Table 1 The direction of motion of Earth's plates creates a variety of features at the boundaries between the plates.

▷ Animation

Table 1 Interactions of Earth's Tectonic Plates

Plate Boundary	Relative Motion	Example
Divergent plate boundary When two plates separate a divergent plate boundary forms. This process occurs where the seafloor spreads along a mid-ocean ridge, forming new crust and hydrothermal vents, as shown to the right. This process can also occur in the middle of continents and is referred to as continental rifting.	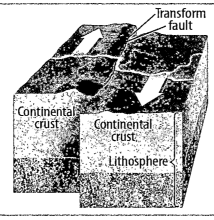	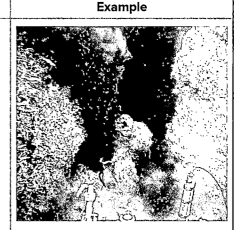
Transform plate boundary Two plates slide horizontally past one another along a transform plate boundary. Earthquakes are common along this type of plate boundary. The San Andreas Fault, shown to the right, is part of the transform plate boundary that extends along the coast of California.	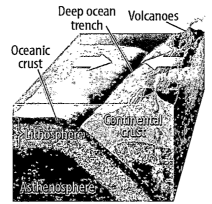	
Convergent plate boundary (ocean-to-continent) When an oceanic and a continental plate collide, they form a convergent plate boundary. The denser plate will subduct. A volcanic mountain, such as Mount Rainier in the Cascade Mountains, forms along the edge of the continent. This process can also occur where two oceanic plates collide, and the denser plate is subducted.	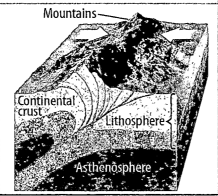	
Convergent plate boundary (continent-to-continent) Convergent plate boundaries can also occur where two continental plates collide. Because both plates are equally dense, neither plate will subduct. Both plates uplift and deform. This creates huge mountains like the Himalayas, shown to the right.		

Evidence for Plate Tectonics

When Wegener proposed the continental drift hypothesis, the technology used to measure how fast the continents move today wasn't yet available. Recall that continents move apart or come together at speeds of a few centimeters per year. This is about the length of a small paperclip.

Today, scientists can measure how fast continents move. A network of satellites orbiting Earth monitors plate motion. By keeping track of the distance between these satellites and Earth, it is possible to locate and determine how fast a tectonic plate moves. This network of satellites is called the Global Positioning System (GPS).

The theory of plate tectonics also provides an explanation for why earthquakes and volcanoes occur in certain places. Because plates are rigid, tectonic activity occurs where plates meet. When plates separate, collide, or slide past each other along a plate boundary, stress builds. A rapid release of energy can result in earthquakes. Volcanoes form where plates separate along a mid-ocean ridge or a continental rift or collide along a subduction zone. Mountains can form where two continents collide. **Figure 12** illustrates the relationship between plate boundaries and the occurrence of earthquakes and volcanoes. Refer back to the lesson opener photo. Find these islands on the map. Are they located near a plate boundary?

 Key Concept Check How are earthquakes and volcanoes related to the theory of plate tectonics?

Figure 12 Notice that most earthquakes and volcanoes occur near plate boundaries.

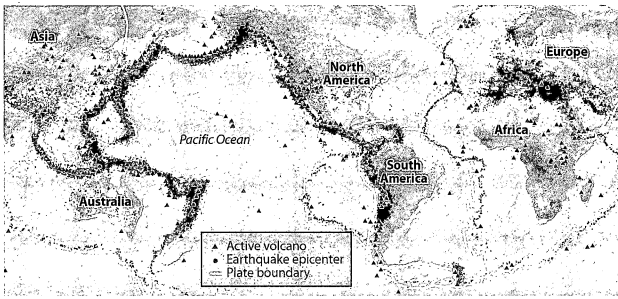

Active volcano
Earthquake epicenter
Plate boundary

Asia
Europe
North America
Pacific Ocean
Africa
South America
Australia

Visual Check Do earthquakes and volcanoes occur anywhere away from plate boundaries?

Plate Motion

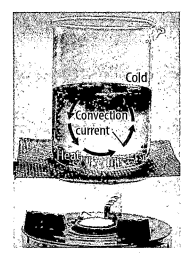

 Personal Tutor

Figure 13 When water is heated, it expands. Less dense heated water rises because the colder water sinks, forming convection currents.

The main objection to Wegener's continental drift hypothesis was that he could not explain why or how continents move. Scientists now understand that continents move because the asthenosphere moves underneath the lithosphere.

Convection Currents

You are probably already familiar with the process of **convection,** *the circulation of material caused by differences in temperature and density.* For example, the upstairs floors of homes and buildings are often warmer. This is because hot air rises while dense, cold air sinks. Look at **Figure 13** to see convection in action.

 Reading Check What causes convection?

Plate tectonic activity is related to convection in the mantle, as shown in **Figure 14.** Radioactive elements, such as uranium, thorium, and potassium, heat Earth's interior. When materials such as solid rock are heated, they expand and become less dense. Hot mantle material rises upward and comes in contact with Earth's crust. Thermal energy is transferred from hot mantle material to the colder surface above. As the mantle cools, it becomes denser and then sinks, forming a convection current. These currents in the asthenosphere act like a conveyor belt moving the lithosphere above.

Key Concept Check Why do tectonic plates move?

MiniLab

20 minutes

How do changes in density cause motion?

Convection currents drive plate motion. Material near the base of the mantle is heated, which decreases its density. This material then rises to the base of the crust, where it cools, increasing in density and sinking.

1. Read and complete a lab safety form.
2. Copy the table to the right into your Science Journal and add a row for each minute. Record your observations.
3. Pour 100 mL of **carbonated water** or **clear soda** into a **beaker** or a **clear glass.**
4. Drop five **raisins** into the water. Observe the path that the raisins follow for 5 minutes.

Time Interval	Observations
First minute	
Second minute	
Third minute	

Analyze and Conclude

1. **Observe** Describe each raisin's motion.

2. **Key Concept** How does the behavior of the raisin model compare to the motion in Earth's mantle?

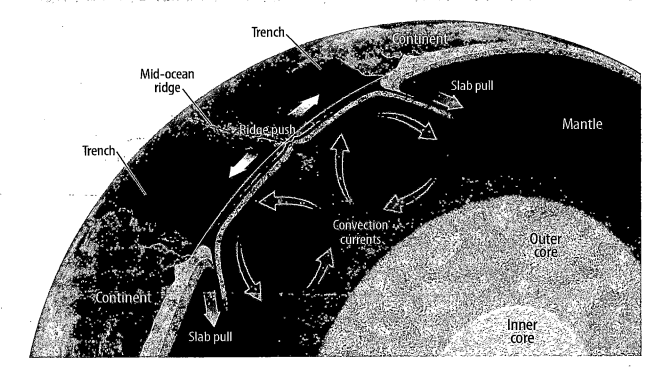

Forces Causing Plate Motion

How can something as massive as the Pacific Plate move? **Figure 14** shows the processes that determine how convection affects the movement of tectonic plates.

Basal Drag Convection currents in the mantle produce a force that causes motion called basal drag. Notice in **Figure 14** how convection currents in the asthenosphere circulate and drag the lithosphere similar to the way a conveyor belt moves items along at a supermarket checkout.

Ridge Push Recall that mid-ocean ridges have greater elevation than the surrounding seafloor. Because mid-ocean ridges are higher, gravity pulls the surrounding rocks down and away from the ridge. *Rising mantle material at mid-ocean ridges creates the potential for plates to move away from the ridge with a force called* **ridge push**. Ridge push moves lithosphere in opposite directions away from the mid-ocean ridge.

Slab Pull As you read earlier in this lesson, when tectonic plates collide, the denser plate will sink into the mantle along a subduction zone. This plate is called a slab. Because the slab is old and cold, it is denser than the surrounding mantle and will sink. *As a slab sinks, it pulls on the rest of the plate with a force called* **slab pull**. Slab pull is thought to be a more significant force than ridge push in moving tectonic plates.

Figure 14 Convection occurs in the mantle underneath Earth's tectonic plates. Three forces act on plates to make them move: basal drag from convection currents, ridge push at mid-ocean ridges, and slab pull from subducting plates.

Ø **Visual Check** What is happening to a plate that is undergoing slab pull?

Use Proportions

The plates along the Mid-Atlantic Ridge spread at an average rate of 2.5 cm/y. How long will it take the plates to spread 1 m? Use proportions to find the answer.

1 Convert the distance to the same unit.

$$1 \text{ m} = 100 \text{ cm}$$

2 Set up a proportion:

$$\frac{2.5 \text{ cm}}{1 \text{ y}} = \frac{100 \text{ cm}}{x \text{ y}}$$

3 Cross multiply and solve for *x* as follows:

$$2.5 \text{ cm} \times x\text{y} = 100 \text{ cm} \times 1 \text{ y}$$

4 Divide both sides by 2.5 cm.

$$x = \frac{100 \text{ cm y}}{2.5 \text{ cm}}$$

$$x = 40 \text{ y}$$

Practice

The Eurasian plate travels the slowest, at about 0.7 cm/y. How long would it take the plate to travel 3 m?

(1 m = 100 cm)

 Math Practice

 Personal Tutor

A Theory in Progress

Plate tectonics has become the unifying theory of geology. It explains the connection between continental drift and the formation and destruction of crust along plate boundaries. It also helps to explain the occurrence of earthquakes, volcanoes, and mountains.

The investigation that Wegener began nearly a century ago is still being revised. Several unanswered questions remain.

• Why is Earth the only known planet in the solar system that currently has plate tectonic activity? Different hypotheses have been proposed to explain this. Scientists have found evidence of plate tectonics in Mars's past.

• Why do some earthquakes and volcanoes occur far away from plate boundaries? Perhaps it is because the plates are not perfectly rigid. Different thicknesses and weaknesses exist within the plates. Also, the mantle is much more active than scientists originally understood.

• What forces dominate plate motion? Currently accepted models suggest that convection currents occur in the mantle. However, there is no way to measure or observe them.

• What will scientists investigate next? **Figure 15** shows an image produced by a new technique called anisotropy that creates a 3-D image of seismic wave velocities in a subduction zone. This developing technology might help scientists better understand the processes that occur within the mantle and along plate boundaries.

 Reading Check Why does the theory of plate tectonics continue to change?

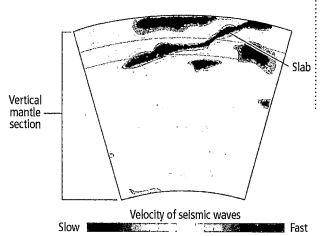

Velocity of seismic waves
Slow — Fast

Vertical mantle section

Slab

Figure 15 Seismic waves were used to produce this tomography scan. These colors show a subducting plate. The blue colors represent rigid materials with faster seismic wave velocities.

Online Quiz
Virtual Lab

Visual Summary

Tectonic plates are made of cold and rigid slabs of rock.

Mantle convection—the circulation of mantle material due to density differences—drives plate motion.

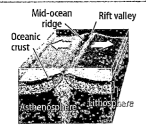

The three types of plate boundaries are divergent, convergent, and transform boundaries.

FOLDABLES

Use your lesson Foldable to review the lesson. Save your Foldable for the project at the end of the chapter.

What do you think NOW?

You first read the statements below at the beginning of the chapter.

5. Continents drift across a molten mantle.

6. Mountain ranges can form when continents collide.

Did you change your mind about whether you agree or disagree with the statements? Rewrite any false statements to make them true.

Use Vocabulary

1 The theory that proposes that Earth's surface is broken into moving, rigid plates is called

_____.

Understand Key Concepts

2 **Compare and contrast** the geological activity— that occurs along the three types of plate boundaries.

3 **Explain** why mantle convection occurs.

4 Tectonic plates move because of
 A. convection currents.
 B. Earth's increasing size.
 C. magnetic reversals.
 D. volcanic activity.

Interpret Graphics

5 **Identify** Name the type of boundary between the Eurasian Plate and the North American Plate and between the Nazca Plate and South American Plate.

6 **Determine Cause and Effect** Copy and fill in the graphic organizer below to list the cause and effects of convection currents.

Critical Thinking

7 **Explain** why earthquakes occur at greater depths along convergent plate boundaries.

Math Skills   Math Practice

8 Two plates in the South Pacific separate at an average rate of 15 cm/y. How far will they have separated after 5,000 years?

Movement of Plate Boundaries

Earth's surface is broken into 12 major tectonic plates. Plates may collide and crumple or fold to make mountains. One plate may subduct under another, forming volcanoes. They may move apart and form a mid-ocean ridge, or they may slide past each other causing earthquakes. This investigation models plate movements.

Question

What happens where two plates come together?

Procedure

Part I

1. Read and complete a lab safety form.
2. Obtain the materials from your teacher.
3. Break a graham cracker along the perforation line into two pieces.
4. Lay the pieces side by side on a piece of waxed paper.
5. Slide crackers in opposite directions so that the edges of the crackers rub together.

Part II

6. Place two new graham crackers side by side but not touching.
7. In the space between the crackers, add several drops of water.
8. Slide the crackers toward each other and observe what happens.

Part III

9. Place a spoonful of frosting on the waxed-paper square.
10. Place two graham crackers on top of the frosting so that they touch.
11. Push the crackers down and spread them apart in one motion.

Materials

graham crackers

waxed paper (four 10×10-cm squares)

dropper

frosting

plastic spoon

Safety

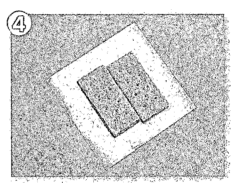

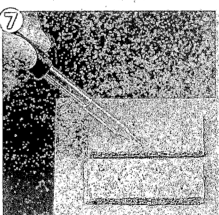

Analyze and Conclude

⑫ Analyze the movement of the crackers in each of your models.

Part I

⑬ What type of plate boundary do the graham crackers in this model represent?

⑭ What do the crumbs in the model represent?

⑮ Did you feel or hear anything when the crackers moved past each other? Explain.

⑯ How does this model simulate an earthquake?

Part II

⑰ What does the water in this model represent?

⑱ What type of plate boundary do the graham crackers in this model represent?

⑲ Why didn't one graham cracker slide beneath the other in this model?

Part III

⑳ What type of plate boundary do the graham crackers in this model represent?

㉑ What does the frosting represent?

㉒ What shape does the frosting create when the crackers move?

㉓ What is the formation formed from the crackers and frosting?

Communicate Your Results

Create a flip book of one of the boundaries to show a classmate who was absent. Show how each boundary plate moves and the results of those movements.

Place a graham cracker and a piece of cardboard side by side. Slide the two pieces toward each other. What type of plate boundary does this model represent? How is this model different from the three that you observed in the lab?

Lab Tips

☑ Use fresh graham crackers.

☑ Slightly heat frosting to make it more fluid for experiments.

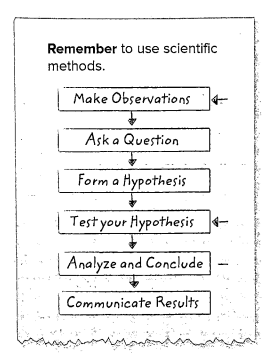

Remember to use scientific methods.

> Make Observations

> Ask a Question

> Form a Hypothesis

> Test your Hypothesis

> Analyze and Conclude

> Communicate Results

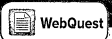
 The theory of plate tectonics states that Earth's lithosphere is broken up into rigid plates that move over Earth's surface.

Key Concepts Summary

Vocabulary

Lesson 1: The Continental Drift Hypothesis

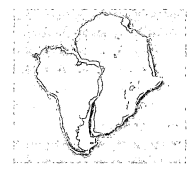

- The puzzle piece fit of continents, fossil evidence, climate, rocks, and mountain ranges supports the hypothesis of **continental drift.**
- Scientists were skeptical of continental drift because Wegener could not explain the mechanism for movement.

Pangaea p. 307
continental drift p. 307

Lesson 2: Development of a Theory

- **Seafloor spreading** provides a mechanism for continental drift.
- Seafloor spreading occurs at **mid-ocean ridges.**
- Evidence of **magnetic reversal** in rock, thermal energy trends, and the discovery of seafloor spreading all contributed to the development of the theory of plate tectonics.

mid-ocean ridge p. 315
seafloor spreading p. 316
normal polarity p. 318
magnetic reversal p. 318
reversed polarity p. 318

Lesson 3: The Theory of Plate Tectonics

- Types of plate boundaries, the location of earthquakes, volcanoes, and mountain ranges, and satellite measurement of plate motion support the theory of **plate tectonics.**
- Mantle **convection, ridge push,** and **slab pull** are the forces that cause plate motion. Radioactivity in the mantle and thermal energy from the core produce the energy for convection.

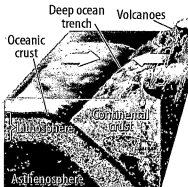

Deep ocean trench Volcanoes
Oceanic crust
Continental crust
Lithosphere
Asthenosphere

plate tectonics p. 323
lithosphere p. 324
divergent plate boundary p. 325
transform plate boundary p. 325
convergent plate boundary p. 325
subduction p. 325
convection p. 328
ridge push p. 329
slab pull p. 329

Personal Tutor

 Vocabulary eFlashcards
Vocabulary eGames

FOLDABLES

Chapter Project

Assemble your lesson Foldables as shown to make a Chapter Project. Use the project to review what you have learned in this chapter.

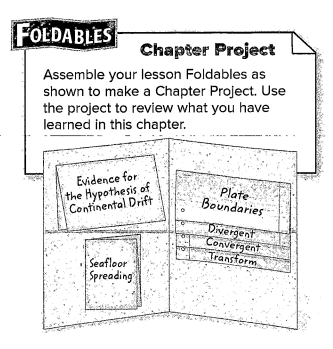

Evidence for the Hypothesis of Continental Drift

Seafloor Spreading

Plate Boundaries

Divergent
Convergent
Transform

Use Vocabulary

1. The process in which hot mantle rises and cold mantle sinks is called _____.

2. What is the plate tectonics theory?

3. What was Pangaea?

4. Identify the three types of plate boundaries and the relative motion associated with each type.

5. Magnetic reversals occur when _____.

6. Explain seafloor spreading in your own words.

Link Vocabulary and Key Concepts

 Interactive Concept Map

Copy this concept map, and then use vocabulary terms from the previous page to complete the concept map.

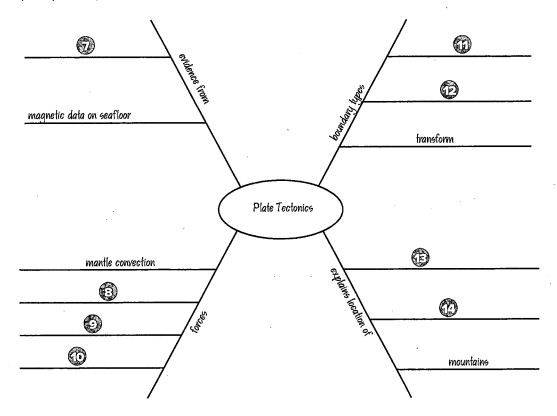

7.

magnetic data on seafloor

mantle convection

8.

9.

10.

11.

12.

transform

13.

14.

mountains

Plate Tectonics

evidence from

boundary types

forces

explains location of

Understand Key Concepts

1 Alfred Wegener proposed the _____ hypothesis.
   A. continental drift
   B. plate tectonics
   C. ridge push
   D. seafloor spreading

2 Ocean crust is
   A. made from submerged continents.
   B. magnetically produced crust.
   C. produced at the mid-ocean ridge.
   D. produced at all plate boundaries.

3 What technologies did scientists NOT use to develop the theory of seafloor spreading?
   A. echo-sounding measurements
   B. GPS (global positioning system)
   C. magnetometer measurements
   D. seafloor thickness measurements

4 The picture below shows Pangaea's position on Earth approximately 280 million years ago. Where did geologists discover glacial features associated with a cooler climate?
   A. Antarctica
   B. Asia
   C. North America
   D. South America

Pangaea

5 Mid-ocean ridges are associated with
   A. convergent plate boundaries.
   B. divergent plate boundaries.
   C. hot spots.
   D. transform plate boundaries.

6 Two plates of equal density form mountain ranges along
   A. continent-to-continent convergent boundaries.
   B. ocean-to-continent convergent boundaries.
   C. divergent boundaries.
   D. transform boundaries.

7 Which type of plate boundary is shown in the figure below?
   A. convergent boundary
   B. divergent boundary
   C. subduction zone
   D. transform boundary

8 What happens to Earth's magnetic field over time?
   A. It changes polarity.
   B. It continually strengthens.
   C. It stays the same.
   D. It weakens and eventually disappears.

9 Which of Earth's outermost layers includes the crust and the upper mantle?
   A. asthenosphere
   B. lithosphere
   C. mantle
   D. outer core

Critical Thinking

10 Evaluate The oldest seafloor in the Atlantic Ocean is located closest to the edge of continents, as shown in the image below. Explain how this age can be used to figure out when North America first began to separate from Europe.

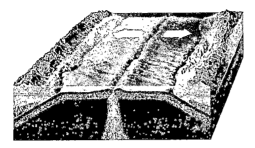

11 Examine the evidence used to develop the theory of plate tectonics. How has new technology strengthened the theory?

12 Explain Sediments deposited by glaciers in Africa are surprising because Africa is now warm. How does the hypothesis of continental drift explain these deposits?

13 Draw a diagram to show subduction of an oceanic plate beneath a continental plate along a convergent plate boundary. Explain why volcanoes form along this type of plate boundary.

14 Infer Warm peanut butter is easier to spread than cold peanut butter. How does knowing this help you understand why the mantle is able to deform in a plastic manner?

Writing in Science

15 Predict If continents continue to move in the same direction over the next 200 million years, how might the appearance of landmasses change? Write a paragraph to explain the possible positions of landmasses in the future. Based on your understanding of the plate tectonic theory, is it possible that new supercontinents will form in the future?

REVIEW THE BIG IDEA

16 What is the theory of plate tectonics? Distinguish between continental drift, seafloor spreading, and plate tectonics. What evidence was used to support the theory of plate tectonics?

17 Use the image below to interpret how the theory of plate tectonics helps to explain the formation of huge mountains like the Himalayas.

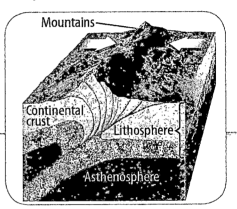

Math Skills Math Practice

Use Proportions

18 Mountains on a convergent plate boundary may grow at a rate of 3 mm/y. How long would it take a mountain to grow to a height of 3,000 m? (1 m = 1,000 mm)

19 The North American Plate and the Pacific Plate have been sliding horizontally past each other along the San Andreas fault zone for about 10 million years. The plates move at an average rate of about 5 cm/y.

a. How far have the plates traveled, assuming a constant rate, during this time?

b. How far has the plate traveled in kilometers? (1 km = 100,000 cm)

Record your answers on the answer sheet provided by your teacher or on a sheet of paper.

Multiple Choice

Use the diagram below to answer questions 1 and 2.

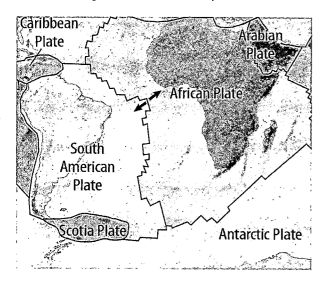

1 In the diagram above, what does the irregular line between tectonic plates represent?

 A abyssal plain

 B island chain

 C mid-ocean ridge

 D polar axis

2 What do the arrows indicate?

 A magnetic polarity

 B ocean flow

 C plate movement

 D volcanic eruption

3 What evidence helped to support the theory of seafloor spreading?

 A magnetic equality

 B magnetic interference

 C magnetic north

 D magnetic polarity

4 Which plate tectonic process creates a deep ocean trench?

 A conduction

 B deduction

 C induction

 D subduction

5 What causes plate motion?

 A convection in Earth's mantle

 B currents in Earth's oceans

 C reversal of Earth's polarity

 D rotation on Earth's axis

6 New oceanic crust forms and old oceanic crust moves away from a mid-ocean ridge during

 A continental drift.

 B magnetic reversal.

 C normal polarity.

 D seafloor spreading.

Use the diagram below to answer question 7.

7 What is the name of Alfred Wegener's ancient supercontinent pictured in the diagram above?

 A Caledonia

 B continental drift

 C *Glossopteris*

 D Pangaea

Use the diagram below to answer question 8.

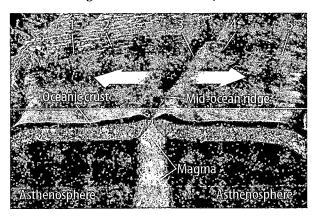

8 The numbers in the diagram represent seafloor rock. Which represent the oldest rock?

  A 1 and 5

  B 2 and 4

  C 3 and 4

  D 4 and 5

9 Which part of the seafloor contains the thickest sediment layer?

  A abyssal plain

  B deposition band

  C mid-ocean ridge

  D tectonic zone

10 What type of rock forms when lava cools and crystallizes on the seafloor?

  A a fossil

  B a glacier

  C basalt

  D magma

Constructed Response

Use the table below to answer questions 11 and 12.

Plate Boundary	Location

11 In the table above, identify the three types of plate boundaries. Then describe a real-world location for each type.

12 Create a diagram to show plate motion along one type of plate boundary. Label the diagram and draw arrows to indicate the direction of plate motion.

13 Identify and explain all the evidence that Wegener used to help support his continental drift hypothesis.

14 Why was continental drift so controversial during Alfred Wegener's time? What explanation was necessary to support his hypothesis?

15 How did scientists prove the theory of seafloor spreading?

16 If new oceanic crust constantly forms along mid-ocean ridges, why isn't Earth's total surface area increasing?

NEED EXTRA HELP?																
If You Missed Question...	1	2	3	4	5	6	7	8	9	10	11	12	13	14	15	16
Go to Lesson...	3	3	2	3	3	2	1	2	2	2	3	3	1	1	2	3

Chapter 10

7.ESS.3, SEPS.1, SEPS.2, SEPS.3, SEPS.5, SEPS.8, 6-8.LST.4.1, 6-8.LST.5.2, 6-8. LST.7.1, 6-8.LST.7.3

Earth Dynamics

THE BIG IDEA How is Earth's surface shaped by plate motion?

Inquiry) Why is Mount Everest different?

You might think that seashells are only found near oceans. But some of the rocks in Mount Everest contain seashells from the ocean floor!

• How do you think seashells got to the top of Mount Everest?

• What are the different ways tectonic plates move to make mountains such as these—or deep-sea trenches, valleys, and plateaus?

• How is Earth's surface shaped by plate motion?

©Imageshop/Alamy

Get Ready to Read

What do you think?

Before you read, decide if you agree or disagree with each of these statements. As you read this chapter, see if you change your mind about any of the statements.

1. Forces created by plate motion are small and do not deform or break rocks.

2. Plate motion causes only horizontal motion of continents.

3. New landforms are created only at plate boundaries.

4. The tallest and deepest landforms are created at plate boundaries.

5. Metamorphic rocks formed deep below Earth's surface sometimes can be located near the tops of mountains.

6. Mountain ranges can form over long periods of time through repeated collisions between plates.

7. The centers of continents are flat and old.

8. Continents are continually shrinking because of erosion.

Mc Graw Hill Education connectED

Your one-stop online resource
connectED.mcgraw-hill.com

 LearnSmart™

 Project-Based Learning Activities

 Chapter Resources Files, Reading Essentials, Get Ready to Read, Quick Vocabulary

 Lab Manuals, Safety Videos, Virtual Labs & Other Tools

 Animations, Videos, Interactive Tables

 Vocabulary, Multilingual eGlossary, Vocab eGames, Vocab eFlashcards

 Self-checks, Quizzes, Tests

Personal Tutors

Lesson 1

Reading Guide

Key Concepts

ESSENTIAL QUESTIONS

- How do continents move?
- What forces can change rocks?
- How does plate motion affect the rock cycle?

Vocabulary

isostasy p. 344

subsidence p. 345

uplift p. 345

compression p. 345

tension p. 345

shear p. 345

strain p. 346

 Multilingual eGlossary

 Science Video

SEPS.2, SEPS.3, SEPS.5, 6-8.LST.4.1, 6-8.LST.5.2, 6-8. LST.7.3

Forces That Shape Earth

Inquiry Can rocks talk?

This campsite in Thingvellir, Iceland, can tell a story about Earth if you ask the right questions. Why is this cliff next to a flat, grassy valley? How did it get like this? Has it always been this way? You can find some answers by looking at the forces that shape Earth.

Do rocks bend?

As Earth's continents move, rocks get smashed between them and bend or break. Land can take on different shapes, depending on the temperature and composition of the rocks and the size and direction of the force.

1. Read and complete a lab safety form.

2. Spread out a **paper towel** on your work area, and place an unwrapped **candy bar** on the paper towel.

3. Gently pull on the edges of your candy bar. Observe any changes to the candy bar. Draw your observations in your Science Journal.

4. Reassemble your candy bar and gently squeeze the two ends of your candy bar together. Draw your observations.

Think About This

1. How are the results of pulling and pushing different?

2. What would be different if the candy bar were warm? What if it were cold?

3. 🗝️ **Key Concept** What kinds of forces do you think can change rocks?

Plate Motion

How far is your school from the nearest large mountain? If you live in the west or along the east coast of the United States, you are probably close to mountains. In contrast, the central region of the United States is flat. Why are these regions so different?

The Rocky Mountains in the west are high and have sharp peaks, but the Appalachian Mountains in the east are lower and gently rounded, as shown in Figure 1.

📖 **Reading Check** How are the Rocky Mountains different from the Appalachian Mountains?

Mountains do not last forever. Weathering and erosion gradually wear them down. The Appalachian Mountains are shorter and smoother than the Rocky Mountains because they are older. They formed hundreds of millions of years ago. The Rockies formed just 50 to 100 million years ago.

Mountain ranges are produced by plate tectonics. The theory of plate tectonics states that Earth's surface is broken into rigid plates that move horizontally on Earth's more fluid upper mantle. Mountains, valleys, and other features form where plates collide, move away from each other, or slide past each other.

Rocky Mountains

Appalachian Mountains

Figure 1 The younger Rocky Mountains are high and have sharp peaks. The older Appalachian Mountains are low and gently rounded.

Vertical Motion

To understand how massive pieces of Earth can rise vertically and form mountainous regions, you need to understand the forces that produce vertical motion.

Balance in the Mantle

Think of an iceberg floating in water. The iceberg floats with its top above the water, but most of it is under the surface of the water, as shown in Figure 2. It floats this way because ice is less dense than water and because the mass of the ice equals the mass of the water it displaces, or pushes out of the way.

Similarly, continents rise above the seafloor because continental crust is made of rocks that are less dense than Earth's mantle. Continental crust displaces some of the mantle below it until an equilibrium, or balance, is reached. **Isostasy** (i SAHS tuh see) *is the equilibrium between continental crust and the denser mantle below it.* A continent floats on top of the mantle because the mass of the continent is equal to the mass of the mantle it displaces. Mountains act the same way on a smaller scale.

Reading Check What is isostasy?

Continental crust changes over time due to plate tectonics and erosion. If a part of the continental crust becomes thicker, it sinks deeper into the mantle, as shown in Figure 3. But it also rises higher until a balance is reached. This is why mountains are taller than the continental crust around them. Although the mountain is massive, it is still less dense than the mantle, so it "floats." Below Earth's surface, the mountain extends deep into the mantle. Above Earth's surface, the mountain rises above the surrounding continental crust. As illustrated in Figure 3, as a mountain erodes, the continental crust rises.

Figure 2 The massive lower portion of an iceberg is under water. Similarly, the root of a mountain extends deep into the mantle.

WORD ORIGIN

isostasy
from Greek *iso,* means "equal";
and Greek *stasy,* means "standing"

Maintaining Balance

 Personal Tutor

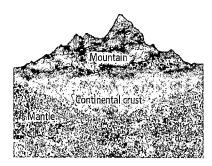 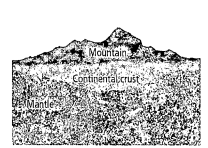 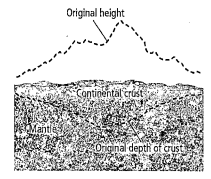

Original height

Original depth of crust

Figure 3 Over time, erosion and weathering remove the top of a mountain. To maintain isostasy, continents move up or down until the mass of the continent equals the mass of mantle it displaces.

©Ralph A. Clevenger/Corbis

Subsidence and Uplift

Much of North America was covered by glaciers more than 1 km thick 20,000 years ago. The weight of the ice pushed the crust downward into the mantle, as shown in **Figure 4.** *The downward vertical motion of Earth's surface is called* **subsidence.** When the ice melted and the water ran off, the isostatic balance was upset again. In response, the crust moved upward. *The upward vertical motion of Earth's surface is called* **uplift.** In the center of Hudson Bay in Canada, the land surface is still rising 1 cm each year as it moves toward isostatic balance.

 Key Concept Check What can cause Earth's surface to move up or down?

Horizontal Motion

Find a small rock and squeeze it. You've just applied force to the rock. Did its shape change? Did it break? Horizontal motion at plate boundaries applies much greater forces to rocks. Forces at plate boundaries are strong enough to break rocks or change the shape of rocks. The same forces also can form mountains.

Types of Stress

Stress is the force acting on a surface. There are three types of stress, as illustrated in **Figure 5.** *Squeezing stress is* **compression.** *Stress that pulls something apart is* **tension.** *Parallel forces acting in opposite directions are* **shear.** These are all stresses that can change rock as plates move horizontally.

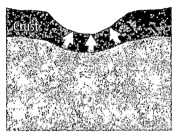
Glacial ice

Figure 4 The weight of a glacier pushes down on the land. When the glacier melts, the land rises until isostasy is restored.

Stresses

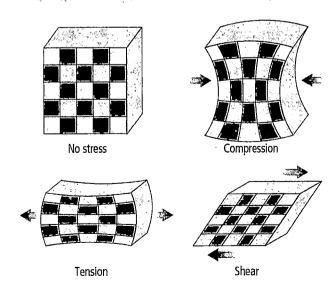

No stress

Compression

Tension

Shear

Figure 5 Compression, tension, and shear stresses cause rocks to change shape.

Figure 6 Compression can fold rocks. Tension can stretch them. Whether rocks go back to their original shape depends on the type of strain.

Visual Check Which of these two illustrations shows tension?

SCIENCE USE V. COMMON USE

plastic
Science Use capable of being molded

Common Use a commonly used synthetic material

Types of Strain

Rocks can change when stress acts on them. *A change in the shape of rock caused by stress is called* **strain.** There are two main types of strain.

Elastic strain does not permanently change, or deform, rocks. When stress is removed, rocks return to their original shapes. Elastic strain occurs when stresses are small or rocks are very strong. Plastic strain creates a permanent change in shape. Even if the stress is removed, the rocks do not go back to their original shapes. Plastic strain occurs when rocks are weak or hot.

 Reading Check Which type of strain permanently changes rocks?

Deformation in the Crust

In the hotter lower crust and upper mantle, rocks tend to deform plastically like putty. As illustrated in **Figure 6**, compression thickens and folds layers of rock. Tension stretches and thins layers of rock. In the colder, upper part of the crust, rocks can break before they deform plastically. When strain breaks rocks rather than just changing their shape, it is called failure. When rocks fail, fractures–or faults–form.

Key Concept Check What can cause rocks to thicken or fold?

MiniLab

10 minutes

What will happen?

If enough force is put on a rock, it will begin to strain, or change shape. Depending on the nature of the force and the rock, sometimes the rock will bend and sometimes it will break.

① Read and complete a lab safety form.

② Knead a piece of **putty,** and pull it apart slowly. Shape the putty into an oval ball. Try to pull it apart quickly. Record your observations in your Science Journal.

③ Shape your putty into an oval. Put your putty in a warm water bath for 2 min. Pull it apart. Record your observations.

④ Shape the putty into an oval shape. Put the putty in an **ice water** bath for 2 min. Pull it apart. Record your observations.

⑤ Try to break your putty by pulling on it and by pushing on it. Record your observations in your Science Journal.

Analyze and Conclude

1. **Summarize** the effects of rate of strain, temperature, and type of stress on the putty.

2. **Key Concept** Relate your experience with your putty model to the forces that can change rocks and to the conditions in Earth that will cause them to change.

Hutchings Photography/Digital Light Source

Plate Tectonics and the Rock Cycle

Although it might seem as if rocks are always the same, rocks are moving around—usually very slowly. Rocks never stop moving through the rock cycle, as illustrated in **Figure 7**. The theory of plate tectonics combined with uplift and subsidence explain why there is a rock cycle on Earth.

The forces that cause plate tectonics produce horizontal motion. Isostasy results in vertical motion within continents. Together, plate motion, uplift, and subsidence keep rocks moving through the rock cycle.

Uplift brings metamorphic and igneous rocks from deep in the crust up to the surface. At the surface, erosion breaks down rocks into sediment. Sediment gets buried by still more sediment. Buried sediment becomes sedimentary rocks. Pressure and temperature increase as rocks are buried, and eventually sedimentary rocks become metamorphic rocks. Subduction takes all types of rocks deep into Earth, where they can create new igneous or metamorphic rocks.

Key Concept Check How does plate motion affect the rock cycle?

 Animation

The Rock Cycle

Figure 7 Horizontal tectonic motion and vertical motion by uplift and subsidence help move rocks through the rock cycle.

Visual Check What happens to eroded sediment?

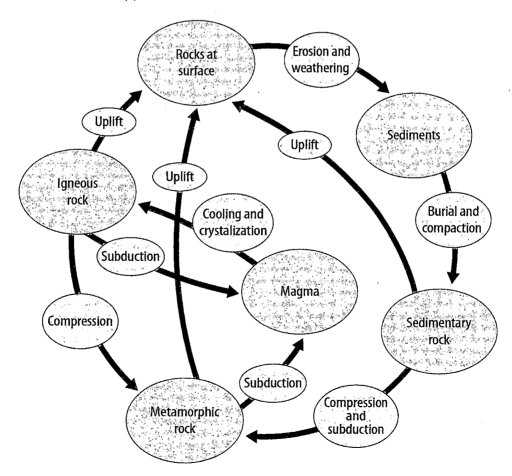

Visual Summary

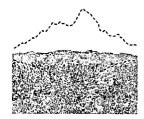

As a mountain is eroded away, the continent will rise until isostatic balance is restored.

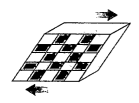

Different types of stress change rocks in different ways.

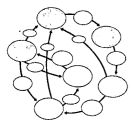

Horizontal and vertical motions are part of what keep rocks moving through the rock cycle.

FOLDABLES

Use your lesson Foldable to review the lesson. Save your Foldable for the project at the end of the chapter.

What do you think NOW?

You first read the statements below at the beginning of the chapter.

1. Forces created by plate motion are small and do not deform or break rocks.

2. Plate motion causes only horizontal motion of continents.

Did you change your mind about whether you agree or disagree with the statements? Rewrite any false statements to make them true.

Use Vocabulary

1 The opposite of uplift is _____.

2 The balance between the crust and the mantle below it is _____.

3 **Explain** the difference between the two types of strain.

Understand Key Concepts

4 **Describe** what happens to the elevation of the land surface when crust thickens.

5 **Name** one result of rock failure.

6 Which type of deformation is produced by compression of plastic crust?
  A. failure   **C.** folds
  B. faults   **D.** shear

Interpret Graphics

7 **List** Copy the graphic organizer below, and use it to show three types of stress.

8 **Identify** the type of stress that deformed the rocks shown below. What kind of strain resulted from the stress?

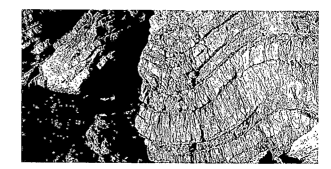

Critical Thinking

9 **Predict** what would happen to the height of the land surface of Antarctica if the ice sheet started to melt.

10 **Reflect** on the relationship between vertical and horizontal motion. How are they related? When are they not related?

Sinclair Stammers/Science Source

Materials

assorted
weights

cardboard

ruler

stopwatch

putty

Safety

🧤

Can you measure how stress deforms putty?

Scientists who study rocks study how the stress, or force applied to a rock, causes the rock to change shape, or deform. Because rocks are hard and they only deform with enormous forces at slow speeds, special equipment is needed to study rocks. In this lab, you will apply forces to putty and take measurements similar to ones scientists take on rocks.

Learn It

A scientist makes many decisions before beginning an investigation. Some decisions involve figuring out how to make the needed measurements. In this lab, you will **design** instruments and an **experiment** to measure stress and deformation of putty.

Try It

① Read and complete a lab safety form.

② Determine how you will use the materials provided to measure stress, deformation, and the time it takes to deform the putty.

③ Write a procedure in your Science Journal, and ask your teacher to approve your plan.

④ Test your procedures. Modify them if necessary.

⑤ Collect your data, and record them in a data table such as the one shown below.

Apply It

⑥ **Summarize** the relationship between stress and rate of deformation.

⑦ 🔑 **Key Concept** Relate the deformation of putty to how forces change rocks.

	Stress Applied	Measured Deformation	Measured Time	Rate of Deformation (deformation / time)
Trial 1				
Trial 2				

Landforms at Plate Boundaries

Reading Guide

Key Concepts

ESSENTIAL QUESTIONS

- What features form where two plates converge?
- What features form where two plates diverge?
- What features form where two plates slide past each other?

Vocabulary

ocean trench p. 352

volcanic arc p. 353

transform fault p. 355

fault zone p. 355

 Multilingual eGlossary

7.ESS.3, 6-8.LST.4.1, 6-8.LST.7.1

Inquiry What happened here?

What tore this landscape apart? Have you ever seen a place like this? Probably not, because places like this are usually under the ocean! Whether it is under the ocean or on dry land, there's a lot of action at plate boundaries.

Philippe Bourseiller/Getty Images

What happens when tectonic plates collide?

As Earth's continents move, tectonic plates can come together, pull apart, or slide past each other. Each of these interactions produces different landforms.

① Using **construction paper** and **index cards,** set up a model plate boundary. Draw your model in your Science Journal.

② Label the two tectonic plates, the fault between them, and the mantle. Title it *Before Stress.*

③ Model tension by pulling the plates apart. Draw and label your model. Title it *Tension.*

④ Model shear by sliding one plate forward and the other backward. Draw and label your model. Title it *Shear.*

⑤ Model compression by pushing the plates together. Experiment until you get two different results. Draw and label both results. Title it *Compression.*

Think About This

1. What might happen if compression and shear occurred together?

2. 🔑 **Key Concept** How are the features that form under the different types of stresses different? How are they similar?

Landforms Created by Plate Motion

Tectonic plates move slowly, only 1–9 cm per year. But these massive, slow-moving plates have so much force they can build tall mountains, form deep valleys, and rip Earth's surface apart.

Compression, tension, and shear stresses are at work at plate boundaries. Each type of stress produces different types of landforms. For example, the San Andreas Fault on the west coast of the United States is the result of shear stresses where plates move past each other. Tall mountains, such as the Dolomites shown in **Figure 8,** are created by compression stresses where plates collide.

Reading Check How fast do tectonic plates move?

Figure 8 The Dolomites in Italy are the result of a collision long ago between landmasses that are now the continents of Europe and Africa.

(t)Hutchings Photography/Digital Light Source; (b)Buena Vista Images/Getty Images

Figure 9 Three stages in the growth of the Himalayas are illustrated. The plates beneath India and Asia started colliding almost 50 million years ago and continue colliding today. Because the plates are still colliding, the Himalayas grow a few millimeters each year due to compression.

Visual Check Which two landforms collided?

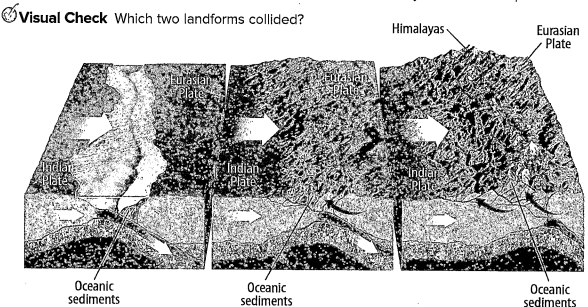

Himalayas

Eurasian Plate

Oceanic sediments

Oceanic sediments

Oceanic sediments

Landforms Created by Compression

The largest landforms on Earth are produced by compression at convergent plate boundaries. The types of landforms that form depend on whether the plates are oceanic or continental.

Mountain Ranges

A collision between two continental plates can produce tall mountains. But the mountains form slowly and in stages over millions of years. The history of the Himalayas is illustrated in **Figure 9.** The Himalayas continue to grow even now as continental collision pushes them higher. Note that although the plates move horizontally, the collision causes the crust to move vertically also.

Ocean Trenches

When two plates collide, one can go under the other and be forced into the mantle in a process called subduction. As shown in **Figure 10,** a deep trench forms where the two plates meet. **Ocean trenches** *are deep, underwater troughs created by an oceanic plate subducting under another plate at a convergent plate boundary.* Ocean trenches, also called deep-sea trenches, are the deepest places in Earth's oceans.

Key Concept Check What are two landforms that can form where two plates converge?

Volcanic Arcs

Volcanic mountains can form in the ocean where oceanic plates converge and one plate subducts under another one. These volcanoes emerge as islands. *A curved line of volcanoes that forms parallel to a plate boundary is called a* **volcanic arc.** Most of the active volcanoes in the United States are part of the Aleutian volcanic arc in Alaska. There are about 40 active volcanoes there. They formed as a result of the Pacific Plate subducting under the North American Plate.

Volcanic arcs in the ocean are also called island arcs. But a volcanic arc can also form where an oceanic plate subducts under a continental plate. Because the continent is above sea level, the volcanoes sit on top of the continent, as does Mount Shasta in California, shown in Figure 10.

Reading Check Where do volcanic arcs form?

Landforms Created by Tension

Where plates move apart, tension stresses stretch Earth's crust. Distinct landforms are produced by tension.

Mid-Ocean Ridges

It might surprise you that tension stresses under the ocean can produce long mountain ranges more than 2 km tall. They form under water at divergent boundaries as oceanic plates move away from each other.

As tension stresses cause oceanic crust to spread apart, hot rock from the mantle rises. Because hot rock is less dense than cold rock, the hot mantle pushes the seafloor upward. In this way, long, high ridges are created in Earth's oceans. You might have already learned that a long, tall mountain range that forms where oceanic plates diverge is called a mid-ocean ridge. Figure 11 shows a mid-ocean ridge near the North American west coast.

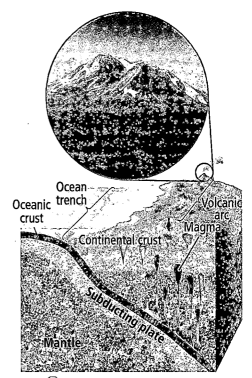

Figure 10 ☞ Volcanic arcs also can form on continents. Mount Shasta in California is part of the Cascade volcanic arc.

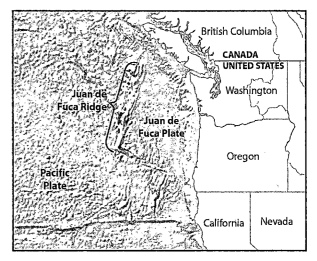

Figure 11 The Juan de Fuca Ridge off the coast of Washington and Oregon is a mid-ocean ridge.

Visual Check What direction is the Juan de Fuca Plate moving relative to the Pacific Plate?

Figure 12 🔑 A divergent boundary has created a continental rift in Africa. This rift eventually will separate Africa into two parts.

Continental Rifts

When divergent boundaries occur within a continent, they can form continental rifts, or enormous splits in Earth's crust. Tension stresses in the cold upper part of the crust create faults. At these faults, large blocks of crust move downward, creating valleys between two ridges.

The East African Rift, pictured in **Figure 12**, is an example of an active continental rift that is beginning to split the African continent into two parts. Each year, the two parts move 3–6 mm farther from each other. One day, millions of years from now, the divergent boundary will have created two separate landmasses. Water will fill the space between them.

🔍 **Reading Check** Where on Earth is a continental rift forming now?

The valley at this rift also is subsiding. The warm lower part of the crust acts like putty. As the crust stretches, it becomes thinner and subsides, as shown in **Figure 12**.

🔑 **Key Concept Check** What features form at divergent boundaries?

⚡ MiniLab

20 minutes

What is the relationship between plate motion and landforms?

As tectonic plates move, they create landforms in predictable patterns. Can you analyze the motion of the plates and predict what landforms will form?

① Examine the world map shown here indicating the movement of tectonic plates. Determine the meaning of the arrows and the lines.

② On a **copy of the map,** label plate boundaries as divergent, convergent, or transform.

③ On your map, predict the landforms that will form at each plate boundary.

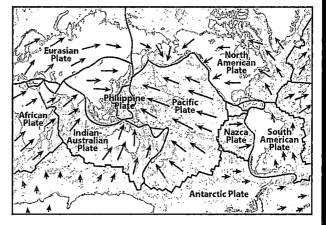

Analyze and Conclude

1. **Describe** the landform that is found around the edge of the Pacific Ocean. Hypothesize why this is called the Ring of Fire.

2. **Compare and contrast** the landforms on the east and west coasts of South America. Support your answer with data.

3. 🔑 **Key Concept** Create a table that relates the type of stress (compression, tension, shear) and the location of the plate boundary (middle of a continent, edge of a continent, middle of an ocean). Fill in the table with the landforms found in each situation. List one place on Earth where each is occurring.

Figure 13 On the left, a transform fault forms as crust moves past each other. On the right, the yellow line shows the mid-ocean ridge. The red lines are transform faults.

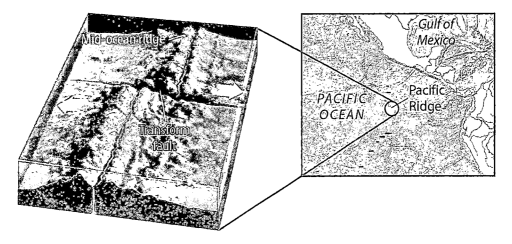

Visual Check In the figure on the right, where are the fracture zones?

Landforms Created by Shear Stresses

Recall that as plates slide horizontally past each other, shear stresses produce transform boundaries. Landforms created by shear stresses are not as obvious as landforms created by tension or compression. Transform boundaries are characterized by long faults and fault zones.

Transform Faults

Where blocks of crust slide horizontally past each other, they form **transform faults.** Some transform faults form perpendicular to mid-ocean ridges, as shown on the left in **Figure 13.** Recall that tension produces mid-ocean ridges at divergent boundaries. As the plates slide away from each other, transform faults also form and can separate sections of mid-ocean ridges. The map in **Figure 13** shows the transform faults along the Pacific Ridge.

 Key Concept Check What features form where plates slide past each other?

Fault Zones

Some transform faults can be seen at Earth's surface. For example, the San Andreas Fault in California is visible in many places. Although the San Andreas Fault is visible at Earth's surface, much of this fault system is underground. As shown in **Figure 14,** the San Andreas Fault is not a single fault. Many smaller faults exist in the area around the San Andreas Fault. *An area of many fractured pieces of crust along a large fault is called a* **fault zone.**

WORD ORIGIN · · · · · · · · · · · · ·
transform
from Latin *trans,* means "across"; and *formare,* means "to form"

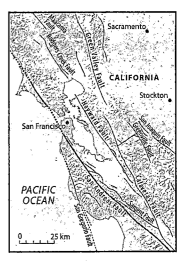

Figure 14 Shear stresses create faulting at Earth's surface. Below the surface there might be many other faults that are part of the same fault zone.

Visual Summary

 The deepest and tallest landforms on Earth are created at plate boundaries.

 Tension stresses within continents can produce enormous splits in Earth's surface.

 Faults at Earth's surface can be part of much larger fault zones that have many underground faults.

FOLDABLES

Use your lesson Foldable to review the lesson. Save your Foldable for the project at the end of the chapter.

What do you think NOW?

You first read the statements below at the beginning of the chapter.

3. New landforms are created only at plate boundaries.

4. The tallest and deepest landforms are created at plate boundaries.

Did you change your mind about whether you agree or disagree with the statements? Rewrite any false statements to make them true.

Use Vocabulary

1 **Use the terms** *volcanic arc* and *trench* in a sentence.

2 **Relate** a transform fault to a fault zone.

3 **Define** *fault zone* in your own words.

Understand Key Concepts

4 Which type of stress is currently producing the East African Rift?
A. shear stress
B. tension stress
C. compression and tension stresses
D. shear and compression stresses

5 **Compare** the development of tall mountains to how ocean trenches form.

6 **Summarize** the processes involved in the formation of a volcanic arc.

Interpret Graphics

7 **Connect** Copy the graphic organizer below. Use it to relate stresses at plate boundaries to the landforms associated with each type of boundary.

Stresses	Landforms
Compression	
Tension	
Shear	

Critical Thinking

8 **Apply** The rocks at the top of Mount Everest contain marine fossils. Describe the tectonic processes that brought sediments and fossils once buried at the bottom of the sea to the top of the tallest mountain.

9 **Relate** a continental rift to a mid-ocean ridge.

10 **Create** a diagram that explains how tectonic plates are in constant motion, resulting in the formation of landforms on Earth's surface over time.

Hot Spots!

Volcanoes on a Plate

Not all volcanoes form at plate boundaries. Some, called hot spot volcanoes, pop up in the middle of a tectonic plate. A hot spot volcano forms over a rising column of magma called a mantle plume. The origin of mantle plumes is still uncertain, but evidence shows they probably rise up from the boundary between Earth's mantle and core.

As a tectonic plate passes over a mantle plume, a volcano forms above the plume. The tectonic plate continues to move, and a chain of volcanoes forms. If the volcanoes are in the ocean and if they get large enough, they become islands, such as the Hawaiian Islands. Here is how this happens:

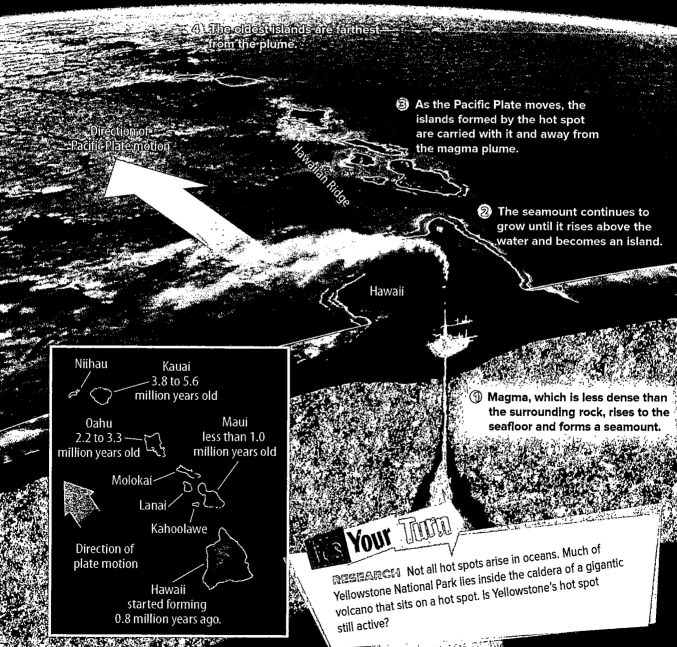

4 The oldest islands are farthest from the plume.

Direction of Pacific Plate motion

Hawaiian Ridge

3 As the Pacific Plate moves, the islands formed by the hot spot are carried with it and away from the magma plume.

2 The seamount continues to grow until it rises above the water and becomes an island.

Hawaii

1 Magma, which is less dense than the surrounding rock, rises to the seafloor and forms a seamount.

Niihau

Kauai
3.8 to 5.6
million years old

Oahu
2.2 to 3.3
million years old

Maui
less than 1.0
million years old

Molokai

Lanai

Kahoolawe

Direction of
plate motion

Hawaii
started forming
0.8 million years ago.

Is Your Turn

RESEARCH Not all hot spots arise in oceans. Much of Yellowstone National Park lies inside the caldera of a gigantic volcano that sits on a hot spot. Is Yellowstone's hot spot still active?

Reading Guide

Key Concepts 🔑

ESSENTIAL QUESTIONS

- How do mountains change over time?

- How do different types of mountains form?

Vocabulary

folded mountain p. 361

fault-block mountain p. 362

 Multilingual eGlossary

 BrainPOP®

 7.ESS.3, SEPS.1, SEPS.2, SEPS.5, SEPS.8, 6-8.LST.7.1, 6-8.LST.7.3

Mountain Building

(Inquiry) Is this a safe place to live?

Is it safe to live next to this mountain? Will lava erupt from it? Will there be earthquakes nearby? Not all mountains are the same. Once you know how a mountain formed, you can predict what is likely to happen in the future.

What happens when Earth's tectonic plates diverge?

When tectonic plates diverge, the crust gets thinner. Sometimes large blocks of crust subside and form valleys. Blocks next to them move up and become fault-block mountains. This is how the Basin and Range Province in the western United States formed.

① Stand 5–6 **hardbound books** on a desk with the bindings vertical.

② Using a **ruler,** measure the width and the height of the books, as shown. Record the results in a table in your Science Journal.

③ Holding the books together, tilt them sideways at the same time to about a 30° angle. Measure the width and the height of the books. Record the results in your table.

④ Tilt the books to about a 60° angle. Measure the width and the height of the books. Record the results in your table.

⑤ Draw a diagram of the tilted books in your Science Journal, and label mountains, valleys, and faults.

Think About This

1. How does the thickness of the crust relate to the height of a mountain?

2. 🔑 **Key Concept** How do you think fault-block mountains form?

The Mountain-Building Cycle

Mountain ranges are built slowly, and they change slowly. Because they are the result of many different plate collisions over many millions of years, they are made of many different types of rocks. The processes of weathering and erosion can remove part or all of a mountain.

 Reading Check What processes can remove part of a mountain?

Converging Plates

Recall that when plates collide at a plate boundary, a combination of folds, faults, and uplift creates mountains. Eventually, after millions of years, the forces that originally caused the plates to move together can become inactive. As shown in **Figure 15,** a single new continent is created from two old ones, and the plate boundary becomes inactive. With no compression at a convergent plate boundary, the mountains stop increasing in size.

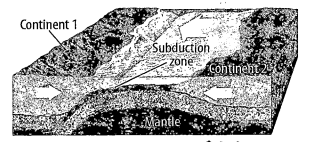
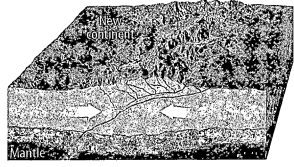

Figure 15 The forces that originally caused plates to move together eventually become inactive. A single continent is created from the two old ones, and the plate boundary becomes inactive.

Folded Mountain

Fault-block Mountain

Uplifted Mountain

WORD ORIGIN ···········

Appalachian
from the Apalachee *abalahci*,
means "other side of the river"

Collisions and Rifting

Continents are continuously changing because Earth's tectonic plates are always moving. When continents split at a divergent plate boundary, they often break close to the place where they first collided. First a large split, or rift, forms. The rift grows, and seawater flows into it, forming an ocean.

Eventually plate motion changes again, and the continents collide. New mountain ranges form on top of or next to older mountain ranges. The cycle of repeated collisions and rifting can create old and complicated mountain ranges, such as the Appalachian Mountains.

 Reading Check Where do plates tend to break apart?

Figure 16 illustrates the history of the plate collisions and rifting that produced the mountain range as it is today. Rocks that make up mountain ranges such as the Appalachian Mountains record the history of plate motion and collisions that formed the mountains.

Weathering

The Appalachian Mountains are an old mountain range that stretches along most of the eastern United States. They are not as high and rugged as the Rocky Mountains in the west because they are much older. They are no longer growing. Weathering has rounded the peaks and lowered the elevations.

Formation of the Appalachians ☐→   ▷ **Animation**

Figure 16 The Appalachian Mountains formed over several hundred million years.

Visual Check Which mountain range is between Valley and Ridge and Piedmont?

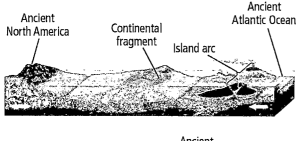

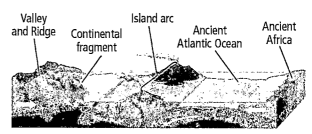

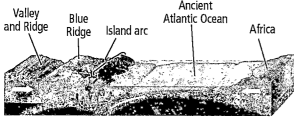

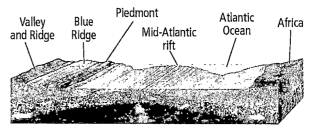

Erosion and Uplift

Over time, natural processes wear down mountains, smooth their peaks, and reduce their height. But some mountain ranges are hundreds of millions of years old. How do they last so long? Recall how isostasy works. As a mountain erodes, the crust under it must rise to restore the balance between what is left of the mountain and how it floats on the mantle. Therefore, rocks deep under continents rise slowly toward Earth's surface. In old mountain ranges, metamorphic rocks that formed deep below the surface are exposed on the top of mountains, such as the rocks in **Figure 17.**

 Key Concept Check How can mountains change over time?

Types of Mountains

You learned in the first lesson that stresses caused by plate movement can pull or compress crust. This is one way plate motion is involved in creating many types of mountains. But the effect of plate movement is also responsible for changing the positions of rocks and the rocks themselves within a mountain range.

Folded Mountains

Rocks that are deeper in the crust are warmer than rocks closer to Earth's surface. Deeper rocks are also under much more pressure. When rocks are hot enough or under enough pressure, folds form instead of faults, as shown in **Figure 18. Folded mountains** *are made of layers of rocks that are folded.* Folded mountains form as continental plates collide, folding and uplifting layers of rock. When erosion removes the upper part of the crust, folds are exposed on the surface.

The arrangement of the folds is not accidental. You can demonstrate this by taking a piece of paper and gently pushing the ends toward one another to form a fold. The fold is a long ridge that is perpendicular to the direction in which you pushed. Folded mountains are similar. The folds are perpendicular to the direction of the compression that created them.

Figure 17 Metamorphic rocks, such as these, formed deep below Earth's surface. After the material above them eroded, the rock rose due to isostasy. Now they are on Earth's surface.

ACADEMIC VOCABULARY

perpendicular
(adj.) being at right angles to a line or plane

Figure 18 Compression stresses folded these rocks. Because the folds run up and down, the compression must have come from the sides.

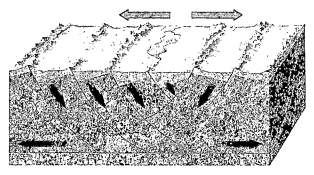

Animation

Figure 19 In the middle of a continent, tension can pull crust apart. Where the crust breaks, fault-block mountains and valleys can form as huge blocks of Earth rise or fall.

**Visual Check** Which way is the tension pulling?

Fault-Block Mountains

Sometimes tension stresses within a continent create mountains. As tension pulls crust apart, faults form, as shown in **Figure 19.** At the faults, some blocks of crust fall and others rise. **Fault-block mountains** *are parallel ridges that form where blocks of crust move up or down along faults.*

The Basin and Range Province in the western United States consists of dozens of parallel fault-block mountains that are oriented north to south. The tension that created the mountains pulled in the east-west directions. One of these mountains is shown at the beginning of this lesson. Notice how a high, craggy ridge is right next to a valley. Somewhere between the two, there is a fault where huge movement once occurred.

Key Concept Check How do folded and fault-block mountains form?

MiniLab

15 minutes

How do folded mountains form?

When two continental plates converge, rocks crumple and fold, forming folded mountains. If the rocks formed in layers, such as sedimentary rocks, the folds can be visible.

1. Read and complete a lab safety form.
2. On a piece of **waxed paper,** shape four balls of different **colored dough** into rectangles about 1 cm thick.
3. Stack the rectangles on top of each other. Using a **plastic knife,** trim the edges so that all layers are clearly visible. Draw a side view of the unfolded layers in your Science Journal.
4. Compress the dough by pushing the short ends together into an S-shape. Try to get at least one upward and one downward fold. Draw a side view of the folded layers in your Science Journal.
5. Using the knife, simulate erosion by slicing off the top of your folded mountains. Draw a top view of the eroded mountains in your Science Journal.

Analyze and Conclude

1. **Relate** the direction of compression to the direction of the peaks of the mountains.
2. **Key Concept** Describe how folded mountains form and change over time.

Hutchings Photography/Digital Light Source

Uplifted Mountains

To the west of the Basin and Range Province is the Sierra Nevada range. The rocks in the Sierra Nevada are made of granite, which is an igneous rock originally formed several kilometers below Earth's surface. The granite on top of the Sierra Nevada's Mount Whitney was once 10 km below Earth's surface. Now it is on top of a 4,420-m-tall mountain. When large regions rise vertically with very little deformation, uplifted mountains form.

 Reading Check What type of rocks are found in the Sierra Nevada?

The entire Sierra Nevada can be thought of as a gigantic tilted fault block. Uplift caused by faulting, and erosion, have exposed it on Earth's surface. But why is it continuing to rise? Scientists do not fully understand how uplifted mountains like the Sierra Nevada range form. One hypothesis proposes that cold mantle under the crust detaches from the crust and sinks deeper into the mantle, as shown in **Figure 20**. The sinking mantle pulls the crust and creates compression closer to the surface. As the crust thickens, the upper part of the crust rises to maintain isostasy.

Volcanic Mountains

You might not think of volcanoes as mountains, but scientists consider volcanoes to be special types of mountains. In fact, some of the largest mountains on Earth are made by volcanic eruptions. As molten rock and ash erupt onto Earth's surface, they harden. Over time, many eruptions can build huge volcanic mountains such as the ones that make up the Hawaiian Islands.

Not all volcanic mountains erupt all the time. Some volcanic mountains are dormant, which means they might erupt again someday. Some volcanic mountains will never erupt again.

 Key Concept Check How do uplifted and volcanic mountains form?

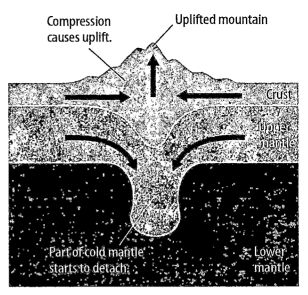

Figure 20 ☞ One possible explanation for how uplifted mountains form is that sinking mantle creates compression of the crust. The crust rises to regain isostasy, forming mountains.

Math Skills

Use Proportions

An equation showing two equal ratios is a proportion. Some mountains in the Himalayas are rising 0.001 m/y. How long would it take the mountains to reach a height of 7,000 m?

1. Set up a proportion.

$$\frac{0.001\ m}{1y} = \frac{7,000\ m}{xy}$$

2. Cross multiply.

$$0.001x = 7,000$$

3. Divide both sides by 0.001.

$$\frac{0.001x}{0.001} = \frac{7,000}{0.001}$$

4. Solve for x.

$$x = 7,000,000\ y$$

Practice

If the uplift rate of Mount Everest is 0.0006 m/y, how long did it take Mount Everest to reach a height of 8,848 m?

✔ **Math Practice**

💬 **Personal Tutor**

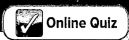
Visual Summary

 Mountain ranges can be the result of repeated continental collision and rifting.

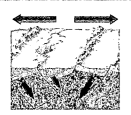 Tension stresses create mountain ranges that are a series of faults, ridges, and valleys.

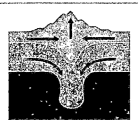 Uplifted mountains form as a result of compression near Earth's surface.

FOLDABLES

Use your lesson Foldable to review the lesson. Save your Foldable for the project at the end of the chapter.

What do you think NOW?

You first read the statements below at the beginning of the chapter.

5. Metamorphic rocks formed deep below Earth's surface sometimes can be located near the tops of mountains.

6. Mountain ranges can form over long periods of time through repeated collisions between plates.

Did you change your mind about whether you agree or disagree with the statements? Rewrite any false statements to make them true.

Use Vocabulary

1. Compression stress can create _____.

2. **Name** two types of mountains that can form far from plate boundaries.

3. Rocks formed deep inside Earth can be found at the surface as _____.

Understand Key Concepts

4. **Contrast** folded and fault-block mountains.

5. Which type of mountains form with little deformation?
   A. fault-block mountains
   B. folded mountains
   C. uplifted mountains
   D. volcanic mountains

6. **Identify** the type of plate boundary where the Appalachian Mountains formed.

Interpret Graphics

7. **Summarize** the plate tectonic events that built the Appalachian Mountains, using a graphic organizer like the one below.

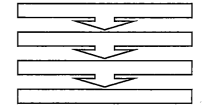

Critical Thinking

8. **Critique** the generalization that mountains only form at convergent boundaries. Explain how other processes can produce mountains.

Math Skills   **Math Practice**

9. Volcanoes in Hawaii began forming on the seafloor, about 5,000 m below the surface. If a volcano reaches the surface in 300,000 years, what was its rate of vertical growth per year?

What tectonic processes are most responsible for shaping North America?

Materials

metric ruler

North America map

Mountains are important structures of the North American landscape. By studying the types of mountains, scientists can figure out what processes have shaped the continent over the last several hundred million years.

Learn It

Before scientists can make conclusions about the formation of a continent, they have to know what happened in all of its parts. Scientists **research information** so they can answer questions and draw conclusions about the continent as a whole.

Try It

① Study the map shown. Choose a mountain range to research. With your teacher's approval, you may research a range that is not shown on this map.

② Using sources approved by your teacher, research your mountain range. Be sure to make a list of the sources you used for your research. Answer the following questions.

- What is the name and location of your mountain range?
- What type of plate boundary is near your mountain range?
- What tectonic plates form the boundary near your mountain range?
- What type(s) of mountains make up your mountain range?
- How did the mountains form?
- What type(s) of rocks make up the mountains?
- How tall are the mountains in your range?
- How old is your mountain range?
- What other factors have affected the height or the shape of the mountains?

③ Record your results in your Science Journal.

Apply It

④ **Create** a demonstration that explains how the movement of tectonic plates resulted in the formation of your mountain range.

⑤ **Compare and Contrast** Combine your research with the other groups' research. How are your mountain ranges similar? How are they different?

⑥ 🔑 **Key Concept** What forces have shaped North America?

Lesson 4

Continent Building

Key Concepts 🔑

ESSENTIAL QUESTIONS

- What are two ways continents grow?
- What are the differences between interior plains, basins, and plateaus?

Vocabulary

plains p. 369

basin p. 369

plateau p. 370

 Multilingual eGlossary

 7.ESS.3, SEPS.2, SEPS.3, SEPS.8, 6-8.LST.5.2, 6-8.LST.7.1

Inquiry What is it really?

You might have heard that the Grand Canyon is just a big hole in the ground. In fact, it's not a hole at all. What do you think it might be? How did it form? You may be surprised at the answer.

Michael Busselle/Digital Vision/SuperStock

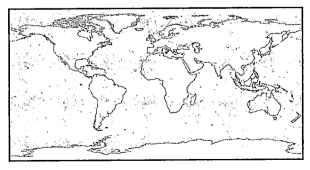

How do continents grow?

Over the history of Earth, continents have been slowly increasing in size. Continents can grow when fragments of crust that formed in other parts of the world stick to the edges of the continent at convergent plate boundaries.

① Read and complete a lab safety form.

② Place **waxed paper** on the lab bench, and place a **block of wood** on one end of the paper.

③ Using **shaving cream,** create a volcanic arc on the waxed paper.

④ Pull the waxed paper under the wood and observe what happens. Record your observations in your Science Journal.

Think About This

1. Using the vocabulary from the chapter (words such as *compression, convergence, folded mountains, volcanic mountains*), describe what occurred as you completed the lab.

2. Create a labeled diagram showing the motion of the ocean plate and the continental plate. Include the volcanic arc and describe what happened to it when it ran into the continent.

3. **Key Concept** How do you think continents grow?

The Structure of Continents

If you look at the map shown on the left in **Figure 21,** you will notice that most of the highest elevations are located near the edges of continents. Why do you think that is?

In contrast, the interiors of most continents are flat. Usually, the middle of a continent is only a few hundred meters above sea level. Continental interiors have very few mountains. In these regions, the rocks are old igneous and metamorphic rocks. A map showing the old, stable interiors of the world's continents is on the right in **Figure 21.** Notice that they usually lie near the middle of the continent. These areas are usually smooth and flat because millions or even billions of years of erosion have smoothed them out.

Reading Check Where are high elevations usually located? Where are the low elevations?

Figure 21 The map on the left shows areas of high elevation in white. They are usually near the edges of continents. The map on the right shows old, stable continental interiors.

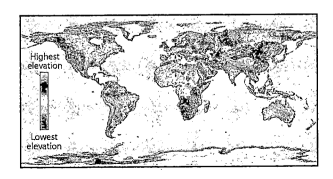

Highest elevation

Lowest elevation

Hutchings Photography/Digital Light Source

 Animation

Figure 22 The green areas show parts of present-day North America that were once attached to other continents in other parts of the world.

How Continents Grow

The shapes and the sizes of the continents have changed many times over Earth's history. Continents can break up and get smaller, or they can get bigger. One way continents get bigger is through the addition of igneous rocks by erupting volcanoes. A second way is when tectonic plates carry island arcs, whole continents, or fragments of continents with them.

When a plate carrying fragments reaches a continent at a convergent boundary, the least dense fragments get pushed onto the edge of the continent. **Figure 22** is a map showing fragments that have been added to the west coast of North America within the last 600 million years. Fragments in the western United States include volcanic arcs, ancient seafloor, and small pieces from other continents.

Key Concept Check What are two ways continents grow?

If rock were not being added to continents, what do you think would happen to the size of continents? Rifting would change their sizes and shapes. Weathering and erosion gradually would wear them down.

(Inquiry) MiniLab

20 minutes

Can you analyze a continent?

As tectonic plates move across Earth's surface, they interact in predictable patterns. Suppose you could get a glimpse of a continent on Earth at some other time. You can use what you know to figure out what that continent is like.

① Read and complete a lab safety form.

② Copy the imaginary continent shown at right into your Science Journal. Arrow length is proportional to the speed of the plates.

③ Use **colored pencils** to differentiate regions of compression, tension, and shear.

④ Identify the locations and types of landforms that would be present on Gigantia. Label fault-block mountains, faults, and folded mountains.

⑤ Determine the locations of the interior plains and where continental fragments are being added.

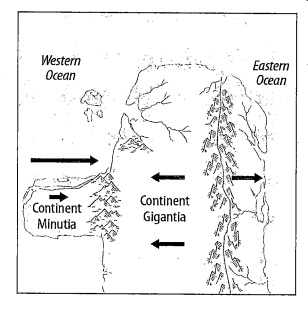

Analyze and Conclude

1. **Select** a region of Earth that has similar plate interactions to those on Gigantia.

2. **Key Concept** Describe how the continent is changing.

Continental Interiors

Rocks in continental interiors tend to be stable, flat, very old, and very strong. They are usually more than 500 million years old. In some continental interiors, the rocks are much older than that! Figure 23 shows rocks that might be the oldest on Earth's surface. Although they might not look very exciting, it is incredible to think they are more than 4.2 billion years old!

Formation of Interior Plains

A **plain** *is an extensive area of level or rolling land.* Most of the central region of North America is referred to as the Interior Plains. The rocks in these plains came from collisions of several smaller plates about 1 billion years ago. At different times in Earth's history, the plains were covered by shallow seas. The plains have been flattened by millions of years of weathering and erosion.

 Key Concept Check What is a plain?

Formation of Basins

Just as plate motion and isostasy create mountains, they also can cause subsidence. *Areas of subsidence and regions with low elevation are called* **basins.** Sediments eroded from mountains accumulate in basins. Figure 24 is a map showing the largest basins in North America. Can you find a relationship between the locations of basins and large mountain ranges?

Reading Check What is the name of the feature where sediment accumulates?

Basins can have great economic importance. Under the right conditions, the remains of plants and animals are buried in the sediments that accumulate in basins. Over millions of years, heat and pressure convert the plant and animal remains into oil, natural gas, and coal. Most of our energy resources are extracted from sedimentary basins. The world's largest oil and natural gas fields also lie in sedimentary basins.

Figure 23 The Canadian rocks pictured here have existed throughout much of Earth's history. They are more than 4.2 billion years old.

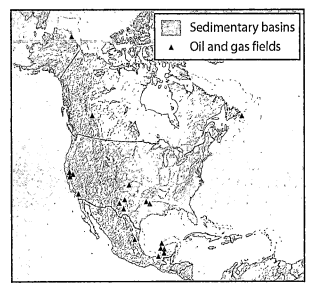

Figure 24 Ancient sedimentary basins are important because oil, natural gas, and coal usually are found in basins.

Visual Check Where are oil and gas fields in relation to sedimentary basins?

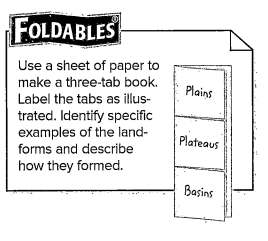

Use a sheet of paper to make a three-tab book. Label the tabs as illustrated. Identify specific examples of the landforms and describe how they formed.

Plains
Plateaus
Basins

Courtesy: Jonathan O'Neil/National Science Foundation

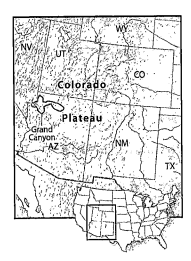

Figure 25 The Colorado Plateau is an example of an uplifted plateau.

🔎 **Visual Check** Which states are partly covered by the Colorado Plateau?

REVIEW VOCABULARY

lava
molten rock that erupts on Earth's surface.

Formation of Plateaus

Some regions are high above sea level but are flat. *Flat regions with high elevations are called* **plateaus.** Some plateaus form through uplift. An example of an uplifted plateau is the Colorado Plateau, shown in **Figure 25.** In the last 5 million years, this region has been uplifted by more than 1 km.

Notice in **Figure 25** that the Grand Canyon is only a small part of the Colorado Plateau. It was created as the Colorado River cut through and eroded the uplifting plateau. So, the Grand Canyon was created by water!

The eruption of lava also can create large plateaus. For example, more than 200,000 km³ of lava flooded the Columbia Plateau shown in **Figure 26.** Over 2 million years, multiple eruptions built up layers of rock. In some places, the plateau is more than 3 km thick!

🔑 **Key Concept Check** What are the differences between plains, basins, and plateaus?

Dynamic Landforms

When you started reading this chapter, you might have thought Earth had always looked the same. Now you know that Earth's surface is constantly changing. Mountains form only to be eroded away. Continents grow, shift, and shrink. Nothing stays the same for long on dynamic Earth.

The Columbia Plateau 🔑

Figure 26 The map shows the area that was covered by multiple eruptions of lava over millions of years. The lava cooled and formed the Columbia River basalt. The layers of basalt are visible in the photograph. Some parts of the Columbia Plateau are more than 3 km thick.

Visual Summary

Rocks at the center of most continents are very old, very strong, and flat.

Fragments of crust are added to continents at convergent boundaries.

Large, elevated plateaus are created through uplift and lava flows.

FOLDABLES

Use your lesson Foldable to review the lesson. Save your Foldable for the project at the end of the chapter.

What do you think NOW?

You first read the statements below at the beginning of the chapter.

7. The centers of continents are flat and old.

8. Continents are continually shrinking because of erosion.

Did you change your mind about whether you agree or disagree with the statements? Rewrite any false statements to make them true.

Use Vocabulary

1 As a mountain erodes, sediment can accumulate in a nearby _____.

2 The central, flat region of North America is known as the _____.

3 The Grand Canyon was eroded out of a large _____.

Understand Key Concepts

4 Which term best describes the center of North America?
- **A.** basin
- **B.** lava
- **C.** plateau
- **D.** plain

5 **Describe** how continents change over time.

6 **Contrast** basins and plateaus.

Interpret Graphics

7 **Summarize** Use a graphic organizer like the one below to show the different stages involved in continent growth. Begin with an old continental interior and end with a new continent.

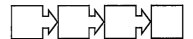

Critical Thinking

8 **Infer** In this lesson you learned that fragments of other continents were added to the west coast of North America. Where in the United States have other continental fragments been added?

9 **Generalize** How are landforms near the edges of continents different from landforms in continental interiors? How are these landforms related to plate tectonics or processes in the rock cycle?

10 **Infer** What would happen to the Grand Canyon if there were further uplift of the Colorado Plateau?

Materials

tub

measuring cup

cornstarch

hooked weights

---

thermometer

flour

hot plate

Also needed:
stopwatch, spoon, metric ruler, ice

Safety

Design Landforms

Suppose you are a museum designer and you want to show people that different landforms form under different circumstances. Sometimes rocks fold, sometimes they break, sometimes they form mountains, and sometimes they sink into Earth and create trenches. What they do depends on the properties of the rock and the type of stress. Unfortunately, rocks do all of these things so slowly that it is hard to see rocks in motion. What materials would you use to model the formation of landforms? What factors affect how rocks behave? How could you change your materials to model how rocks behave?

Ask a Question

What materials could represent rocks? How are the materials different from rocks?

Make Observations

① Read and complete the lab safety form.

② Mix some ingredients in your plastic bin or mixing bowl. Try different combinations until you make a material you can use to model landforms.

③ Experiment with the materials, and try to create different landforms.

④ Record your observations in your Science Journal. How do the materials behave like rocks, and how are they different?

(t to b, 4-5, 7, r)Hutchings Photography/Digital Light Source; (2, 6)Michael Scott/McGraw-Hill Education; (3)Jacques Cornell/McGraw-Hill Education

Form a Hypothesis

(5) After observing the behavior of your material, think of factors that cause rocks to behave differently. How might you recreate these different situations? Pick one factor and develop a hypothesis about how you can use the materials to model the behavior of rocks.

Test Your Hypothesis

(6) Develop a procedure to test your hypothesis. What is your dependent variable and your independent variable? How will you make quantitative measurements of both variables?

(7) Create a table to record your results.

(8) Have your teacher approve your procedure and your table.

(9) Conduct your experiment, and record your results.

Analyze and Conclude

(10) **Create** a graph displaying your results.

(11) **Interpret** your graph and explain the relationship between the variables.

(12) **Critique** your procedure and your results.

(13) **The Big Idea** Relate your results to how Earth's surface is shaped by plate motion.

Communicate Your Results

Design a museum exhibit that models the formation of one or more landforms.

What materials could represent Earth's crust? Now that you have modeled Earth's landforms, put the landforms on tectonic plates. Model plate motion, and describe how your landforms change at different types of plate boundaries.

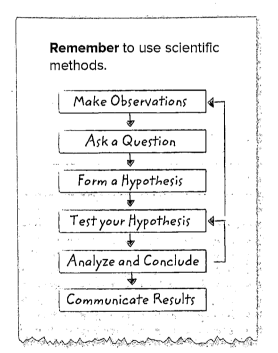

Lab Tips

☑ This lab might be messy! Clean up dry cornstarch and flour with a broom and dustpan.

☑ Be quantitative! Figure out concrete ways to measure both the variable you are changing (the independent variable) and the variable you are measuring (the dependent variable).

☑ If your first try is not successful, try something different! Science rarely works on the first try.

Remember to use scientific methods.

Make Observations →

Ask a Question

Form a Hypothesis

Test your Hypothesis ←

Analyze and Conclude

Communicate Results

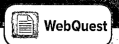

The forces created by the movement of tectonic plates are responsible for the variety of Earth's constantly changing landforms.

Key Concepts Summary 🔑

Key Concepts Summary 🔑	Vocabulary
Lesson 1: Forces That Shape Earth • As continents float in the mantle, they rise and fall to maintain the balance of **isostasy.** • **Compression, tension,** and **shear** stresses can deform or break rocks. • **Uplift** and plate motion move rocks through the rock cycle. 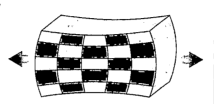	**isostasy** p. 344 **subsidence** p. 345 **uplift** p. 345 **compression** p. 345 **tension** p. 345 **shear** p. 345 **strain** p. 346
Lesson 2: Landforms at Plate Boundaries 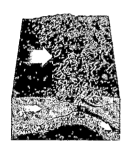 • When two continental plates collide, tall mountain ranges form. When an oceanic plate subducts below another one, an **ocean trench** and a **volcanic arc** form. • At divergent boundaries, mid-ocean ridges and continental rifts form. • **Transform faults** can create large areas of faulting and fracturing, not all of which can be seen at Earth's surface.	**ocean trench** p. 352 **volcanic arc** p. 353 **transform fault** p. 355 **fault zone** p. 355
Lesson 3: Mountain Building • Mountain ranges can grow from repeated plate collisions. Erosion reduces the sizes of continents. • Different types of mountains form from folded layers of rock, blocks of crust moving up and down at faults, uplift, and volcanic eruptions. 	**folded mountain** p. 361 **fault-block mountain** p. 362
Lesson 4: Continent Building  • Continents shrink because of erosion and rifting. Continents grow through volcanic activity and continental collisions. • **Plains** are generally flat areas of land, usually in the center of continents. **Basins** are regions at low elevation where sediment accumulates or once accumulated. **Plateaus** are large, flat regions at high elevation.	**plains** p. 369 **basin** p. 369 **plateau** p. 370

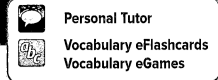

Personal Tutor

Vocabulary eFlashcards
Vocabulary eGames

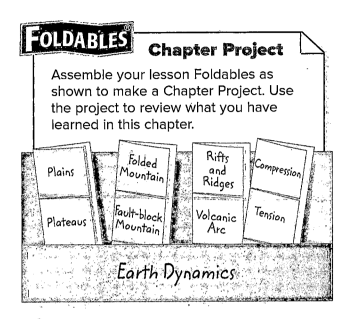

Chapter Project

Assemble your lesson Foldables as shown to make a Chapter Project. Use the project to review what you have learned in this chapter.

Plains | Folded Mountain | Rifts and Ridges | Compression

Plateaus | Fault-block Mountain | Volcanic Arc | Tension

Earth Dynamics

Use Vocabulary

① Plastic and elastic deformation are types of _____.

② Areas of fractured crust along a fault are called _____.

③ Mountains that rise with little deformation of rock are _____.

④ Repeated volcanic eruptions on land can create large _____.

⑤ The downward vertical motion of Earth's surface is _____.

⑥ Parallel ridges separated by faults and valleys are _____.

Link Vocabulary and Key Concepts

 Interactive Concept Map

Copy this concept map, and then use vocabulary terms from the previous page and other terms from the chapter to complete the concept map.

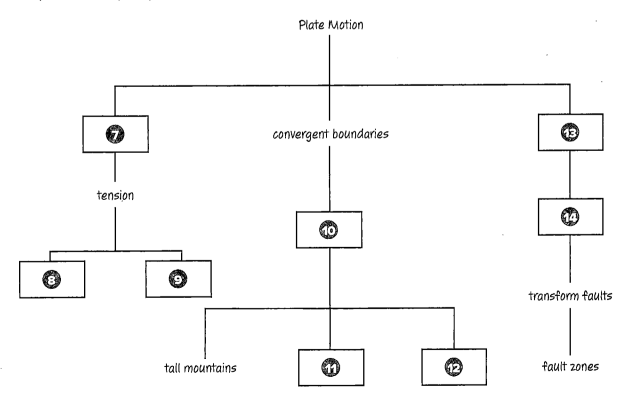

Plate Motion

⑦ — tension
  ⑧
  ⑨

convergent boundaries
  ⑩
  tall mountains ⑪ ⑫

⑬
  ⑭
  transform faults
  fault zones

Understand Key Concepts

1 The fact that land surface is high where crust is thick is due to what?

A. isostasy
B. subduction
C. shear stresses
D. tension stresses

2 The highest mountains form at which type of plate boundary?

A. convergent
B. divergent
C. oceanic
D. transform

3 Why does plastic deformation occur in the lower crust?

A. Rocks are hot.
B. Rocks are strong.
C. Tension occurs in the lower crust.
D. The mantle is plastic.

4 Lake Baikal in Siberia, pictured below, fills a continental rift valley. What type of stress is creating the rift?

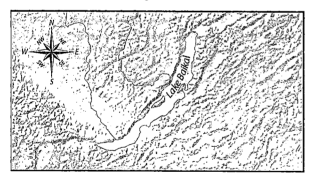

A. compression in the north-south direction
B. shear in the northeast-southwest direction.
C. tension in the north-south direction
D. tension in the northwest-southeast direction

5 When an oceanic plate converges with a continental plate, an island arc

A. does not form.
B. forms on both plates.
C. forms on the continental plate.
D. forms on the larger plate.

6 Which feature is indicated by the arrow in the illustration below?

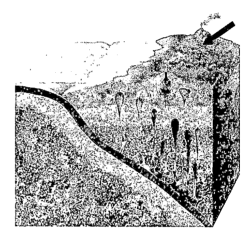

A. a fault zone
B. an ocean trench
C. an uplifted mountain
D. a volcanic arc

7 Which of the following locations in the United States has grown due to the addition of colliding fragments?

A. in the center
B. along the west coast
C. the Hawaiian Islands
D. along the Gulf of Mexico

8 Which are the cause of rocks being exposed at Earth's surface?

A. erosion and subsidence
B. erosion and uplift
C. faulting and folding
D. folding and subsidence

Critical Thinking

9 Compare a floating iceberg with a continent floating on the mantle.

10 Explain how seashells got on top of Mount Everest.

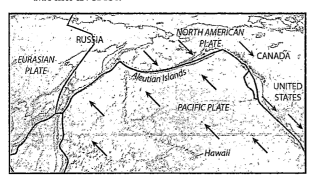

11 Infer Look at the illustration above. Where will the Hawaiian Islands be added to another continent?

12 Assess the statement, "Isostasy never stops causing uplift and subsidence."

13 Suggest the source for the sediment that filled the basins in North Dakota and Colorado.

14 Defend the statement that the large mountains of the Hawaiian Islands did not form at a plate boundary.

15 Predict where on Earth the crust is thickest.

16 Infer Why is the area in southern Africa flat but elevated?

17 Illustrate a possible future for the Appalachian Mountains. How do you think the Appalachian Mountains will look in 200 million years? What processes will change these mountains?

Writing in Science

18 Write a paragraph describing the history of an imaginary mountain range. Use the terms *fold, volcanic arc, convergent,* and *divergent* in your paragraph.

REVIEW THE BIG IDEA

19 If plate tectonics were suddenly to stop, how would Earth's surface change?

20 The photo below shows Mount Everest in the Himalayas. How did it get to be so tall?

Math Skills ✓ Math Practice

Use Proportions

21 The Himalayas formed when the Indian sub-continent collided with the Eurasian Plate. The Indian subcontinent moved about 10 cm/y.

a. How far would it have moved in 24,000,000 years?

b. How many kilometers did the plate move? (1 km = 100,000 cm)

22 A continent travels 0.006 m/y. How long would it take the continent to travel 100 m?

23 Mount Whitney is 4,421 m high. It started as a hill with an elevation of only 457 m about 40 mya. What was the rate of uplift for Mount Whitney in m/y? (Hint: Figure out the total elevation gain first.)

Record your answers on the answer sheet provided by your teacher or on a sheet of paper.

Multiple Choice

1   Which is the result of isostasy?

   A   a basin filling with sediment

   B   an iceberg floating in the ocean

   C   magma rising beneath a mountain

   D   one plate subducting under another one

2   The San Andreas Fault is classified as a transform fault. Which type of stress can create transform faults?

   A   compression

   B   shear

   C   fracture

   D   tension

Use the figure below to answer question 3.

Glacial ice

3   Which processes are shown in the figure?

   A   compression and divergence

   B   shearing and tension

   C   subsidence and uplift

   D   uplifting and subduction

4   What happens when rock fails?

   A   It breaks.

   B   It deforms elastically.

   C   It deforms plastically.

   D   It folds.

5   What part does subduction play in the rock cycle?

   A   It breaks rocks into sediment.

   B   It decreases pressure on buried rocks.

   C   It pulls rocks deep into Earth.

   D   It pushes rocks up to Earth's surface.

Use the figure below to answer questions 6 and 7.

6   Which force is shown in the figure?

   A   compression

   B   shearing

   C   tension

   D   uplift

7   What type of mountain results from the force shown in the figure?

   A   folded

   B   fault-block

   C   uplifted

   D   volcanic

8   Which continental landform can result when two plates diverge?

   A   basin

   B   continental rift

   C   mid-ocean ridge

   D   transform fault

Use the figure below to answer question 9.

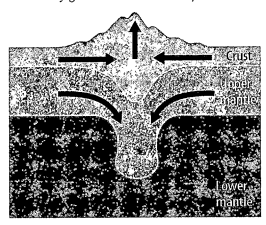

9 Which kind of mountain is shown in the figure?

A fault-block

B folded

C uplifted

D volcanic

10 Which feature is a flat region at a high elevation?

A a basin

B a mountain

C a plain

D a plateau

11 Which landforms are most likely to have coal, oil, and gas deposits?

A basins

B mountains

C plains

D plateaus

Constructed Response

Use the figure below to answer questions 12 and 13.

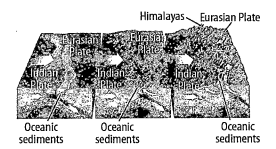

12 Use the figure to explain how the Himalayas formed. Identify the forces involved.

13 What would happen if the plate motion were reversed? Describe possible scenarios for the stages shown on the left and the right of the figure.

Use the figure below to answer question 14.

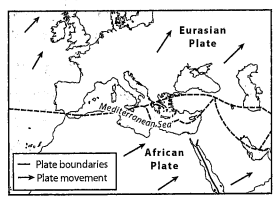

14 Each year, the African Plate moves closer to the Eurasian Plate. Predict how the Mediterranean Sea and the continents, shown in the figure, will change in 100 million years.

NEED EXTRA HELP?													
If You Missed Question...	1	2	3	4	5	6	7	8	9	10	11	12	13	14
Go to Lesson...	1	2	1	2	1	1	2	3	4	4	2	3	4	4

Chapter 11

7.ESS.2, SEPS.2, SEPS.4, SEPS.5, SEPS.7, SEPS.8, 6-8.LST.5.1, 6-8.LST.7.1

Earth's History

How have natural events changed Earth over time?

(inquiry) What is this place?

Molten rock flowing everywhere, steaming volcanoes, asteroid and meteorite showers—ancient Earth was a very different place compared to today.

- Can you think of a place where this environment exists?

- Could you live there?

- What has happened during Earth's long history to make it look as it does today?

Get Ready to Read

What do you think?

Before you read, decide if you agree or disagree with each of these statements. As you read this chapter, see if you change your mind about any of the statements.

1. All rocks contain fossils.

2. Humans produce all radioactive materials.

3. When Earth first formed, oceans were much larger than they are today.

4. Earth's early atmosphere was different from Earth's present-day atmosphere.

5. Fish were the first organisms in the oceans.

6. Asteroids no longer crash into Earth.

Your one-stop online resource
connectED.mcgraw-hill.com

 LearnSmart™

 Chapter Resources Files, Reading Essentials, Get Ready to Read, Quick Vocabulary

 Animations, Videos, Interactive Tables

 Self-checks, Quizzes, Tests

 Project-Based Learning Activities

 Lab Manuals, Safety Videos, Virtual Labs & Other Tools

 Vocabulary, Multilingual eGlossary, Vocab eGames, Vocab eFlashcards

 Personal Tutors

Lesson 1

Reading Guide

Key Concepts 🔑

ESSENTIAL QUESTIONS

- What evidence supports the idea that Earth is very old?
- What evidence did scientists use to develop the geologic time scale?
- How does the geologic time scale compare to the human time scale?

Vocabulary

principle of superposition p. 384

fossil p. 384

radioactive decay p. 385

half-life p. 385

geologic time scale p. 386

 Multilingual eGlossary

 BrainPOP®

 SEPS.5

Geologic Time

Inquiry Do these layers tell a story?

Geologists study the type of rock and special characteristics of the rock to learn about Earth's long history. How much of Earth's history is contained in these rock layers? What makes each one different from the next? Earth formed 4.6 billion years ago, and much of its story is contained in its rocks.

What happened? 🔬 📋

It might be hard to imagine that rocks change over time. How can you model rock layers to show how Earth processes change rock?

① Read and complete a lab safety form.

② Use at least four balls of **clay** to make a model of a sequence of rock layers.

③ Use **colored pencils** to make a detailed drawing of your model in your Science Journal. Exchange models with another student.

④ Spend about 5 minutes changing your partner's rock sequence.

⑤ Get your original rock sequence back. In your Science Journal, draw the changed model and try to explain what happened to the rocks.

Think About This

1. How did you change your partner's rock sequence?

2. What happened to your original rock sequence?

3. 🔑 **Key Concept** How do you think rocks show that Earth has changed?

Evidence That Earth Has Changed

You have changed in many ways throughout your life. What kind of evidence could you use to investigate these changes? Maybe you have some old family photographs, some clothes that you wore years ago that no longer fit, or even a book or toy that you loved when you were younger. These items can be used to show you have changed. Similarly, scientists search for evidence that Earth has changed over time.

Scientists study Earth's past, and they develop ideas and theories about how it formed and how it has changed. Sometimes when scientists make new discoveries, they must change their theories. As time passes, scientists either improve or revise scientific theories completely.

✔️ **Reading Check** Why are scientific theories sometimes revised?

What kinds of evidence do scientists use to show that Earth has changed? Some evidence is under your feet. As shown in Figure 1, rock layers above and below Earth's surface hold the clues to Earth's past.

Figure 1 These rock layers have been folded and deformed. This is one type of evidence that tells of Earth's past.

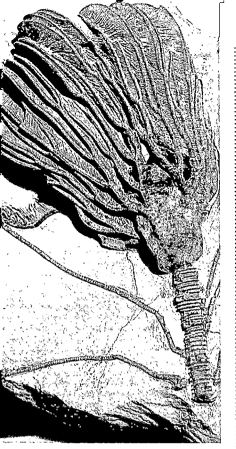

Rock Layers and Fossils

Weathering breaks rocks exposed at Earth's surface into smaller pieces called sediment. Over time, gravity, water, and wind carry sediment downhill and deposit it in low areas called basins. Eventually, layers of sediment form. The increasing weight of the sediment slowly causes the layers to compress, forming layers of rock. The rock layers, such as those shown in the photograph at the beginning of this lesson, formed over millions of years. Therefore, scientists know that Earth must be very old.

Key Concept Check How are rocks evidence of Earth's age?

Because new sediment layers are always collecting on top of older layers, the oldest layer is usually on the bottom. Geologists use this observation to organize rock layers according to their ages. They use the **principle of superposition,** *which states that in rock layers that have not been folded or deformed, the oldest rock layers are on the bottom.* The principle of superposition cannot give the actual ages of rock layers in years, called the absolute age. Instead, it gives the relative ages of rock layers, which tells you whether the layers are younger or older than other rock layers.

Sometimes as sediment builds up, it buries organisms within the layers. Under certain conditions, the organisms become rock along with the layers, as shown in **Figure 2.** *The preserved remains or evidence of past living organisms are called* **fossils.** Many fossils represent species that no longer live on Earth.

Figure 2 The rock layers and the fossils they contain provide information about Earth's past. This fossil crinoid was an animal that lived in a shallow ocean that once covered part of North America.

(Inquiry) MiniLab

15 minutes

What was that?

Scientists study fossils to learn about organisms and environments in Earth's history. What can you learn from these fossils?

① Use a **magnifying lens** to closely examine each **fossil or photograph of a fossil.**

② In your Science Journal, make and complete a data table such as the one shown. Add more rows as necessary.

③ Use **colored pencils** to draw each of the fossils you observe.

Drawing of Fossil	Plant/ Animal/ Other	Where the Organism Might Have Lived

Analyze and Conclude

1. **Compare and Contrast** How are your fossils alike? How do they differ?

2. **Analyze Data** What characteristics helped you determine the types of organisms and where they might have lived?

3. **Key Concept** What do you think fossils can tell you about Earth's past?

Radioactivity

Tiny particles called atoms make up all matter on Earth. An element is a substance that contains only one type of atom. Most elements are stable, which means they remain unchanged under normal conditions. But some elements are unstable. Over time they decay, or break down, and form different elements. **Radioactive decay** *is the process by which one element naturally changes into another.* The decay occurs when the atom's nucleus ejects particles. The original element is called the parent element, and the new element that forms is called the daughter element.

 Reading Check How do unstable elements change?

A radioactive element decays at a rate that is constant for that particular element. Scientists have calculated these rates. The **half-life** *of an element is the time required for half of the amount of a radioactive parent element to decay into a stable daughter element.* The graph in Figure 3 shows how the percentage of parent atoms decreases as parent atoms decay and form daughter atoms.

Because radioactive elements decay at a constant rate, we can use them as clocks to measure time. First, scientists must know the element's half-life. Then, by comparing the amount of parent element to the amount of daughter element in a sample, scientists can calculate the age of the sample. Analyzing radioactive elements shows that some rocks are billions of years old.

 Key Concept Check What evidence supports the idea that Earth is very old?

Figure 3 As time passes, more and more parent atoms decay and form daughter atoms. With each half-life, the percentage of parent atoms decreases by half.

 Animation

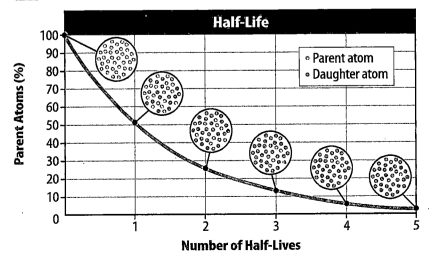

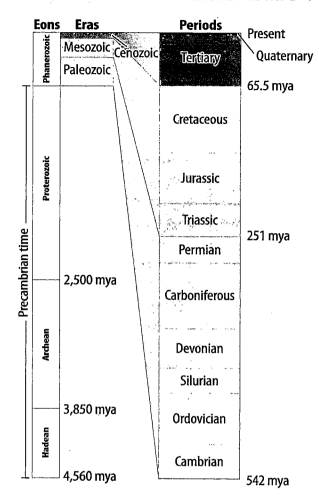

Figure 4 The divisions of geologic time are based on changes in rocks and fossils.

 **Personal Tutor**

WORD ORIGIN ·······················

Cambrian
from Latin *Cambria*, the Roman name for Wales
·····························

The Geologic Time Scale

During the 1800s, geologists organized the rocks and the rock layers they studied. They based their organization on superposition and the fossils present in the rock layers. They observed that older rock layers usually were positioned below younger rock layers. So, when they made charts showing the rock layers, they put the oldest rock layers at the bottom. They also assigned names to the rock layers. Each name represented a certain time in Earth's history. Rocks and rock layers that were all about the same age were assigned the same name. Eventually, they drew a standardized chart that represented all of the individual time periods in Earth's history. The **geologic time scale** *is a visual record of Earth's history, with the individual units based on changes in the rocks and fossils.* It is always drawn with the oldest rocks at the bottom and the youngest rocks at the top, as shown in **Figure 4**.

 Key Concept Check What evidence did scientists use to develop the geologic time scale?

Eons, Eras, Periods, and Epochs

You can divide the history of your life into years, months, weeks, and days. You might use special events, such as your first day of school, to mark divisions in your life. The geologic time scale shows the units used to describe Earth's history. Geologists divide Earth's history into eons, eras, periods, and epochs. They use the fossil record to mark geologic divisions. The divisions are not all the same length but mark places in the rock record where there are significant changes in the types of fossils present in the rocks.

For example, the beginning of the Cambrian period is marked by an abrupt appearance of complex life-forms. The end of the Permian period is marked by a significant and catastrophic die-off of organisms. You will learn more about these changes in Lessons 2 and 3 of this chapter.

Comparing Time Scales

Earth is 4.6 billion years old. Can you imagine that much time? You probably think only in terms of your own lifetime and maybe the lives of your parents and grandparents. Comparing the geologic time scale to something familiar, such as 1 year, can help.

Imagine all of Earth's history taking place within 1 year, starting January 1. The first tiny organisms float in the ocean on February 21. The earliest animals crawl onto land on November 20. The last of the dinosaurs become extinct on December 25. And human ancestors appear on the afternoon of December 31. Humans have experienced only a small part of Earth's history.

 Key Concept Check How does the geologic time scale compare to the human time scale?

Observing Slow and Rapid Changes

According to the geologic time scale, Earth has changed over billions of years. Most of these changes occurred slowly. For example, it takes millions of years for a mountain range to erode. However, some changes occur rapidly. The mountain in **Figure 5** became over 300 m tall in 1 year. It formed when eruptions from fissures, or cracks in the ground, formed a volcano in the middle of a cornfield. Likewise, an earthquake can change Earth's surface in just seconds.

Make a vertical four-tab Foldable. Label the sections as illustrated. Cut them to show the relationships among the units used to describe geologic time.

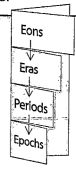

Eons → Eras → Periods → Epochs

Figure 5 Mount Paricutín formed when ash and lava erupted in this corn field in Michoacán, Mexico. Everything was buried in the town of Paricutín except the steeple of a church.

Visual Summary

Many ancient organisms that lived on Earth have been preserved in rocks. Scientists use them to help interpret Earth's history.

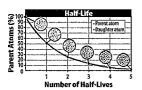

Radioactive elements contained within rocks can be used to calculate the age of rocks.

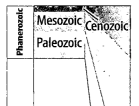

Eons, eras, periods and epochs are divisions of the geologic time scale.

FOLDABLES

Use your lesson Foldable to review the lesson. Save your Foldable for the project at the end of the chapter.

What do you think NOW?

You first read the statements below at the beginning of the chapter.

1. All rocks contain fossils.

2. Humans produce all radioactive materials.

Did you change your mind about whether you agree or disagree with the statements? Rewrite any false statements to make them true.

Use Vocabulary

① The preserved remains of organisms are called _____.

② **Define** *geologic time scale* in your own words.

③ **Use the terms** *radioactive decay* and *half-life* in a sentence.

Understand Key Concepts

④ What is the longest unit of time on the geologic time scale?
   A. eon
   B. epoch
   C. era
   D. period

⑤ **Relate** How were fossils used in the development of the geologic time scale?

⑥ **Compare** the ages of rocks determined by the principle of superposition and ages determined by radioactive decay.

Interpret Graphics

⑦ **Sequence** Use the graphic organizer to correctly order the following three phrases: *new discoveries are made, people develop scientific theories, scientific theories are modified.*

Critical Thinking

⑧ **Suggest** how the geologic time scale might be different if there were no radioactive elements.

⑨ **Explain** In 1978, the start of the Paleozoic era was placed at 570 million years ago. Today, it is placed at 542 million years. Discuss how this change is possible.

Math Skills 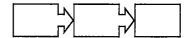 Math Practice

⑩ If you begin with 140 g of an element, how much remains after 3 half-lives? [Hint: Use the same process for grams as for atoms.]

©Layne Kennedy/Corbis

What do these numbers tell you about a rock's age?

Imagine you are part of a research team studying the Grand Canyon. You have collected some rock samples to identify. When you return to the lab, you plan to use the half-life data of the radiometric isotope Uranium 235 (U-235) to calculate the ages of the rock samples. The results will allow you to identify the source of each rock sample.

Materials

scientific calculator

Also needed:
U-235 radioactive decay pairs table, rock sample data table

Learn It

When you **analyze data,** you make observations about your results so you can draw conclusions about the data.

Try It

① Obtain a copy of Table 1, and complete it by converting the number of half-lives elapsed into decimal format.

② Radiometric dating reveals the amount of parent material left in each sample: Rock A has 18.7 percent parent material left; rock B has 70.7 percent; rock C has 42.7 percent; and rock D has 35.4 percent. Use Table 1 to determine the number of half-lives that have elapsed.

③ Calculate the age of each rock sample. The half-life of U-235 is 700 million (700 x 10⁶) years. Multiply the number of half-lives in Table 1 by the half-life of U-235.

④ Obtain a copy of Table 2. Match the age of your rock samples to the Grand Canyon rock layers listed in Table 2.

Apply It

⑤ **Analyze** Obtain a chart showing the rock layers of the Grand Canyon. Locate the rock layers from Table 2 on the chart. Determine to which geologic era the rocks belong. Copy Table 2, and record this information.

⑥ **Speculate** You collected one more rock sample on your hike, and identified it as Hermit Shale (265 million years old). Radiometric analysis reveals that it contains 95.8 percent parent material. Is your identification correct? Explain.

⑦ 🔑 **Key Concept** How does radiometric dating compare to relative-age dating? How does radiometric dating support the idea that Earth is very old?

Lesson 2

Reading Guide

Key Concepts

ESSENTIAL QUESTIONS

- How did gravity affect Earth's formation?
- How did the oceans and atmosphere form?
- What conditions made early Earth able to support life?
- How did environmental changes affect the evolution of life?

Vocabulary

Hadean eon p. 392

Archean eon p. 394

protocontinent p. 394

Proterozoic eon p. 396

 Multilingual eGlossary

 SEPS.2, SEPS.7, 6-8.LST.5.1, 6-8.LST.7.1

Ancient Earth

Inquiry Could this be Earth?

Earth's surface has not always been a hospitable place. Over the past 4.6 billion years, the surface has changed from a boiling mass of melted rock to one covered by warm, shallow oceans and finally to a combination of deep oceans, shallow seas and continents.

How might Earth's crust have formed?

Earth today is much different from Earth billions of years ago. One major difference is temperature. Early Earth was extremely hot. But as the planet cooled, things changed.

1. Read and complete a lab safety form.
2. Add 2–3 **wax sticks** to a 500-mL **beaker** half-filled with water.
3. Set the beaker on a **hot plate.** Turn on the hot plate.
4. Heat the water until all of the wax melts. Turn off the hot plate.
5. Put on **heat-resistant gloves** and remove the beaker from the hot plate.
6. As the water cools, observe the contents of the beaker. Record your observations in your Science Journal.

Think About This

1. Describe what you observed as the wax melted.

2. What happened to the wax as the water cooled?

3. **Key Concept** How do you think Earth's continental crust might have formed?

Earth's Earliest History

How do you know about the beginning of your life? You probably don't remember it, but you can search for evidence to learn about it. Maybe there are photographs, video or tape recordings, or family stories that hold some clues. Earth, however, is so old that no one knows how it formed. So, scientists must search for evidence of its beginning.

Gravity and the Solar System

Before Earth or even the solar system existed, a cloud of gas, ice, and dust, called a nebula (NEB yuh luh), floated in space, as shown in Figure 6.

First, gravity pulled the particles together into a flattened disk shape that began to rotate. Then, the material in the center of the disk became dense, and the Sun formed. Finally, the pieces of material remaining in the disk attracted each other, and the planets formed. Some smaller bits of rock and ice remained as asteroids and comets.

Formation of the Solar System

Figure 6 Scientists hypothesize that the solar system formed when a nebula was pulled together by gravity.

REVIEW VOCABULARY

thermal energy
energy that moves from one place to another because of differences in temperature.

Figure 7 The seas of molten rock that covered Hadean Earth might have looked like this pool of lava.

Spherical Earth

Earth became larger as more particles came together. Collisions produce thermal energy, so colliding particles warmed the new planet. Because the hot rocks that made up ancient Earth were soft enough to flow, gravity pulled them into the shape of a sphere. Asteroids continued to crash into the surface, making Earth even hotter.

Key Concept Check What effect did gravity have on Earth's formation?

The Hadean Eon

Collisions with asteroids were not the only source of thermal energy. The young planet had large amounts of radioactive elements, and thermal energy is a by-product of radioactive decay. These two sources of thermal energy made early Earth much hotter than it is today. Because it was so hot, that time in history was named after the Greek god of the underworld, Hades (HAY deez). *The first 640 million years of Earth history are called the* **Hadean** (hay DEE un) **eon.**

Formation of Earth's Core

At first, Earth was a mixture of solid particles. When it became hot enough to melt metal, the denser metal began to flow because of the force of gravity. This is how Earth developed distinct layers of different materials. For example, when molten iron and small amounts of other metals flowed toward Earth's center, they formed the core.

Reading Check How did gravity affect Earth after its formation?

A hot Earth cools.

Throughout the Hadean eon, fewer and fewer asteroids struck Earth. And, as radioactive elements decayed and formed stable elements, less radioactive material was present. As a result, Earth began to cool. It continues to cool even today.

Seas of Molten Rock

How might Hadean Earth's surface have been different from Earth's surface today? Recall that sometimes volcanoes form when thermal energy escapes from inside Earth. Volcanoes produce lava, such as that shown in **Figure 7.** Because Earth was much hotter during the Hadean eon, scientists hypothesize that there must have been more lava produced. In fact, they think that a sea of molten rock covered Earth's surface.

©Jason Weingart Photography

Changes in the Seas

The pool of lava shown in Figure 7 appears much like a small version of the huge molten seas of the Hadean eon. As Earth cooled, small islands of solid rock might have floated on the sea's surface. But motion in the molten seas or asteroid impacts would have destroyed them.

Earth continued to cool. Some of the material in the molten seas started to solidify, forming an ancient crust. This crust was not like Earth's crust today. Because of its composition, the crust would have melted very easily.

Reading Check Why isn't the earliest formed crust present on Earth today?

The Ancient Atmosphere

Lava was not the only thing that came from Hadean Earth's interior. Like present-day volcanic activity, Hadean eruptions produced gases. These volcanic gases formed Earth's earliest atmosphere. This atmosphere would have been poisonous for modern organisms. It contained water vapor, carbon dioxide, and poisonous gases, but no oxygen.

Key Concept Check How did Earth's early atmosphere form?

MiniLab
15 minutes

How might Earth's early atmosphere have formed?

You can't see it, taste it, or smell it. Yet the thin blanket of air that surrounds Earth is essential to you and most of the other life-forms that call this planet home. How might this blanket of gases have formed?

① Read and complete a lab safety form.

② Use the **hot plate** to boil 400 mL of water.

③ Place a **250-mL beaker** into each **bowl** as shown.

④ Pack **ice cubes** around one of the beakers.

⑤ Using **heat-resistant gloves** and **beaker tongs,** carefully pour the hot water into the bowl without the ice cubes, around the beaker.

⑥ Pour half of a **can of carbonated water** into the beaker in ice. Pour the other half into the beaker in hot water. Record your observations in your Science Journal.

Analyze and Conclude

1. **Compare and Contrast** What happened to the carbonated water in both beakers?

2. **Draw Conclusions** Why did the carbonated water in the two beakers react differently?

3. **Key Concept** How does this lab explain how Earth's early atmosphere might have formed?

Figure 8 During the Archean eon, the first continental crust formed protocontinents, which were smaller than present-day continents.

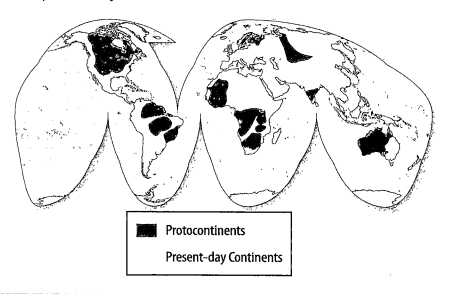

Protocontinents

Present-day Continents

ACADEMIC VOCABULARY

occur
(verb) to come into being—
as an event, to come to pass

The Archean Eon

The period of time that occurred from about 4 to 2.5 million years ago is called the **Archean** (ar KEE un) **eon.** Earth continued to cool after the Hadean eon. And during the Archean eon, Earth had its first solid surface. Portions of this first crust are still present on most of Earth's continents, as shown in **Figure 8.** Though Earth was cooler than during the Hadean eon, it still produced about twice as much internal thermal energy as present-day Earth. So far, the oldest rocks discovered on Earth formed during the Archean eon.

Extensive Volcanic Activity

You might have already learned that ocean crust forms when magma rises to the surface through cracks in the ocean floor. During the Archean eon, extensive volcanic activity formed Earth's first oceanic crust. Convection currents, formed by the rising and sinking of hot material below Earth's surface, moved the crust along Earth's surface in much the same way that convection moves tectonic plates today. But, with more thermal energy driving convection, the crust moved faster.

The Earliest Continents

Along with the first oceanic crust, the first continental crust formed during the Archean eon. As shown in **Figure 8,** the Archean continents were smaller than present-day continents, and there were more of them. *Scientists call the small, early continents* **protocontinents.** Throughout the Archean eon, convection caused collisions between these protocontinents. Sometimes they came together and formed larger landmasses.

Earth's Oceans Form

During the Archean eon, the temperature in Earth's atmosphere dropped. As a result, the water vapor in the air condensed. For the first time in Earth's history, it started to rain. Gases in the atmosphere made the rain acidic. So, when the rain fell on Earth's solid surface, it quickly dissolved mineral salts from rocks. By the time the low areas of the oceanic crust filled with water, the new oceans were salty. Where did all the water come from?

Recall that volcanic eruptions throughout the Hadean and Archean eons released water vapor into the atmosphere. Icy comets probably added more water vapor to the atmosphere each time one passed close to Earth or collided with it. Earth's warm atmosphere changed the ice to water vapor.

Key Concept Check How did Earth's oceans form?

Fossil Bacteria and Stromatolites The earliest evidence of life is present in rocks that formed in the warm Archean oceans. These fossils are uncommon and difficult to see because they are often microscopic. The fossils are the remains of unicellular bacteria and cyanobacteria (si an oh bak TIH ree uh), also called blue-green algae. Sometimes sticky strands of cyanobacteria trap sediment from the ocean and form visible mounds called stromatolites (stroh MA tuh lites). The fossil stromatolites shown in the inset photo in **Figure 9**, have a similar structure to the present-day stromatolites shown in the larger photo.

Key Concept Check What conditions made early Earth able to support life?

Life in Extreme Environments The Archean oceans were extreme environments. Most present-day organisms would not have survived in them. However, investigating extreme environments today can provide clues to how early life survived on Earth.

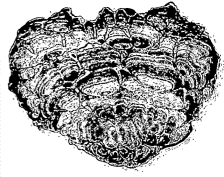

SCIENCE USE V. COMMON USE

salt
Science Use an ionic crystalline compound

Common Use a substance used to season or preserve food

Figure 9 Sometimes mats of cyanobacteria trap calcium carbonate and form visible mounds called stromatolites. Fossil stromatolites formed in the same way that modern stromatolites form. This slice through a fossil stromatolite shows its layered structure.

The Proterozoic Eon

After the Archean eon, Earth began to look more like the planet we know today. *The time from 2.5 to 0.542 billion years ago is known as the* **Proterozoic** (PROH ter oh zoh ihk) **eon.** As Earth cooled, convection currents in the mantle slowed, but collisions of protocontinents continued. Eventually, larger landmasses the size of present-day continents formed.

Changes in the Atmosphere

Changes in the composition of Earth's atmosphere were also occurring during this time. Two distinct processes caused these changes.

Increase in Oxygen First, energy from the Sun split water molecules, separating hydrogen from oxygen. Second, unicellular organisms in the ocean produced oxygen from carbon dioxide and water through photosynthesis. As time passed, the amount of oxygen in the atmosphere increased from about 3 percent to 20 percent. This increase is called the Great Oxygenation Event. It also is called the Oxygen Catastrophe (kuh TAS truh fee) because the new oxygen-rich atmosphere was harmful to species that had evolved in an oxygen-poor environment.

Key Concept Check How did changes in Earth's environment affect the evolution of life?

Snowball Earth Some scientists hypothesize that 800 to 600 million years ago, the entire planet might have been a harsh environment. The Snowball Earth hypothesis suggests that changes in the atmosphere caused the surface of Earth to completely freeze over. One interpretation of Earth's frozen surface is shown in **Figure 10.**

WORD ORIGIN

catastrophe
from Greek *katastrephein,* means "to overturn"

Figure 10 According to the Snowball Earth hypothesis, the whole Earth might have been covered with ice during the late Proterozoic eon. Ice formed at the poles and spread all the way to the equator.

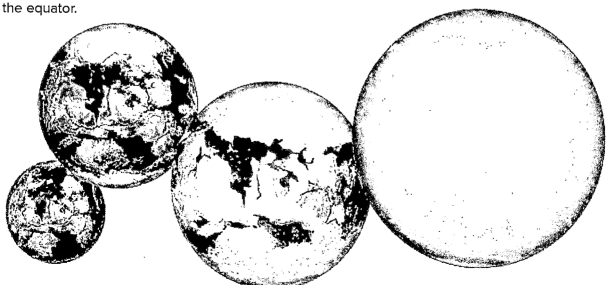

Supercontinents and Shallow Seas

You might have already learned about Pangaea. It was a supercontinent that formed during the Late Paleozoic. But it was not Earth's only supercontinent. Scientists hypothesize that a different supercontinent existed during the Proterozoic. They call it Rodinia. It formed as separate continents collided and stuck together. They also think that it took millions of years for Rodinia to form. The environments along the coasts of Rodinia were similar to the environments that are present along the ocean's shores today. The ocean close to the shoreline was shallow. It was also relatively warm in some places. These environments were favorable for the developing Proterozoic organisms.

Figure 11 Fossils, such as these from the Ediacara fauna of Australia, are evidence of the evolutionary changes taking place during the Proterozoic eon. The central image is an artist's interpretation of the environment in which these organisms lived.

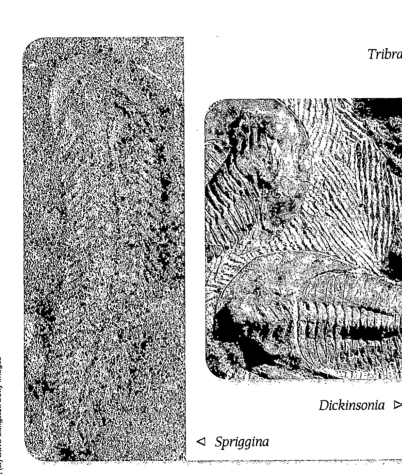

Tribrachidium ▷

Dickinsonia ▷

◁ *Spriggina*

Proterozoic Life

Unicelluar organisms remained the dominant life-forms during the Proterozoic eon. And life was still restricted to the water. An important change occurred near the end of this eon. The first multicellular organisms evolved in the oceans. These life-forms had no hard parts, such as teeth, bones, or shells. So, like earlier organisms, their fossils are not abundant. However, there are some locations where soft mud preserved their delicate remains, such as those shown in Figure 11. They provide a preview of the evolutionary changes to come.

Visual Summary

The Hadean eon is marked by a molten Earth and the development of Earth's core.

■ Protocontinents
Present-day Continents

During the Archean eon, protocontinents and oceans formed, and the atmosphere became hospitable to life.

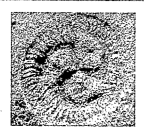

Oxygen became abundant in the atmosphere during the Proterozoic eon, and new and complex life-forms evolved.

FOLDABLES

Use your lesson Foldable to review the lesson. Save your Foldable for the project at the end of the chapter.

What do you think NOW?

You first read the statements below at the beginning of the chapter.

3. When Earth first formed, oceans were much larger than they are today.

4. Earth's early atmosphere was different from Earth's present-day atmosphere.

Did you change your mind about whether you agree or disagree with the statements? Rewrite any false statements to make them true.

Use Vocabulary

1 **Use the term** *Archean* in a sentence.

2 **Define** What is a protocontinent?

Understand Key Concepts

3 What heat sources caused melting in early Earth?
   A. the Sun and stars
   B. collisions and the Sun
   C. radioactivity and the Sun
   D. radioactivity and collisions

4 **Relate** the presence of oxygen in the atmosphere to life-forms.

5 **Sort** Use a Venn diagram to sort the following list into two groups, Archean and Proterozoic: *unicellular organism, first oceans, multicellular organism, Snowball Earth*

Interpret Graphics

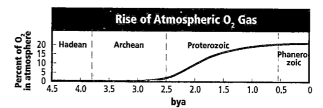

6 **Assess** What does the graph above show about the level of oxygen in the atmosphere over the last 450 million years?

7 **Draw** a graphic organizer such as the one below, and put the following terms in order of occurrence: *breakdown of water, oxygen-rich atmosphere, breakdown of carbon dioxide.*

Critical Thinking

8 **Imagine** radioactivity did not exist. How would Earth history change?

9 **Critique** the name *Proterozoic* for the third eon in Earth history. The word is derived from the Greek words for "first life."

Global Cooling?

AMERICAN MUSEUM NATURAL HISTORY

A Different Kind of Climate Change

As if global warming weren't bad enough, imagine extreme global cooling. Geological evidence shows that our planet has been through more than one episode of Snowball Earth. This climate change was so severe the polar ice caps grew so large they actually met at the equator.

Although Earth did thaw, much of the planet is still very cold, even today. On average, more than 70 percent of Earth's ecosystems are below or close to 0°C, including the deep ocean and frozen alpine and polar regions. Over time, humans have learned how to survive on much of Earth's frozen surface. By building strong shelters, wearing warm clothing, and preserving food, humans have learned to live with the ever-present cold.

▲ Could humans live in a place like this?

But what if it got so cold that no plants could grow? Like many animals, humans depend on plants for food. Plants could not survive on another Snowball Earth. Without plants, we would soon run out of food. Could we survive such extreme global cooling? Not likely.

What about global warming? Although scientists are researching ways to reverse global warming, it could be 100 years or more before the effects of today's actions are realized. Meanwhile, societies must adjust to increasingly warmer climates. Some societies already are doing just that. In France, farmers are planting crops that can tolerate warmer temperatures. In Austria, ski resorts are planning hiking trails and golf courses for a future without snow. In Copenhagen, Denmark, the new subway system will be built with raised structures that allow for the rise in sea level that is expected from global warming.

The question, however, remains: can entire societies really adjust? The answer might depend on how warm the climate gets and whether societies can change as quickly as the climate does.

▲ What if snow never fell on these ski slopes again?

It's Your Turn

FORM AN OPINION Can society adjust to changing environments? Will it? Research the question and form an opinion. Write a report to convince society that they must adjust to the changing environment. Provide strong reasons for your position and include examples of how they might adjust.

(l) Imagebroker/Alamy, (r) Thorsten Milse/Getty Images, (b) ©Bauphoto/Alamy

The Cambrian Explosion

Reading Guide

Key Concepts

ESSENTIAL QUESTIONS

- How were Phanerozoic life-forms different from earlier life-forms?

- How did asteroid impacts affect Earth's environment?

- What natural processes change Earth's surface?

Vocabulary

Phanerozoic eon p. 401

adaptation p. 402

extinct p. 402

Multilingual eGlossary

7.ESS.2, SEPS.2, SEPS.4, SEPS.8

Inquiry) What kind of animal is this?

Organisms live in all environments, from the coldest to the warmest, from the wettest to the driest. But, Earth's organisms haven't always lived in so many environments. Over time, they have adapted to changing environments. Where did Earth's earliest organisms first appear? How did they come to live where they do now? Why are so many of these early species no longer living on Earth?

What types of organisms are likely to become fossils?

There is little fossil evidence of Earth's earliest life-forms. But why? What about them made them less likely to become preserved as fossils?

1. Read and complete a lab safety form.
2. Flatten the **salt dough** into a slab about 1 cm thick.
3. Inflate a **small, round balloon** halfway. Tie off the balloon.
4. Place the **shell** and the balloon side by side on top of the dough. Predict which model "organism" has a better chance of becoming fossilized. Write your prediction in your Science Journal.
5. Cover the organisms with a piece of **waxed paper.**
6. Place a **book** over the organisms. After a minute or two, remove the book and the waxed paper. Observe the organisms and the dough, and record your observations.

Think About This

1. What does the book represent in this model?

2. Describe what both model organisms and the clay looked liked after you removed the book.

3. **Key Concept** Which organism represents the earliest life-forms on Earth? Why?

The Cambrian Explosion

Have you ever watched fireworks? At first, the sky looks dark and empty. Then suddenly there is an explosion, and the sky fills with sparkling light. This sudden explosion is similar to what happened at the beginning of the **Phanerozoic** (FAN uh ruh ZO ihk) **eon,** *the time in Earth's history from 542 million years ago to the present.* *Phanerozoic* means "visible life." Remember that early fossils are rare and mostly microscopic. Some rock layers from the Phanerozoic eon appear different from rocks that formed earlier. Phanerozoic rocks contain a great number of fossils that are large enough to observe without using a magnifying device.

The beginning of the Phanerozoic eon is called the Cambrian (KAM bree un) Period. During this time, some organisms, such as the trilobite (TRI luh bite) pictured in the photo on the opposite page, developed hard parts such as shells. Shells and bones are more easily fossilized than soft bodies. Fossils from the Cambrian period show a great diversity of organisms. This change in life on Earth is called the Cambrian Explosion.

WORD ORIGIN ·············
trilobite
from Greek *tri,* means "three";
and Greek *lobos,* means "lobe"
················

 Key Concept Check How were Phanerozoic life-forms different from earlier life-forms?

Hutchings Photography/Digital Light Source

How do glaciers affect sea level?

① Read and complete a lab safety form.

② Place a wide-rimmed **soup bowl** upside down in the center of a **plastic tub.**

③ Add water to the container until it reaches the point where the rim meets the bowl.

④ In your Science Journal, make a drawing of your setup as viewed from the side. Use a **blue pencil** and a **ruler** to accurately mark the water level on your drawing.

⑤ Use two **small paper cups** to remove two cups of water from the container. Place the full cups on top of the bowl.

⑥ Use a **red pencil** and the ruler to accurately mark the new water level on your drawing.

Analyze and Conclude

1. **Infer** What do the cups of water represent?

2. **Recognize Cause and Effect** On your drawing, use the colored pencils to show how the drop in sea level affected organisms that lived in the warm, shallow seas during the Cambrian period.

3. 🔑 **Key Concept** What natural process changed Earth and may have caused the Cambrian extinctions?

Environmental Changes

What caused the Cambrian Explosion? Scientists hypothesize that it resulted from changes in Earth's environments. Early in the Phanerozoic eon, continents were breaking apart, temperatures were increasing, and sea levels were rising. These changes produced many new, warm, shallow seas. They are the light blue areas in **Figure 12**. These seas provided environments for rapid evolution of new organisms.

Figure 12 🔑 Earth's surface during the Cambrian period had many separate continents and no ice caps.

🔍 **Visual Check** How did sea level during the Cambrian period compare to sea level today?

Adaptations and Extinctions

Some organisms are better suited to an environment than others. **Adaptations** *are the characteristics that species develop over time that help them survive in a particular environment.* Species that do not adapt as environments change eventually die off. *A species is considered* **extinct** *when all of its members have died.* Recall that divisions in the geologic time scale mark places in the rock record where there are major changes in the types of fossils. These changes often mark mass extinction events. These are times when many species become extinct within a short time.

✓ **Reading Check** How did the breaking apart of continents result in the formation of more hospitable environments?

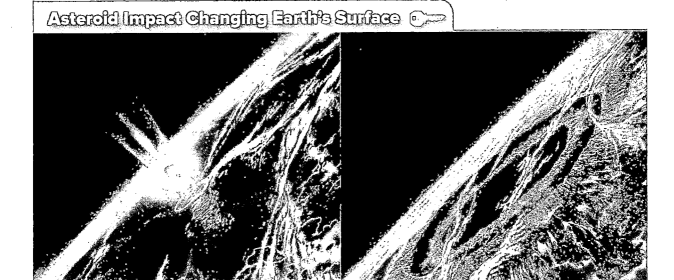

Figure 13 An asteroid impact might have contributed to the mass extinction that occurred at the end of the Cretaceous period.

The Impact of Asteroids

What kinds of environmental changes can cause a mass extinction? One example is the result of an asteroid impact. You read earlier that when the solar system formed, not all of the material in the dust and gas cloud became the Sun and planets. Some smaller space objects, including asteroids, remained. Sometimes asteroids collide with Earth. If an asteroid is large enough, the collision can change Earth's environment. Figure 13 shows what such an event might look like.

Scientists hypothesize that an asteroid impact might have contributed to the mass extinction that occurred at the end of the Cretaceous period. Large impact events throw crushed rock and dust into the atmosphere blocking out sunlight. This leads to global cooling and changing climates. These environment-changing events occur over a short period of time. This is not long enough for species to adapt to these changes. Some marine reptiles, flying reptiles, and land plants, as well as the last of the dinosaurs, became extinct at the end of the Cretaceous.

 Key Concept Check How can an asteroid impact change Earth's environment?

Mass extinction events generally are followed by rapid evolutionary changes. The surviving species adapt to unoccupied environments. This process has resulted in a continuous change of the life-forms on Earth. Within this chapter, you have seen a small sample of the variety of organisms that have inhabited our planet throughout Earth's history.

FOLDABLES

Use a sheet of notebook paper to make a four-tab Foldable. Label as illustrated and use it to record what you learn about the environmental changes that led to the Cambrian Explosion.

Continents Breaking Apart

Temperatures Increasing

Sea Levels Rising

Asteroid Impact

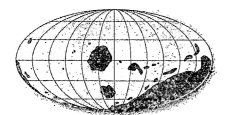

Cambrian

Devonian

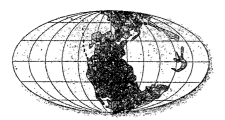

Pennsylvanian

Triassic

Cretaceous

Neogene

Earth's Changing Surface

Earth's surface has been evolving since its formation 4.6 billion years ago. The same sources of internal thermal energy that drove the earliest volcanism and plate tectonics operate today. **Figure 14** is a series of maps that shows how the position of the continents has changed throughout the Phanerozoic eon. Because thermal energy still escapes from Earth's interior, the tectonic plates and the continents that are part of them have not stopped moving.

Volcanic Activity

Although volcanic activity has decreased over the past 4.6 billion years, it continues today. The greatest amount of activity is at the boundaries between tectonic plates. Volcanoes form oceanic crust, help build mountains, and fuel part of the rock cycle.

Mountain Building

During the Phanerozoic eon, the supercontinent Pangaea formed. As the tectonic plates came together, mountains formed. The last three maps in **Figure 14** show that as Pangaea broke apart, Africa moved toward Europe. As the continents on the plates pushed against each other, the Alps formed in the area that is now Europe.

Changes Continue

The processes that changed ancient Earth continue to change present-day Earth. And, as you have learned, the evidence of these changes is recorded in the rock layers that make up Earth. Scientists study present-day processes as well as fossils and rock layers to develop theories about how Earth has changed throughout history.

Key Concept Check What natural processes change Earth's surface?

◄ **Figure 14** The surface of Earth has been changing since its formation. These maps illustrate how landmasses have moved throughout geologic time.

 Animation

Visual Summary

The Cambrian Explosion marks the appearance of new and different life-forms.

Changes in climate and the environment influenced the development of life on Earth.

Earth's surface has been changed, partly as a result of volcanic activity, mountain building, and asteroid impacts.

FOLDABLES

Use your lesson Foldable to review the lesson. Save your Foldable for the project at the end of the chapter.

What do you think

You first read the statements below at the beginning of the chapter.

5. Fish were the first organisms in the oceans.

6. Asteroids no longer crash into Earth.

Did you change your mind about whether you agree or disagree with the statements? Rewrite any false statements to make them true.

Use Vocabulary

1 **Use the term** *Phanerozoic eon* in a sentence.

2 When all members of a species have died, that species is _____.

3 **Define** *adaptations* in your own words.

Understand Key Concepts

4 What important changes developed in Cambrian life-forms?
- **A.** ability to swim
- **B.** better hunting skills
- **C.** growth of hard parts
- **D.** ability to breathe oxygen

5 **Summarize** how plate tectonic activity during the Phanerozoic eon resulted in changes to Earth's surface.

Interpret Graphics

6 **Observe** the trilobite in the figure below. Give an example of an adaptation they developed living in the Cambrian ocean.

7 **Organize** Use a graphic organizer to sequence the following events: rock and debris in the atmosphere, global cooling, changing climates, asteroid impact, some species become extinct, sunlight blocked

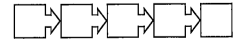

Critical Thinking

8 **Relate** the environmental changes resulting from an asteroid impact to adaptations that might be beneficial when one occurred.

9 **Describe** how an organism might adapt to living in muddy water.

Mark Steinmetz

Materials

meterstick

tape measure

poster board

colored markers

colored paper

string

maps

Modeling Geologic Time

Evidence suggests that Earth formed approximately 4.6 billion years ago. But how long is 4,600,000,000 years? It is difficult to comprehend time that extends so far into the past unless you can relate it to your own experience. In this activity, you will develop a metaphor for geologic time using a scale that is familiar to you. Then, you will create a model to share with your class.

Question

How can you model geologic time using a familiar scale?

Procedure

1. Think of something you are familiar with that can model a long period of time. For example, you might choose the length of a football field or the distance between two U.S. cities on a map—one on the east coast and one on the west coast.

2. Make a model of your metaphor using a metric scale. On your model, display the events listed in the table on the next page. Use the equation below to generate true-to-scale dates in your model.

$$\frac{\text{Known age of past event (years before present)}}{\text{Known age of Earth (years before present)}} = \frac{X \text{ time scale unit location}}{\text{Maximum distance or extent of metaphor}}$$

Example: To find where "first fish" would be placed on your model if you used a meterstick (100 cm), set up your equation as follows:

$$\frac{500,000,000 \text{ years}}{4,600,000,000 \text{ years}} = \frac{X \text{ (location on meterstick)}}{100 \text{ cm}}$$

3. In your Science Journal, keep a record of all the math equations you used. You can use a calculator, but show all equations.

Analyze and Conclude

④ **Calculate** What percentage of geologic time have modern humans occupied? Set up your equation as follows:

$$\frac{100{,}000}{4{,}600{,}000{,}000} \times 100 = \text{\% of time occupied by } H.\ sapiens$$

⑤ **Estimate** Where does the Precambrian end on your model? Estimate how much of geologic time falls within the Precambrian.

⑥ **Evaluate** What other milestone events in Earth's history, other than those listed in the table, could you include on your model?

⑦ **Appraise** the following sentence as it relates to your life: "Time is relative."

⑧ 🔵 **The Big Idea** The Earth events on the model you constructed are based mostly on evidence from rock layers and fossil records. How did this evidence help you to understand how the geologic time scale is used to organize Earth's 4.6-billion-year-old history?

Communicate Your Results

Share your model with the class. Explain why you chose the model you did, and demonstrate how you calculated the scale on your model.

Imagine that you were asked to teach a class of kindergartners about Earth's time. How would you do it? What metaphor would you use? Why?

Some Important Approximate Dates in the History of Earth:	
MYA	Event
4,600	Origin of Earth
3,500	Oldest evidence of life
500	First fish
375	Tiktaalik appears
320	First reptiles
252	Permian extinction event
220	Mammals and dinosaurs appear
155	Archaeopteryx appears
145	Atlantic Ocean forms
66	Cretaceous extinction event
6	Human ancestors appear
2.6	Pleistocene Ice Age begins
0.1	Homo sapiens appear
0.00052	Columbus lands in New World
??	Your birth date

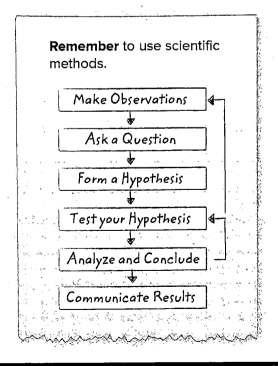

Remember to use scientific methods.

Make Observations → Ask a Question → Form a Hypothesis → Test your Hypothesis → Analyze and Conclude → Communicate Results

Over geologic time, oceans formed, continents grew due to constructive and destructive forces, and the composition of the atmosphere changed. The organisms that lived on Earth evolved as these conditions changed.

Key Concepts Summary

Vocabulary

Lesson 1: Geologic Time

- Thick layers of rock and the **fossils** they contain, along with rock ages derived from measuring radioactive elements, show that Earth is billions of years old.
- Scientists used the **principle of superposition** and the fossils in rock layers to develop the **geologic time scale.**
- The geologic time scale is extremely long compared to the human time scale.

principle of superposition p. 384
fossil p. 384
radioactive decay p. 385
half-life p. 385
geologic time scale p. 386

Lesson 2: Ancient Earth

- Gravity is the force that pulled together material in space, forming a sphere.
- The atmosphere and oceans formed from gases that escaped from inside Earth and water vapor from comets.
- Moderate temperatures and liquid water made early Earth able to support life.
- Changes in temperature, the depth of oceans, and the composition of the atmosphere have all affected the evolution of life.

Hadean eon p. 392
Archean eon p. 394
protocontinent p. 394
Proterozoic eon p. 396

Lesson 3: The Cambrian Explosion

- Phanerozoic life-forms were more abundant and more diverse than earlier life-forms. Many also produced hard parts, which earlier organisms did not have.
- Asteroid impacts altered the atmosphere by adding dust particles and blocking out sunlight, which resulted in global cooling.
- Volcanism, plate tectonic motion, weathering, and erosion continuously change Earth's surface.

Phanerozoic eon p. 401
adaptation p. 402
extinct p. 402

(t) © Layne Kennedy/Corbis, (c) Jason Edwards/Getty Images, (b) Mark Steinmetz

Personal Tutor

Vocabulary eFlashcards

Vocabulary eGames

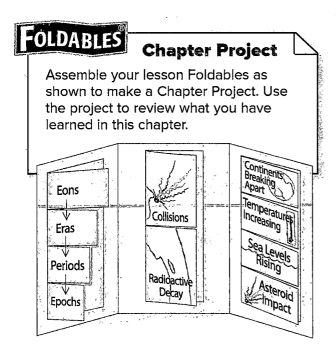

Chapter Project

Assemble your lesson Foldables as shown to make a Chapter Project. Use the project to review what you have learned in this chapter.

Eons → Eras → Periods → Epochs

Collisions

Radioactive Decay

Continents Breaking Apart

Temperature Increasing

Sea Levels Rising

Asteroid Impact

Use Vocabulary

1 Define the principle of superposition in your own words.

2 Use the term *fossil* in a sentence.

3 Distinguish between the Hadean and the Proterozoic.

4 Explain radioactive decay in your own words.

5 Humans are living during the _____.

6 Use the term *extinct* in a sentence.

 Interactive Concept Map

Link Vocabulary and Key Concepts

Copy this concept map, and then use vocabulary terms from the previous page to complete the concept map.

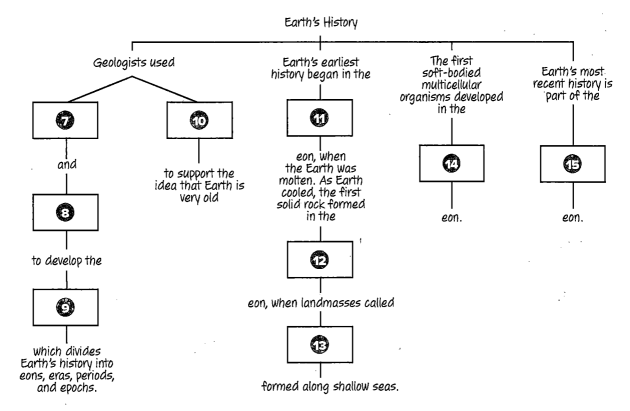

Earth's History

Geologists used

7 and **8** to develop the **9** which divides Earth's history into eons, eras, periods, and epochs.

10 to support the idea that Earth is very old

Earth's earliest history began in the **11** eon, when the Earth was molten. As Earth cooled, the first solid rock formed in the **12** eon, when landmasses called **13** formed along shallow seas.

The first soft-bodied multicellular organisms developed in the **14** eon.

Earth's most recent history is part of the **15** eon.

Understand Key Concepts

1 What evidence could you use to determine which rock layer is oldest in the figure below?

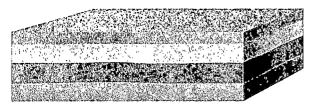

A. observation of layer order
B. observation of layer colors
C. measurement of layer thicknesses
D. classification of particle size in layers

2 What is needed to make a fossil?
A. rock and sediment
B. sand and sediment
C. an organism and water
D. an organism and sediment

3 After 2 half-lives of a radioactive element, how much of the parent element is left?
A. one-half
B. one-third
C. one-fourth
D. one-eighth

4 Over time, which of these break down?
A. all elements
B. stable elements
C. parent elements
D. daughter elements

5 What molten metal formed most of Earth's core?
A. iron
B. nickel
C. cobalt
D. hematite

6 What product of volcanic eruptions made the atmosphere's composition more similar to that of today?
A. oxygen
B. nitrogen
C. water vapor
D. carbon dioxide

7 How did the amount of volcanic activity change as Earth aged?
A. It decreased.
B. It increased.
C. It remained the same.
D. It stopped completely.

8 Which characteristic distinguishes the Precambrian fossil from the Phanerozoic fossil pictured below?

A. The Precambrian organism had adaptations for life on land.
B. The Phanerozoic organism had adaptations for life on land.
C. The Precambrian organism had hard body parts.
D. The Phanerozoic organism had hard body parts.

9 Which feature could mammals develop to adapt to a warming global climate?
A. larger eyes
B. larger bodies
C. thicker coats of fur
D. thinner coats of fur

10 What improves an organism's chances for preservation as a fossil?
A. hair
B. hard shell
C. muscles
D. skin

11 Which classification for fossils distinguishes Phanerozoic-aged fossils from Proterozoic-aged fossils?
A. old or young
B. hard parts or soft parts
C. unicellular or multicellular
D. well-adapted or poorly adapted

Mark Steinmetz

Critical Thinking

12 Suggest how scientists might revise their estimate for Earth's age if they discovered a 6-billion-year-old rock.

13 Explain how rock layers containing older fossils can occur above rock layers that contain younger fossils.

14 Choose what evidence you might use to determine the relative age of two rock layers in your neighborhood.

15 Hypothesize why the oldest rocks on Earth are from the Archean eon, not the Hadean eon.

16 Describe how the event above might impact Earth's surface, atmosphere, and organisms.

17 Discuss why there are no fossils of Hadean age.

18 Suppose that all the internal heat had completely escaped from inside Earth. How would this change Earth's surface?

19 Support the decision to name the evolutionary changes occurring at the start of the Phanerozoic eon the Cambrian Explosion.

Writing in Science

20 Write A haiku is a poem with three lines. The lines contain five, seven, and five syllables respectively. Write a haiku about the changes Earth has gone through since it formed.

REVIEW THE BIG IDEA

21 Will the natural events that change Earth's surface continue indefinitely?

22 How have natural events changed over time?

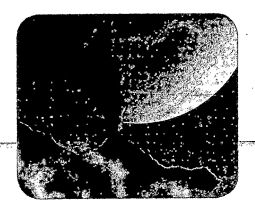

Math Skills **Math Practice**

Using Percentages

23 If you begin with 68 g of an isotope, how many grams of the original isotope will remain after 4 half-lives?

24 After 6 days, only 25 percent of a sample of a radioactive element remains. What is the half-life of the element?

25 Fifty atoms of a radioactive element remain after 5 half-lives. How many atoms were in the original sample?

Record your answers on the answer sheet provided by your teacher or on a sheet of paper.

Multiple Choice

1   Which is NOT a cause of the Cambrian Explosion?

    A   Continents were breaking apart.

    B   Temperatures were increasing.

    C   Sea levels were rising.

    D   Ice caps were increasing.

Use the figure below to answer questions 2 and 3.

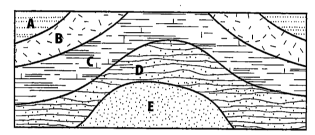

2   According to the principle of superposition, which rock layer in this cross section is youngest?

    F   layer A

    G   layer B

    H   layer C

    I   layer D

3   Which is probably true of fossils in layer B?

    A   They are younger than fossils in layer A.

    B   They are younger than fossils in layer C.

    C   They are older than fossils in layer D.

    D   They are older than fossils in layer E.

4   Which force do scientists hypothesize formed our solar system?

    F   collision

    G   electromagnetism

    H   gravity

    I   magnetism

5   Which caused the formation of Earth's earliest atmosphere?

    A   blue-green algae

    B   colliding continents

    C   multicellular organisms

    D   volcanic activity

6   During which event does evidence show that life on Earth diversified greatly?

    F   Cambrian Explosion

    G   Hadean Earth

    H   Oxygen Catastrophe

    I   Snowball Earth

Use the graph below to answer question 7.

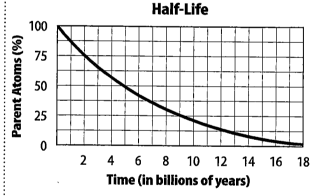

7   What is the half-life of the radioactive element shown in the graph?

    A   2 billion years

    B   5 billion years

    C   9 billion years

    D   12 billion years

8   Which conditions led to the evolution of new species during the Cambrian?

    F   decreasing temperatures

    G   unchanging positions of the continents

    H   the presence of warm, shallow seas

    I   multiple asteroid impacts

9 Which process or action is responsible for Earth's continual surface changes over the last 4.6 billion years?

   A plate tectonics

   B asteroid impacts

   C volcanic activity

   D mountain building

10 What do geologists use to divide geologic time into eons, eras, and periods?

   F fossils

   G radioactive dating

   H changes in rocks and fossils

   I radioactive dating and the principle of superposition

Use the table below to answer questions 11 and 12.

Some Radioactive Elements		
Parent Element	**Daughter Element**	**Half-life (in years)**
Carbon-14	Nitrogen-14	5,730
Uranium-235	Lead-207	704 million

11 Which element in the table above would be better for dating a sample from Precambrian time?

   A carbon-14

   B lead-207

   C nitrogen-14

   D uranium-235

12 A sample of wood contains 25 percent of the carbon-14 that a living plant contains. What is the approximate age of the wood?

   F 2,865 years

   G 5,730 years

   H 11,460 years

   I 17,190 years

13 A geologist is trying to determine the relative age of rock layers in a certain area, but he or she cannot rely on the principle of superposition. Which clue will help the geologist determine whether a rock layer has been overturned?

   A Igneous rock usually forms below sedimentary rock.

   B Rock layers erode at an average rate of 1.5 m per year.

   C The largest sediment particles are usually deposited near the bottom of a rock layer.

   D Metamorphic rocks are the lightest type of rock, so they will be deposited at the top of a rock layer.

14 Which term states that the oldest rock layer is found at the bottom in an undisclosed stack of rock layers?

   F half-life

   G geologic time scale

   H superposition

   I radioactive decay

NEED EXTRA HELP?														
If You Missed Question...	1	2	3	4	5	6	7	8	9	10	11	12	13	14
Go to Lesson...	3	1	1	2	2	2	1	2	2	3	1	1	1	1

Chapter 12

7.ESS.7, SEPS.2, SEPS.4, SEPS.5, SEPS.6, SEPS.7, SEPS.8, 6-8.LST.4.2, 6-8.LST.5.1, 6-8.LST.7.1, 6-8.LST.7.3

Natural Resources

THE BIG IDEA Why is it important to manage natural resources wisely?

Inquiry What do these colors mean?

This image shows where thermal energy escapes from the inside of a house. Red and yellow areas represent the greatest loss. Blue areas represent low or no loss.

- Which energy resources are used to heat this house?

- Why is it important to reduce thermal energy loss from houses, cars, or electrical appliances?

- Why is it important to manage natural resources wisely?

Get Ready to Read

What do you think?

Before you read, decide if you agree or disagree with each of these statements. As you read this chapter, see if you change your mind about any of the statements.

1. Nonrenewable energy resources include fossil fuels and uranium.

2. Energy use in the United States is lower than in other countries.

3. Renewable energy resources do not pollute the environment.

4. Burning organic material can produce electricity.

5. Cities cover most of the land in the United States.

6. Minerals form over millions of years.

7. Humans need oxygen and water to survive.

8. About 10 percent of Earth's total water can be used by humans.

Your one-stop online resource
connectED.mcgraw-hill.com

 LearnSmart®

 Chapter Resources Files, Reading Essentials, Get Ready to Read, Quick Vocabulary

Animations, Videos, Interactive Tables

 Self-checks, Quizzes, Tests

 Project-Based Learning Activities

 Lab Manuals, Safety Videos, Virtual Labs & Other Tools

 Vocabulary, Multilingual ·eGlossary, Vocab eGames, Vocab eFlashcards

 Personal Tutors

Reading Guide

Key Concepts

ESSENTIAL QUESTIONS

- What are the main sources of nonrenewable energy?

- What are the advantages and disadvantages of using nonrenewable energy resources?

- How can individuals help manage nonrenewable resources wisely?

Vocabulary

nonrenewable resource p. 417

renewable resource p. 417

nuclear energy p. 421

reclamation p. 423

 Multilingual eGlossary

7.ESS.7, SEPS.2, SEPS.7, 6-8.LST.4.2

Energy Resources

Inquiry — What's in the pipeline?

The Trans-Alaska Pipeline System carries oil more than 1,200 km from beneath Prudhoe Bay, Alaska, to the port city of Valdez, Alaska. How might the pipeline's construction and operation affect the habitats and the organisms living along it? How do getting and using fossil fuels impact the environment?

bonfey45/iStock/Getty Images

How do you use energy resources?

In the United States today, the energy used for most daily activities is easily available at the flip of a switch or the push of a button. How do you use energy in your daily activities?

1. Design a three-column data chart in your Science Journal. Title the columns *Activity, Type of Energy Used,* and *Amount of Time.*

2. Record every instance that you use energy during a 24-hr period.

3. Total your usage of the different forms of energy, and record them in your Science Journal.

Think About This

1. How many times did you use each type of energy?

2. Compare and contrast your usage with that of other members of your class.

3. 🔑 **Key Concept** Are there instances of energy use when you could have conserved energy? Explain how you would do it.

Sources of Energy

Think about all the times you use energy in one day. Are you surprised by how much you depend on energy? You use it for electricity, transportation, and other needs. That is one reason it is important to know where energy comes from and how much is available for humans to use.

Table 1 lists different energy sources. Most energy in the United States comes from nonrenewable resources. **Nonrenewable resources** *are resources that are used faster than they can be replaced by natural processes.* Fossil fuels, such as coal and oil, and uranium, which is used in nuclear reactions, are both nonrenewable energy resources.

Renewable resources *are resources that can be replaced by natural processes in a relatively short amount of time.* The Sun's energy, also called solar energy, is a renewable energy resource. You will read more about renewable energy resources in Lesson 2.

🔑 **Key Concept Check** What are the main nonrenewable energy resources?

Table 1 Energy resources can be nonrenewable or renewable.

Table 1 Energy Sources	
Nonrenewable Energy Resources	**Renewable Energy Resources**
fossil fuels uranium	solar wind water geothermal biomass

WORD ORIGIN

resource
from Latin *resurgere*, means "to rise again"

Spencer Grant/PhotoEdit

Nonrenewable Energy Resources

You might turn on a lamp to read, turn on a heater to stay warm, or ride the bus to school. In the United States, the energy to power lamps, heat houses, and run vehicles probably comes from nonrenewable energy resources, such as fossil fuels.

Fossil Fuels

Coal, oil, also called petroleum, and natural gas are fossil fuels. They are nonrenewable because they form over millions of years. The fossil fuels used today formed from the remains of prehistoric organisms. The decayed remains of these organisms were buried by layers of sediment and changed chemically by extreme temperatures and pressure. The type of fossil fuel that formed depended on three factors:

- the type of organic matter
- the temperature and pressure
- the length of time that the organic matter was buried

Reading Check What factors determine which type of fossil fuel forms?

Coal Earth was very different 350 million years ago, when the coal used today began forming. Plants, such as ferns and trees, grew in prehistoric swamps. As shown in Figure 1, the first step of coal formation occurred when those plants died.

Bacteria, extreme temperatures, and pressure acted on the plant remains over time. Eventually a brownish material, called peat, formed. Peat can be used as a fuel. However, peat contains moisture and produces a lot of smoke when it burns. As shown in Figure 1, peat eventually can change into harder and harder types of coal. The hardest coal, anthracite, contains the most carbon per unit of volume and burns most efficiently.

 **Animation**

Figure 1 Much of the coal used today began forming more than 300 million years ago from the remains of prehistoric plants.

Coal Formation

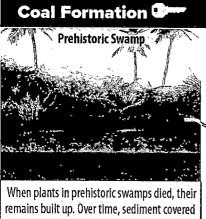

Prehistoric Swamp

When plants in prehistoric swamps died, their remains built up. Over time, sediment covered the plant remains. Inland seas formed where the swamps once were.

Inland Sea

Bacteria broke down the organic remains, leaving behind mostly carbon. Extreme temperatures and pressure compressed the material and squeezed out gas and moisture. A brownish material, called peat, formed.

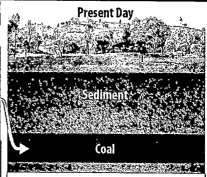

Present Day

As additional layers of sediment covered and compacted the peat, over time it changed into successively harder types of coal.

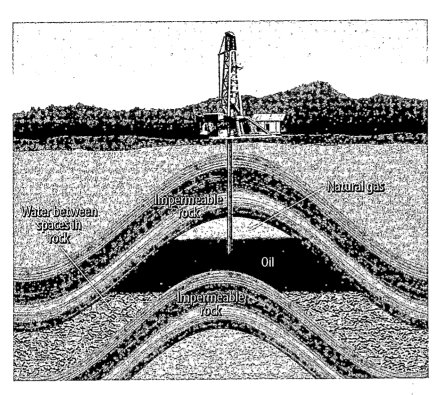

Figure 2 Reservoirs of oil and natural gas often are under layers of impermeable rock.

Visual Check What prevents oil and natural gas from rising to the surface?

Oil and Natural Gas Like coal, the oil and natural gas used today formed millions of years ago. The process that formed oil and natural gas is similar to the process that formed coal. However, oil and natural gas formation involves different types of organisms. Scientists theorize that oil and natural gas formed from the remains of microscopic marine organisms called plankton. The plankton died and fell to the ocean floor. There, layers of sediment buried their remains. Bacteria decomposed the organic matter, and then pressure and extreme temperatures acted on the sediments. During this process, thick, liquid oil formed first. If the temperature and pressure were great enough, natural gas formed.

Most of the oil and natural gas used today formed where forces within Earth folded and tilted thick rock layers. Often hundreds of meters of sediments and rock layers covered oil and natural gas. However, oil and natural gas were less dense than the surrounding sediments and rock. As a result, oil and natural gas began to rise to the surface by passing through the pores, or small holes, in rocks. As shown in Figure 2, oil and natural gas eventually reached layers of rock through which they could not pass, or impermeable rock layers. Deposits of oil and natural gas formed under these impermeable rocks. The less-dense natural gas settled on top of the denser oil.

Reading Check How is coal formation different from oil formation?

Advantages of Fossil Fuels

Do you know that fossil fuels store chemical energy? Burning fossil fuels transforms this energy. The steps involved in changing chemical energy in fossil fuels into electric energy are fairly easy and direct. This process is one advantage of using these nonrenewable resources. Also, fossil fuels are relatively inexpensive and easy to transport. Coal is often transported by trains, and oil is transported by pipelines or large ships called tankers.

Disadvantages of Fossil Fuels

Although fossil fuels provide energy, there are disadvantages to using them.

Limited Supply One disadvantage of fossil fuels is that they are nonrenewable. No one knows for sure when supplies will be gone. Scientists estimate that, at current rates of consumption, known reserves of oil will last only another 50 years.

Habitat Disruption In addition to being nonrenewable, the process of obtaining fossil fuels disturbs environments. Coal comes from underground mines or strip mines, such as the one shown in Figure 3. Oil and natural gas come from wells drilled into Earth. Mines in particular disturb habitats. Forests might be fragmented, or broken into areas of trees that are no longer connected. Fragmentation can negatively affect birds and other organisms that live in forests.

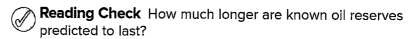

Reading Check How much longer are known oil reserves predicted to last?

Figure 3 Strip-mining involves removing layers of rock and soil to reach coal deposits.

Pollution Another disadvantage of fossil fuels as an energy resource is pollution. For example, runoff from coal mines can pollute soil and water. Oil spills from tankers can harm living things, such as the bird shown in **Figure 4.**

Pollution also occurs when fossil fuels are used. Burning fossil fuels releases chemicals into the atmosphere. These chemicals react in the presence of sunlight and produce a brownish haze. This haze can cause respiratory problems, particularly in young children. The chemicals also can react with water in the atmosphere and make rain and snow more acidic. The acidic precipitation can change the chemistry of soil and water and harm living things.

 Key Concept Check What is one advantage and one disadvantage of obtaining and using fossil fuels in Indiana?

Nuclear Energy

Atoms are too small to be seen with the unaided eye. Even though they are small, atoms can release large amounts of energy. *Energy released from atomic reactions is called* **nuclear energy.** Stars release nuclear energy by fusing atoms. The type of nuclear energy used on Earth involves a different process.

Figure 4 One disadvantage of fossil fuels is pollution, which can harm living things. This bird was covered with oil after an oil spill.

MiniLab

20 minutes

What is your reaction?

When atoms split during nuclear fission, the chain reaction releases thermal energy and by-products. What happens when your class participates in a simulation of a nuclear reaction?

① Read and complete a lab safety form.

② Use a **marker** to label three **sticky notes.** Label one note *U-235.* Label two notes *Neutron.* Stick the U-235 note on your **apron.** Hold the Neutron notes in one hand and a **Thermal Energy Card** in the other. You now represent a uranium-235 atom.

③ When you are tagged with a Neutron label from another student, tag two other student U-235 atoms with your Neutron labels. Drop your Thermal Energy Card into the **Energy Box.**

④ Observe as the remainder of the U-235 atoms are split, and imagine this happening extremely fast at the atomic level.

Analyze and Conclude

1. **Describe** what the simulation illustrated about nuclear fission.

2. **Predict** what would happen if, in the simulation, your classroom was filled wall-to-wall with U-235 atoms and the chain reaction got out of control.

3. **Key Concept** Identify one advantage and one disadvantage of nuclear energy.

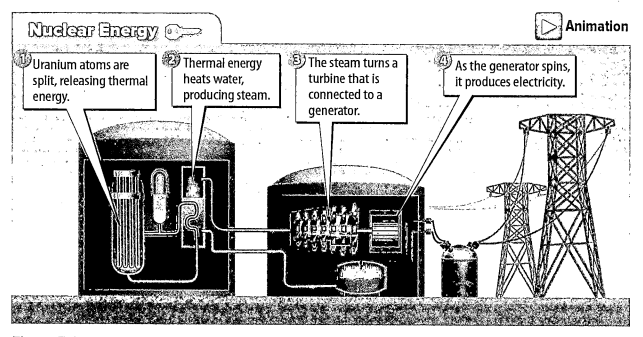

Nuclear Energy

① Uranium atoms are split, releasing thermal energy.

② Thermal energy heats water, producing steam.

③ The steam turns a turbine that is connected to a generator.

④ As the generator spins, it produces electricity.

Figure 5 In a nuclear power plant, thermal energy released from splitting uranium atoms is transformed into electrical energy.

Nuclear Fission Nuclear power plants, such as the one shown in Figure 5, produce electricity using nuclear fission. This process splits atoms. Uranium atoms are placed into fuel rods. Neutrons are aimed at the rods and hit the uranium atoms. Each atom splits and releases two to three neutrons and thermal energy. The released neutrons hit other atoms, causing a chain reaction of splitting atoms. Countless atoms split and release large amounts of thermal energy. This energy heats water and changes it to steam. The steam turns a turbine connected to a generator, which produces electricity.

Reading Check What are the steps in nuclear fission?

Advantages and Disadvantages of Nuclear Energy

One advantage of using nuclear energy is that a relatively small amount of uranium produces a large amount of energy. In addition, a well-run nuclear power plant does not pollute the air, the soil, or the water.

However, using nuclear energy has disadvantages. Nuclear power plants use a nonrenewable resource—uranium—for fuel. In addition, the chain reaction in the nuclear reactor must be carefully monitored. If it gets out of control, it can lead to a release of harmful radioactive substances into the environment.

The waste materials from nuclear power plants are highly radioactive and dangerous to living things. The waste materials remain dangerous for thousands of years. Storing them safely is important for both the environment and public health.

Reading Check Why is it important to control a chain reaction?

Managing Nonrenewable Energy Resources

As shown in **Figure 6**, fossil fuels and nuclear energy provide about 87 percent of U.S. energy. Because these sources eventually will be gone, we must understand how to manage and conserve them. This is particularly important because energy use in the United States is higher than in other countries. Although only about 4.5 percent of the world's population lives in the United States, it uses more than 18 percent of the world's total energy.

Management Solutions

Mined land must be reclaimed. **Reclamation** *is a process in which mined land must be recovered with soil and replanted with vegetation.* Laws also help ensure that mining and drilling take place in an environmentally safe manner. In the United States, the Clean Air Act limits the amount of pollutants that can be released into the air. In addition, the U.S. Atomic Energy Act and the Energy Policy Act include regulations that protect people from nuclear emissions.

What You Can Do

Have you ever heard of vampire energy? Vampire energy is the energy used by appliances and other electronic equipment, such as microwave ovens, washing machines, televisions, and computers, that are plugged in 24 h a day. Even when turned off, they still consume energy. These appliances consume about 5 percent of the energy used each year. You can conserve energy by unplugging DVD players, printers, and other appliances when they are not in use.

You also can walk or ride your bike to help conserve energy. And, you can use renewable energy resources, which you will read about in the next lesson.

 Key Concept Check How can you help manage nonrenewable resources wisely?

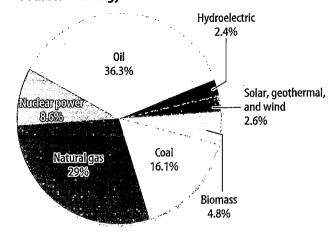

Sources of Energy Used in the U.S. in 2015

Hydroelectric 2.4%
Oil 36.3%
Solar, geothermal, and wind 2.6%
Nuclear power 8.6%
Coal 16.1%
Natural gas 29%
Biomass 4.8%

Figure 6 About 87 percent of the energy used in the United States comes from nonrenewable resources.

⌀ **Visual Check** Which energy source is used most in the United States?

ACADEMIC VOCABULARY · · · · · · · · · · · · · ·

regulation
(noun) a rule dealing with procedures, such as safety

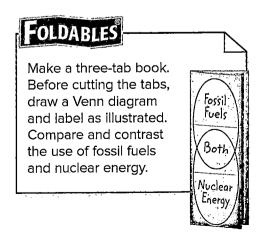

FOLDABLES®

Make a three-tab book. Before cutting the tabs, draw a Venn diagram and label as illustrated. Compare and contrast the use of fossil fuels and nuclear energy.

Fossil Fuels
Both
Nuclear Energy

Online Quiz

Visual Summary

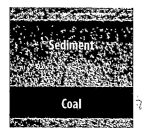

Fossil fuels include coal, oil, and natural gas. Fossil fuels take millions of years to form. Humans use fossil fuels at a much faster rate.

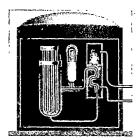

Nuclear energy comes from splitting atoms, or fission. Nuclear power plants must be monitored for safety, and nuclear waste must be stored properly.

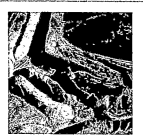

It is important to manage nonrenewable energy resources wisely. This includes mine reclamation, limiting air pollutants, and conserving energy.

FOLDABLES

Use your lesson Foldable to review the lesson. Save your Foldable for the project at the end of the chapter.

What do you think NOW?

You first read the statements below at the beginning of the chapter.

1. Nonrenewable energy resources include fossil fuels and uranium.

2. Energy use in the United States is lower than in other countries.

Did you change your mind about whether you agree or disagree with the statements? Rewrite any false statements to make them true.

Use Vocabulary

1 Energy produced from atomic reactions is called _____.

2 **Distinguish** between renewable and nonrenewable resources.

3 **Use the term** *reclamation* in a sentence.

Understand Key Concepts

4 What is the source of most energy in the United States?
   A. coal   C. natural gas
   B. oil   D. nuclear energy

5 **Summarize** the advantages and disadvantages of using nuclear energy.

6 **Illustrate** Make a poster showing how you can conserve energy.

Interpret Graphics

7 **Sequence** Draw a graphic organizer like the one below to sequence the events in the formation of oil.

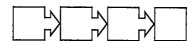

8 **Describe** Use the diagram below to describe the energy conversions that take place in a nuclear power plant.

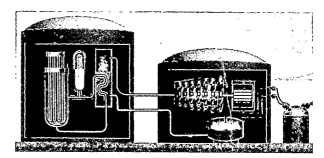

Critical Thinking

9 **Suppose** that a nuclear power plant will be built near your town. Would you support the plan? Why or why not?

10 **Consider** Do the advantages of obtaining and using fossil fuels in Indiana outweigh the disadvantages? Explain.

How can you identify bias and its source?

Whenever an author is trying to persuade, or convince, readers to share a particular opinion, you must read and evaluate carefully for bias. Bias is a way of thinking that tells only one side of a story, sometimes with inaccurate information.

Learn It

Sometimes a scientific investigation involves making judgments. When you make a judgment, you form an opinion. It is important to be honest and not allow any expectations of results to **bias** your judgments.

Try It

1. Read the passage to the right for sources of bias, such as

- claims not supported by evidence;

- persuasive statements;

- the author wanting to believe what he or she is saying, whether or not it is true.

Apply It

2. Analyze the passage, and identify two instances of bias and the source of each. Record this information in your Science Journal.

3. If you were the moderator at an EPA hearing about the issue, what would you do to solve the problem of bias?

4. **Key Concept** In your own words, explain how you would formulate an argument about the wise management of air resources while avoiding bias.

Factory Spews Out Air Pollution

Environmental organizations claim a coal-burning factory is polluting the air with toxic particulate matter in violation of U.S. Environmental Protection Agency (EPA) standards. Particulate matter is a mix of both solid and liquid particles in the air.

Citizens of the town collected air samples for a period of six months. An independent laboratory analysis of the samples showed a dangerously high level of the toxic particulate materials. Levels this high have been cited in medical journals as contributing to illness and death from asthma, respiratory disease, and lung cancer.

The factory has not updated its pollution control equipment, claiming that it cannot afford the cost. At a town meeting, a company spokesperson claimed that the particulate matter is not harmful to human health. The state environmental director, who previously worked at the factory, stated that the jobs provided by the factory are more important to the state than environmental concerns.

Lesson 2

Reading Guide

Key Concepts 🔑

ESSENTIAL QUESTIONS

- What are the main sources of renewable energy?

- What are the advantages and disadvantages of using renewable energy resources?

- What can individuals do to encourage the use of renewable energy resources?

Vocabulary

solar energy p. 427

wind farm p. 428

hydroelectric power p. 428

geothermal energy p. 429

biomass energy p. 429

 Multilingual eGlossary

 7.ESS.7, SEPS.4, SEPS.5

Renewable Energy Resources

Inquiry) What do these panels do?

These solar panels convert energy from the Sun into electrical energy. This solar power plant, at Nellis Air Force Base in Nevada, produces up to 42 percent of the electricity used on the base. What are some of the advantages of using energy from the Sun? What are some of the disadvantages?

How can renewable energy sources generate energy in your home?

Renewable energy technologies can contribute to reducing our dependence on fossil fuels.

① Review the table below. It shows how much energy, in Watt-hours, it takes to run certain appliances.

② In one hour, a typical bicycle generator generates 200 W-h of electric energy; a small solar panel generates 150 W-h; and small wind turbines typically generate 100 W-h. Complete the table by calculating the time it would take for each alternative form of energy to generate the electricity needed to run each appliance for 1 h.

Hint: Use the following equation to solve for the time used by each energy source:

$$\left(\begin{array}{l}\text{Time used by}\\\text{energy source}\end{array}\right) = \frac{\left(\begin{array}{l}\text{Time to use}\\\text{appliance}\end{array}\right) \times \left(\begin{array}{l}\text{Energy used per hour}\\\text{by appliance}\end{array}\right)}{\left(\begin{array}{l}\text{Energy produced per hour}\\\text{by energy source}\end{array}\right)}$$

Think About This

1. Which appliance required the longest energy-generating time from the alternative energy sources? Why?

2. 🔑 **Key Concept** What issues would you have to consider when using solar or wind energy to generate electricity in your home?

Appliance	Energy Used Per Hour	Time on Bike	Time for Solar Panel	Time for Wind Turbine
Desktop computer	75 W-h			
Hair dryer	1000 W-h			
Television	200 W-h			

Renewable Energy Resources

Could you stop the Sun from shining or the wind from blowing? These might seem like silly questions, but they help make an important point about renewable resources. Renewable resources come from natural processes that have been happening for billions of years and will continue to happen.

Solar Energy

Solar energy *is energy from the Sun.* Solar cells, such as those in watches and calculators, capture light energy and transform it to electrical energy. Solar power plants can generate electricity for large areas. They transform energy in sunlight, which then turns turbines connected to generators.

Some people use solar energy in their homes, as shown in **Figure 7**. Active solar energy uses technology, such as solar panels, that gathers and stores solar energy that heats water and homes. Passive solar energy uses design elements that capture energy in sunlight. For example, windows on the south side of a house can let in sunlight that helps heat a room.

Figure 7 👉 People can use solar energy to provide electricity for their homes.

Wind Energy

Have you ever dropped your school papers outside and had them scattered by the wind? If so, you experienced wind energy. This renewable resource has been used since ancient times to sail boats and to turn windmills. Today, wind turbines, such as the ones shown in Figure 8, can produce electricity on a large scale. *A group of wind turbines that produce electricity is called a* **wind farm.**

Reading Check How is wind energy a renewable resource?

Water Energy

Like wind energy, flowing water has been used as an energy source since ancient times. Today, water energy produces electricity using different methods, such as hydroelectric power and tidal power.

Hydroelectric Power *Electricity produced by flowing water is called* **hydroelectric power.** To produce hydroelectric power, humans build a dam across a powerful river. Figure 9 shows how flowing water is used to produce electricity.

Tidal Power Coastal areas that have great differences between high and low tides can be a source of tidal power. Water flows across turbines as the tide comes in during high tides and as it goes out during low tides. The flowing water turns turbines connected to generators that produce electricity.

▲ **Figure 8** ☞ Offshore wind farms are called wind parks. This wind park is in Denmark.

Figure 9 ☞ In a hydroelectric power plant, energy from flowing water produces electricity. ▽

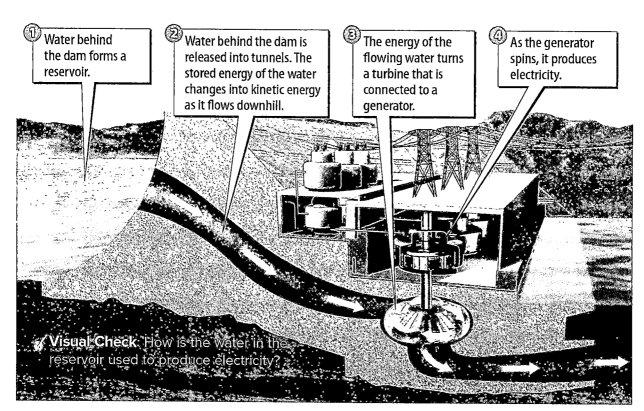

1. Water behind the dam forms a reservoir.

2. Water behind the dam is released into tunnels. The stored energy of the water changes into kinetic energy as it flows downhill.

3. The energy of the flowing water turns a turbine that is connected to a generator.

4. As the generator spins, it produces electricity.

Visual Check How is the water in the reservoir used to produce electricity?

Clynt Garnham Renewable Energy/Alamy

EXPLAIN

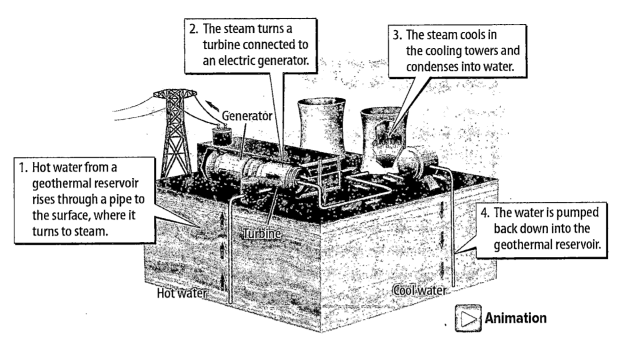

2. The steam turns a turbine connected to an electric generator.

3. The steam cools in the cooling towers and condenses into water.

1. Hot water from a geothermal reservoir rises through a pipe to the surface, where it turns to steam.

4. The water is pumped back down into the geothermal reservoir.

Generator

Turbine

Hot water

Cool water

▷ Animation

Figure 10 ⌐
Geothermal power plants use thermal energy from Earth's interior and produce electricity.

WORD ORIGIN · · · · · · · · · · · ·
geothermal
from Greek *ge-*, means "Earth"; and Greek *therme*, means "heat"

Geothermal Energy

Earth's core is nearly as hot as the Sun's surface. This thermal energy flows outward to Earth's surface. *Thermal energy from Earth's interior is called* **geothermal energy**. It can be used to heat homes and generate electricity in power plants, such as the one shown in **Figure 10**. People drill wells to reach hot, dry rocks or bodies of magma. The thermal energy from the hot rocks or magma heats water that makes steam. The steam turns turbines connected to generators that produce electricity.

Biomass Energy

Since humans first lit fires for warmth and cooking, biomass has been an energy source. **Biomass energy** *is energy produced by burning organic matter, such as wood, food scraps, and alcohol.* Wood is the most widely used biomass. Industrial wood scraps and organic materials, such as grass clippings and food scraps, are burned to generate electricity on a large scale.

Biomass also can be converted into fuels for vehicles. Ethanol is made from sugars in plants, such as corn. Ethanol often is blended with gasoline. This reduces the amount of oil used to make the gasoline. Adding ethanol to gasoline also reduces the amount of carbon monoxide and other pollutants released by vehicles. Another renewable fuel, biodiesel, is made from vegetable oils and fats. It emits few pollutants and is the fastest-growing renewable fuel in the United States.

 Key Concept Check What are the main sources of renewable energy?

FOLDABLES

Make a vertical five-tab Foldable. Label the tabs as illustrated. Identify the advantages and disadvantages of alternative fuels.

Solar

Wind

Water

Geothermal

Biomass

Advantages and Disadvantages of Renewable Resources

A big advantage of using renewable energy resources is that they are renewable. They will be available for millions of years to come. In addition, renewable energy resources produce less pollution than fossil fuels.

There are disadvantages associated with using renewable resources, however. Some are costly or limited to certain areas. For example, large-scale geothermal plants are limited to areas with tectonic activity. Recall that tectonic activity involves the movement of Earth's plates. **Table 2** lists the advantages and disadvantages of using renewable energy resources.

Table 2 Most renewable energy resources produce little or no pollution.

 Visual Check What are the advantages and the disadvantages of biomass energy?

☞ **Key Concept Check** What are some advantages and disadvantages of using renewable energy resources?

 **Interactive Table**

Table 2 Renewable Resources—Advantages and Disadvantages

Renewable Resource	Advantages	Disadvantages
Solar energy	• nonpolluting • available in the United States	• less energy produced on cloudy days • no energy produced at night • high cost of solar cells • requires a large surface area to collect and produce energy on a large scale
Wind energy	• nonpolluting • relatively inexpensive • available in the United States	• large-scale use limited to areas with strong, steady winds • best sites for wind farms are far from urban areas and transmission lines • potential impact on bird populations
Water energy	• nonpolluting • available in the United States	• large-scale use limited to areas with fast-flowing rivers or great tidal differences • negative impact on aquatic ecosystems • production of electricity affected by long periods of little or no rainfall
Geothermal energy	• produces little pollution • available in the United States	• large-scale use limited to tectonically active areas • habitat disruption from drilling to build a power plant
Biomass energy	• reduces amount of organic material discarded in landfills • available in the United States	• air pollution results from burning some forms of biomass • less energy efficient than fossil fuels, costly to transport

Managing Renewable Energy Resources

Renewable energy currently meets only 9.8 percent of U.S. energy needs. As shown in **Figure 11**, most renewable energy comes from biomass. Solar energy, wind energy, and geothermal energy meet only a small percentage of U.S. energy needs. However, some states are passing laws that require the state's power companies to produce a percentage of electricity using renewable resources. Management of renewable resources often focuses on encouraging their use.

Management Solutions

The U.S. government has begun programs to encourage use of renewable resources. In 2009, billions of dollars were granted to the U.S. Department of Energy's Office of Energy Efficiency and Renewable Energy for renewable energy research and programs that reduce the use of fossil fuels.

What You Can Do

You might be too young to own a house or a car, but you can help educate others about renewable energy resources. You can talk with your family about ways to use renewable energy at home. You can participate in a renewable energy fair at school. As a consumer, you also can make a difference by buying products that are made using renewable energy resources.

 Key Concept Check What can you do to encourage the use of renewable energy resources?

Energy Resources in the United States

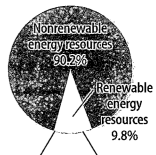

Energy Resource	Percent
Biomass	54%
Hydroelectric	26%
Wind	18%
Solar	4%
Geothermal	2%

Figure 11 The renewable energy resource used most in the United States is biomass energy.

MiniLab
20 minutes

How are renewable energy resources used at your school?
Complete a survey about the use of renewable resources in your school.

① Prepare interview questions about the use of renewable energy resources at your school. Each group member should come up with at least two questions.

② Choose one group member to interview a school staff member.

③ Copy the table at the right into your Science Journal, and fill in the interview data.

Renewable Energy Source	Yes/No	Where is it used?	Why is it used? or Why isn't it used?
Sun			
Wind			
Water			
Geothermal			
Biomass			

Analyze and Conclude

1. **Explain** Which renewable energy resources are and are not being used? Why or why not?

2. **Key Concept** Choose one "why not" reason and describe how it could be addressed by communication with school planners.

Lesson 2 Review

Visual Summary

Renewable energy resources can be used to heat homes, produce electricity, and power vehicles.

Advantages of renewable energy resources include little or no pollution and availability.

Management of renewable energy resources includes encouraging their use and continuing to research more about their use.

FOLDABLES

Use your lesson Foldable to review the lesson. Save your Foldable for the project at the end of the chapter.

What do you think NOW?

You first read the statements below at the beginning of the chapter.

3. Renewable energy resources do not pollute the environment.

4. Burning organic material can produce electricity.

Did you change your mind about whether you agree or disagree with the statements? Rewrite any false statements to make them true.

Use Vocabulary

1. **Define** *hydroelectric power* in your own words.

2. Burning wood is an example of _____ energy.

Understand Key Concepts

3. Which can reduce the amount of organic material discarded in landfills?
   - **A.** biomass energy
   - **C.** water energy
   - **B.** solar energy
   - **D.** wind energy

4. **Compare and contrast** solar energy and wind energy.

5. **Determine** Your family wants to use renewable energy to heat your home. Which renewable energy resource is best suited to your area? Explain your answer.

Interpret Graphics

6. **Organize** Copy and fill in the graphic organizer below. In each oval, list a type of renewable energy resource.

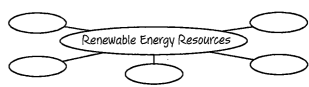
Renewable Energy Resources

7. **Compare** the use of renewable resources and nonrenewable resources in the production of electricity in the United States, based on the table below.

Sources of Electricity Generation, 2015	
Energy Source	**Percent**
Fossil fuels	67%
Nuclear power	20%
Solar, wind, geothermal, biomass	7%
Hydroelectric	6%

Critical Thinking

8. **Design** and explain a model that shows how a renewable resource produces energy.

How can you analyze energy-use data for information to help conserve energy?

As a student, you are not making large governmental policy decisions about uses of resources. As an individual, however, you can analyze data about energy use. You can use your analysis to determine some personal actions that can be taken to conserve energy resources.

Learn It

To **analyze the data** of fuel usage, you will need to look for patterns in the data, compare and categorize them, and determine cause and effect.

Try It

1. Study the fuel usage graph shown below. The data were collected from a house that uses natural gas as a source of energy to heat it.

2. Identify the time period that is covered by the graph.

3. Explain what is represented by the values on the vertical axis of the graph.

4. Describe the range of monthly gas usage over the 12-month period.

5. Group the monthly gas usage into three levels. Give each level a title. Enter these in your Science Journal.

Apply It

6. Categorize the three levels based on the amount of natural gas use.

7. Identify the three highest and four lowest months of gas usage. What might explain the usage patterns during these months?

8. Suppose the house from which the data came was heated with an electric furnace, instead of a furnace that used natural gas. What would you expect a usage graph for an electric furnace to look like?

9. **Key Concept** Formulate a list of heat conservation practices for homes.

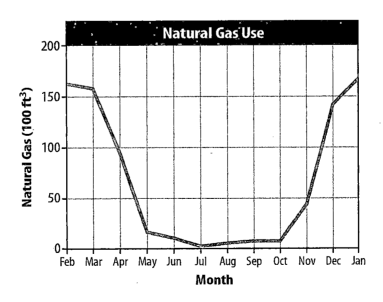

Lesson 3

Reading Guide

Key Concepts 🔑
ESSENTIAL QUESTIONS

- Why is land considered a resource?

- What are the advantages and disadvantages of using land as a resource?

- How can individuals help manage land resources wisely?

Vocabulary
ore p. 437

deforestation p. 438

 Multilingual eGlossary

 What's Science Got to do With It?

 SEPS.5, SEPS.6

Land Resources

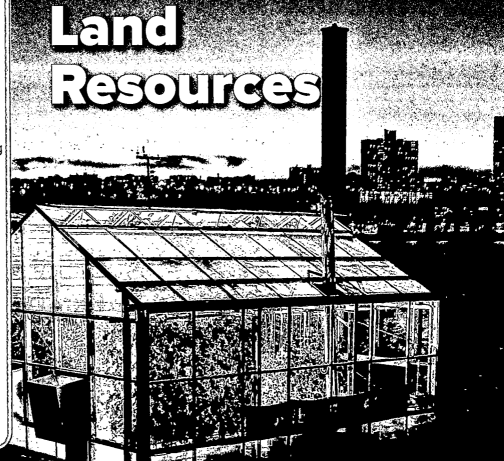

Inquiry A Garden on the Water?

The Science Barge is an experimental farm in New York City, New York. It saves space and reduces pollution and fossil fuel use while growing crops to feed people in an urban area. Why are people experimenting with ways to grow food that have fewer environmental impacts? Why is it important for humans to use land resources wisely?

Tyrone Turner/National Geographic Stock

What resources from the land do you use every day?

The land on which humans live is part of Earth's crust. It provides resources that enable humans and other organisms to survive.

① Make a list of every item you use in a 24-h period as you carry out your daily activities.

② Combine your list with your group members' lists and decide which items contain resources from the land. Design a graphic organizer to group the materials into categories.

③ Fill in the graphic organizer on **chart paper.** Use a **highlighter** or **colored markers** to show which resources are renewable and which are nonrenewable.

④ Post your chart and compare it with the others in your class.

Think About This

1. Are there any times in your day when you do not use a resource from the land? Provide an example.

2. Describe the major categories that you used to organize your list of resources.

3. 🗝️ **Key Concept** Why do you think land is considered a resource?

Land as a Resource

A natural resource is something from Earth that living things use to meet their needs. People use soil for growing crops and forests to harvest wood for making furniture, houses, and paper products. They mine minerals from the land and clear large areas for roads and buildings. In each of these cases, people use land as a natural resource to meet their needs.

🗝️ **Key Concept Check** Why is land considered a resource?

Living Space

No matter where you live, you and all living things use land for living space. Living space includes natural habitats, as well as the land on which buildings, sidewalks, parking lots, and streets are built. As shown in **Figure 12,** cities make up only a small percentage of land use in the United States. Most land is used for agriculture, grasslands, and forests.

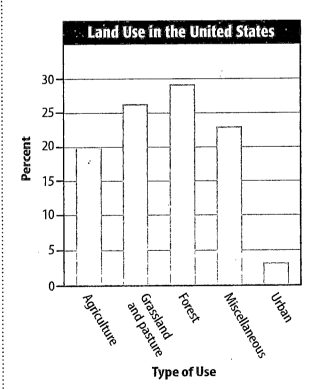

Land Use in the United States

Percent — Type of Use: Agriculture, Grassland and pasture, Forest, Miscellaneous, Urban

Figure 12 🗝️ Forests and grasslands make up the largest categories of U.S. land use.

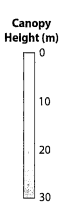
Canopy
Height (m)

0

10

20

30

1650

1920

Figure 13 Much of the U.S. eastern forest has been replaced by cities, farms, and other types of development.

Visual Check
Compare forest cover in the eastern United States in 1650 and 1920.

Forests and Agriculture

As shown in Figure 13, forests covered much of the eastern United States in 1650. By 1920, the forests had nearly disappeared. Although some of the trees have grown back, they are not as tall and the forests are not as complex as they were originally.

Forests w ere cut down for the same reasons that forests are cut down today: for fuel, paper products, and wood products. People also cleared land for development and agriculture. Today, about one-fifth of U.S. land is used for growing crops and about one-fourth is used for grazing livestock.

Reading Check Why are forests cut down?

**MiniLab** **20 minutes**

How can you manage land resource use with environmental responsibility?

You inherited a 100-acre parcel of forested land. Your relative's will stated that you must support all of your needs by using or selling resources from the land. To receive the inheritance, you must create an environmentally responsible land-use plan.

① Copy the table into your Science Journal.

② Your relative's will stated that you must support all of your needs by using or selling resources from the land. Decide how you will use the land, and complete the table.

③ Draw your land use plan on **graph paper.**

④ Present your group's land use plan to the class, and explain your reasoning.

Land Use	Percent of Total Area	Reasoning
Forest		
House and yard		
Garden		
Mineral mine		
Other		

Analyze and Conclude

1. **Compare and contrast** the design and reasoning of your plan with another group's plan.

2. **Identify** additional information about the land parcel that you would need to refine your plan.

3. **Key Concept** Summarize two environmentally responsible practices that were used by more than one group in their plan.

Mineral Resources

Recall that coal, an energy resource, is mined from the land. Certain minerals also are mined to make products you use every day. These minerals often are called ores. **Ores** *are deposits of minerals that are large enough to be mined for a profit.*

The house in Figure 14 contains many examples of common items made from mineral resources. Some of these come from metallic mineral resources. Ores such as bauxite and hematite are metallic mineral resources. They are used to make metal products. The aluminum in automobiles and refrigerators comes from bauxite. The iron in nails and faucets comes from hematite. Some mineral resources come from nonmetallic mineral resources, such as gypsum, halite, and minerals found in sand and gravel. Nonmetallic mineral resources also are mined from the land. The sulfur used in paints and rubber and the fluorite used in paint pigments are other examples of nonmetal mineral resources.

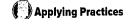 **Applying Practices**

Which natural resources are used to make synthetic materials? Go online to research which natural resources are used to make plastics and other common synthetic materials.

WORD ORIGIN ···········

ore
from Old English *ora*, means "unworked metal"

Figure 14 Many common products are made from mineral resources.

Visual Check Identify two products made from nonmetallic mineral resources.

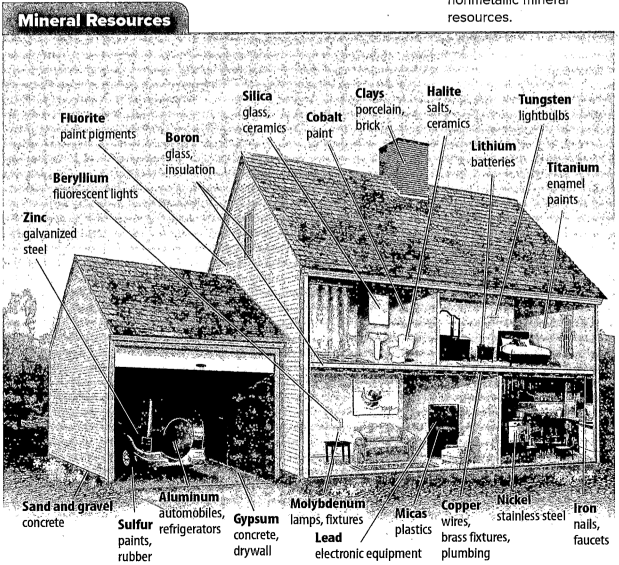

Mineral Resources

- **Fluorite** paint pigments
- **Boron** glass, insulation
- **Beryllium** fluorescent lights
- **Zinc** galvanized steel
- **Silica** glass, ceramics
- **Cobalt** paint
- **Clays** porcelain, brick
- **Halite** salts, ceramics
- **Tungsten** lightbulbs
- **Lithium** batteries
- **Titanium** enamel paints
- **Sand and gravel** concrete
- **Aluminum** automobiles, refrigerators
- **Sulfur** paints, rubber
- **Gypsum** concrete, drywall
- **Molybdenum** lamps, fixtures
- **Lead** electronic equipment
- **Micas** plastics
- **Copper** wires, brass fixtures, plumbing
- **Nickel** stainless steel
- **Iron** nails, faucets

Advantages and Disadvantages of Using Land Resources

Land resources such as soil and forests are widely available and easy to access. In addition, crops and trees are renewable–they can be replanted and grown in a relatively short amount of time. These are all advantages of using land resources.

Some land resources, however, are nonrenewable. It can take millions of years for minerals to form. This is one disadvantage of using land resources. Other disadvantages include deforestation and pollution.

Deforestation

As shown in **Figure 15**, humans sometimes cut forests to clear land for grazing, farming, and other uses. **Deforestation** *is the cutting of large areas of forests for human activities.* It leads to soil erosion and loss of animal habitats. In tropical rain forests–complex ecosystems that can take hundreds of years to replace–deforestation is a serious problem.

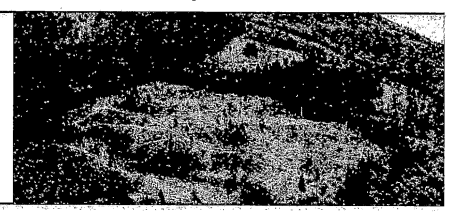

Figure 15 Deforestation occurs when humans cut forests to clear land for agricultural uses or development.

Deforestation also can affect global climates. Trees remove carbon dioxide from the atmosphere during photosynthesis. Rates of photosynthesis decrease when large areas of trees are cut down, and more carbon dioxide remains in the atmosphere. Carbon dioxide helps trap thermal energy within Earth's atmosphere. Increased concentrations of carbon dioxide can cause Earth's average surface temperatures to increase.

Pollution

Recall that runoff from coal mines can affect soil and water quality. The same is true of mineral mines. Runoff that contains chemicals from these mines can pollute soil and water. In addition, many farmers use chemical fertilizers to help grow crops. Runoff containing fertilizers can pollute rivers, soil, and underground water supplies.

REVIEW VOCABULARY

runoff
rainwater that does not soak into the ground and flows over Earth's surface

Key Concept Check What are some advantages and disadvantages of using land resources?

Karen Huntt/Getty Images

Managing Land Resources

Because some land uses involve renewable resources while others do not, managing land resources is complex. For example, a tree is renewable. But forests can be nonrenewable because some can take hundreds of years to fully regrow. In addition, the amount of land is limited, so there is competition for space. Those who manage land resources must balance all of these issues.

Management Solutions

One way governments can manage forests and other unique ecosystems is by preserving them. On preserved land, logging and development is either banned or strictly controlled. Large areas of forests cannot be cut. Instead, loggers cut selected trees and then plant new trees to replace ones they cut.

Land mined for mineral resources also must be preserved. On both public and private lands, mined land must be restored according to government regulations.

Land used for farming and grazing can be managed to conserve soil and improve crop yield. Farmers can leave crop stalks after harvesting to protect soil from erosion. They also can use organic farming techniques that do not use synthetic fertilizers.

What You Can Do

You can help conserve land resources by recycling products made from land resources. You can use yard waste and vegetable scraps to make rich compost for gardening, reducing the need to use synthetic fertilizers. Compost is a mix of decayed organic material, bacteria and other organisms, and small amounts of water. Figure 16 shows another way you can help manage land resources wisely.

Key Concept Check What can you do to help manage land resources wisely?

Jeff Greenberg/Alamy

Figure 16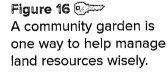
A community garden is one way to help manage land resources wisely.

Visual Summary

Land is a natural resource that humans use to meet their needs.

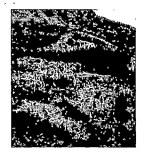

Disadvantages of using land as a resource include deforestation, which leads to increased erosion and increased carbon dioxide in the atmosphere.

Individuals can help manage land resources wisely by recycling, composting, and growing food in community gardens.

FOLDABLES

Use your lesson Foldable to review the lesson. Save your Foldable for the project at the end of the chapter.

What do you think NOW?

You first read the statements below at the beginning of the chapter.

5. Cities cover most of the land in the United States.

6. Minerals form over millions of years.

Did you change your mind about whether you agree or disagree with the statements? Rewrite any false statements to make them true.

Use Vocabulary

1. Cutting down forests for human activities is called _____.

2. **Use the word** *ore* in a sentence.

Understand Key Concepts

3. One disadvantage of using metallic mineral resources is that these resources are
   A. easy to mine.   C. nonrenewable.
   B. inexpensive.   D. renewable.

4. **Give an example** of how people use land as a resource.

5. **Compare** the methods used by governments and individuals to manage land resources wisely.

Interpret Graphics

6. **Take Notes** Copy the graphic organizer below, and list at least two land resources mentioned in this lesson. Describe how using each affects the environment.

Land Resource	How Use Affects Environment

7. **Identify** whether the resources shown here are from metallic or nonmetallic mineral resources.

Sand and gravel — concrete
Sulfur — paints, rubber
Aluminum — automobiles, refrigerators

Critical Thinking

8. **Design** a way to manage land resources wisely. Use a method that is not discussed in this lesson.

9. **Decide** Land is a limited resource. There often is pressure to develop preserved land. Do you think this should happen? Why or why not?

A Greener Greensburg

A town struck by disaster makes the world a greener place.

In May 2007, a powerful tornado struck the small Kansas town of Greensburg. The tornado destroyed almost every home, school, and business. Six months later, the town's officials and residents decided to rebuild Greensburg as a model green community.

The town's residents pledged to use fewer natural resources; to produce clean, renewable energy; and to reuse and recycle waste. As part of this effort, every new home and building would be designed for energy efficiency. The homes also would be constructed of materials that are healthful for the people who live and work in them.

What is a model green town? Here are some ways Greensburg will help the environment, save money, and make life better for its residents.

▲ **Rain gardens help improve water quality by filtering pollutants from runoff.**

USE RENEWABLE ENERGY

- **Produce clean energy** with renewable energy sources such as wind and sunlight. Wind turbines capture the abundant wind power of the Kansas plains.

- **Cut back on greenhouse gas emissions** with electric or hybrid city vehicles.

BUILD GREEN BUILDINGS

- **Design every home, school, and office** to use less energy and promote better health.

- **Make the most of natural daylight** for indoor lighting with many windows, which also can be opened for fresh air.

- **Use green materials** that are nontoxic and locally grown or made from recycled materials.

CONSERVE WATER

- **Capture runoff and rainwater** with landscape features such as rain gardens, bowl-shaped gardens designed to collect and absorb excess rainwater.

- **Use low-flow** faucets, shower heads, and toilets.

CREATE A HEALTHY ENVIRONMENT

- **Provide parks and green spaces** filled with native plants that need little water or care.

- **Create a "walkable community"** to encourage people to drive less and be more active, with a town center connected to neighborhoods by sidewalks and trails.

It's Your Turn With your group, choose one of Greensburg's projects. Make a plan describing how it could be implemented in your community and what its benefits would be.

(t)©Saxon Holt/Alamy; (b) LARRY W. SMITH/EPA/Newscom; (bkgd)Jim Watson/AFP/Getty Images

Air and Water Resources

Reading Guide

Key Concepts 🔑

ESSENTIAL QUESTIONS

- Why is it important to manage air and water resources wisely?

- How can individuals help manage air and water resources wisely?

Vocabulary

photochemical smog p. 444

acid precipitation p. 444

 Multilingual eGlossary

 BrainPOP®

 7.ESS.7, SEPS.2, SEPS.4, SEPS.5, SEPS.6, SEPS.7, SEPS.8, 6-8.LST.5.1, 6-8. LST.7.1, 6-8.LST.7.3

(Inquiry) Are these crop circles?

No, this dotted landscape in Colorado is the result of circle irrigation. The fields are round because the irrigation equipment pivots from the center of the field and moves in a circle to water the crops. Crop irrigation accounts for about 34 percent of water used in the United States.

Kris Hanke/Getty

How often do you use water each day?

In most places in the United States, people are fortunate to have an adequate supply of clean water. When you turn on the faucet, do you think about the value of water as a resource?

① Prepare a two-column table to collect data on the number of times you use water in one day. Title the first column *Purpose* and the second column *Times Used*.

② In the *Purpose* column, describe how you used the water, such as *Faucet, Toilet, Shower/Bath, Dishwasher, Laundry, Leaks,* and *Other.*

③ In the *Times Used* column, record and tally the total number of times you used water.

④ Calculate the percent that you use water for each category. Construct a circle graph showing the percentages of use in a day.

Think About This

1. For which purpose did you use water the most? The least?

2. **Key Concept** In which category, or categories, could you conserve water? How?

Importance of Air and Water

Using some natural resources, such as fossil fuels and minerals, makes life easier. You would miss them if they were gone, but you would still survive.

Air and water, on the other hand, are resources that you cannot live without. Most living things can survive only a few minutes without air. Oxygen from air helps your body provide energy for your cells.

Water also is needed for many life functions. As shown in **Figure 17**, water is the main component of blood. Water helps protect body tissues, helps maintain body temperature, and has a role in many chemical reactions, such as the digestion of food. In addition to drinking water, people use water for other purposes that you will learn about later in this lesson, including agriculture, transportation, and recreation.

Reading Check What are the functions of water in the human body?

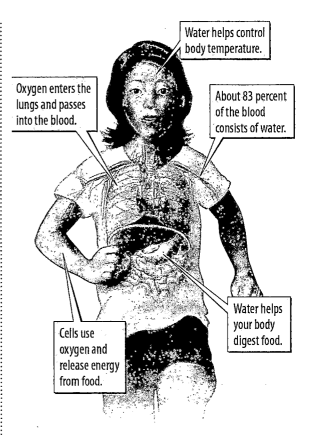

Water helps control body temperature.

Oxygen enters the lungs and passes into the blood.

About 83 percent of the blood consists of water.

Water helps your body digest food.

Cells use oxygen and release energy from food.

Figure 17 Your body needs oxygen and water to carry out its life-sustaining functions.

Personal Tutor

Figure 18 Sometimes a layer of warm air can trap smog in the cooler air close to Earth's surface. The smog can cover an area for days.

⊘ **Visual Check** Where does the pollution that forms smog come from?

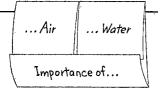
Figure 19 Gas and dust released by erupting volcanoes, such as Karymsky Volcano in Russia, can pollute the air.

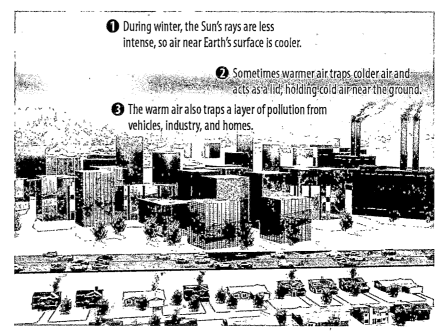

❶ During winter, the Sun's rays are less intense, so air near Earth's surface is cooler.

❷ Sometimes warmer air traps colder air and acts as a lid, holding cold air near the ground.

❸ The warm air also traps a layer of pollution from vehicles, industry, and homes.

Air

Most living things need air to survive. However, polluted air, such as the air in Figure 18, can actually harm humans and other living things. Air pollution is produced when fossil fuels burn in homes, vehicles, and power plants. It also can be caused by natural events, such as volcanic eruptions or forest fires.

⊘ **Reading Check** What activities can cause air pollution?

Smog Burning fossil fuels releases not only energy, but also substances, such as nitrogen compounds. **Photochemical smog** *is a brownish haze produced when nitrogen compounds and other pollutants in the air react in the presence of sunlight.* Smog can irritate your respiratory system. In some individuals, it can increase the chance of asthma attacks. Smog can be particularly harmful when it is trapped under a layer of warm air and remains in an area for several days, also shown in Figure 18.

Acid Precipitation Nitrogen and sulfur compounds released when fossil fuels burn can react with water in the atmosphere and produce acid precipitation. **Acid precipitation** *is precipitation that has a pH less than 5.6.* When it falls into lakes, it can harm fish and other organisms. It also can pollute soil and kill trees and other plants. Acid precipitation can even damage buildings and statues made of some types of rocks.

Natural Events Forest fires and volcanic eruptions, such as the one shown in Figure 19, release gases, ash, and dust into the air. Dust and ash from one volcanic eruption can spread around the world. Materials from forest fires and volcanic eruptions can cause health problems similar to those caused by smog.

Klaus Nigge/Getty Images

Water

Suppose you saved $100, but you were only allowed to spend 90 cents. You might be very frustrated! If all of the water on Earth were your $100, freshwater that we can use is like that 90 cents you can spend. As shown in **Figure 20**, most water on Earth is salt water. Only 3 percent is freshwater, and most of that is frozen in glaciers. That leaves just a small part, 0.9 percent, of the total amount of water on Earth for humans to use.

This relatively small supply of freshwater must meet many needs. In addition to drinking water, people use water for farming, industry, electricity production, household activities, transportation, and recreation. Each of these uses can affect water quality. For example, water used to irrigate fields can mix with fertilizers. This polluted water then can run off into rivers and groundwater, reducing the quality of these water supplies. Water used in industry often is heated to high temperatures. The hot water can harm aquatic organisms when it is returned to the environment.

 Reading Check How can farming affect water quality?

Water Distribution on Earth

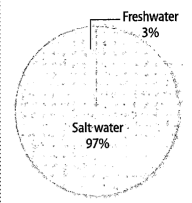

Figure 20 Freshwater makes up only 3 percent of Earth's water.

MiniLab

20 minutes

How much water can a leaky faucet waste?

You are competing for the job of environmental consultant at your school. One of the competition requirements is to complete an analysis of water waste from existing faucets.

① Read and complete a lab safety form.

② Catch the water from a **leaking faucet** in a **beaker.** Time the collection for 1 min with a **stopwatch.**

③ Use a **50-mL graduated cylinder** to measure the amount of water lost. Record the amount of water, in milliliters per minute, that leaked from the faucet in your Science Journal.

④ Make a table to show the amount of water that would leak from the faucet in 1 hour, 1 day, 1 week, 1 month, and 1 year.

Analyze and Conclude

1. **Construct** a graph of your data. Label the axes and title your graph. Explain what the graph illustrates.

2. **Describe** how many liters of water would be wasted by the leak over a period of one year. Explain how you arrived at that figure.

3. **Key Concept** As an environmental consultant, what information and recommendations would your report contain about water waste in the school?

Figure 21 The amount of sulfur compounds in the atmosphere decreased following the passage of the Clean Air Act.

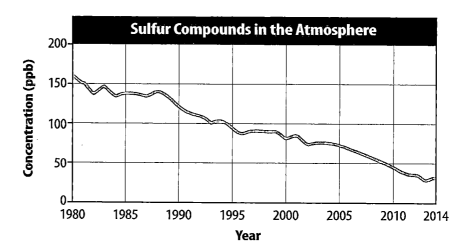

Sulfur Compounds in the Atmosphere

Math Skills

Use Percentages

The carbon monoxide (CO) level in Portland air went from 6.3 parts per million (ppm) in 1990 to 1.3 ppm in 2014. What was the percent change in CO levels?

1. Subtract the starting value from the final value.

   1.3 ppm − 6.3 ppm = −5.0 ppm

2. Divide the difference by the starting value.

   −5.0 ppm/6.3 ppm = −0.794

3. Multiply by 100 and add a % sign.

   −0.794 × 100 = −79.4%.

It decreased by 79.4%.

Practice

Between 1990 and 2014 the ozone (O₃) levels in Richmond went from 0.084 ppm to 0.062 ppm. What was the percent change in ozone levels?

 Math Practice

 Personal Tutor

Managing Air and Water Resources

Animals and plants do not use natural resources to produce electricity or to raise crops. But they do use air and water. Management of these important resources must consider both human needs and the needs of other living things.

Key Concept Check Why is it important to manage air and water resources wisely?

Management Solutions

Legislation is an effective way to reduce air and water pollution. The regulations of the U.S. Clean Air Act, passed in 1970, limit the amount of certain pollutants that can be released into the air. The graph in **Figure 21** shows how levels of sulfur compounds have decreased since the act became law.

Similar laws are now in place to maintain water quality. The U.S. Clean Water Act legislates the reduction of water pollution. The Safe Drinking Water Act legislates the protection of drinking water supplies. By reducing pollution, these laws help ensure that all living things have access to clean air and water.

What You Can Do

You have learned that reducing fossil fuel use and improving energy efficiency can reduce air pollution. You can make sure your home is energy efficient by cleaning air-conditioning or heating filters and using energy-saving lightbulbs.

You can help reduce water pollution by properly disposing of harmful chemicals so that less pollution runs off into rivers and streams. You can volunteer to help clean up litter from a local stream. You also can conserve water so there is enough of this resource for you and other living things in the future.

Key Concept Check How can individuals help manage air and water resources wisely?

Visual Summary

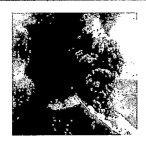

Sources of air pollution include the burning of fossil fuels in vehicles and power plants, and natural events such as volcanic eruptions and forest fires.

Water Distribution on Earth

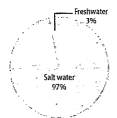

Freshwater 3%

Salt water 97%

Only a small percentage of Earth's water is available for humans to use. Humans use water for agriculture, industry, recreation, and cleaning.

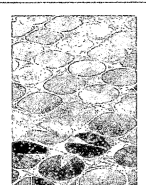

Management of air and water resources includes passing laws that regulate sources of air and water pollution. Individuals can reduce energy use and dispose of chemicals properly to help keep air and water clean.

FOLDABLES

Use your lesson Foldable to review the lesson. Save your Foldable for the project at the end of the chapter.

What do you think NOW?

You first read the statements below at the beginning of the chapter.

7. Humans need oxygen and water to survive.

8. About 10 percent of Earth's total water can be used by humans.

Did you change your mind about whether you agree or disagree with the statements? Rewrite any false statements to make them true.

Use Vocabulary

1 **Define** *acid precipitation* in your own words.

2 Air pollution caused by the reaction of nitrogen compounds and other pollutants in the presence of sunlight is _____.

Understand Key Concepts

3 About how much of Earth's water is available for humans to use?
   A. 0.01 percent   C. 3.0 percent
   B. 0.90 percent   D. 97.0 percent

4 **Relate** In terms of human health, why is it important to manage air resources wisely?

5 **List** ways your classroom could improve its energy efficiency.

Interpret Graphics

6 **Determine Cause and Effect** Copy and fill in the graphic organizer below to describe three effects of acid precipitation.

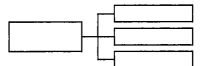

Critical Thinking

7 **Evaluate** The top three categories of household water use in the United States are flushing the toilet, washing clothes, and taking showers. Evaluate your water use, and list one thing you could do to reduce your use in each category.

Math Skills   Math Practice

8 Between 1990 and 2014, the amount of sulfur dioxide (SO_2) in Miami's air went from 14 ppb to 1 ppb. What was the percent change of SO_2?

(t)Klaus Nigge/Getty Images; (b)Kris Hanke/Getty Images

Research Efficient Energy and Resource Use

A community organization is encouraging your school's board of education to participate in the "Green Schools" program. Your class has been nominated to research and report on the present status of energy efficiency and resource use in the school. The results of the report will be used as information for the presentation. Your task is to choose a natural resource and collect data about how it is presently used in the school. Your group will then recommend environmentally responsible management practices.

Question
How can a natural resource be used more wisely at school?

Procedure
① Read and complete a lab safety form.

② With your group, choose one of these resources to research its use in your school: water, land, air, or a renewable or nonrewable energy resource.

③ For your chosen resource, plan how you will research resource use. What questions will you ask? How much of the resource is used by the school? Is it used efficiently? How could it be used more efficiently, or how could it be conserved? Have your teacher approve your plan.

④ Prepare data collection forms like the one below to record the results of your research in your Science Journal.

⑤ Conduct your research, and enter the data on the forms.

Sample Data Table				
Resource: Water				
Areas of Research: Water Loss Through Leaks and Recycling System				
Location	Faucets	Water Fountains	Toilets	"Gray" Water Recycling System
Washroom	6 good 2 poor 2 leaking		4 good 1 leaking	no
Hallway		3 good 1 leaking		no
Classroom 101	1 good			no
Classroom 102	1 good			no
Classroom 103	1 leaking			no

⑥ Review and summarize the data. Perform any necessary calculations to convert values to annual usage.

⑦ Conduct interviews, or collect more data about areas of research for which you need additional information.

⑧ After analyzing your data, write a proposal suggesting how the resource can be wisely managed in your school.

⑨ Compare the elements you addressed in your research with those recommended by a state or a national environmental organization. Did your research include everything?

⑩ Modify your proposal, if necessary. Record your revisions in your Science Journal.

Analyze and Conclude

⑪ **Graph** and explain the results of your data analysis.

⑫ **Describe** the positive and negative environmental impacts of obtaining and using your resource in Indiana.

⑬ 🔵 **The Big Idea** Describe two recommendations that you would make to the school's board of education about changes in resource management practices.

Communicate Your Results

Present the results of your research and your proposal to the class. Use appropriate visual aids to help make your points.

Combine information and reports from groups that investigated other resources from the list in step 2 so that all four resources are represented. Make a final report that includes recommendations for efficient use of each resource at your school. Use your report to determine which energy resources are most beneficial and efficient.

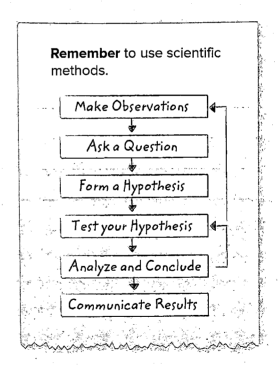

Remember to use scientific methods.

| Make Observations |
| Ask a Question |
| Form a Hypothesis |
| Test your Hypothesis |
| Analyze and Conclude |
| Communicate Results |

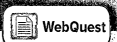

Wise management of natural resources helps extend the supply of nonrenewable resources, reduce pollution, and improve soil, air, and water quality.

Key Concepts Summary

Vocabulary

Lesson 1: Energy Resources

- **Nonrenewable resources** include fossil fuels and uranium, which is used for **nuclear energy.**
- Nonrenewable energy resources are widely available and easy to convert to energy. However, using these resources can cause pollution and habitat disruption. Safety concerns also are an issue.
- People can conserve energy to help manage these resources.

nonrenewable resource p. 417

renewable resource p. 417

nuclear energy p. 421

reclamation p. 423

Lesson 2: Renewable Energy Resources

- Renewable energy resources include **solar energy,** wind energy, water energy, **geothermal energy,** and **biomass energy.**
- Renewable resources cause little to no pollution. However, some types of renewable energy are costly or limited to certain areas.
- Individuals can help educate others about renewable resources.

solar energy p. 427

wind farm p. 428

hydroelectric power p. 428

geothermal energy p. 429

biomass energy p. 429

Lesson 3: Land Resources

- Land is considered a resource because it is used by living things to meet their needs for food, shelter, and other things.
- Some land resources are renewable, while others are not.
- Individuals can recycle and compost to help conserve land resources.

ore p. 437

deforestation p. 438

Lesson 4: Air and Water Resources

- Most living things cannot survive without clean air and water.
- Individuals can make their homes and schools more energy efficient.

photochemical smog p. 444

acid precipitation p. 444

(t)stanley45/iStock/Getty Images; (b)Jeff Greenberg/Alamy

FOLDABLES

Chapter Project

Assemble your lesson Foldables as shown to make a Chapter Project. Use the project to review what you have learned in this chapter.

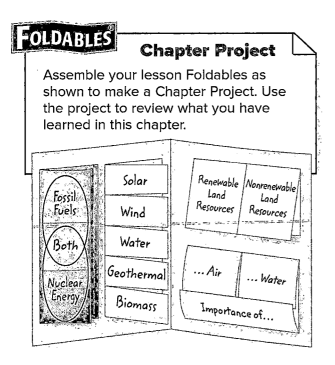

Use Vocabulary

1 Distinguish between renewable resources and nonrenewable resources.

2 Replace the underlined words with the correct vocabulary word: <u>Energy produced from atomic reactions</u> can be used to generate electricity.

3 How does biomass energy differ from geothermal energy?

4 Energy from the Sun is _____.

5 Define the term *ore* in your own words.

6 Distinguish between photochemical smog and acid precipitation.

Link Vocabulary and Key Concepts

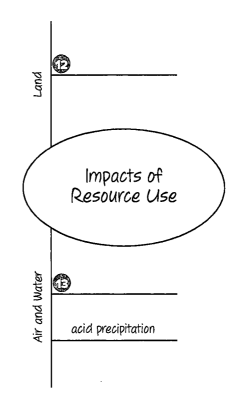 **Interactive Concept Map**

Copy these concept maps, and then use vocabulary terms from the previous page and other terms from the chapter to complete the concept maps.

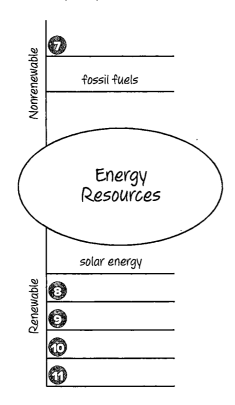

Understand Key Concepts

1 Which energy source produces radioactive waste?
   A. biomass
   B. geothermal
   C. hydroelectric power
   D. nuclear power

2 The table below shows the energy sources used to produce electricity in the United States. What can you infer from the table?

Electricity Production	
Energy Source	**Percent**
Coal	33
Natural gas	33
Nuclear power	20
Solar, wind, geothermal, biomass	7
Hydroelectric power	6
Oil	1
Other	<1

   A. About 19 percent of U.S. electricity comes from renewable sources.
   B. Hydroelectric power is more widely used for electricity than nuclear power.
   C. About 87 percent of U.S. electricity comes from nonrenewable sources.
   D. Oil is more widely used for electricity than hydroelectric power.

3 Which factor would best determine whether a home is suitable for solar energy?
   A. difference in tidal heights
   B. strength of daily winds
   C. nearness to tectonically active areas
   D. number of sunny days per year

4 Which product comes from a metallic mineral resource?
   A. aluminum
   B. drywall
   C. gravel
   D. table salt

5 Which is a renewable land resource?
   A. forests
   B. minerals
   C. soil
   D. trees

6 Where is most water on Earth located?
   A. lakes
   B. oceans
   C. rivers
   D. underground

7 Which natural event can result in air pollution?
   A. burning fossil fuels
   B. littering a stream
   C. runoff from farms
   D. volcanic eruption

8 The graph below shows how the amount of sulfur compounds in the atmosphere has changed since the passage of the Clean Air Act. Based on the data in the graph, what can you infer about the act?

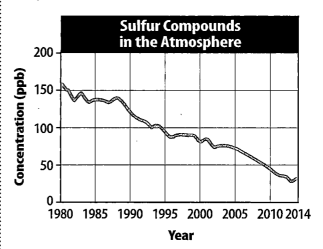

   A. The act has helped decrease pollutants in the atmosphere.
   B. The act has helped increase pollutants in the atmosphere.
   C. The act has incentives for use of renewable resources.
   D. The act has not impacted the amount of pollutants in the atmosphere.

Critical Thinking

9 **Organize** the list of energy sources into renewable and nonrenewable energy resources.

• coal	• nuclear energy
• solar energy	• wind energy
• oil	• natural gas
• geothermal energy	• tidal power
• hydroelectric power	• biomass

10 **Create** a cartoon showing a chain reaction in a nuclear power plant.

11 **Compare** hydroelectric and tidal power.

12 **Design** a way to use passive solar energy in your classroom.

13 **Distinguish** between geothermal energy and solar energy.

14 **Consider** What factors must governments consider when managing land resources?

15 **Evaluate** the use of forests as natural resources. Do the advantages outweigh the disadvantages? Explain.

16 **Infer** When would you expect more smog to form—on cloudy days or on sunny days? Explain.

17 **Design** a way to remove salt from salt water. Then evaluate your plan. Could it be used to produce freshwater on a large scale? Why or why not?

18 **Formulate** a way to demonstrate the importance of air and water resources to younger students.

Writing in Science

19 **Compose** a song about vampire energy. The lyrics should describe vampire energy and explain how it can be reduced.

REVIEW THE BIG IDEA

20 Select a natural resource and explain why it is important to manage the resource wisely.

21 Suppose the house below is heated by electricity produced from burning coal. Which areas of the house have the greatest loss of thermal energy? Why is it important for this house to reduce thermal energy loss?

Math Skills ☑ **Math Practice**

Use Percentages

22 Between 2012 and 2013, the carbon monoxide level in the air in Denver, Colorado, went from 2 ppm to 2.5 ppm. What was the percent change in CO?

23 There often is a considerable difference between pollutants in surface water and pollutants in groundwater in the same area. For example, in Portland, Oregon, there were 4.6 ppm of sulfates in the groundwater and 0.9 ppm in the surface water. What was the percent difference? (Hint: Use 4.6 ppm as the starting value.)

Tyrone Turner/National Geographic Stock

Record your answers on the answer sheet provided by your teacher or on a sheet of paper.

Multiple Choice

1 Which activity does NOT reduce the use of fossil fuels?

A riding a bicycle to school

B unplugging DVD players

C walking to the store

D watering plants less often

Use the graph below to answer questions 2 and 3.

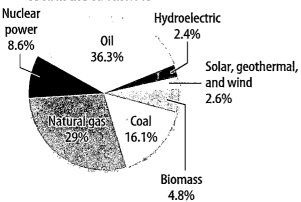

Sources of Energy Used in the U.S. in 2015

Nuclear power 8.6%
Oil 36.3%
Hydroelectric 2.4%
Solar, geothermal, and wind 2.6%
Natural gas 29%
Coal 16.1%
Biomass 4.8%

2 Which is the most-used renewable energy resource in the United States?

A biomass

B hydroelectric

C natural gas

D nuclear energy

3 What percentage of the energy used in the United States comes from burning fossil fuels?

A About 40 percent

B About 45 percent

C About 80 percent

D About 93 percent

4 Which practice emphasizes the use of renewable energy resources?

A buying battery-operated electronics

B installing solar panels on buildings

C replacing sprinklers with watering cans

D teaching others about vampire energy

5 Which is a nonrenewable land resource?

A crops

B minerals

C streams

D trees

Use the figure below to answer question 6.

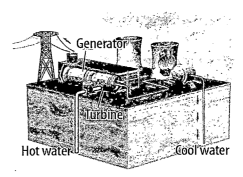

6 Which alternative energy resource is used to make electricity in the figure?

A solar energy

B tidal power

C geothermal energy

D hydroelectric power

7 Which practice is a wise use of land resources?

A composting

B conserving water

C deforestation

D strip mining

Use the figure below to answer question 8.

8 Which type of air pollution is labeled *A* in the figure?

   A acid precipitation

   B fertilizer runoff

   C nuclear waste

   D photochemical smog

9 Approximately how much water on the Earth is in oceans?

   A 1 percent

   B 3 percent

   C 75 percent

   D 97 percent

10 Which is a source of biomass energy?

   A sunlight

   B uranium

   C wind

   D wood

Constructed Response

Use the figure below to answer questions 11 and 12.

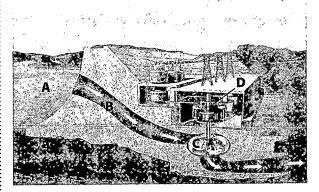

11 Which resource powers the turbine in the figure? Describe what happens at steps A–D to produce electricity.

12 What are two advantages and two disadvantages of producing electricity in the way shown in the figure?

13 Describe an example of how forests are used as a resource. What is one advantage of using the resource in this way? What is a disadvantage?

14 Agree or disagree with the following statement: "Known oil reserves will last only another 50 years. Thus, the United States should build more nuclear power plants to deal with the upcoming energy shortage." Support your answer with at least two advantages or two disadvantages of using nuclear energy.

NEED EXTRA HELP?														
If You Missed Question...	1	2	3	4	5	6	7	8	9	10	11	12	13	14
Go to Lesson...	1	2	1	2	3	2	3	4	4	2	2	2	3	1

Unit 5

LIFE: Structure & Function

Steer clear of those mitochondria. Too much energy!

Passing through some lysosomes. Their enzymes digest food particles.

Now entering cell!

1600   **1650**   **1800**

1665
Robert Hooke discovers cells while examining thin slices of cork under a microscope.

1674
Anton van Leeuwenhoek observes living cells under a microscope and names the moving organisms *animalcules.*

1831
The nucleus is given its name by Robert Brown.

1839
Theodor Schwann publishes a book suggesting that the cell is the basic unit of life.

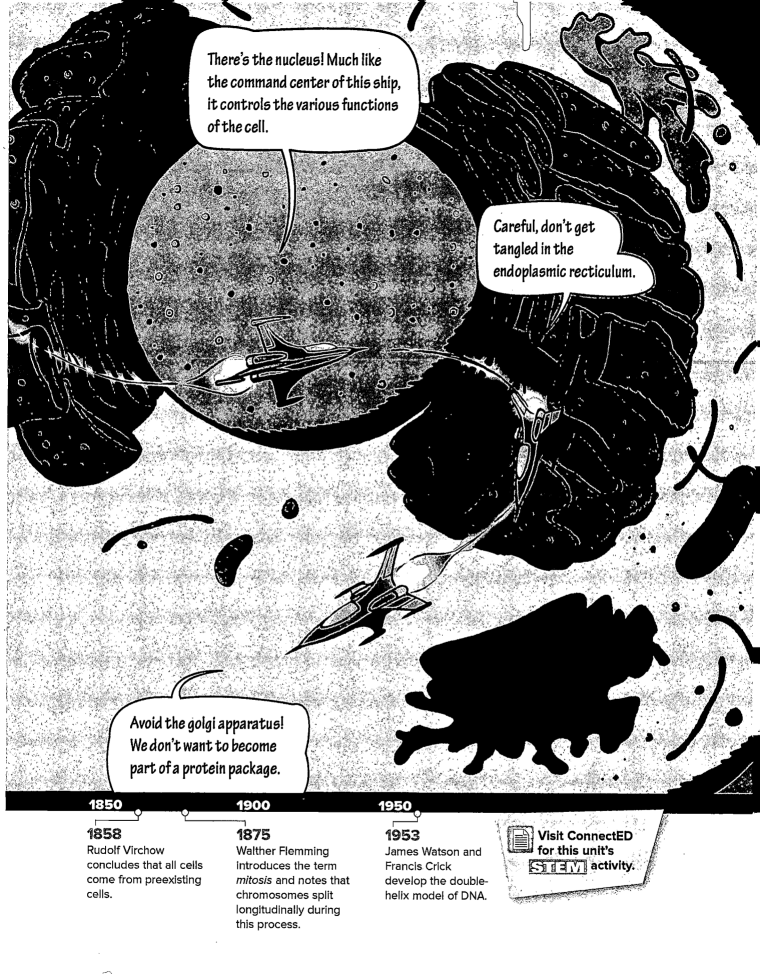

Models

What would you do without your heart—one of the most important muscles in your body? Worldwide, people are on donor lists, patiently waiting for heart transplants because their hearts are not working properly. Today, doctors can diagnose and treat heart problems with the help of models.

A **model** is a representation of an object, a process, an event, or a system that is similar to the physical object or idea being studied. Models can be used to study things that are too big or too small, happen too quickly or too slowly, or are too dangerous or too expensive to study directly. However, some models can replace organs or bones in the body that are not functioning properly.

A magnetic resonance image (MRI) is a type of model created by using a strong magnetic field and radio waves. MRI machines produce high-resolution images of the body from a series of images of different layers of the heart. For example, an MRI model of the heart allows cardiologists to diagnose heart disease or damage. To obtain a clear MRI, the patient must be still. Even the beating of the heart can limit the ability of an MRI to capture clear images.

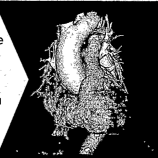

A computer tomography (CT) scan combines multiple X-ray images into a detailed 3-D visual model of structures in the body. Cardiologists use this model to diagnose a malfunctioning heart or blocked arteries. A limitation of a CT scan is that some coronary artery diseases, especially if they do not involve a buildup of calcium, may not be detected by the scan.

An artificial heart is a physical model of a human heart that can pump blood throughout the body. For a patient with heart failure, a doctor might suggest temporarily replacing the heart with an artificial model while they wait for a transplant. Because of its size, the replacement heart is suitable for about only 50 percent of the male population. And, it is stable only for about 2 years before it wears out.

A cardiologist might use a physical model of a heart to explain a diagnosis to a patient. The parts of the heart can be touched and manipulated to explain how a heart works and the location of any complications. However, this physical model does not function like a real heart, and it cannot be used to diagnose disease.

Maps as Models

One way to think of a computer model, such as an MRI or a CT scan, is as a map. A map is a model that shows how locations are arranged in space. A map can be a model of a small area, such as your street. Or, maps can be models of very large areas, such as a state, a country, or the world.

Biologists study maps to understand where different animal species live, how they interact, and how they migrate. Most animals travel in search of food, water, specific weather, or a place to mate. By placing small electronic tracking devices on migrating animals biologists can create maps of their movements, such as the map of elephant movement in Figure 1. These maps are models that help determine how animals survive, repeat the patterns of their life cycle, and respond to environmental changes.

Limitations of Models

It is impossible to include all the details about an object or an idea in one model. A map of elephant migration does not tell you whether the elephant is eating, sleeping, or playing with other elephants. Scientists must consider the limitations of the models they use when drawing conclusions about animal behavior.

All models have limitations. When making decisions about a patient's diagnosis and treatment, a cardiologist must be aware of the information each type of model does and does not provide. CT scans and MRIs each provide different diagnostic information. A doctor needs to know what information is needed before choosing which model to use. Scientists and doctors consider the purpose and limitations of the models they use to ensure that they draw the most accurate conclusions possible.

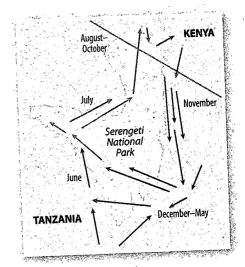

Figure 1 This map is a model of elephants' movements. The colored lines show the paths of three elephants that were equipped with tracking devices for a year.

MiniLab

40 minutes

How can you model an elephant enclosure?

You are part of a zoo design firm hired to design a model of a new elephant enclosure that mimics a natural habitat.

① Read and complete a lab safety form.

② Research elephants and study the map above to understand the needs of elephants.

③ Create a detailed map of your enclosure using **colored pencils** and a **ruler.** Be sure to include the scale, labels, and a legend.

④ Trade maps with a classmate.

⑤ Using **salt dough** and **craft supplies,** build a physical 3-D model of the elephant enclosure.

Analyze and Conclude

1. **Describe** How did you decide on the scale for your map?

2. **Compare** What are some similarities between your map and your physical model?

3. **Contrast** What are the benefits and the limitations of your physical model?

Classifying and Exploring Life

THE BIG IDEA

What are living things, and how can they be classified?

Science Photo Library/Alamy

Inquiry **Dropped Dinner Rolls?**

At first glance, you might think someone dropped dinner rolls on a pile of rocks. These objects might look like dinner rolls, but they're not.

- What do you think the objects are? Do you think they are alive?

- Why do you think they look like this?

- What are living things, and how can they be classified?

Get Ready to Read

What do you think?

Before you read, decide if you agree or disagree with each of these statements. As you read this chapter, see if you change your mind about any of the statements.

1. All living things move.
2. The Sun provides energy for almost all organisms on Earth.
3. A dichotomous key can be used to identify an unknown organism.
4. Physical similarities are the only traits used to classify organisms.
5. Most cells are too small to be seen with the unaided eye.
6. Only scientists use microscopes.

Mc Graw Hill Education

connectED

Your one-stop online resource
connectED.mcgraw-hill.com

LS — LearnSmart

Chapter Resources Files, Reading Essentials, Get Ready to Read, Quick Vocabulary

Animations, Videos, Interactive Tables

Self-checks, Quizzes, Tests

PBL — Project-Based Learning Activities

Lab Manuals, Safety Videos, Virtual Labs & Other Tools

Vocabulary, Multilingual eGlossary, Vocab eGames, Vocab eFlashcards

Personal Tutors

Reading Guide

Key Concept 🔑

ESSENTIAL QUESTION

- What characteristics do all living things share?

Vocabulary

organism p. 463

cell p. 464

unicellular p. 464

multicellular p. 464

homeostasis p. 467

 Multilingual eGlossary

 7.LS.1

Characteristics of Life

Inquiry) What's missing?

This toy looks like a dog and can move, but it is a robot. What characteristics are missing to make it alive? Let's find out.

Angela Wyant/Getty Images

Is it alive?

Living organisms have specific characteristics. Is a rock a living organism? Is a dog? What characteristics describe something that is living?

1. Read and complete a lab safety form.
2. Place three pieces of **pasta** in the bottom of a **clear plastic cup.**
3. Add **carbonated water** to the cup until it is 2/3 full.
4. Observe the contents of the cup for 5 minutes. Record your observations in your Science Journal.

Think About This

1. Think about living things. How do you know they are alive?

2. Which characteristics of life do you think you are observing in the cup?

3. **Key Concept** Is the pasta alive? How do you know?

Characteristics of Life

Look around your classroom and then at **Figure 1.** You might see many nonliving things, such as lights and books. Look again, and you might see many living things, such as your teacher, your classmates, and plants. What makes people and plants different from lights and books?

People and plants, like all living things, have all the characteristics of life. All living things are organized, grow and develop, reproduce, respond, maintain certain internal conditions, and use energy. Nonliving things might have some of these characteristics, but they do not have all of them. Books might be organized into chapters, and lights use energy. However, only those things that have all the characteristics of life are living. *Things that have all the characteristics of life are called* **organisms.**

Reading Check How do living things differ from nonliving things?

Figure 1 A classroom might contain living and nonliving things.

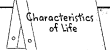
Organization

Your home is probably organized in some way. For example, the kitchen is for cooking, and the bedrooms are for sleeping. Living things are also organized. Whether an organism is made of one **cell**—*the smallest unit of life*—or many cells, all living things have structures that have specific functions.

Living things that are made of only one cell are called **unicellular** *organisms.* Within a unicellular organism are structures with specialized functions just like a house has rooms for different activities. Some structures take in nutrients or control cell activities. Other structures enable the organism to move.

Living things that are made of two or more cells are called **multicellular** *organisms.* Some multicellular organisms only have a few cells, but others have trillions of cells. The different cells of a multicellular organism usually do not perform the same function. Instead, the cells are organized into groups that have specialized functions, such as digestion or movement.

Growth and Development

The tadpole in **Figure 2** is not a frog, but it will soon lose its tail, grow legs, and become an adult frog. This happens because the tadpole, like all organisms, will grow and develop. When organisms grow, they increase in size. A unicellular organism grows as the cell increases in size. Multicellular organisms grow as the number of their cells increases.

Figure 2 A tadpole grows in size while developing into an adult frog.

Growth and Development

 Animation

Visual Check What characteristics of life can you identify in this figure?

1 A frog egg develops into a tadpole.

2 As the tadpole grows, it develops legs.

Changes that occur in an organism during its lifetime are called development. In multicellular organisms, development happens as cells become specialized into different cell types, such as skin cells or muscle cells. Some organisms undergo dramatic developmental changes over their lifetime, such as a tadpole developing into a frog.

Reading Check What happens in development?

Reproduction

As organisms grow and develop, they usually are able to reproduce. Reproduction is the process by which one organism makes one or more new organisms. In order for living things to continue to exist, organisms must reproduce. Some organisms within a population might not reproduce, but others must reproduce if the species is to survive.

Organisms do not all reproduce in the same way. Some organisms, like the ones in Figure 3, can reproduce by dividing and become two new organisms. Other organisms have specialized cells for reproduction. Some organisms must have a mate to reproduce, but others can reproduce without a mate. The number of offspring produced varies. Humans usually produce only one or two offspring at a time. Other organisms, such as the frog in Figure 2, can produce hundreds of offspring at one time.

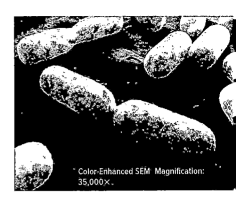
Color-Enhanced SEM Magnification: 35,000×.

Figure 3 Some unicellular organisms, like the bacteria shown here, reproduce by dividing. The two new organisms are identical to the original organism.

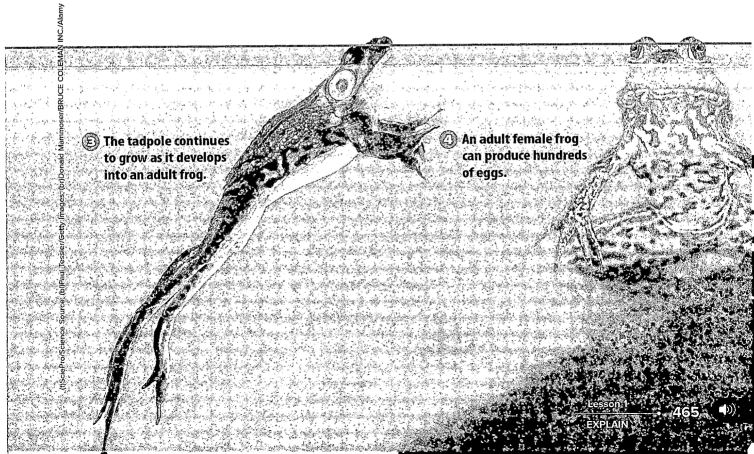

3 The tadpole continues to grow as it develops into an adult frog.

4 An adult female frog can produce hundreds of eggs.

Responses to Stimuli

If someone throws a ball toward you, you might react by trying to catch it. This is because you, like all living things, respond to changes in the environment. These changes can be internal or external and are called stimuli (STIHM yuh li).

Internal Stimuli

You respond to internal stimuli (singular, stimulus) every day. If you feel hungry and then look for food, you are responding to an internal stimulus–the feeling of hunger. The feeling of thirst that causes you to find and drink water is another example of an internal stimulus.

External Stimuli

Changes in an organism's environment that affect the organism are external stimuli. Some examples of external stimuli are light and temperature.

Many plants, like the one in **Figure 4**, will grow toward light. You respond to light, too. Your skin's response to sunlight might be to darken, turn red, or freckle.

Some animals respond to changes in temperature. The response can be more or less blood flowing to the skin. For example, if the temperature increases, the diameter of an animal's blood vessels increases. This allows more blood to flow to the skin, cooling an animal.

Figure 4 The leaves and stems of plants like this one will grow toward a light source.

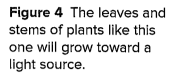

MiniLab

20 minutes

Did you blink?

Like all living organisms, you respond to changes, or stimuli, in your environment. When you react to a stimulus without thinking, the response is known as a reflex. Let's see what a reflex is like.

① Read and complete a lab safety form.

② Sit on a chair with your hands in your lap.

③ Have your partner gently toss a **soft, foam ball** at your face five times. Your partner will warn you when he or she is going to toss the ball. Record your responses in your Science Journal.

④ Have your partner gently toss the ball at your face five times without warning you. Record your responses.

⑤ Switch places with your partner, and repeat steps 3 and 4.

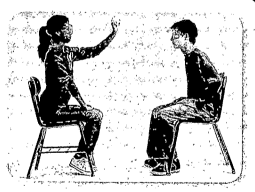

Analyze and Conclude

1. **Compare** your responses when you were warned and when you were not warned.

2. **Decide** if any of your reactions were reflex responses, and explain your answer.

3. 🔑 **Key Concept** Infer why organisms have reflex responses to some stimuli.

Homeostasis

Have you ever noticed that if you drink more water than usual, you have to go to the bathroom more often? That is because your body is working to keep your internal environment under normal conditions. *An organism's ability to maintain steady internal conditions when outside conditions change is called* homeostasis (hoh mee oh STAY sus).

The Importance of Homeostasis

Are there certain conditions you need to do your homework? Maybe you need a quiet room with a lot of light. Cells also need certain conditions to function properly. Maintaining certain conditions–homeostasis–ensures that cells can function. If cells cannot function normally, then an organism might become sick or even die.

Methods of Regulation

A person might not survive if his or her body temperature changes more than a few degrees from 37°C. When your outside environment becomes too hot or too cold, your body responds. It sweats, shivers, or changes the flow of blood to maintain a body temperature of 37°C.

Unicellular organisms, such as the paramecium in **Figure 5**, also have ways of regulating homeostasis. A structure called a contractile vacuole (kun TRAK tul • VA kyuh wohl) collects and pumps excess water out of the cell.

Figure 5 This paramecium lives in freshwater. Water continuously enters its cell and collects in contractile vacuoles. The vacuoles contract and expel excess water from the cell. This maintains normal water levels in the cell.

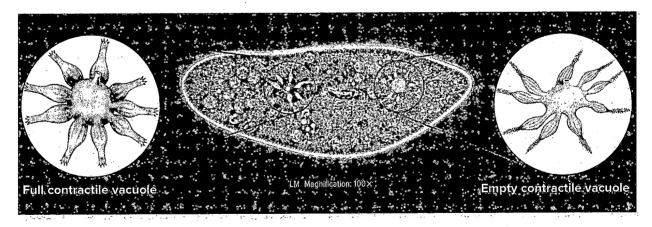

Full contractile vacuole   LM Magnification: 100×   Empty contractile vacuole

There is a limit to the amount of change that can occur within an organism. For example, you are able to survive only a few hours in water that is below 10°C. No matter what your body does, it cannot maintain steady internal conditions, or homeostasis, under these circumstances. As a result, your cells lose their ability to function.

 Reading Check Why is maintaining homeostasis important to organisms?

M. I. Walker/Science Source

Energy

Everything you do requires energy. Digesting your food, sleeping, thinking, reading and all of the characteristics of life shown in Table 1 on the next page require energy. Cells continuously use energy to transport substances, make new cells, and perform chemical reactions. Where does this energy come from?

For most organisms, this energy originally came to Earth from the Sun, as shown in Figure 6. For example, energy in the cactus came from the Sun. The squirrel gets energy by eating the cactus, and the coyote gets energy by eating the squirrel.

Key Concept Check What characteristics do all living things share?

Energy Use

Personal Tutor

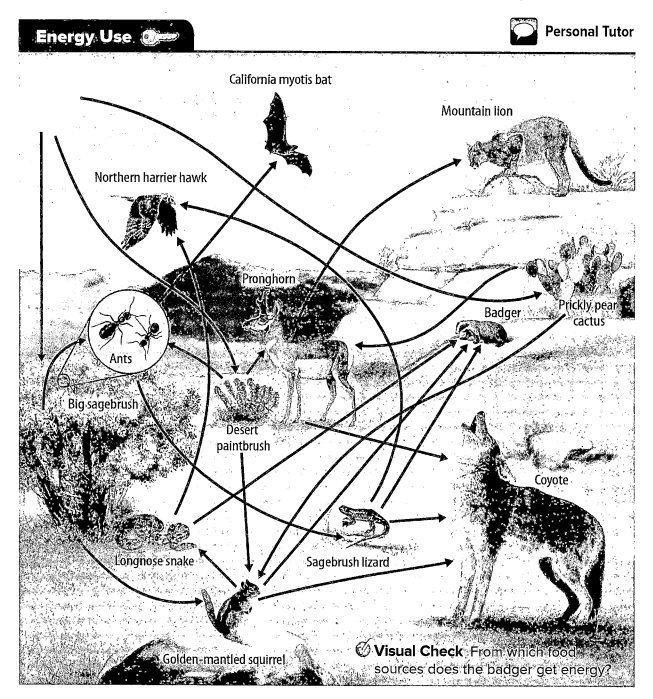

Figure 6 All organisms require energy to survive. In this food web, energy passes from one organism to another and to the environment.

Table 1 Characteristics of Life

Characteristic	Definition	Example
Organization	Living things have specialized structures with specialized functions. Living things with more than one cell have a greater level of organization because groups of cells function together.	
Growth and development	Living things grow by increasing cell size and/or increasing cell number. Multicellular organisms develop as cells develop specialized functions.	
Reproduction	Living things make more living things through the process of reproduction.	
Response to stimuli	Living things adjust and respond to changes in their internal and external environments.	
Homeostasis	Living things maintain stable internal conditions.	
Use of energy	Living things use energy for all the processes they perform. Living things get energy by making their own food, eating food, or absorbing food.	

Online Quiz

Visual Summary

An organism has all the characteristics of life.

Unicellular organisms have specialized structures, much like a house has rooms for different activities.

Homeostasis enables living things to maintain a steady internal environment.

FOLDABLES

Use your lesson Foldable to review the lesson. Save your Foldable for the project at the end of the chapter.

What do you think NOW?

You first read the statements below at the beginning of the chapter.

1. All living things move.

2. The Sun provides energy for almost all organisms on Earth.

Did you change your mind about whether you agree or disagree with the statements? Rewrite any false statements to make them true.

Use Vocabulary

1 A(n) _____ is the smallest unit of life.

2 Distinguish between unicellular and multicellular.

3 Define the term *homeostasis* in your own words.

Understand Key Concepts

4 Which is NOT a characteristic of all living things?
- **A.** breathing
- **B.** growing
- **C.** reproducing
- **D.** using energy

5 Compare the processes of reproduction and growth.

6 Choose the characteristic of living things that you think is most important. Explain why you chose that characteristic.

7 Critique the following statement: A candle flame is a living thing.

Interpret Graphics

8 Summarize Copy and fill in the graphic organizer below to summarize the characteristics of living things.

Characteristics of Living Things

9 Describe all the characteristics of life that are represented in the figure below.

Critical Thinking

10 Suggest how organisms would be different if they were not organized.

11 Hypothesize what would happen if living things could not reproduce.

AMERICAN
MUSEUM&
NATURAL
HISTORY

CAREERS
in SCIENCE

The Amazing Adaptation of an Air-Breathing Catfish

Discover how some species of armored catfish breathe air.

Have you ever thought about why animals need oxygen? All animals, including you, get their energy from food. When you breathe, the oxygen you take in is used in your cells. Chemical reactions in your cells use oxygen and change the energy in food molecules into energy that your cells can use. Mammals and many other animals get oxygen from air. Most fish get oxygen from water. Either way, after an animal takes in oxygen, red blood cells carry oxygen to cells throughout its body.

Adriana Aquino is an ichthyologist (IHK thee AH luh jihst) at the American Museum of Natural History in New York City. She discovers and classifies species of fish, such as the armored catfish in the family Loricariidae from South America. It lives in freshwater rivers and pools in the Amazon. Its name comes from the bony plates covering its body. Some armored catfish can take in oxygen from water and from air!

Some armored catfish live in fast-flowing rivers. The constant movement of the water evenly distributes oxygen throughout it. The catfish can easily remove oxygen from this oxygen-rich water.

But other armored catfish live in pools of still water, where most oxygen is only at the water's surface. This makes the pools low in oxygen. To maintain a steady level of oxygen in their cells, these fish have adaptations that enable them to take in oxygen directly from air. These catfish can switch from removing oxygen from water through their gills to removing oxygen from air through the walls of their stomachs. They can only do this when they do not have much food in their stomachs. Some species can survive up to 30 hours out of water!

Meet an Ichthyologist

Aquino examines hundreds of catfish specimens. Some she collects in the field, and others come from museum collections. She compares the color, the size, and the shape of the various species. She also examines their internal and external features, such as muscles, gills, and bony plates.

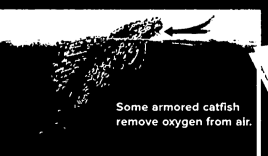

Some armored catfish remove oxygen from air.

Your Turn

BRAINSTORM Work with a group. Choose an animal and list five physical characteristics. Brainstorm how these adaptations help the animal be successful in its habitat. Present your findings to the class.

Classifying Organisms

Reading Guide

Key Concept 🔑
ESSENTIAL QUESTION

- What methods are used to classify living things into groups?

- Why does every species have a scientific name?

Vocabulary

binomial nomenclature p. 475

species p. 475

genus p. 475

dichotomous key p. 476

cladogram p. 476

 Multilingual eGlossary

 BrainPOP®

Inquiry Alike or Not?

In a band, instruments are organized into groups, such as brass and woodwinds. The instruments in a group are alike in many ways. In a similar way, living things are classified into groups. Why are living things classified?

Launch Lab

15 minutes

How do you identify similar items?

Do you separate your candies by color before you eat them? When your family does laundry, do you sort the clothes by color first? Identifying characteristics of items can enable you to place them into groups.

1. Read and complete a lab safety form.

2. Examine twelve **leaves.** Choose a characteristic that you could use to separate the leaves into two groups. Record the characteristic in your Science Journal.

3. Place the leaves into two groups, *A* and *B,* using the characteristic you chose in step 2.

4. Choose another characteristic that you could use to further divide group A. Record the characteristic, and divide the leaves.

5. Repeat step 4 with group B.

Think About This

1. What types of characteristics did other groups in class choose to separate the leaves?

2. **Key Concept** Why would scientists need rules for separating and identifying items?

Classifying Living Things

How would you find your favorite fresh fruit or vegetable in the grocery store? You might look in the produce section, such as the one shown in Figure 7. Different kinds of peppers are displayed in one area. Citrus fruits such as oranges, lemons, and grapefruits are stocked in another area. There are many different ways to organize produce in a grocery store. In a similar way, there have been many different ideas about how to organize, or classify, living things.

A Greek philosopher named Aristotle (384 B.C.–322 B.C.) was one of the first people to classify organisms. Aristotle placed all organisms into two large groups, plants and animals. He classified animals based on the presence of "red blood," the animal's environment, and the shape and size of the animal. He classified plants according to the structure and size of the plant and whether the plant was a tree, a shrub, or an herb.

Figure 7 The produce in this store is classified into groups.

Visual Check What other ways can you think of to classify and organize produce?

(t)Hutchings Photography/Digital Light Source, (b)PhotoLink/Getty Images

Lesson 2

473

EXPLORE

Determining Kingdoms

In the 1700s, Carolus Linnaeus, a Swedish physician and botanist, classified organisms based on similar structures. Linnaeus placed all organisms into two main groups, called kingdoms. Over the next 200 years, people learned more about organisms and discovered new organisms. In 1969 American biologist Robert H. Whittaker proposed a five-kingdom system for classifying organisms. His system included kingdoms Monera, Protista, Plantae, Fungi, and Animalia.

Determining Domains

The classification system of living things is still changing. The current classification method is called systematics. Systematics uses all the evidence that is known about organisms to classify them. This evidence includes an organism's cell type, its habitat, the way an organism obtains food and energy, structure and function of its features, and the common ancestry of organisms. Systematics also includes molecular analysis–the study of molecules such as DNA within organisms.

Using systematics, scientists identified two distinct groups in Kingdom Monera–Bacteria and Archaea (ar KEE uh). This led to the development of another level of classification called domains. All organisms are now classified into one of three domains–Bacteria, Archaea, or Eukarya (yew KER ee uh) –and then into one of six kingdoms, as shown in **Table 2.**

Key Concept Check What evidence is used to classify living things into groups?

Table 2 Domains and Kingdoms

Domain	Bacteria	Archaea	Eukarya			
Kingdom	Bacteria	Archaea	Protista	Fungi	Plantae	Animalia
Example						
Characteristics	Bacteria are simple unicellular organisms.	Archaea are simple unicellular organisms that often live in extreme environments.	Protists are unicellular and are more complex than bacteria or archaea.	Fungi are unicellular or multicellular and absorb food.	Plants are multicellular and make their own food.	Animals are multicellular and take in their food.

Scientific Names

Suppose you did not have a name. What would people call you? All organisms, just like people, have names. When Linnaeus grouped organisms into kingdoms, he also developed a system for naming organisms. This naming system, called binomial nomenclature (bi NOH mee ul · NOH mun klay chur), is the system we still use today.

Binomial Nomenclature

Linneaus's naming system, **binomial nomenclature,** *gives each organism a two-word scientific name,* such as *Ursus arctos* for a brown bear. This two-word scientific name is the name of an organism's species (SPEE sheez). *A* **species** *is a group of organisms that have similar traits and are able to produce fertile offspring.* In binomial nomenclature, the first word is the organism's genus (JEE nus) name, such as *Ursus. A* **genus** *is a group of similar species.* The second word might describe the organism's appearance or its behavior.

How do species and genus relate to kingdoms and domains? Similar species are grouped into one genus (plural, genera). Similar genera are grouped into families, then orders, classes, phyla, kingdoms, and finally domains, as shown for the grizzly bear in **Table 3.**

WORD ORIGIN

genus
from Greek *genos,* means
"race, kind"

Table 3 The classification of the brown bear or grizzly bear shows that it belongs to the order Carnivora.

Table 3 Classification of the Brown Bear		
Taxonomic Group	**Number of Species**	**Examples**
Domain Eukarya	About 4–10 million	
Kingdom Animalia	About 2 million	
Phylum Chordata	About 50,000	
Class Mammalia	About 5,000	
Order Carnivora	About 270	
Family Ursidae	8	
Genus *Ursus*	4	
Species *Ursus arctos*	1	

Visual Check What domain does the brown bear belong to?

PHOTO 24/Getty Images

▲ **Figure 8** These trees are two different species. *Pinus strobus* has long needles, and *Tsuga canadensis* has short needles.

FOLDABLES

Make a horizontal two-tab book to compare two of the tools scientists use to identify organisms—dichotomous keys and cladograms.

Uses of Scientific Names

When you talk about organisms, you might use names such as bird, tree, or mushroom. However, these are common names for a number of different species. Sometimes there are several common names for one organism. The animal in **Table 3** on the previous page might be called a brown bear or a grizzly bear, but it has only one scientific name, *Ursus arctos.*

Other times, a common name might refer to several different types of organisms. For example, you might call both of the trees in **Figure 8** pine trees. But these trees are two different species. How can you tell? Scientific names are important for many reasons. Each species has its own scientific name. Scientific names are the same worldwide. This makes communication about organisms more effective because everyone uses the same name for the same species.

Key Concept Check Why does every species have a scientific name?

Classification Tools

Suppose you go fishing and catch a fish you don't recognize. How could you figure out what type of fish you have caught? There are several tools you can use to identify organisms.

Dichotomous Keys

A **dichotomous key** *is a series of descriptions arranged in pairs that leads the user to the identification of an unknown organism.* The chosen description leads to either another pair of statements or the identification of the organism. Choices continue until the organism is identified. The dichotomous key shown in **Figure 9** identifies several species of fish.

Dichotomous Key

1. a. This fish has a mouth that extends past its eye. It is an arrow goby.

b. This fish does not have a mouth that extends past its eye. Go to step 2.

2. a. This fish has a dark body with stripes. It is a chameleon goby.

b. This fish has a light body with no stripes. Go to step 3.

3. a. This fish has a black-tipped dorsal fin. It is a bay goby.

b. This fish has a speckled dorsal fin. It is a yellowfin goby.

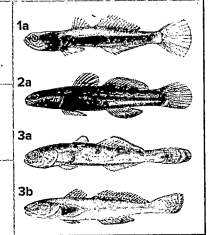

1a

2a

3a

3b

▲ **Figure 9** Dichotomous keys include a series of questions to identify organisms.

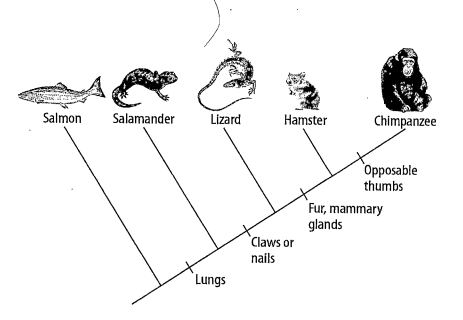

Salmon Salamander Lizard Hamster Chimpanzee

Opposable
thumbs

Fur, mammary
glands

Claws or
nails

Lungs

Figure 10 A cladogram shows relationships among species. In this cladogram, salamanders are more closely related to lizards than they are to hamsters.

 **Animation**

Cladograms

A family tree shows the relationships among family members, including common ancestors. Biologists use a similar diagram, called a cladogram. *A* **cladogram** *is a branched diagram that shows the relationships among organisms, including common ancestors.* A cladogram, as shown in **Figure 10,** has a series of branches. Notice that each branch follows a new characteristic. Each characteristic is observed in all the species to its right. For example, the salamander, lizard, hamster, and chimpanzee have lungs, but the salmon does not. Therefore, they are more closely related to each other than they are to the salmon.

MiniLab

20 minutes

How would you name an unknown organism?

Assign scientific names to four unknown alien organisms from a newly discovered planet.

① Use the table to assign scientific names to identify each alien.

② Compare your names with those of your classmates.

Analyze and Conclude

1. **Explain** why you chose the two-word names for each organism.

2. **Compare** your names to those of a classmate. Explain any differences.

3. **Key Concept** Discuss how two-word scientific names help scientists identify and organize living things.

Prefix	Meaning	Suffix	Meaning
mon–	one	–antennius	antenna
di–	two	–ocularus	eye
rectanguli–	square	–formus	shape
trianguli–	triangle	–uris	tail

Lesson 2

EXPLAIN

477

Online Quiz

Virtual Lab

Visual Summary

All organisms are classified into one of three domains: Bacteria, Archaea, or Eukarya.

Every organism has a unique species name.

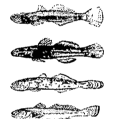
A dichotomous key helps to identify an unknown organism through a series of paired descriptions.

FOLDABLES

Use your lesson Foldable to review the lesson. Save your Foldable for the project at the end of the chapter.

What do you think NOW?

You first read the statements below at the beginning of the chapter.

3. A dichotomous key can be used to identify an unknown organism.

4. Physical similarities are the only traits used to classify organisms.

Did you change your mind about whether you agree or disagree with the statements? Rewrite any false statements to make them true.

Use Vocabulary

1 A naming system that gives every organism a two-word name is _____ _____.

2 **Use the term** *dichotomous key* in a sentence.

3 **Organisms** of the same _____ are able to produce fertile offspring.

Understand Key Concepts

4 **Describe** how you write a scientific name.

5 **Compare** the data available today on how to classify things with the data available during Aristotle's time.

6 Which is NOT used to classify organisms?
A. ancestry
B. habitat
C. age of the organism
D. molecular evidence

Interpret Graphics

7 **Organize Information** Copy and fill in the graphic organizer below to show how organisms are classified.

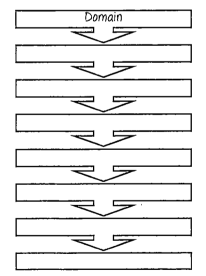

Domain

Critical Thinking

8 **Suggest** a reason scientists might consider changing the current classification system.

9 **Evaluate** the importance of scientific names.

PHOTO 24/Getty Images

How can you identify a beetle?

A dichotomous key is one of the tools scientists use to identify an unknown organism and **classify** it into a group. To use a dichotomous key, a scientist examines specific characteristics of the unknown organism and compares them to characteristics of known organisms.

Ⓐ

Ⓑ

Learn It

Sorting objects or events into groups based on common features is called classifying. When classifying, select one feature that is shared by some members of the group, but not by all. Place those members that share the feature in a subgroup. You can **classify** objects or events into smaller and smaller subgroups based on characteristics.

Try It

① Use the dichotomous key to identify beetle A. Choose between the first pair of descriptions. Follow the instructions for the next choice. Notice that each description either ends in the name of the beetle or instructs you to go on to another set of choices.

② In your Science Journal, record the identity of the beetle using both its common name and scientific name.

③ Repeat steps 1 and 2 for beetles B, C, and D.

Apply It

④ Think about the choices in each step of the dichotomous key. What conclusion can be made if you arrive at a step and neither choice seems correct?

⑤ Predict whether a dichotomous key will work if you start at a location other than the first description. Support your reasoning.

⑥ 🗝️ **Key Concept** How did the dichotomous key help you classify the unknown beetles?

Ⓒ

Dichotomous Key	
1A.	The beetle has long, thin antennae. Go to 5.
1B.	The beetle does not have long, thin antennae. Go to 2.
2A.	The beetle has short antennae that branch. Go to 3.
2B.	The beetle does not have short antennae that branch. It is a stag beetle, *Lucanus cervus*.
3A.	The beetle has a triangular structure between wing covers and upper body. It is a Japanese beetle, *Popillia japonica*.
3B.	The beetle does not have a triangular structure. Go to 4.
4A.	The beetle has a wide, rounded body. It is a June bug, *Cotinis nitida*.
4B.	The beetle does not have a wide, rounded body. It is a death watch beetle, *Xestobium rufovillosum*.
5A.	The beetle has a distinct separation between body parts. Go to 6.
5B.	The beetle has no distinct separation between body parts. It is a firefly, *Photinus pyralis*.
6A.	The beetle has a black, gray, and white body with two black eyespots. It is an eyed click beetle, *Alaus oculatis*.
6B.	The beetle has a dull brown body with light stripes. It is a click beetle, *Chalcolepidius limbatus*.

Ⓓ

Exploring Life

Reading Guide

Key Concepts

ESSENTIAL QUESTIONS

- How did microscopes change our ideas about living things?

- What are the types of microscopes, and how do they compare?

Vocabulary

light microscope p. 482

compound microscope p. 482

electron microscope p. 483

 Multilingual eGlossary

7.LS.1, SEPS.5

1quiry Giant Insect?

Although this might look like a giant insect, it is a photo of a small tick taken with a high-powered microscope. This type of microscope can enlarge an image of an object up to 200,000 times. How can seeing an enlarged image of a living thing help you understand life?

Eye of Science/Science Source

Can a water drop make objects appear bigger or smaller?

For centuries, people have been looking for ways to see objects in greater detail. How can something as simple as a drop of water make this possible?

1. Read and complete a lab safety form.

2. Lay a sheet of **newspaper** on your desk. Examine a line of text, noting the size and shape of each letter. Record your observations in your Science Journal.

3. Add a large drop of **water** to the center of a piece of **clear plastic.** Hold the plastic about 2 cm above the same line of text.

4. Look through the water at the line of text you viewed in step 2. Record your observations.

Think About This

1. Describe how the newsprint appeared through the drop of water.

2. **Key Concept** How might microscopes change your ideas about living things?

The Development of Microscopes

Have you ever used a magnifying lens to see details of an object? If so, then you have used a tool similar to the first microscope. The invention of microscopes enabled people to see details of living things that they could not see with the unaided eye. The microscope also enabled people to make many discoveries about living things.

In the mid 1600s English scientist Robert Hooke made one of the most significant discoveries using a microscope. He observed and named cells. Before microscopes, people did not know that living things are made of cells. In the late 1600s the Dutch merchant Anton van Leeuwenhoek (LAY vun hook) made improvements to the first microscopes. His microscope, similar to the one shown in Figure 11, had one lens and could magnify an image about 270 times its original size. This made it easier to view organisms.

Key Concept Check How did microscopes change our ideas about living things?

Figure 11 Anton van Leeuwenhoek observed pond water and insects using a microscope like the one shown above.

Use Multiplication

The magnifying power of a lens is expressed by a number and a multiplication symbol (×). For example, a lens that makes an object look ten times larger has a power of 10×. To determine a microscope's magnification, multiply the power of the ocular lens by the power of the objective lens. A microscope with a 10× ocular lens and a 10× objective lens magnifies an object 10 × 10, or 100 times.

Practice

What is the magnification of a compound microscope with a 10× ocular lens and a 4× objective lens?

 Math Practice

 Personal Tutor

Types of Microscopes

One characteristic of all microscopes is that they magnify objects. Magnification makes an object appear larger than it really is. Another characteristic of microscopes is resolution–how clearly the magnified object can be seen. The two main types of microscopes–light microscopes and electron microscopes–differ in magnification and resolution.

Light Microscopes

If you have used a microscope in school, then you have probably used a light microscope. **Light microscopes** *use light and lenses to enlarge an image of an object.* A simple light microscope has only one lens. *A light microscope that uses more than one lens to magnify an object is called a* **compound microscope.** A compound microscope magnifies an image first by one lens, called the objective lens. The image is then further magnified by another lens, called the ocular lens. The total magnification of the image is equal to the magnifications of the ocular lens and the objective lens multiplied together.

Light microscopes can enlarge images up to 1,500 times their original size. The resolution of a light microscope is about 0.2 micrometers (μm), or two-millionths of a meter. A resolution of 0.2 μm means you can clearly see points on an object that are at least 0.2 μm apart.

Light microscopes can be used to view living or nonliving objects. In some light microscopes, an object is placed directly under the microscope. For other light microscopes, an object must be mounted on a slide. In some cases, the object, such as the white blood cells in **Figure 12,** must be stained with a dye in order to see any details.

 Reading Check What are some ways an object can be examined under a light microscope?

Compound Light Microscope

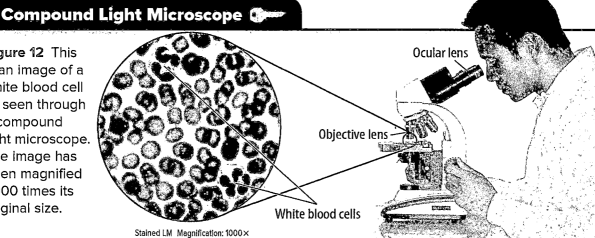

Figure 12 This is an image of a white blood cell as seen through a compound light microscope. The image has been magnified 1,000 times its original size.

Ocular lens

Objective lens

White blood cells

Stained LM Magnification: 1000×

(l)Steve Gschmeissner/Science Source; (r)JGI/Blend Images/Getty Images

Electron Microscopes

You might know that electrons are tiny particles inside atoms. **Electron microscopes** *use a magnetic field to focus a beam of electrons through an object or onto an object's surface.* An electron microscope can magnify an image up to 100,000 times or more. The resolution of an electron microscope can be as small as 0.2 nanometers (nm), or two-billionths of a meter. This resolution is up to 1,000 times greater than a light microscope. The two main types of electron microscopes are transmission electron microscopes (TEMs) and scanning electron microscopes (SEMs).

TEMs are usually used to study extremely small things such as cell structures. Because objects must be mounted in plastic and then very thinly sliced, only dead organisms can be viewed with a TEM. In a TEM, electrons pass through the object and a computer produces an image of the object. A TEM image of a white blood cell is shown in **Figure 13.**

SEMs are usually used to study an object's surface. In an SEM, electrons bounce off the object and a computer produces a three-dimensional image of the object. An image of a white blood cell from an SEM is shown in **Figure 13.** Note the difference in detail in this image compared to the image in **Figure 12** of a white blood cell from a light microscope.

 Key Concept Check What are the types of microscopes, and how do they compare?

FOLDABLES

Make a two-column folded chart. Label the front *Types of Microscopes*, and label the inside as shown. Use it to organize your notes about microscopes.

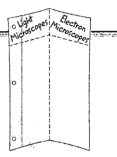

Figure 13 A TEM greatly magnifies thin slices of an object. An SEM is used to view a three-dimensional image of an object.

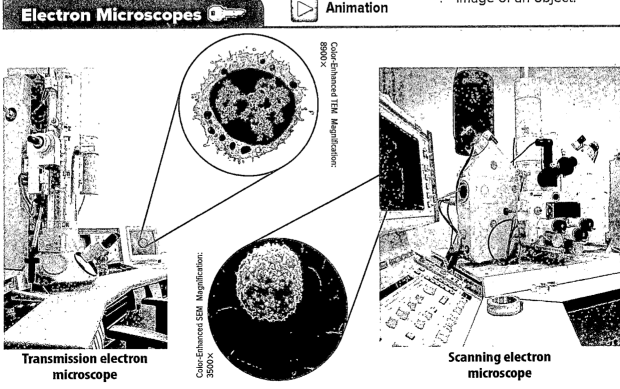

Electron Microscopes   ▷ Animation

Transmission electron microscope

Color-Enhanced TEM Magnification: 8900×

Color-Enhanced SEM Magnification: 3500×

Scanning electron microscope

(l)Stewart Sutton/Getty Images; (c)Don W. Fawcett/Science Source; (cr)A. Syred/Science Source; (r)Javier Larrea/age fotostock/SuperStock

How do microscopes help us compare living things?

A microscope enables scientists to study objects in greater detail than is possible with the unaided eye. Compare what objects look like with the unaided eye to those same objects observed using a microscope.

① Read and complete a lab safety form.

② Examine a **sea sponge,** a **leaf,** and **salt crystals.** Draw each object in your Science Journal.

③ Observe **microscope slides of each object** using a **microscope** on low power.

④ Draw each object as it appears under low power.

Analyze and Conclude

1. **Compare** your sketches of the objects observed with your unaided eye and observed with a microscope.

2. 🔑 **Key Concept** Explain how studying an object under a microscope might help you understand it better.

WORD ORIGIN ·

microscope
from Latin *microscopium,* means "an instrument for viewing what is small"

ACADEMIC VOCABULARY · · · · · · · · · · · · · · ·

identify
(verb) to determine the characteristics of a person or a thing

Using Microscopes

The microscopes used today are more advanced than the microscopes used by Leeuwenhoek and Hooke. The quality of today's light microscopes and the invention of electron microscopes have made the microscope a useful tool in many fields.

Health Care

People in health-care fields, such as doctors and laboratory technicians, often use microscopes. Microscopes are used in surgeries, such as cataract surgery and brain surgery. They enable doctors to view the surgical area in greater detail. The area being viewed under the microscope can also be displayed on a TV monitor so that other people can watch the procedure. Laboratory technicians use microscopes to analyze body fluids, such as blood and urine. They also use microscopes to determine whether tissue samples are healthy or diseased.

Other Uses

Health care is not the only field that uses microscopes. Have you ever wondered how police determine how and where a crime happened? Forensic scientists use microscopes to study evidence from crime scenes. The presence of different insects can help identify when and where a homicide happened. Microscopes might be used to identify the type and age of the insects.

People who study fossils might use microscopes. They might examine a fossil and other materials from where the fossil was found.

Some industries also use microscopes. The steel industry uses microscopes to examine steel for impurities. Microscopes are used to study jewels and identify stones. Stones have some markings and impurities that can be seen only by using a microscope.

✅ **Reading Check** List some uses of microscopes.

Hutchings Photography/Digital Light Source

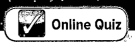
Visual Summary

Living organisms can be viewed with light microscopes.

A compound micro-scope is a type of light microscope that has more than one lens.

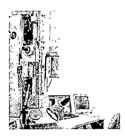

Living organisms cannot be viewed with a transmission electron microscope.

FOLDABLES

Use your lesson Foldable to review the lesson. Save your Foldable for the project at the end of the chapter.

What do you think NOW?

You first read the statements below at the beginning of the chapter.

5. Most cells are too small to be seen with the unaided eye.

6. Only scientists use microscopes.

Did you change your mind about whether you agree or disagree with the statements? Rewrite any false statements to make them true.

Use Vocabulary

1 Define the term *light microscope* in your own words.

2 A(n) _____ focuses a beam of electrons through an object or onto an object's surface.

Understand Key Concepts

3 Explain how the discovery of microscopes has changed what we know about living things.

4 Which microscope would you use if you wanted to study the surface of an object?
A. compound microscope
B. light microscope
C. scanning electron microscope
D. transmission electron microscope

Interpret Graphics

5 Identify Copy and fill in the graphic organizer below to identify four uses of microscopes.

Microscope Uses

6 Compare the images of the white blood cells below. How do they differ?

Critical Thinking

7 Develop a list of guidelines for choosing a microscope to use.

Math Skills Math Practice

8 A student observes a blood sample with a compound microscope that has a 10× ocular lens and a 40× objective lens. How much larger do the blood cells appear under the microscope?

(l to r, t to b)Dr. Jeremy Burgess/Science Source; (2)JGI/Blend Images/Getty Images; (3)Stewart Sutton/Getty Images; (4)Steve Gschmeissner/Science Source; (5)Don W. Fawcett/Science Source (6)A. Syred/Science Source

Materials

a collection of objects

Constructing a Dichotomous Key

A dichotomous key is a series of descriptions arranged in pairs. Each description leads you to the name of the object or to another set of choices until you have identified the organism. In this lab, you will create a dichotomous key to classify objects.

Question

How can you create a dichotomous key to identify objects?

Procedure

① Read and complete a lab safety form.

② Obtain a container of objects from your teacher.

③ Examine the objects, and then brainstorm a list of possible characteristics. You might look at each object's size, shape, color, odor, texture, or function.

④ Choose a characteristic that would separate the objects into two groups. Separate the objects based on whether or not they have this characteristic. This characteristic will be used to begin a dichotomous key, like the example below.

Dichotomous Key to Identify Office Supplies

| The object is made of wood. Go to 1. |
| The object is not made of wood. Go to 2. |
| 1. The object is longer than 20 cm. Go to 5. |
| 3. The object is not longer than 20 cm. Go to 9. |
| 2. The object is made of metal. Go to 6. |
| 4. The object is not made of metal. Go to 10. |

Hutchings Photography/Digital Light Source

⑤ Write a sentence to describe the characteristic in step 4, and then write "Go to 1." Write another sentence that has the word "not" in front of the characteristic. Then write "Go to 2."

⑥ Repeat steps 4 and 5 for the two new groups. Give sentences for new groups formed from the first group consecutive odd numbers. Give sentences for groups formed from the second group consecutive even numbers. Remember to add the appropriate "Go to" directions.

⑦ Repeat steps 4–6 until there is one object in each group. Give each object an appropriate two-word name.

⑧ Give your collection of objects and your dichotomous key to another group. Have them identify each object using your dichotomous key. Have them record their answers.

Analyze and Conclude

⑨ **Evaluate** Was the other team able to correctly identify the collection of objects using your dichotomous key? Why or why not?

⑩ 🔵 **The Big Idea** Summarize how dichotomous keys are useful in identifying unknown objects.

Communicate Your Results

Create a poster using drawings or photos of each object you identified. Include your two-word names for the objects.

Teach a peer how to use a dichotomous key. Let the peer use your collection to have a first-hand experience with how a key works.

Lab Tips

☑ Base the questions in your key on observable, measurable, or countable characteristics. Avoid questions that refer to how something is used or how you think or feel about an item.

☑ Remember to start with general questions and then get more and more specific.

Remember to use scientific methods.

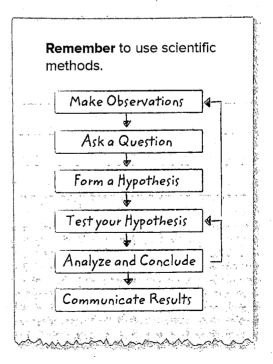

Make Observations

Ask a Question

Form a Hypothesis

Test your Hypothesis

Analyze and Conclude

Communicate Results

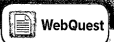
 All living things have certain characteristics in common and can be classified using several methods. The invention of the microscope has enabled us to explore life further, which has led to changes in classification.

Key Concepts Summary

Vocabulary

Lesson 1: Characteristics of Life

- An **organism** is classified as a living thing because it has all the characteristics of life.

- All living things are organized, grow and develop, reproduce, respond to stimuli, maintain **homeostasis,** and use energy.

organism p. 463
cell p. 464
unicellular p. 464
multicellular p. 464
homeostasis p. 467

Lesson 2: Classifying Organisms

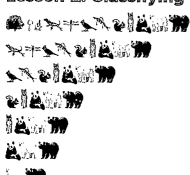

- Living things are classified into different groups based on physical or molecular similarities.

- Some **species** are known by many different common names. To avoid confusion, every species has a scientific name based on a system called **binomial nomenclature.**

binomial nomenclature p. 475
species p. 475
genus p. 475
dichotomous key p. 476
cladogram p. 477

Lesson 3: Exploring Life

- The invention of microscopes allowed scientists to view cells, which enabled them to further explore and classify life.

- A **light microscope** uses light and has one or more lenses to enlarge an image up to about 1,500 times its original size. An **electron microscope** uses a magnetic field to direct beams of electrons, and it enlarges an image 100,000 times or more.

light microscope p. 482
compound microscope p. 482
electron microscope p. 489

(t)Paul Tessier/Getty Images; (b)Javier Larrea/age fotostock/SuperStock

Personal Tutor

Vocabulary eFlashcards
Vocabulary eGames

FOLDABLES Chapter Project

Assemble your lesson Foldables as shown to make a Chapter Project. Use the project to review what you have learned in this chapter.

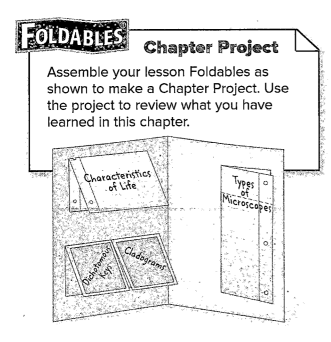

Use Vocabulary

1. A(n) _____ organism is made of only one cell.

2. Something with all the characteristics of life is a(n) _____.

3. A(n) _____ shows the relationships among species.

4. A group of similar species is a(n) _____.

5. A(n) _____ has a resolution up to 1,000 times greater than a light microscope.

6. A(n) _____ is a light microscope that uses more than one lens to magnify an image.

Link Vocabulary and Key Concepts

 Interactive Concept Map

Copy this concept map, and then use vocabulary terms from the previous page to complete the concept map.

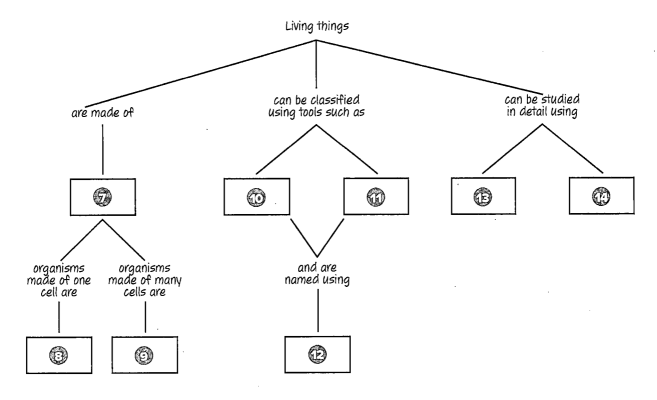

Understand Key Concepts

1 Which is an internal stimulus?
A. an increase in moisture
B. feelings of hunger
C. number of hours of daylight
D. the temperature at night

2 Which is an example of growth and development?
A. a caterpillar becoming a butterfly
B. a chicken laying eggs
C. a dog panting
D. a rabbit eating carrots

3 Based on the food web below, what is an energy source for the mouse?

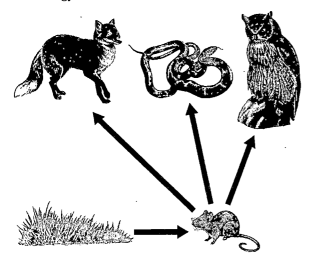

A. fox
B. grass
C. owl
D. snake

4 Which shows the correct order for the classification of species?
A. domain, kingdom, class, order, phylum, family, genus, species
B. domain, kingdom, phylum, class, order, family, genus, species
C. domain, kingdom, phylum, class, order, family, species, genus
D. domain, kingdom, phylum, order, class, family, genus, species

5 The organism shown below belongs in which kingdom?

A. Animalia
B. Archaea
C. Bacteria
D. Plantae

6 Which was discovered using a microscope?
A. blood
B. bones
C. cells
D. hair

7 What type of microscope would most likely be used to obtain an image of a live roundworm?
A. compound light microscope
B. scanning electron microscope
C. simple light microscope
D. transmission electron microscope

8 Which best describes a compound microscope?
A. uses electrons to magnify the image of an object
B. uses multiple lenses to magnify the image of an object
C. uses one lens to magnify the image of an object
D. uses sound waves to magnify the image of an object

Critical Thinking

9 **Distinguish** between a unicellular organism and a multicellular organism.

10 **Critique** the following statement: An organism that is made of only one cell does not need organization.

11 **Infer** In the figure below, which plant is responding to a lack of water in its environment? Explain your answer.

12 **Explain** how using a dichotomous key can help you identify an organism.

13 **Describe** how the branches on a cladogram show the relationships among organisms.

14 **Assess** the effect of molecular evidence on the classification of organisms.

15 **Compare** light microscopes and electron microscopes.

16 **State** how microscopes have changed the way living things are classified.

17 **Compare** magnification and resolution.

18 **Evaluate** the impact microscopes have on our daily lives.

Writing in Science

19 **Write** a five-sentence paragraph explaining the importance of scientific names. Be sure to include a topic sentence and a concluding sentence in your paragraph.

REVIEW THE BIG IDEA

20 Identify the characteristics that all living things share.

21 The photo below shows living and nonliving things. How would you classify the living things by domain and kingdom?

Math Skills ×÷ ✓ **Math Practice**

Use Multiplication

22 A microscope has an ocular lens with a power of 5× and an objective lens with a power of 50×. What is the total magnification of the microscope?

23 A student observes a unicellular organism with a microscope that has a 10× ocular lens and a 100× objective lens. How much larger does the organism look through this microscope?

24 The ocular lens on a microscope has a power of 10×. The microscope makes objects appear 500 times larger. What is the power of the objective lens?

Record your answers on the answer sheet provided by your teacher or on a sheet of paper.

Multiple Choice

1 What feature of living things do the terms *unicellular* and *multicellular* describe?

  A how they are organized

  B how they reproduce

  C how they maintain temperature

  D how they produce macromolecules

Use the diagram below to answer question 2.

2 Which characteristic of life does the diagram show?

  A homeostasis

  B organization

  C growth and development

  D response to stimuli

3 A newly discovered organism is 1 m tall, multicellular, green, and it grows on land and performs photosynthesis. To which kingdom does it most likely belong?

  A Animalia

  B Fungi

  C Plantae

  D Protista

4 Unicellular organisms are members of which kingdoms?

  A Animalia, Archaea, Plantae

  B Archaea, Bacteria, Protista

  C Bacteria, Fungi, Plantae

  D Fungi, Plantae, Protista

5 Which microscope would best magnify the outer surface of a cell?

  A compound light

  B scanning electron

  C simple dissecting

  D transmission electron

Use the diagram below to answer question 6.

6 Which discovery was NOT made with the instrument above?

  A Bacterial cells have thick walls.

  B Blood is a mixture of components.

  C Insects have small body parts.

  D Tiny organisms live in pond water.

7 Which statement is false?

  A Binomial names are given to all known organisms.

  B Binomial names are less precise than common names.

  C Binomial names differ from common names.

  D Binomial names enable scientists to communicate accurately.

Use the diagram below to answer question 8.

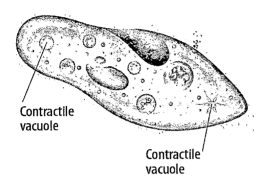

Contractile
vacuole

Contractile
vacuole

8 Which is the function of the structures in this paramecium?

A growth

B homeostasis

C locomotion

D reproduction

9 Which sequence is from the smallest group of organisms to the largest group of organisms?

A genus → family → species

B genus → species → family

C species → family → genus

D species → genus → family

10 Which information about organisms is excluded in the study of systematics?

A calendar age

B molecular analysis

C energy source

D normal habitat

Constructed Response

11 Copy and complete the table below about the six characteristics of life.

Characteristic	Explanation

12 Choose one characteristic of living things and explain how it affects everyday human life. From your own knowledge, give a specific example.

Use the diagram below to answer question 13.

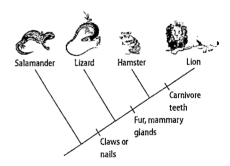

Salamander Lizard Hamster Lion

Carnivore
teeth

Fur, mammary
glands

Claws or
nails

13 Explain why the lion is more closely related to the hamster than the hamster is related to the salamander.

NEED EXTRA HELP?													
If You Missed Question...	1	2	3	4	5	6	7	8	9	10	11	12	13
Go to Lesson...	1	1	2	2	3	3	2	1	2	2	1	1	2

Chapter 14

7.LS.1, 7.LS.5, SEPS.3, SEPS.7, 6-8.LST.4.1, 6-8.LST.5.2, 6-8.LST.7.1

Cell Structure and Function

THE BIG IDEA How do the structures and processes of a cell enable it to survive?

Inquiry Alien Life?

You might think this unicellular organism looks like something out of a science-fiction movie. Although it looks scary, the hairlike structures in its mouth enable the organism to survive.

- What do you think the hairlike structures do?

- How might the shape of the hairlike structures relate to their function?

- How do you think the structures and processes of a cell enable it to survive?

Get Ready to Read

What do you think?

Before you read, decide if you agree or disagree with each of these statements. As you read this chapter, see if you change your mind about any of the statements.

1. Nonliving things have cells.

2. Cells are made mostly of water.

3. Different organisms have cells with different structures.

4. All cells store genetic information in their nuclei.

5. Diffusion and osmosis are the same process.

6. Cells with large surface areas can transport more than cells with smaller surface areas.

7. ATP is the only form of energy found in cells.

8. Cellular respiration occurs only in lung cells.

Your one-stop online resource
connectED.mcgraw-hill.com

 LearnSmart®

 Chapter Resources Files, Reading Essentials, Get Ready to Read, Quick Vocabulary

 Animations, Videos, Interactive Tables

 Self-checks, Quizzes, Tests

 Project-Based Learning Activities

 Lab Manuals, Safety Videos, Virtual Labs & Other Tools

 Vocabulary, Multilingual eGlossary, Vocab eGames, Vocab eFlashcards

 Personal Tutors

Cells and Life

Reading Guide

Key Concepts 🔑
ESSENTIAL QUESTIONS

- How did scientists' understanding of cells develop?

- What basic substances make up a cell?

Vocabulary

cell theory p. 498

macromolecule p. 499

nucleic acid p. 500

protein p. 501

lipid p. 501

carbohydrate p. 501

 Multilingual eGlossary

 7.LS.1, 6-8.LST.7.1

Inquiry Two of a Kind?

At first glance, the plant and animal in the photo might seem like they have nothing in common. The plant is rooted in the ground, and the rabbit can move quickly. Are they more alike than they appear? How can you find out?

Jason Harris/Getty Images

What's in a cell?

Most plants grow from seeds. A seed began as one cell, but a mature plant can be made up of millions of cells. How does a seed change and grow into a mature plant?

1. Read and complete a lab safety form.

2. Use a **toothpick** to gently remove the thin outer covering of a **bean seed** that has soaked overnight.

3. Open the seed with a **plastic knife,** and observe its inside with a **magnifying lens.** Draw the inside of the seed in your Science Journal.

4. Gently remove the small, plantlike embryo, and weigh it on a **balance.** Record its mass in your Science Journal.

5. Gently pull a **bean seedling** from the soil. Rinse the soil from the roots. Weigh the seedling, and record the mass.

Think About This

1. How did the mass of the embryo and the bean seedling differ?

2. **Key Concept** If a plant begins as one cell, where do all the cells come from?

Understanding Cells

Have you ever looked up at the night sky and tried to find other planets in our solar system? It is hard to see them without using a telescope. This is because the other planets are millions of kilometers away. Just like we can use telescopes to see other planets, we can use microscopes to see the basic units of all living things—cells. But people didn't always know about cells. Because cells are so small, early scientists had no tools to study them. It took hundreds of years for scientists to learn about cells.

More than 300 years ago, an English scientist named Robert Hooke built a microscope. He used the microscope to look at cork, which is part of a cork oak tree's bark. What he saw looked like the openings in a honeycomb, as shown in Figure 1. The openings reminded him of the small rooms, called cells, where monks lived. He called the structures cells, from the Latin word *cellula* (SEL yuh luh), which means "small rooms."

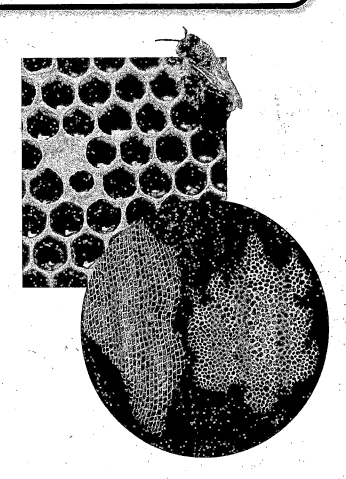

Figure 1 To Robert Hooke, the cells of cork looked like the openings in a honeycomb.

(t)Hutchings Photography/Digital Light Source, (c)Bon Appetit/Alamy, (b)Omikron/Science Source

The Cell Theory

After Hooke's discovery, other scientists began making better microscopes and looking for cells in many other places, such as pond water and blood. The newer microscopes enabled scientists to see different structures inside cells. Matthias Schleiden (SHLI dun), a German scientist, used one of the new microscopes to look at plant cells. Around the same time, another German scientist, Theodor Schwann, used a microscope to study animal cells. Schleiden and Schwann realized that plant and animal cells have similar features. You'll read about many of these features in Lesson 2.

Almost two decades later, Rudolf Virchow (VUR koh), a German doctor, proposed that all cells come from preexisting cells, or cells that already exist. The observations made by Schleiden, Schwann, and Virchow were combined into one theory. As illustrated in Table 1, *the cell theory states that all living things are made of one or more cells, the cell is the smallest unit of life, and all new cells come from preexisting cells.* After the development of the cell theory, scientists raised more questions about cells. If all living things are made of cells, what are cells made of?

Key Concept Check How did scientists' understanding of cells develop?

REVIEW VOCABULARY

theory
explanation of things or events based on scientific knowledge resulting from many observations and experiments

Table 1 Scientists developed the cell theory after studying cells with microscopes.

Table 1 The Cell Theory

Principle	Example
All living things are made of one or more cells.	Leaf cells
The cell is the smallest unit of life.	This unicellular amoeba is surrounding an algal cell to get food and energy. Amoeba Algal cell
All new cells come from preexisting cells.	Existing cell Cell dividing New cells

Basic Cell Substances

Have you ever watched a train travel down a railroad track? The locomotive pulls train cars that are hooked together. Like a train, many of the substances in cells are made of smaller parts that are joined together. *These substances, called* **macromolecules,** *form by joining many small molecules together.* As you will read later in this lesson, macromolecules have many important roles in cells. But macromolecules cannot function without one of the most important substances in cells—water.

The Main Ingredient—Water

The main ingredient in any cell is water. It makes up more than 70 percent of a cell's volume and is essential for life. Why is water such an important molecule? In addition to making up a large part of the inside of cells, water also surrounds cells. The water surrounding your cells helps to insulate your body, which maintains homeostasis, or a stable internal environment.

The structure of a water molecule makes it ideal for dissolving many other substances. Substances must be in a liquid to move into and out of cells. A water molecule has two areas:

- An area that is more negative (−), called the negative end; this end can attract the positive part of another substance.

- An area that is more positive (+), called the positive end; this end can attract the negative part of another substance.

Examine **Figure 2** to see how the positive and negative ends of water molecules dissolve salt crystals.

WORD ORIGIN

macromolecule
from Greek *makro–*, means "long"; and Latin *molecula*, means "mass"

Figure 2 The positive and negative ends of a water molecule attract the positive and negative parts of another substance, similar to the way magnets are attracted to each other.

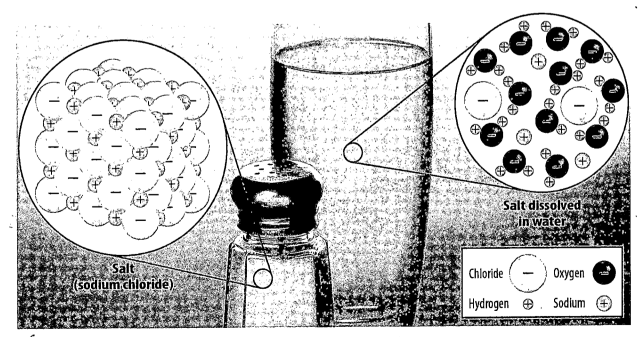

Salt (sodium chloride)

Salt dissolved in water

Chloride	(−)	Oxygen	●
Hydrogen	⊕	Sodium	⊕

✔️ **Visual Check** Which part of the salt crystal is attracted to the oxygen in the water molecule?

Hutchings Photography/Digital Light Source

Macromolecules

Although water is essential for life, all cells contain other substances that enable them to function. Recall that macromolecules are large molecules that form when smaller molecules join together. As shown in Figure 3, there are four types of macromolecules in cells: nucleic acids, proteins, lipids, and carbohydrates. Each type of macromolecule has unique functions in a cell. These functions range from growth and communication to movement and storage.

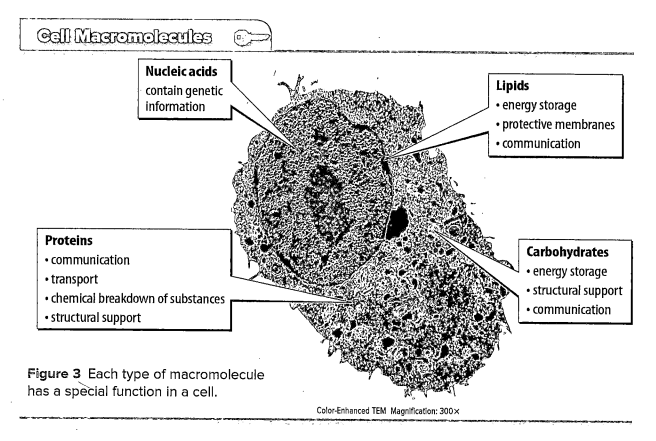

Cell Macromolecules

Nucleic acids
contain genetic information

Lipids
• energy storage
• protective membranes
• communication

Proteins
• communication
• transport
• chemical breakdown of substances
• structural support

Carbohydrates
• energy storage
• structural support
• communication

Figure 3 Each type of macromolecule has a special function in a cell.

Color-Enhanced TEM Magnification: 300×

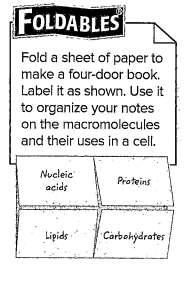

FOLDABLES

Fold a sheet of paper to make a four-door book. Label it as shown. Use it to organize your notes on the macromolecules and their uses in a cell.

| Nucleic acids | Proteins |
| Lipids | Carbohydrates |

Nucleic Acids Both deoxyribonucleic (dee AHK sih ri boh noo klee ihk) acid (DNA) and ribonucleic (ri boh noo KLEE ihk) acid (RNA) are nucleic acids. **Nucleic acids** *are macromolecules that form when long chains of molecules called nucleotides* (NEW klee uh tidz) *join together*. The order of nucleotides in DNA and RNA is important. If you change the order of words in a sentence, you can change the meaning of the sentence. In a similar way, changing the order of nucleotides in DNA and RNA can change the genetic information in a cell.

Nucleic acids are important in cells because they contain genetic information. This information can pass from parents to offspring. DNA includes instructions for cell growth, cell reproduction, and cell processes that enable a cell to respond to its environment. DNA is used to make RNA. RNA is used to make proteins.

Proteins The macromolecules necessary for nearly everything cells do are proteins. **Proteins** *are long chains of amino acid molecules.* You just read that RNA is used to make proteins. RNA contains instructions for joining amino acids together.

Cells contain hundreds of proteins. Each protein has a unique function. Some proteins help cells communicate with each other. Other proteins transport substances around inside cells. Some proteins, such as amylase (AM uh lays) in saliva, help break down nutrients in food. Other proteins, such as keratin (KER uh tun)–a protein found in hair, horns, and feathers–provide structural support.

Lipids Another group of macromolecules found in cells is lipids. *A* **lipid** *is a large macromolecule that does not dissolve in water.* Because lipids do not mix with water, they play an important role as protective barriers in cells. They are also the major part of cell membranes. Lipids play roles in energy storage and in cell communication. Examples of lipids are cholesterol (kuh LES tuh rawl), phospholipids (fahs foh LIH pids), and vitamin A.

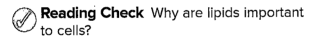 **Reading Check** Why are lipids important to cells?

Carbohydrates *One sugar molecule, two sugar molecules, or a long chain of sugar molecules make up* **carbohydrates** (kar boh HI drayts). Carbohydrates store energy, provide structural support, and are needed for communication between cells. Sugars and starches are carbohydrates that store energy. Fruits contain sugars. Breads and pastas are mostly starch. The energy in sugars and starches can be released quickly through chemical reactions in cells. Cellulose is a carbohydrate in the cell walls in plants that provides structural support.

 Key Concept Check What basic substances make up a cell?

Al Telser/McGraw-Hill Education

MiniLab   **25 minutes**

How can you observe DNA?

Nucleic acids are macromolecules that are important in cells because they contain an organism's genetic information. In this lab, you will observe one type of nucleic acid, DNA, in onion root-tip cells using a compound light microscope.

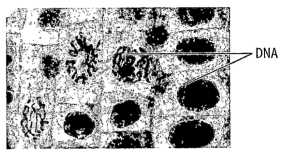

DNA

1. Read and complete a lab safety form.
2. Obtain a **microscope** and a **slide** from your teacher. Use care and properly handle your microscope.
3. Observe the **onion root-tip cells** at the magnifications assigned by your teacher.
4. Determine the approximate number of cells in your field of view and the number of cells with visible DNA. Record these numbers in your Science Journal.

Analyze and Conclude

1. **Calculate** Using your data, find the percentage of cells with visible DNA that you saw in your microscope's field of view.

2. **Compare** your results with the results of other students. Are all the results the same? Explain.

3. **Create** a data table for the entire class that lists individual results.

4. **Calculate** the total percentage of cells with visible DNA at each magnification.

5. **Key Concept** Did looking at the cells at different magnifications change the percentage of cells with visible DNA? Explain.

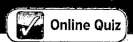
Visual Summary

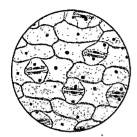

The cell theory summarizes the main principles for understanding that the cell is the basic unit of life.

Water is the main ingredient in every cell.

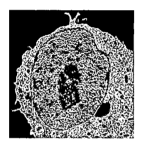

A nucleic acid, such as DNA, contains the genetic information for a cell.

FOLDABLES

Use your lesson Foldable to review the lesson. Save your Foldable for the project at the end of the chapter.

What do you think NOW?

You first read the statements below at the beginning of the chapter.

1. Nonliving things have cells.

2. Cells are made mostly of water.

Did you change your mind about whether you agree or disagree with the statements? Rewrite any false statements to make them true.

Use Vocabulary

1 The _____ _____ states that the cell is the basic unit of all living things.

2 **Distinguish** between a carbohydrate and a lipid.

3 **Use the term** *nucleic acid* in a sentence.

Understand Key Concepts

4 Which macromolecule is made from amino acids?
   A. lipid   **C.** carbohydrate
   B. protein   **D.** nucleic acid

5 **Describe** how the invention of the microscope helped scientists understand cells.

6 **Compare** the functions of DNA and proteins in a cell.

Interpret Graphics

7 **Summarize** Copy and fill in the graphic organizer below to summarize the main principles of the cell theory.

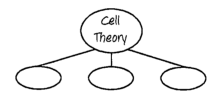

8 **Analyze** How does the structure of the water molecule shown below enable it to interact with other water molecules?

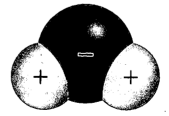

Critical Thinking

9 **Summarize** the functions of lipids in cells.

10 **Hypothesize** why carbohydrates are found in plant cell walls.

HOW IT WORKS

A Very Powerful Microscope

If Robert Hooke had used an atomic force microscope (AFM), he would have observed more than just cells. He would have seen the macromolecules inside them! An AFM can scan objects that are only nanometers in size. A nanometer is one one-billionth of a meter. That's 100,000 times smaller than the width of a human hair. AFM technology has enabled scientists to better understand how cells function. It also has given them a three-dimensional look at the macromolecules that make life possible. This is how it works.

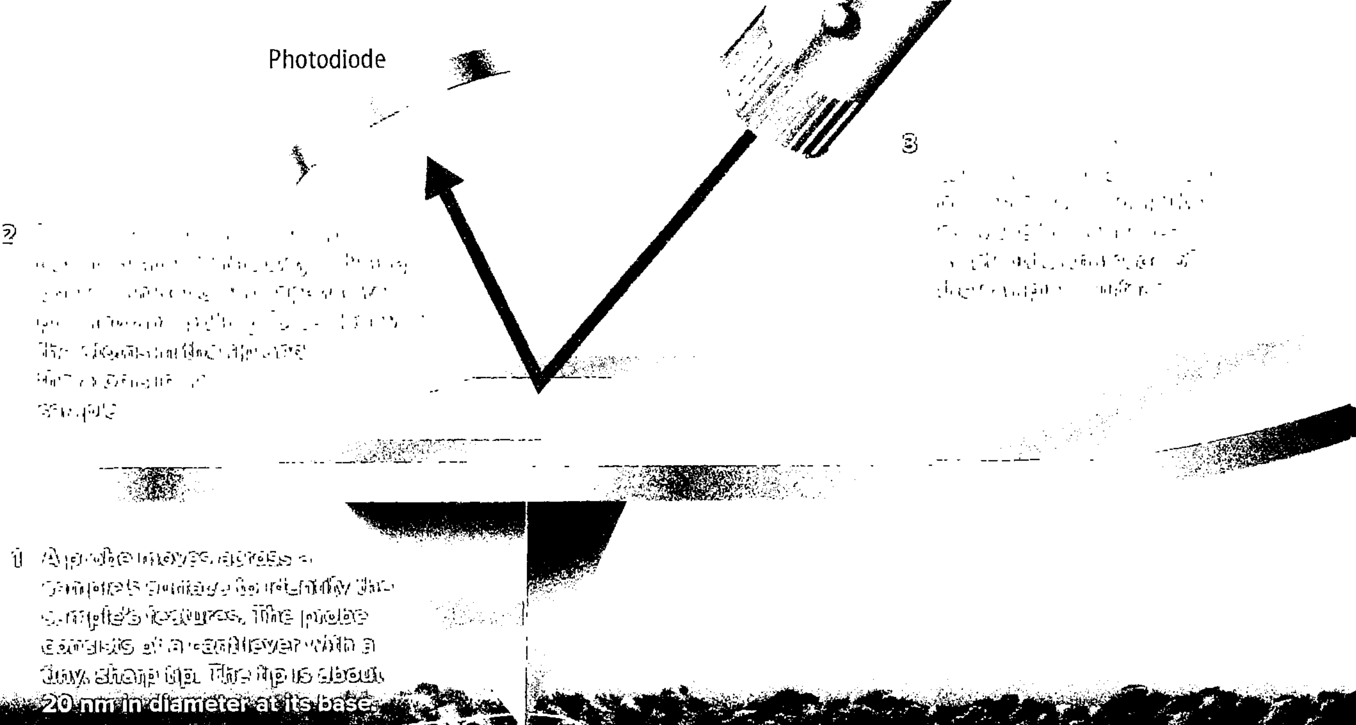

Photodiode
3
2
1 A probe moves across a sample's surface to identify the sample's features. The probe consists of a cantilever with a tiny, sharp tip. The tip is about 20 nm in diameter at its base.

It's Your Turn

NASA's Phoenix Mars Lander included an atomic force microscope. Find out what scientists discovered on Mars with this instrument.

Lesson 2

Reading Guide

Key Concepts

ESSENTIAL QUESTIONS

- How are prokaryotic cells and eukaryotic cells similar, and how are they different?

- What do the structures in a cell do?

Vocabulary

cell membrane p. 506

cell wall p. 506

cytoplasm p. 507

cytoskeleton p. 507

organelle p. 508

nucleus p. 509

chloroplast p. 511

 Multilingual eGlossary

 BrainPOP®

 7.LS.1, 7.LS.5, SEPS.3, SEPS.7

Eye of Science Science Source

Inquiry Hooked Together?

What do you think happens when one of the hooks in the photo above goes through one of the loops? The two sides fasten together. The shapes of the hooks and loops in the hook-and-loop tape are suited to their function—to hold the two pieces together.

Why do eggs have shells?

Bird eggs have different structures, such as a shell, a membrane, and a yolk. Each structure has a different function that helps keep the egg safe and assists in development of the baby bird inside of it.

① Read and complete a lab safety form.

② Place an **uncooked egg** in a bowl.

③ Feel the shell, and record your observations in your Science Journal.

④ Crack open the egg. Pour the contents into the bowl.

⑤ Observe the inside of the shell and the contents of the bowl. Record your observations in your Science Journal.

Think About This

1. What do you think is the role of the eggshell?

2. Are there any structures in the bowl that have the same function as the eggshell? Explain.

3. 🔑 **Key Concept** What does the structure of the eggshell tell you about its function?

Cell Shape and Movement

You might recall from Lesson 1 that all living things are made up of one or more cells. As illustrated in Figure 4, cells come in many shapes and sizes. The size and shape of a cell relates to its job or function. For example, a human red blood cell cannot be seen without a microscope. Its small size and disk shape enable it to pass easily through the smallest blood vessels. The shape of a nerve cell enables it to send signals over long distances. Some plant cells are hollow and make up tubelike structures that carry materials throughout a plant.

The structures that make up a cell also have unique functions. Think about how the players on a football team perform different tasks to move the ball down the field. In a similar way, a cell is made of different structures that perform different functions that keep a cell alive. You will read about some of these structures in this lesson.

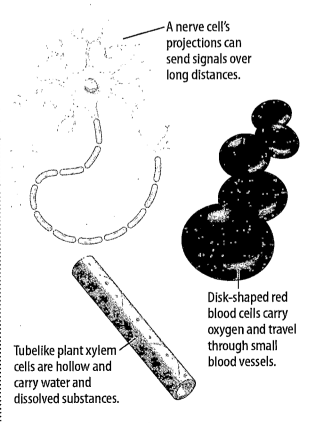

A nerve cell's projections can send signals over long distances.

Disk-shaped red blood cells carry oxygen and travel through small blood vessels.

Tubelike plant xylem cells are hollow and carry water and dissolved substances.

Figure 4 The shape of a cell relates to the function it performs.

Hutchings Photography/Digital Light Source

Figure 5 The cell wall maintains the shape of a plant cell.

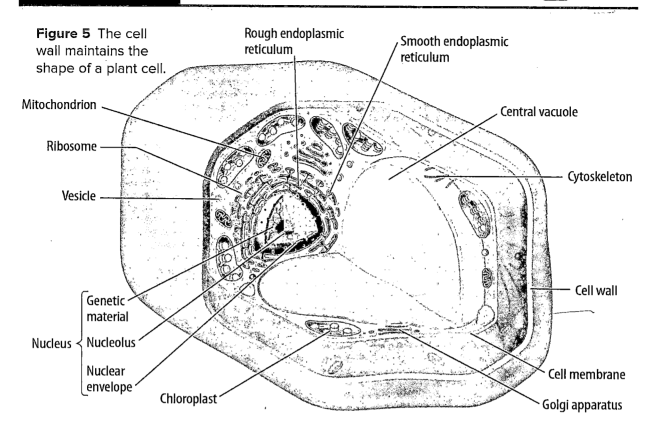

Rough endoplasmic reticulum

Smooth endoplasmic reticulum

Mitochondrion

Ribosome

Vesicle

Central vacuole

Cytoskeleton

Nucleus {
Genetic material
Nucleolus
Nuclear envelope
}

Chloroplast

Cell wall

Cell membrane

Golgi apparatus

ACADEMIC VOCABULARY

function
(*noun*) the purpose for which something is used

Cell Membrane

Although different types of cells perform different functions, all cells have some structures in common. As shown in **Figure 5** and **Figure 6**, every cell is surrounded by a protective covering called a membrane. *The* **cell membrane** *is a flexible covering that protects the inside of a cell from the environment outside a cell.* Cell membranes are mostly made of two different macromolecules—proteins and a type of lipid called phospholipids. Think again about a football team. The defensive line tries to stop the other team from moving forward with the football. In a similar way, a cell membrane protects the cell from the outside environment.

Reading Check What are cell membranes made of?

Cell Wall

Every cell has a cell membrane, but some cells are also surrounded by a structure called the cell wall. Plant cells such as the one in **Figure 5**, fungal cells, bacteria, and some types of protists have cell walls. *A* **cell wall** *is a stiff structure outside the cell membrane.* A cell wall protects a cell from attack by viruses and other harmful organisms. In some plant cells and fungal cells, a cell wall helps maintain the cell's shape and gives structural support.

Animal Cell

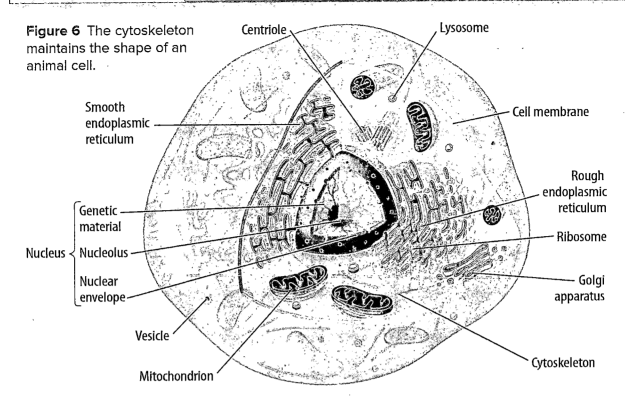

Figure 6 The cytoskeleton maintains the shape of an animal cell.

Centriole

Lysosome

Smooth endoplasmic reticulum

Cell membrane

Rough endoplasmic reticulum

Nucleus
{
Genetic material

Nucleolus

Nuclear envelope
}

Ribosome

Golgi apparatus

Vesicle

Cytoskeleton

Mitochondrion

⊘ **Visual Check** Compare this animal cell to the plant cell in **Figure 5**.

Cell Appendages

Arms, legs, claws, and antennae are all types of appendages. Cells can have appendages too. Cell appendages are often used for movement. Flagella (fluh JEH luh; singular, flagellum) are long, tail-like appendages that whip back and forth and move a cell. A cell can also have cilia (SIH lee uh; singular, cilium) like the ones shown in **Figure 7**. Cilia are short, hairlike structures. They can move a cell or move molecules away from a cell. A microscopic organism called a paramecium (pa ruh MEE shee um) moves around its watery environment using its cilia. The cilia in your windpipe move harmful substances away from your lungs.

Cytoplasm and the Cytoskeleton

In Lesson 1, you read that water is the main ingredient in a cell. Most of this water is in the **cytoplasm**, *a fluid inside a cell that contains salts and other molecules.* The cytoplasm also contains a cell's cytoskeleton. *The* **cytoskeleton** *is a network of threadlike proteins that are joined together.* The proteins form a framework inside a cell. This framework gives a cell its shape and helps it move. Cilia and flagella are made from the same proteins that make up the cytoskeleton.

Color-Enhanced SEM Magnification: Unavailable

Figure 7 Lung cells have cilia that help move fluids and foreign materials.

WORD ORIGIN ·············

cytoplasm
from Greek *kytos*, means "hollow vessel"; and *plasma*, means "something molded"

SPL/Science Source

How do eukaryotic and prokaryotic cells compare?

With the use of better microscopes, scientists discovered that cells can be classified as one of two types—prokaryotic or eukaryotic.

1. Read and complete a lab safety form.

2. Using different **craft items,** make a two-dimensional model of a eukaryotic cell.

3. In your cell model, include the number of cell structures assigned by your teacher.

4. Make each cell structure the correct shape, as shown in this lesson.

5. Make a label for each cell structure of your model.

Analyze and Conclude

1. **Describe** the nucleus of your cell.

2. **Classify** your cell as either a plant cell or an animal cell, and support your classification with evidence.

3. **Key Concept** Compare and contrast a prokaryotic cell, as shown in Figure 8, with your eukaryotic cell model.

Cell Types

Recall that the use of microscopes enabled scientists to discover cells. With more advanced microscopes, scientists discovered that all cells can be grouped into two types—prokaryotic (proh ka ree AH tihk) cells and eukaryotic (yew ker ee AH tihk) cells.

Prokaryotic Cells

The genetic material in a prokaryotic cell is not surrounded by a membrane, as shown in **Figure 8.** This is the most important feature of a prokaryotic cell. Prokaryotic cells also do not have many of the other cell parts that you will read about later in this lesson. Most prokaryotic cells are unicellular organisms and are called prokaryotes.

Figure 8 In prokaryotic cells, the genetic material floats freely in the cytoplasm.

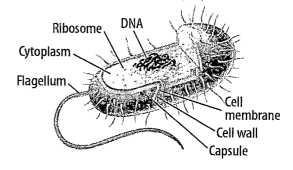

Eukaryotic Cells

Plants, animals, fungi, and protists are all made of eukaryotic cells, such as the ones shown in **Figure 5** and **Figure 6,** and are called eukaryotes. With few exceptions, each eukaryotic cell has genetic material that is surrounded by a membrane. Every eukaryotic cell also has *other structures, called* **organelles,** *which have specialized functions. Most organelles are surrounded by membranes.* Eukaryotic cells are usually larger than prokaryotic cells. About ten prokaryotic cells would fit inside one eukaryotic cell.

Key Concept Check How are prokaryotic cells and eukaryotic cells similar, and how are they different?

Cell Organelles

As you have just read, organelles are eukaryotic cell structures with specific functions. Organelles enable cells to carry out different functions at the same time. For example, cells can obtain energy from food, store information, make macromolecules, and get rid of waste materials all at the same time because different organelles perform the different tasks.

The Nucleus

The largest organelle inside most eukaryotic cells is the nucleus, shown in **Figure 9**. *The* **nucleus** *is the part of a eukaryotic cell that directs cell activities and contains genetic information stored in DNA.* DNA is organized into structures called chromosomes. The number of chromosomes in a nucleus is different for different species of organisms. For example, kangaroo cells contain six pairs of chromosomes. Most human cells contain 23 pairs of chromosomes.

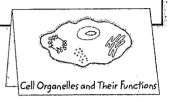

Fold a sheet of paper into a vertical half book. Use it to record information about cell organelles and their functions.

Cell Organelles and Their Functions

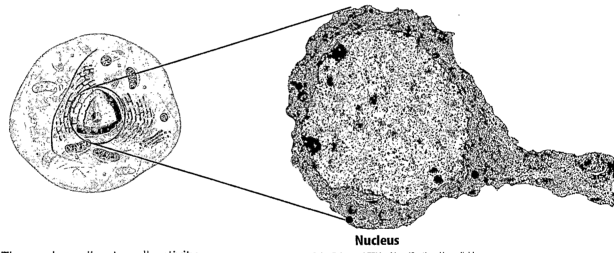

Nucleus
Color-Enhanced TEM   Magnification: Unavailable

Figure 9 The nucleus directs cell activity and is surrounded by a membrane.

In addition to chromosomes, the nucleus contains proteins and an organelle called the nucleolus (new KLEE uh lus). The nucleolus is often seen as a large dark spot in the nucleus of a cell. The nucleolus makes ribosomes, organelles that are involved in the production of proteins. You will read about ribosomes later in this lesson.

Surrounding the nucleus are two membranes that form a structure called the nuclear envelope. The nuclear envelope contains many pores. Certain molecules, such as ribosomes and RNA, move into and out of the nucleus through these pores.

 Reading Check What is the nuclear envelope?

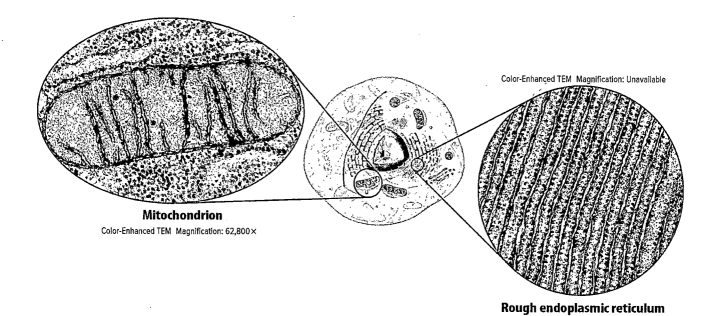

Mitochondrion
Color-Enhanced TEM Magnification: 62,800×

Color-Enhanced TEM Magnification: Unavailable

Rough endoplasmic reticulum

Figure 10 The endoplasmic reticulum is made of many folded membranes. Mitochondria provide a cell with usable energy.

Manufacturing Molecules

You might recall from Lesson 1 that proteins are important molecules in cells. Proteins are made on small structures called ribosomes. Unlike other cell organelles, a ribosome is not surrounded by a membrane. Ribosomes are in a cell's cytoplasm. They also can be attached to a weblike organelle called the endoplasmic reticulum (en duh PLAZ mihk • rih TIHK yuh lum), or ER. As shown in **Figure 10**, the ER spreads from the nucleus throughout most of the cytoplasm. ER with ribosomes on its surface is called rough ER. Rough ER is the site of protein production. ER without ribosomes is called smooth ER. It makes lipids such as cholesterol. Smooth ER is important because it helps remove harmful substances from a cell.

 Reading Check Contrast smooth ER and rough ER.

Processing Energy

All living things require energy in order to survive. Cells process some energy in specialized organelles. Most eukaryotic cells contain hundreds of organelles called mitochondria (mi tuh KAHN dree uh; singular, mitochondrion), shown in **Figure 10**. Some cells in a human heart can contain a thousand mitochondria.

Like the nucleus, a mitochondrion is surrounded by two membranes. Energy is released during chemical reactions that occur in the mitochondria. This energy is stored in high-energy molecules called ATP—adenosine triphosphate (uh DEH nuh seen • tri FAHS fayt). ATP is the fuel for cellular processes such as growth, cell division, and material transport.

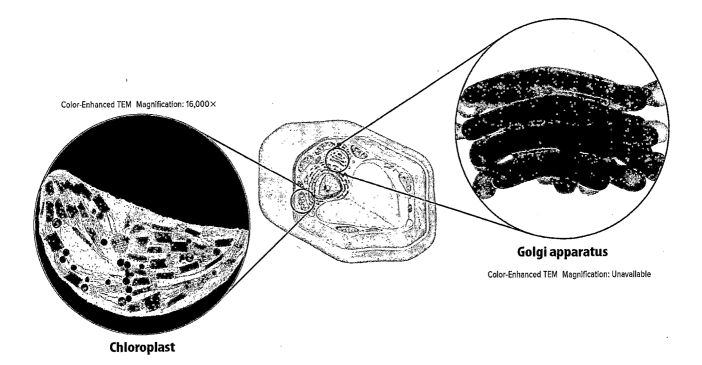

Color-Enhanced TEM Magnification: 16,000×

Chloroplast

Golgi apparatus

Color-Enhanced TEM Magnification: Unavailable

Plant cells and some protists, such as algae, also contain organelles called chloroplasts (KLOR uh plasts), shown in **Figure 11.** **Chloroplasts** *are membrane-bound organelles that use light energy and make food—a sugar called glucose—from water and carbon dioxide in a process known as photosynthesis* (foh toh SIHN thuh sus). The sugar contains stored chemical energy that can be released when a cell needs it. You will read more about photosynthesis in Lesson 4.

Reading Check Which types of cells contain chloroplasts?

Processing, Transporting, and Storing Molecules

Near the ER is an organelle that looks like a stack of pancakes. This is the Golgi (GAWL jee) apparatus, shown in **Figure 11.** It prepares proteins for their specific jobs or functions. Then it packages the proteins into tiny, membrane-bound, ball-like structures called vesicles. Vesicles are organelles that transport substances from one area of a cell to another area of a cell. Some vesicles in an animal cell are called lysosomes. Lysosomes contain substances that help break down and recycle cellular components.

Some cells also have saclike structures called vacuoles (VA kyuh wohlz). Vacuoles are organelles that store food, water, and waste material. A typical plant cell usually has one large vacuole that stores water and other substances. Some animal cells have many small vacuoles.

Key Concept Check What is the function of the Golgi apparatus?

Figure 11 Plant cells have chloroplasts that use light energy and make food. The Golgi apparatus packages materials into vesicles.

(l)Biology Pics/Science Source; (r)David Gunn/Getty Images

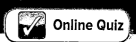
Visual Summary

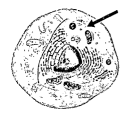

A cell is protected by a flexible covering called the cell membrane.

Cells can be grouped into two types—prokaryotic cells and eukaryotic cells.

In a chloroplast, light energy is used for making sugars in a process called photosynthesis.

FOLDABLES

Use your lesson Foldable to review the lesson. Save your Foldable for the project at the end of the chapter.

What do you think NOW?

You first read the statements below at the beginning of the chapter.

3. Different organisms have cells with different structures.

4. All cells store genetic information in their nuclei.

Did you change your mind about whether you agree or disagree with the statements? Rewrite any false statements to make them true.

Use Vocabulary

1 **Distinguish** between the cell wall and the cell membrane.

2 **Use the terms** *mitochondria* and *chloroplasts* in a sentence.

3 **Define** *organelle* in your own words.

Understand Key Concepts

4 Which organelle is used to store water?
  A. chloroplast   C. nucleus
  B. lysosome   D. vacuole

5 **Explain** the role of the cytoskeleton.

6 **Draw** a prokaryotic cell and label its parts.

7 **Compare** the roles of the endoplasmic reticulum and the Golgi apparatus.

Interpret Graphics

8 **Explain** how the structure of the cells below relates to their function.

9 **Compare** Copy the table below and fill it in to compare the structures of a plant cell to the structures of an animal cell.

Structure	Plant Cell	Animal Cell
Cell membrane	yes	yes
Cell wall		
Mitochondrion		
Chloroplast		
Nucleus		
Vacuole		
Lysosome		

Critical Thinking

10 **Analyze** Why are most organelles surrounded by membranes?

11 **Compare** the features of eukaryotic and prokaryotic cells.

How are plant cells and animal cells similar and how are they different?

A light microscope enables you to observe many of the structures in cells. Increasing the magnification means you see a smaller portion of the object, but lets you see more detail. As you see more details, you can **compare and contrast** different cell types. How are they alike? How are they different?

Materials

microscope

microscope slide and coverslip

forceps

dropper

Elodea plant

Prepared slide of human cheek cells

Safety

Learn It

Observations can be analyzed by noting the similarities and differences between two or more objects that you observe. You **compare** objects by noting similarities. You **contrast** objects by looking for differences.

Try It

1. Read and complete a lab safety form.

2. Using forceps, make a wet-mount slide of a young leaf from the tip of an *Elodea* plant.

3. Use a microscope to observe the leaf on low power. Focus on the top layer of cells.

4. Switch to high power and focus on one cell. The large organelle in the center of the cell is the central vacuole. Moving around the central vacuole are green, disklike objects called chloroplasts. Try to find the nucleus. It looks like a clear ball.

5. Draw a diagram of an *Elodea* cell in your Science Journal. Label the cell wall, central vacuole, chloroplasts, cytoplasm, and nucleus. Return to low power and remove the slide. Properly dispose of the slide.

6. Observe the prepared slide of cheek cells under low power.

7. Switch to high power and focus on one cell. Draw a diagram of one cheek cell. Label the cell membrane, cytoplasm, and nucleus. Return to low power and remove the slide.

Apply It

8. Based on your diagrams, how do the shapes of the *Elodea* cell and cheek cell compare?

9. 🔑 **Key Concept** Compare and contrast the cell structures in your two diagrams. Which structures did you observe in both cells? Which structures did you observe in only one of the cells?

Moving Cellular Material

Reading Guide

Key Concepts 🔑

ESSENTIAL QUESTIONS

- How do materials enter and leave cells?

- How does cell size affect the transport of materials?

Vocabulary

passive transport p. 515

diffusion p. 516

osmosis p. 516

facilitated diffusion p. 517

active transport p. 518

endocytosis p. 518

exocytosis p. 518

 Multilingual eGlossary

 7.LS.1, 6-8.LST.4.1

 Go to the resource tab in ConnectED to find the PBL *It's Alive! Or is it?*

Inquiry Why the Veil?

A beekeeper often wears a hat with a face-covering veil made of mesh. The openings in the mesh are large enough to let air through, yet small enough to keep bees out. In a similar way, some things must be allowed in or out of a cell, while other things must be kept in or out. How do the right things enter or leave a cell?

What does the cell membrane do?

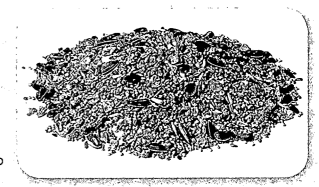

All cells have a membrane around the outside of the cell. The cell membrane separates the inside of a cell from the environment outside a cell. What else might a cell membrane do?

1. Read and complete a lab safety form.

2. Place a square of **wire mesh** on top of a **beaker.**

3. Pour a small amount of **birdseed** on top of the wire mesh. Record your observations in your Science Journal.

Think About This

1. What part of a cell does the wire mesh represent?

2. What happened when you poured birdseed on the wire mesh?

3. 🔑 **Key Concept** How do you think the cell membrane affects materials that enter and leave a cell?

Passive Transport

Recall from Lesson 2 that membranes are the boundaries between cells and between organelles. Another important role of membranes is to control the movement of substances into and out of cells. A cell membrane is semipermeable. This means it allows only certain substances to enter or leave a cell. Substances can pass through a cell membrane by one of several different processes. The type of process depends on the physical and chemical properties of the substance passing through the membrane.

Small molecules, such as oxygen and carbon dioxide, pass through membranes by a process called passive transport. **Passive transport** *is the movement of substances through a cell membrane without using the cell's energy.* Passive transport depends on the amount of a substance on each side of a membrane. For example, suppose there are more molecules of oxygen outside a cell than inside it. Oxygen will move into that cell until the amount of oxygen is equal on both sides of the cell's membrane. Since oxygen is a small molecule, it passes through a cell membrane without using the cell's energy. The different types of passive transport are explained on the following pages.

✓ **Reading Check** Describe a semipermeable membrane.

FOLDABLES

Fold a sheet of paper into a two-tab book. Label the tabs as shown. Use it to organize information about the different types of passive and active transport.

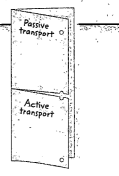

Passive transport

Active transport

Ken Cavanagh/McGraw-Hill Education

Diffusion

What happens when the concentration, or amount per unit of volume, of a substance is unequal on each side of a membrane? The molecules will move from the side with a higher concentration of that substance to the side with a lower concentration. **Diffusion** *is the movement of substances from an area of higher concentration to an area of lower concentration.*

Usually, diffusion continues through a membrane until the concentration of a substance is the same on both sides of the membrane. When this happens, a substance is in equilibrium. Compare the two diagrams in **Figure 12.** What happened to the red dye that was added to the water on one side of the membrane? Water and dye passed through the membrane in both directions until there were equal concentrations of water and dye on both sides of the membrane.

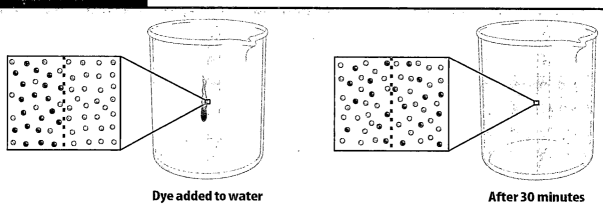

Dye added to water   **After 30 minutes**

⊘ **Visual Check** What would the water in the beaker on the right look like if the membrane did not let anything through?

Figure 12 Over time, the concentration of dye on either side of the membrane becomes the same.

Osmosis—The Diffusion of Water

Diffusion refers to the movement of any small molecules from higher to lower concentrations. However, **osmosis** *is the diffusion of water molecules only through a membrane.* Semipermeable cell membranes also allow water to pass through them until equilibrium occurs. For example, the amount of water stored in the vacuoles of plant cells can decrease because of osmosis. That is because the concentration of water in the air surrounding the plant is less than the concentration of water inside the vacuoles of plant cells. Water will continue to diffuse into the air until the concentrations of water inside the plant's cells and in the air are equal. If the plant is not watered to replace the lost water, it will wilt and eventually die.

WORD ORIGIN

diffusion
from Latin *diffusionem,* means "scatter, pour out"

Facilitated Diffusion

Some molecules are too large or are chemically unable to travel through a membrane by diffusion. *When molecules pass through a cell membrane using special proteins called transport proteins, this is* **facilitated diffusion.** Like diffusion and osmosis, facilitated diffusion does not require a cell to use energy. As shown in Figure 13, a cell membrane has transport proteins. The two types of transport proteins are carrier proteins and channel proteins. Carrier proteins carry large molecules, such as the sugar molecule glucose, through the cell membrane. Channel proteins form pores through the membrane. Atomic particles, such as sodium ions and potassium ions, pass through the cell membrane by channel proteins.

Reading Check How do materials move through the cell membrane in facilitated diffusion?

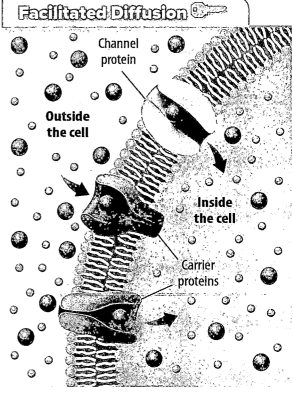

Figure 13 Transport proteins are used to move large molecules into and out of a cell.

MiniLab

20 minutes

How is a balloon like a cell membrane?

Substances within a cell are constantly in motion. How can a balloon act like a cell membrane?

① Read and complete a lab safety form.

② Make a three-column table in your Science Journal to record your data. Label the first column *Balloon Number*, the second column *Substance*, and the third column *Supporting Evidence*.

③ Use your senses to identify what substance is in each of the **numbered balloons.**

④ Record what you think each substance is.

⑤ Record the evidence supporting your choice.

Analyze and Conclude

1. **List** the senses that were most useful in identifying the substances.

2. **Infer** if you could identify the substances if you were blindfolded. If so, how?

3. **Describe** how the substances moved, and explain why they moved this way.

4. **Key Concept** Explain how a balloon is like a cell membrane in terms of the movement of substances.

Figure 14 Active transport is most often used to bring needed nutrients into a cell. Endocytosis and exocytosis move materials that are too large to pass through the cell membrane by other methods.

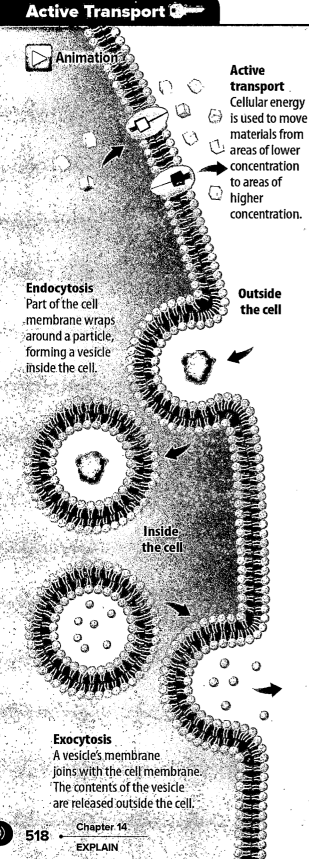

Active Transport 🔑

▷ **Animation**

Active transport
Cellular energy is used to move materials from areas of lower concentration to areas of higher concentration.

Endocytosis
Part of the cell membrane wraps around a particle, forming a vesicle inside the cell.

Outside the cell

Inside the cell

Exocytosis
A vesicle's membrane joins with the cell membrane. The contents of the vesicle are released outside the cell.

Active Transport

Sometimes when cellular materials pass through membranes it requires a cell to use energy. **Active transport** *is the movement of substances through a cell membrane only by using the cell's energy.*

Recall that passive transport is the movement of substances from areas of higher concentration to areas of lower concentration. However, substances moving by active transport move from areas of lower concentration to areas of higher concentration, as shown in **Figure 14.**

Active transport is important for cells and organelles. Cells can take in needed nutrients from the environment through carrier proteins by using active transport. This occurs even when concentrations of these nutrients are lower in the environment than inside the cell. Some other molecules and waste materials also leave cells by active transport.

Endocytosis and Exocytosis

Some substances are too large to enter a cell membrane by diffusion or by using a transport protein. These substances can enter a cell by another process. **Endocytosis** (en duh si TOH sus), shown in **Figure 14,** *is the process during which a cell takes in a substance by surrounding it with the cell membrane.* Many different types of cells use endocytosis. For example, some cells take in bacteria and viruses using endocytosis.

Some substances are too large to leave a cell by diffusion or by using a transport protein. These substances can leave a cell another way. **Exocytosis** (ek soh si TOH sus), shown in **Figure 14,** *is the process during which a cell's vesicles release their contents outside the cell.* Proteins and other substances are removed from a cell through this process.

 Key Concept Check How do materials enter and leave cells?

Cell Size and Transport

Recall that the movement of nutrients, waste material, and other substances into and out of a cell is important for survival. For this movement to happen, the area of the cell membrane must be large compared to its volume. The area of the cell membrane is the cell's surface area. The volume is the amount of space inside the cell. As a cell grows, both its volume and its surface area increase. The volume of a cell increases faster than its surface area. If a cell were to keep growing, it would need large amounts of nutrients and would produce large amounts of waste material. However, the surface area of the cell's membrane would be too small to move enough nutrients and wastes through it for the cell to survive.

 Key Concept Check How does cell size affect the transport of materials?

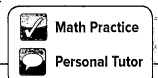
Math Practice

Personal Tutor

Math Skills ÷×   Use Ratios

A ratio is a comparison of two numbers, such as surface area and volume. If a cell were cube-shaped, you would calculate surface area by multiplying its length (ℓ) by its width (w) by the number of sides (6).

You would calculate the volume of the cell by multiplying its length (ℓ) by its width (w) by its height (h).

To find the surface-area-to-volume ratio of the cell, divide its surface area by its volume.

In the table below, surface-area-to-volume ratios are calculated for cells that are 1 mm, 2 mm, and 4 mm per side. Notice how the ratios change as the cell's size increases.

Surface area = $\ell \times w \times 6$

Volume = $\ell \times w \times h$

$$\frac{\text{Surface area}}{\text{Volume}}$$

	1 mm × 1 mm × 1 mm	2 mm × 2 mm × 2 mm	4 mm × 4 mm × 4 mm
Length	1 mm	2 mm	4 mm
Width	1 mm	2 mm	4 mm
Height	1 mm	2 mm	4 mm
Number of sides	6	6	6
Surface area ($\ell \times w \times$ **no. of sides**)	1 mm × 1 mm × 6 = 6 mm^2	2 mm × 2 mm × 6 = 24 mm^2	4 mm × 4 mm × 6 = 96 mm^2
Volume ($\ell \times w \times h$)	1 mm × 1 mm × 1 mm = 1 mm^3	2 mm × 2 mm × 2 mm = 8 mm^3	4 mm × 4 mm × 4 mm = 64 mm^3
Surface-area-to-volume ratio	$\frac{6 \text{ mm}^2}{1 \text{ mm}^3} = \frac{6}{1}$ or 6:1	$\frac{24 \text{ mm}^2}{8 \text{ mm}^3} = \frac{3}{1}$ or 3:1	$\frac{96 \text{ mm}^2}{64 \text{ mm}^3} = \frac{1.5}{1}$ or 1.5:1

Practice

What is the surface-area-to-volume ratio of a cell whose six sides are 3 mm long?

Visual Summary

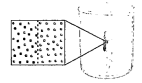

Small molecules can move from an area of higher concentration to an area of lower concentration by diffusion.

In facilitated diffusion, proteins transport larger molecules through a cell membrane.

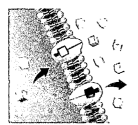

Some molecules move from areas of lower concentration to areas of higher concentration through active transport.

FOLDABLES

Use your lesson Foldable to review the lesson. Save your Foldable for the project at the end of the chapter.

What do you think NOW?

You first read the statements below at the beginning of the chapter.

5. Diffusion and osmosis are the same process.

6. Cells with large surface areas can transport more than cells with smaller surface areas.

Did you change your mind about whether you agree or disagree with the statements? Rewrite any false statements to make them true.

Use Vocabulary

1 **Use the term** *osmosis* in a sentence.

2 **Distinguish** between active transport and passive transport.

3 The process by which vesicles move substances out of a cell is _____.

Understand Key Concepts

4 **Explain** why energy is needed in active transport.

5 **Summarize** the function of endocytosis.

6 **Contrast** osmosis and diffusion.

7 What is limited by a cell's surface-area-to-volume ratio?
 A. cell shape
 B. cell size
 C. cell surface area
 D. cell volume

Interpret Graphics

8 **Identify** the process shown below, and explain how it works.

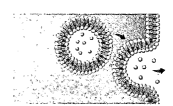

9 **Copy** and fill in the graphic organizer below to describe ways that cells transport substances.

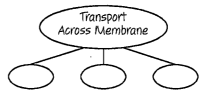

Transport Across Membrane

Critical Thinking

10 **Relate** the surface area of a cell to the transport of materials.

Math Skills  Math Practice

11 **Calculate** the surface-area-to-volume ratio of a cube whose sides are 6 cm long.

How does an object's size affect the transport of materials?

Nutrients, oxygen, and other materials enter and leave a cell through the cell membrane. Does the size of a cell affect the transport of these materials throughout the cell? In this lab, you will **analyze and conclude** how the size of a cube of egg white affects material transport.

Materials

hard-cooked eggs

metric ruler

blue food coloring

250-mL beaker

plastic spoon

plastic knife

paper towels

Safety

Learn It

To **analyze** how an object's size affects material transport, you will need to calculate each object's surface-area-to-volume ratio. The following formulas are used to calculate surface area and volume of a cube.

surface area (mm^2) = (length of 1 side)^2 × 6

volume (mm^3) = (length of 1 side)^3

To calculate the ratio of surface area to volume, divide surface area by volume.

Try It

① Read and complete a lab safety form.

② Measure and cut one large cube of egg white that is 20 mm on each side. Then, measure and cut one small cube of egg white that is 10 mm on each side.

③ Place 100 mL of water in a plastic cup. Add 10 drops of food coloring. Gently add the egg-white cubes, and soak overnight.

④ Remove the cubes from the cup with a plastic spoon and place them on a paper towel. Cut each cube in half.

⑤ Examine the inside surface of each cube. Measure and record in millimeters how deep the blue food coloring penetrated into each cube.

Apply It

⑥ How does the depth of the color compare on the two cubes?

⑦ Calculate the surface area, the volume, and the surface-area-to-volume ratio of each cube. How do the surface-area-to-volume ratios of the two cubes compare?

⑧ 🔑 **Key Concept** Would a cell with a small surface-area-to-volume ratio be able to transport nutrients and waste through the cell as efficiently as a cell with a large surface-area-to-volume ratio?

Reading Guide

Key Concepts
ESSENTIAL QUESTIONS

- How does a cell obtain energy?
- How do some cells make food molecules?

Vocabulary

cellular respiration p. 523

glycolysis p. 523

fermentation p. 524

photosynthesis p. 525

 Multilingual eGlossary

7.LS.1, 6-8.LST.5.2

Cells and Energy

Inquiry Why are there bubbles?

Have you ever seen bubbles on a green plant in an aquarium? Where did the bubbles come from? Green plants use light energy and make sugars and oxygen.

Colin Milkins/Getty Images

What do you exhale?

Does the air you breathe in differ from the air you breathe out?

① Read and complete a lab safety form.

② Unwrap a **straw.** Use the straw to slowly blow into a small **cup** of **bromthymol blue.** Do not splash the liquid out of the cup.

③ In your Science Journal, record any changes in the solution.

Think About This

1. What changes did you observe in the solution?

2. What do you think caused the changes in the solution?

3. 🔑 **Key Concept** Why do you think the air you inhale differs from the air you exhale?

Cellular Respiration

When you are tired, you might eat something to give you energy. All living things, from one-celled organisms to humans, need energy to survive. Recall that cells process energy from food into the energy-storage compound ATP. **Cellular respiration** *is a series of chemical reactions that convert the energy in food molecules into a usable form of energy called ATP.* Cellular respiration is a complex process that occurs in two parts of a cell–the cytoplasm and the mitochondria.

Reactions in the Cytoplasm

The first step of cellular respiration, called glycolysis, occurs in the cytoplasm of all cells. **Glycolysis** *is a process by which glucose, a sugar, is broken down into smaller molecules.* As shown in **Figure 15**, glycolysis produces some ATP molecules. It also uses energy from other ATP molecules. You will read on the following page that more ATP is made during the second step of cellular respiration than during glycolysis.

✓ **Reading Check** What is produced during glycolysis?

Glycolysis 🔑

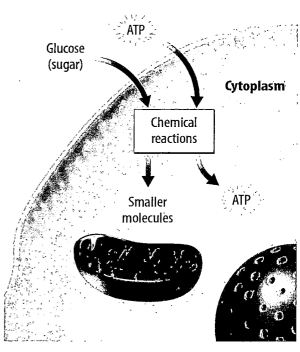

Figure 15 Glycolysis is the first step of cellular respiration.

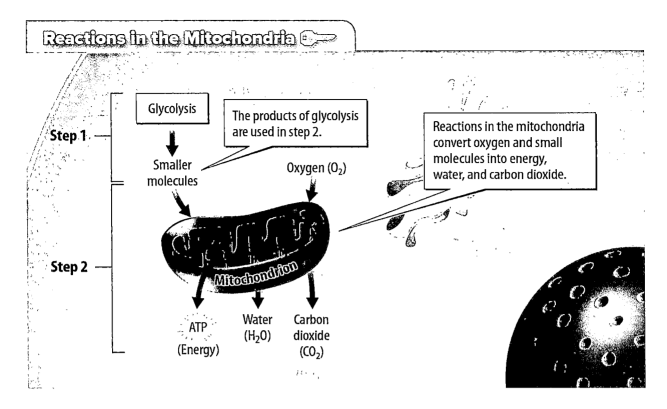

Glycolysis

Step 1

The products of glycolysis are used in step 2.

Smaller molecules

Oxygen (O_2)

Reactions in the mitochondria convert oxygen and small molecules into energy, water, and carbon dioxide.

Mitochondrion

Step 2

ATP (Energy)

Water (H_2O)

Carbon dioxide (CO_2)

Figure 16 After glycolysis, cellular respiration continues in the mitochondria.

Ⓥ **Visual Check** Compare the reactions in mitochondria with glycolysis.

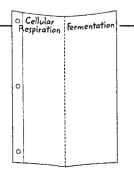

FOLDABLES

Fold a sheet of paper into a half book. Label the columns as shown. Use it to record information about the different types of energy production.

Cellular Respiration | Fermentation

Reactions in the Mitochondria

The second step of cellular respiration occurs in the mitochondria of eukaryotic cells, as shown in **Figure 16**. This step of cellular respiration requires oxygen. The smaller molecules made from glucose during glycolysis are broken down. Large amounts of ATP–usable energy–are produced. Cells use ATP to power all cellular processes. Two waste products–water and carbon dioxide (CO_2)–are given off during this step.

The CO_2 released by cells as a waste product is used by plants and some unicellular organisms in another process called photosynthesis. You will read more about the chemical reactions that take place during photosynthesis in this lesson.

Fermentation

Have you ever felt out of breath after exercising? Sometimes when you exercise, your cells don't have enough oxygen to make ATP through cellular respiration. Then, chemical energy is obtained through a different process called fermentation. This process does not use oxygen.

Fermentation *is a reaction that eukaryotic and prokaryotic cells can use to obtain energy from food when oxygen levels are low.* Because no oxygen is used, fermentation makes less ATP than cellular respiration does. Fermentation occurs in a cell's cytoplasm, not in mitochondria.

Ⓚ **Key Concept Check** How does a cell obtain energy?

Types of Fermentation

One type of fermentation occurs when glucose is converted into ATP and a waste product called lactic acid, as illustrated in **Figure 17**. Some bacteria and fungi help produce cheese, yogurt, and sour cream using lactic-acid fermentation. Muscle cells in humans and other animals can use lactic-acid fermentation and obtain energy during exercise.

Some types of bacteria and yeast make ATP through a process called alcohol fermentation. However, instead of producing lactic acid, alcohol fermentation produces an alcohol called ethanol and CO_2, also illustrated in **Figure 17**. Some types of breads are made using yeast. The CO_2 produced by yeast during alcohol fermentation makes the dough rise.

Reading Check Compare lactic-acid fermentation and alcohol fermentation.

Figure 17 Your muscle cells produce lactic acid as a waste during fermentation. Yeast cells produce carbon dioxide and alcohol as wastes during fermentation.

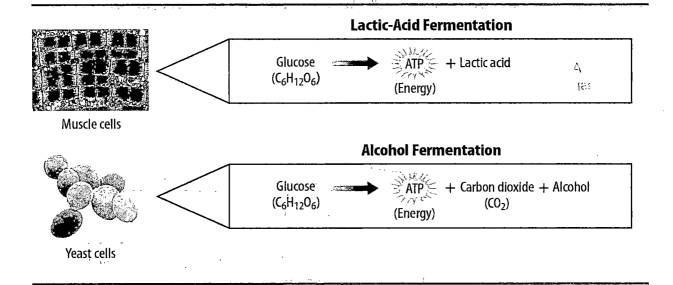

Lactic-Acid Fermentation

Muscle cells

Glucose ($C_6H_{12}O_6$) ⟹ ATP (Energy) + Lactic acid

Alcohol Fermentation

Yeast cells

Glucose ($C_6H_{12}O_6$) ⟹ ATP (Energy) + Carbon dioxide (CO_2) + Alcohol

Photosynthesis

Humans and other animals convert food energy into ATP through cellular respiration. However, plants and some unicellular organisms obtain energy from light. **Photosynthesis** *is a series of chemical reactions that convert light energy, water, and CO_2 into the food-energy molecule glucose and give off oxygen.*

Lights and Pigments

Photosynthesis requires light energy. In plants, pigments such as chlorophyll absorb light energy. When chlorophyll absorbs light, it absorbs all colors except green. Green light is reflected as the green color seen in leaves. However, plants contain many pigments that reflect other colors, such as yellow and red.

WORD ORIGIN
photosynthesis
from Greek *photo*, means "light"; and *synthesis*, means "composition"

Reactions in Chloroplasts

The light energy absorbed by chlorophyll and other pigments powers the chemical reactions of photosynthesis. These reactions occur in chloroplasts, the organelles in plant cells that convert light energy to chemical energy in food. During photosynthesis, light energy, water, and carbon dioxide combine and make sugars. Photosynthesis also produces oxygen that is released into the atmosphere, as shown in **Figure 18**.

 Key Concept Check How do some cells make food molecules?

Importance of Photosynthesis

Recall that photosynthesis uses light energy and CO_2 and makes food energy and releases oxygen. This food energy is stored in the form of glucose. When an organism, such as the bird in **Figure 18**, eats plant material, such as fruit, it takes in food energy. An organism's cells use the oxygen released during photosynthesis and convert the food energy into usable energy through cellular respiration. **Figure 18** illustrates the important relationship between cellular respiration and photosynthesis.

Figure 18 The relationship between cellular respiration and photosynthesis is important for life.

Personal Tutor

Cellular Respiration and Photosynthesis

Light energy

Chloroplast

Carbon dioxide (CO_2)
Water (H_2O)

Glucose ($C_6H_{12}O_6$)
Oxygen (O_2)

Mitochondrion

ATP

$$C_6H_{12}O_6 + 6O_2 \implies 6CO_2 + 6H_2O + ATP \text{ (Energy)}$$

Cellular respiration

$$6CO_2 + 6H_2O \xrightarrow[\text{Chlorophyll}]{\text{Light energy}} C_6H_{12}O_6 + 6O_2$$

Photosynthesis

IMAGEMORE Co.,Ltd./Getty Images

Visual Summary

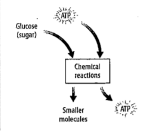

Glycolysis is the first step in cellular respiration.

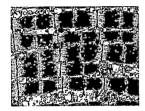

Fermentation provides cells, such as muscle cells, with energy when oxygen levels are low.

Light energy powers the chemical reactions of photosynthesis.

FOLDABLES

Use your lesson Foldable to review the lesson. Save your Foldable for the project at the end of the chapter.

What do you think NOW?

You first read the statements below at the beginning of the chapter.

7. ATP is the only form of energy found in cells.

8. Cellular respiration occurs only in lung cells.

Did you change your mind about whether you agree or disagree with the statements? Rewrite any false statements to make them true.

Use Vocabulary

1. **Define** *glycolysis* using your own words.

2. **Distinguish** between cellular respiration and fermentation.

3. A process used by plants to convert light energy into food energy is _____.

Understand Key Concepts 🔑

4. Which contains pigments that absorb light energy?
   - **A.** chloroplast
   - **B.** mitochondrion
   - **C.** nucleus
   - **D.** vacuole

5. **Relate** mitochondria to cellular respiration.

6. **Describe** the role of chlorophyll in photosynthesis.

7. **Give an example** of how fermentation is used in the food industry.

Interpret Graphics

8. **Draw** a graphic organizer like the one below. Fill in the boxes with the substances used and produced during photosynthesis.

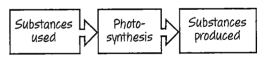

| Substances used | Photosynthesis | Substances produced |

9. **Summarize** the steps of cellular respiration using the figure below.

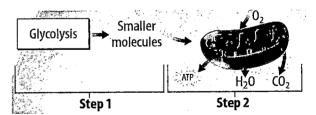

Glycolysis → Smaller molecules → O_2 ... ATP H_2O CO_2

Step 1   Step 2

Critical Thinking

10. **Design** a concept map to show the relationship between cellular respiration in animals and photosynthesis in plants.

11. **Summarize** the roles of glucose and ATP in energy processing.

Photosynthesis and Light

You might think of photosynthesis as a process of give and take. Plant cells take in water and carbon dioxide, and, powered by light energy, make their own food. Plants give off oxygen as a waste product during photosynthesis. Can you determine how the intensity of light affects the rate of photosynthesis?

Ask a Question

How does the intensity of light affect photosynthesis?

Make Observations

① Read and complete a lab safety form.

② Cut the bottom end of an *Elodea* stem at an angle, and lightly crush the cut end. Place the *Elodea* in a test tube with the cut side at the top. Fill the test tube with water. Stand the test tube and a thermometer in a beaker filled with water. (The water in the beaker keeps the water in the test tube from getting too warm under the lamp.)

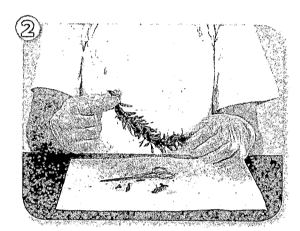

③ Place the beaker containing your test tube on a sheet of paper under a lamp. Measure the temperature of the water in the beaker. Record the temperature in your Science Journal.

④ When bubbles of oxygen begin to rise from the plant, start counting the number of bubbles per minute. Continue to record this data for 10 minutes.

⑤ Record the temperature of the water in the beaker at the end of the test.

⑥ Calculate the average number of bubbles produced per minute by your plant.

⑦ Compare your data with your classmates' data.

Form a Hypothesis

⑧ Use your data to form a hypothesis relating the amount of light to the rate of photosynthesis.

Test Your Hypothesis

⑨ Repeat the experiment, changing the light variable so that you are observing your plant's reaction to getting either more or less light. An increase or decrease in water temperature will indicate a change in the amount of light. Keep all other conditions the same.

⑩ Record your data in a table similar to the one shown at right, and calculate the average number of bubbles per minute.

Analyze and Conclude

⑪ **Use Variables** How does the amount of light affect photosynthesis? What is your evidence?

⑫ **The Big Idea** How do plant cells make food? What do they take in and what do they give off? What source of energy do they use?

Communicate Your Results

Compile all the class data on one graph to show the effects of varying amounts of light on the rate of photosynthesis.

What other variables might affect the rate of photosynthesis? For example, how does different-colored light or a change in temperature affect the rate of photosynthesis? To investigate your question, design a controlled experiment.

Lab Tips

☑ To calculate the average number of bubbles per minute, add the total number of bubbles observed in 10 minutes, and then divide by 10.

Number of Bubbles per Minute		
Time	Control	Less Light
1		
2		
3		
4		
5		
6		
7		
8		
9		
10		

Remember to use scientific methods.

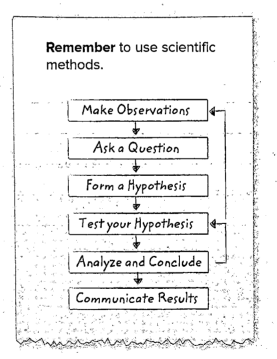

Make Observations
Ask a Question
Form a Hypothesis
Test your Hypothesis
Analyze and Conclude
Communicate Results

 THE BIG IDEA

A cell is made up of structures that provide support and movement; process energy; and transport materials into, within, and out of a cell.

Key Concepts Summary 🔑

Vocabulary

Lesson 1: Cells and Life

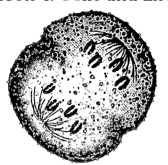

- The invention of the microscope led to discoveries about cells. In time, scientists used these discoveries to develop the **cell theory,** which explains how cells and living things are related.
- Cells are composed mainly of water, **proteins, nucleic acids, lipids,** and **carbohydrates.**

cell theory p. 498
macromolecule p. 499
nucleic acid p. 500
protein p. 501
lipid p. 501
carbohydrate p. 501

Lesson 2: The Cell

- Cell structures have specific functions, such as supporting a cell, moving a cell, controlling cell activities, processing energy, and transporting molecules.
- A prokaryotic cell lacks a nucleus and other **organelles,** while a eukaryotic cell has a nucleus and other organelles.

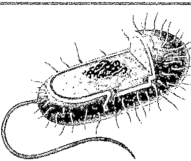

cell membrane p. 506
cell wall p. 506
cytoplasm p. 507
cytoskeleton p. 507
organelle p. 508
nucleus p. 509
chloroplast p. 511

Lesson 3: Moving Cellular Material

- Materials enter and leave a cell through the cell membrane using **passive transport** or **active transport, endocytosis,** and **exocytosis.**
- The ratio of surface area to volume limits the size of a cell. In a smaller cell, the high surface-area-to-volume ratio allows materials to move easily to all parts of a cell.

passive transport p. 515
diffusion p. 516
osmosis p. 516
facilitated diffusion p. 517
active transport p. 518
endocytosis p. 518
exocytosis p. 518

Lesson 4: Cells and Energy

- All living cells release energy from food molecules through **cellular respiration** and/or **fermentation.**
- Some cells make food molecules using light energy through the process of **photosynthesis.**

$$C_6H_{12}O_6 + 6O_2 \implies 6CO_2 + 6H_2O + \underset{\text{(Energy)}}{\text{ATP}}$$

Cellular respiration

$$6CO_2 + 6H_2O \underset{\text{Chlorophyll}}{\overset{\text{Light energy}}{\implies}} C_6H_{12}O_6 + 6O_2$$

Photosynthesis

cellular respiration p. 523
glycolysis p. 523
fermentation p. 524
photosynthesis p. 525

MedicalRF.com

Personal Tutor

Vocabulary eFlashcards
Vocabulary eGames

FOLDABLES® Chapter Project

Assemble your lesson Foldables as shown to make a Chapter Project. Use the project to review what you have learned in this chapter.

Passive transport

Active transport

Nucleic acids   Proteins

Lipids   Carbohydrates

Types of Energy Production

Cell Organelles and Their Functions

Use Vocabulary

1 Substances formed by joining smaller molecules together are called _____.

2 The _____ consists of proteins joined together to create fiberlike structures inside cells.

3 The movement of substances from an area of high concentration to an area of low concentration is called _____.

4 A process that uses oxygen to convert energy from food into ATP is _____

_____.

Link Vocabulary and Key Concepts

 Interactive Concept Map

Copy this concept map, and then use vocabulary terms from the previous page to complete the concept map.

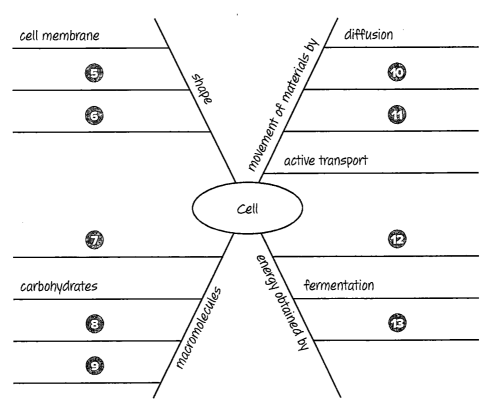

cell membrane

5

6

diffusion

10

11

shape

movement of materials by

active transport

Cell

7

12

carbohydrates

8

9

macromolecules

energy obtained by

fermentation

13

Understand Key Concepts

1 Cholesterol is which type of macromolecule?
- A. carbohydrate
- B. lipid
- C. nucleic acid
- D. protein

2 Genetic information is stored in which macromolecule?
- A. DNA
- B. glucose
- C. lipid
- D. starch

3 The arrow below is pointing to which cell part?

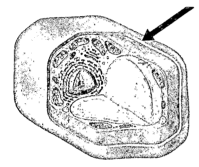

- A. chloroplast
- B. mitochondrion
- C. cell membrane
- D. cell wall

4 Which best describes vacuoles?
- A. lipids
- B. proteins
- C. contained in mitochondria
- D. storage compartments

5 Which is true of fermentation?
- A. does not generate energy
- B. does not require oxygen
- C. occurs in mitochondria
- D. produces lots of ATP

6 Which process eliminates substances from cells in vesicles?
- A. endocytosis
- B. exocytosis
- C. osmosis
- D. photosynthesis

7 Which cell shown below can send signals over long distances?

A.

B.

C.

D.

8 The figure below shows a cell. What is the arrow pointing to?

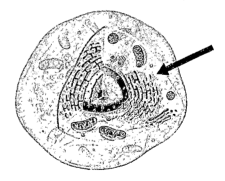

- A. chloroplast
- B. cytoplasm
- C. mitochondrion
- D. nucleus

Critical Thinking

9 **Evaluate** the importance of the microscope to biology.

10 **Summarize** the role of water in cells.

11 **Hypothesize** how new cells form from existing cells.

12 **Distinguish** between channel proteins and carrier proteins.

13 **Explain** osmosis.

14 **Infer** Why do cells need carrier proteins that transport glucose?

15 **Compare** the amounts of ATP generated in cellular respiration and fermentation.

16 **Assess** the role of fermentation in baking bread.

17 **Hypothesize** how air pollution like smog affects photosynthesis.

18 **Compare** prokaryotes and eukaryotes by copying and filling in the table below.

Structure	Prokaryote (yes or no)	Eukaryote (yes or no)
Cell membrane		
DNA		
Nucleus		
Endoplasmic reticulum		.
Golgi apparatus		
Cell wall		

Writing in Science

19 **Write** a five-sentence paragraph relating the cytoskeleton to the walls of a building. Be sure to include a topic sentence and a concluding sentence in your paragraph.

REVIEW THE BIG IDEA

20 How do the structures and processes of a cell enable it to survive? As an example, explain how chloroplasts help plant cells.

21 The photo below shows a protozoan. What structures enable it to get food into its mouth?

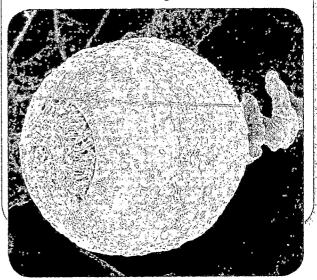

Math Skills ✓ Math Practice

Use Ratios

22 A rectangular solid measures 4 cm long by 2 cm wide by 2 cm high. What is the surface-area-to-volume ratio of the solid?

23 At different times during its growth, a cell has the following surface areas and volumes:

Time	Surface area (μm)	Volume (μm)
1	6	1
2	24	8
3	54	27

What happens to the surface-area-to-volume ratio as the cell grows?

Record your answers on the answer sheet provided by your teacher or on a sheet of paper.

Multiple Choice

1 Which process do plant cells use to capture and store energy from sunlight?

  A endocytosis

  B fermentation

  C glycolysis

  D photosynthesis

Use the diagram below to answer question 2.

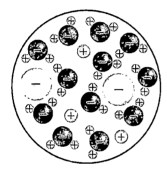

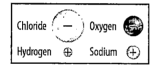

2 The diagram shows salt dissolved in water. What does it show about water molecules and chloride ions?

  A A water molecule consists of oxygen and chloride ions.

  B A water molecule is surrounded by several chloride ions.

  C A water molecule moves away from a chloride ion.

  D A water molecule points its positive end toward a chloride ion.

3 Which transport process requires the use of a cell's energy?

  A diffusion

  B osmosis

  C active transport

  D facilitated diffusion

4 Diffusion differs from active cell transport processes because it

  A forces large molecules from a cell.

  B keeps a cell's boundary intact.

  C moves substances into a cell.

  D needs none of a cell's energy.

Use the diagram below to answer questions 5 and 6.

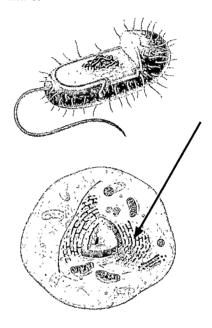

5 Which structure does the arrow point to in the eukaryotic cell?

  A cytoplasm

  B lysosome

  C nucleus

  D ribosome

6 Which feature does a typical prokaryotic cell have that is missing from some eukaryotic cells, like the one above?

  A cytoplasm

  B DNA

  C cell membrane

  D cell wall

7 Which explains why the ratio of cell surface area to volume affects the cell size? Cells with a high surface-to-volume ratio

A consume energy efficiently.

B produce waste products slowly.

C suffer from diseases frequently.

D transport substances effectively.

Use the diagram below to answer question 8.

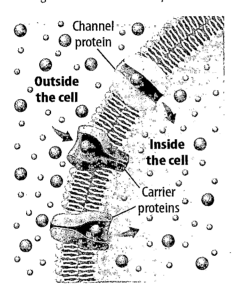

8 Which statement is NOT true of carrier proteins and channel proteins?

A Carrier proteins change shape as they function but channel proteins do not.

B Carrier proteins and channel proteins extend through the cell membrane.

C Channel proteins move items inside a cell but carrier proteins do not.

D Channel proteins and carrier proteins perform facilitated diffusion.

Constructed Response

9 Copy the table below and complete it using these terms: *cell membrane, cell wall, chloroplast, cytoplasm, cytoskeleton, nucleus.*

Cell Structure	Function
	Maintains the shape of an animal cell
	Controls the activities of a cell
	Traps energy from the Sun
	Controls the materials going in and out of a cell
	Holds the structures of a cell in a watery mix
	Maintains the shape of some plant cells

10 Name the kinds of organisms that have cells with cell walls. Name the kinds of organisms that have cells without cell walls. Briefly describe the benefits of cell walls for organisms.

11 Draw simple diagrams of an animal cell and a plant cell. Label the nucleus, the cytoplasm, the mitochondria, the cell membrane, the chloroplasts, the cell wall, and the central vacuole in the appropriate cells. Briefly describe the main differences between the two cells.

NEED EXTRA HELP?											
If You Missed Question...	1	2	3	4	5	6	7	8	9	10	11
Go to Lesson...	4	1	3	3	2	2	3	3	2	2	2

Chapter 15

From a Cell to an Organism

THE BIG IDEA

How can one cell become a multicellular organism?

Inquiry What's happening inside?

From the outside, a chicken egg looks like a simple oval object. But big changes are taking place inside the egg. Over several weeks, the one cell in the egg will grow and divide and become a chick.

- How did the original cell change over time?

- What might have happened to the chick's cells as the chick grew?

- How can one cell become a multicellular chick?

What do you think?

Before you read, decide if you agree or disagree with each of these statements. As you read this chapter, see if you change your mind about any of the statements.

1. Cell division produces two identical cells.

2. Cell division is important for growth.

3. At the end of the cell cycle, the original cell no longer exists.

4. Unicellular organisms do not have all the characteristics of life.

5. All the cells in a multicellular organism are the same.

6. Some organs work together as part of an organ system.

connectED

Your one-stop online resource
connectED.mcgraw-hill.com

 LearnSmart®

 Chapter Resources Files, Reading Essentials; Get Ready to Read, Quick Vocabulary

 Animations, Videos, Interactive Tables

 Self-checks, Quizzes, Tests

 Project-Based Learning Activities

 Lab Manuals, Safety Videos, Virtual Labs & Other Tools

 Vocabulary, Multilingual eGlossary, Vocab eGames, Vocab eFlashcards

 Personal Tutors

The Cell Cycle and Cell Division

Reading Guide

Key Concepts

ESSENTIAL QUESTIONS

- What are the phases of the cell cycle?

- Why is the result of the cell cycle important?

Vocabulary

cell cycle p. 539

interphase p. 540

sister chromatid p. 542

centromere p. 542

mitosis p. 543

cytokinesis p. 543

daughter cell p. 543

 Multilingual eGlossary

 BrainPOP®

 **7.LS.2, 6-8.LST.7.1**

Inquiry Time to Split?

Unicellular organisms such as these reproduce when one cell divides into two new cells. The two cells are identical to each other. What do you think happened to the contents of the original cell before it divided?

Why isn't your cell like mine?

All living things are made of cells. Some are made of only one cell, while others are made of trillions of cells. Where do all those cells come from?

1. Read and complete a lab safety form.

2. Ask your team members to face away from you. Draw an animal cell on a sheet of **paper.** Include as many organelles as you can.

3. Use **scissors** to cut the cell drawing into equal halves. Fold each sheet of paper in half so the drawing cannot be seen.

4. Ask your team members to face you. Give each team member half of the cell drawing.

5. Have team members sit facing away from each other. Each person should use a **glue stick** to attach the cell half to one side of a sheet of paper. Then, each person should draw the missing cell half.

6. Compare the two new cells to your original cell.

Think About This

1. How did the new cells compare to the original cell?

2.  **Key Concept** What are some things that might be done in the early steps to produce two new cells that are more like the original cell?

The Cell Cycle

No matter where you live, you have probably noticed that the weather changes in a regular pattern each year. Some areas experience four seasons—winter, spring, summer, and fall. In other parts of the world, there are only two seasons—rainy and dry. As seasons change, temperature, precipitation, and the number of hours of sunlight vary in a regular cycle.

These changes can affect the life cycles of organisms such as trees. Notice how the tree in Figure 1 changes with the seasons. Like changing seasons or the growth of trees, cells go through cycles. *Most cells in an organism go through a cycle of growth, development, and division called the* **cell cycle.** Through the cell cycle, organisms grow, develop, replace old or damaged cells, and produce new cells.

Figure 1 This maple tree changes in response to a seasonal cycle.

Visual Check List the seasonal changes of this maple tree.

(t)Hutchings Photography/Digital Light Source, (b)Bill Brooks/Alamy

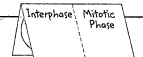
Phases of the Cell Cycle

There are two main phases in the cell cycle—interphase and the mitotic (mi TAH tihk) phase. **Interphase** *is the period during the cell cycle of a cell's growth and development.* A cell spends most of its life in interphase, as shown in **Figure 2.** During interphase, most cells go through three stages:

• rapid growth and replication, or copying, of the membrane-bound structures called organelles;

• copying of DNA, the genetic information in a cell; and

• preparation for cell division.

Interphase is followed by a shorter period of the cell cycle known as the mitotic phase. A cell reproduces during this phase. The mitotic phase has two stages, as illustrated in **Figure 2.** The nucleus divides in the first stage, and the cell's fluid, called the cytoplasm, divides in the second stage. The mitotic phase creates two new identical cells. At the end of this phase, the original cell no longer exists.

Key Concept Check What are the two main phases of the cell cycle?

The Cell Cycle

Figure 2 A cell spends most of its life growing and developing during interphase.

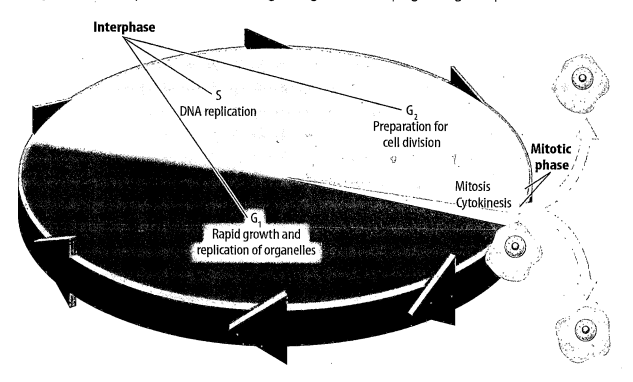

Interphase

S
DNA replication

G$_2$
Preparation for cell division

G$_1$
Rapid growth and replication of organelles

Mitotic phase

Mitosis
Cytokinesis

Visual Check Which stage of interphase is the longest?

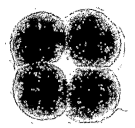

2-cell stage
LM Magnification: Unavailable

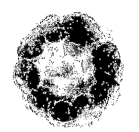

4-cell stage
LM Magnification: Unavailable

32-cell stage
LM Magnification: Unavailable

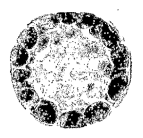

64-cell stage
LM Magnification: Unavailable

Length of a Cell Cycle

The time it takes a cell to complete the cell cycle depends on the type of cell that is dividing. Recall that a eukaryotic cell has membrane-bound organelles, including a nucleus. For some eukaryotic cells, the cell cycle might last only eight minutes. For other cells, the cycle might take as long as one year. Most dividing human cells normally complete the cell cycle in about 24 hours. As illustrated in **Figure 3**, the cells of some organisms divide very quickly.

Interphase

As you have read, interphase makes up most of the cell cycle. Newly produced cells begin interphase with a period of rapid growth—the cell gets bigger. This is followed by cellular activities such as making proteins. Next, actively dividing cells make copies of their DNA and prepare for cell division. During interphase, the DNA is called chromatin (KROH muh tun). Chromatin is long, thin strands of DNA, as shown in **Figure 4**. When scientists dye a cell in interphase, the nucleus looks like a plate of spaghetti. This is because the nucleus contains many strands of chromatin tangled together.

▲ Figure 3 The fertilized egg of a sea star divides into 4 cells in about 2 hours. It divides into 1000 cells in about 10 hours.

Figure 4 During interphase, the nuclei of an animal cell and a plant cell contain long, thin strands of DNA called chromatin. **▼**

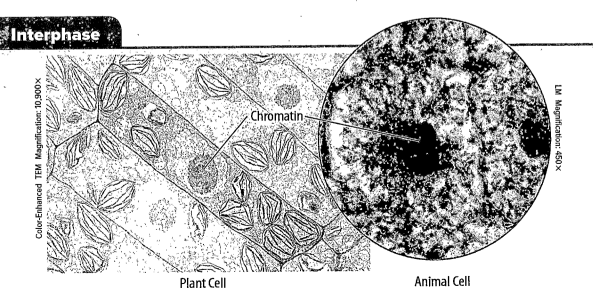

Interphase

Color-Enhanced TEM Magnification: 10,900×

Chromatin

LM Magnification: 450×

Plant Cell

Animal Cell

(l)Science Source; (b)Biophoto Associates/Science Source; (br)Michael Abbey/Science Source

Table 1 Phases of the Cell Cycle

Phase	Stage	Description
Interphase	G₁	growth and cellular functions; organelle replication
	S	growth and chromosome replication; organelle replication
	G₂	growth and cellular functions; organelle replication
Mitotic phase	mitosis	division of nucleus
	cytokinesis	division of cytoplasm

▲ **Table 1** The two phases of the cell cycle can each be divided into different stages.

Figure 5 The coiled DNA forms a duplicated chromosome made of two sister chromatids connected at the centromere. ▼

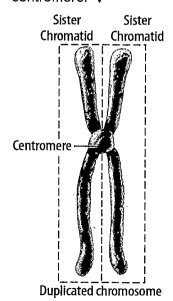

Sister Chromatid   Sister Chromatid

Centromere

Duplicated chromosome

Phases of Interphase

Scientists divide interphase into three stages, as shown in **Table 1.** Interphase begins with a period of rapid growth–the G_1 stage. This stage lasts longer than other stages of the cell cycle. During G_1, a cell grows and carries out its normal cell functions. For example, during G_1, cells that line your stomach make enzymes that help digest your food. Although most cells continue the cell cycle, some cells stop the cell cycle at this point. For example, mature nerve cells in your brain remain in G_1 and do not divide again.

During the second stage of interphase–the S stage–a cell continues to grow and copies its DNA. There are now identical strands of DNA. These identical strands of DNA ensure that each new cell gets a copy of the original cell's genetic information. Each strand of DNA coils up and forms a chromosome. Identical chromosomes join together. The cell's DNA is now arranged as pairs of identical chromosomes. Each pair is called a duplicated chromosome. *Two identical chromosomes, called* **sister chromatids,** *make up a duplicated chromosome,* as shown in **Figure 5.** Notice that the *sister chromatids are held together by a structure called the* **centromere.**

The final stage of interphase–the G_2 stage–is another period of growth and the final preparation for the mitotic phase. A cell uses energy copying DNA during the S stage. During G_2, the cell stores energy that will be used during the mitotic phase of the cell cycle.

 Reading Check Describe what happens in the G_2 phase.

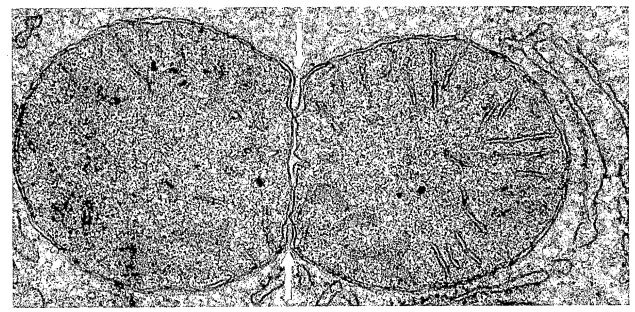

TEM Magnification: Unavailable

Organelle Replication

During cell division, the organelles in a cell are distributed between the two new cells. Before a cell divides, it makes a copy of each organelle. This enables the two new cells to function properly. Some organelles, such as the energy-processing mitochondria and chloroplasts, have their own DNA. These organelles can make copies of themselves on their own, as shown in **Figure 6.** A cell produces other organelles from materials such as proteins and lipids. A cell makes these materials using the information contained in the DNA inside the nucleus. Organelles are copied during all stages of interphase.

The Mitotic Phase

The mitotic phase of the cell cycle follows interphase. It consists of two stages: mitosis (mi TOH sus) and cytokinesis (si toh kuh NEE sus). *In* **mitosis,** *the nucleus and its contents divide. In* **cytokinesis,** *the cytoplasm and its contents divide.* **Daughter cells** *are the two new cells that result from mitosis and cytokinesis.*

During mitosis, the contents of the nucleus divide, forming two identical nuclei. The sister chromatids of the duplicated chromosomes separate from each other. This gives each daughter cell the same genetic information. For example, a cell that has ten duplicated chromosomes actually has 20 chromatids. When the cell divides, each daughter cell will have ten different chromatids. Chromatids are now called chromosomes.

In cytokinesis, the cytoplasm divides and forms the two new daughter cells. Organelles that were made during interphase are divided between the daughter cells.

Figure 6 This mitochondrion is in the final stage of dividing.

 Indiana FYI

How is mitosis related to cancer? Cancer is a disease in which cells undergo mitosis and cell division uncontrollably. This occurs when a change in a cell causes the cell to ignore the signals that usually regulate mitosis and the cell cycle.

WORD ORIGIN ············

mitosis
from Greek *mitos,* means "warp thread"; and Latin *-osis,* means "process"

Don W. Fawcett/Science Source

Phases of Mitosis

Like interphase, mitosis is a continuous process that scientists divide into different phases, as shown in **Figure 7.**

Prophase During the first phase of mitosis, called prophase, the copied chromatin coils together tightly. The coils form visible duplicated chromosomes. The nucleolus disappears, and the nuclear membrane breaks down. Structures called spindle fibers form in the cytoplasm.

Metaphase During metaphase, the spindle fibers pull and push the duplicated chromosomes to the middle of the cell. Notice in **Figure 7** that the chromosomes line up along the middle of the cell. This arrangement ensures that each new cell will receive one copy of each chromosome. Metaphase is the shortest phase in mitosis, but it must be completed successfully for the new cells to be identical.

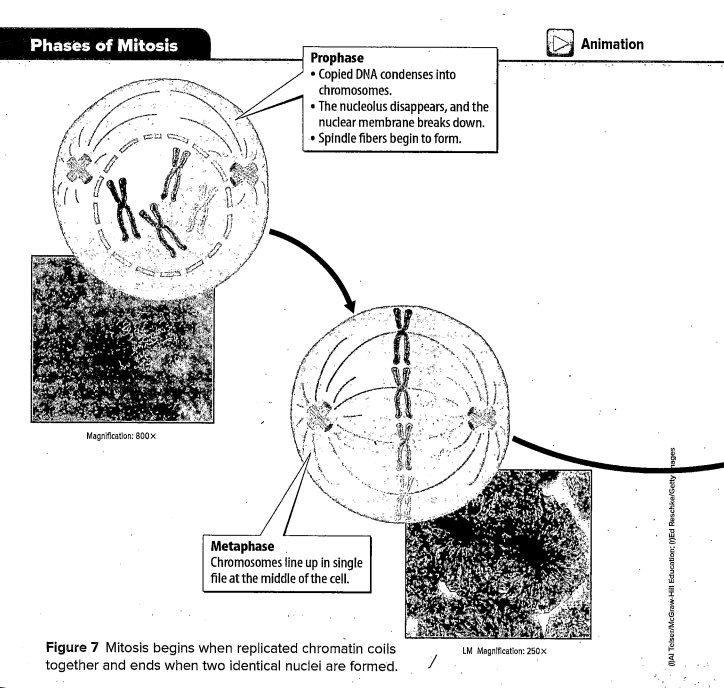

Phases of Mitosis

▷ **Animation**

Prophase
- Copied DNA condenses into chromosomes.
- The nucleolus disappears, and the nuclear membrane breaks down.
- Spindle fibers begin to form.

Magnification: 800×

Metaphase
Chromosomes line up in single file at the middle of the cell.

LM Magnification: 250×

Figure 7 Mitosis begins when replicated chromatin coils together and ends when two identical nuclei are formed.

(l)Al Telser/McGraw-Hill Education; (r)Ed Reschke/Getty Images

Anaphase In anaphase, the third stage of mitosis, the two sister chromatids in each chromosome separate from each other. The spindle fibers pull them in opposite directions. Once separated, the chromatids are now two identical single-stranded chromosomes. As they move to opposite sides of a cell, the cell begins to get longer. Anaphase is complete when the two identical sets of chromosomes are at opposite ends of a cell.

Telophase During telophase, the spindle fibers begin to disappear. Also, the chromosomes begin to uncoil. A nuclear membrane forms around each set of chromosomes at either end of the cell. This forms two new identical nuclei. Telophase is the final stage of mitosis. It is often described as the reverse of prophase because many of the processes that occur during prophase are reversed during telophase.

Reading Check What are the phases of mitosis?

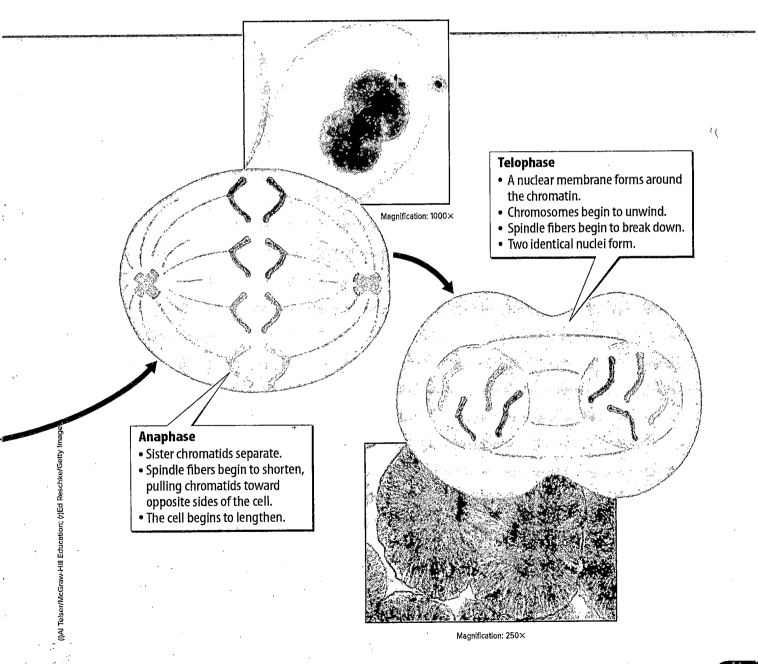

Magnification: 1000×

Telophase
- A nuclear membrane forms around the chromatin.
- Chromosomes begin to unwind.
- Spindle fibers begin to break down.
- Two identical nuclei form.

Anaphase
- Sister chromatids separate.
- Spindle fibers begin to shorten, pulling chromatids toward opposite sides of the cell.
- The cell begins to lengthen.

Magnification: 250×

(l)Al Telser/McGraw-Hill Education; (r)Ed Reschke/Getty Images

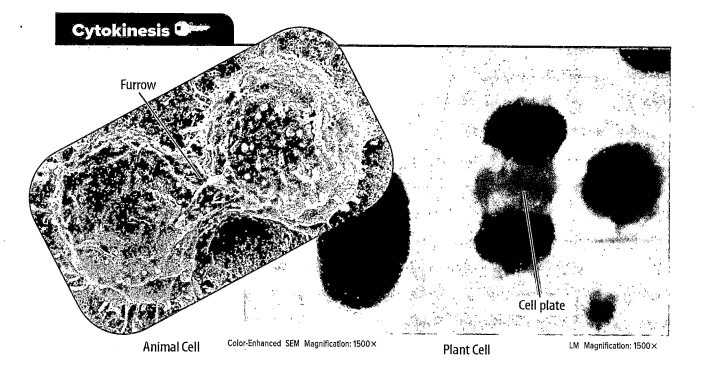

Furrow

Cell plate

Animal Cell   Color-Enhanced SEM Magnification: 1500×   Plant Cell   LM Magnification: 1500×

Figure 8 Cytokinesis differs in animal cells and plant cells.

Math Skills

Use Percentages

A percentage is a ratio that compares a number to 100. If the length of the entire cell cycle is 24 hours, 24 hours equals 100%. If part of the cycle takes 6.0 hours, it can be expressed as 6.0 hours/ 24 hours. To calculate percentage, divide and multiply by 100. Add a percent sign.

$$\frac{6.0}{24} = 0.25 \times 100 = 25\%$$

Practice

Interphase in human cells takes about 23 hours. If the cell cycle is 24 hours, what percentage is interphase?

 Math Practice

Personal Tutor

Dividing the Cell's Components

Following the last phase of mitosis, a cell's cytoplasm divides in a process called cytokinesis. The specific steps of cytokinesis differ depending on the type of cell that is dividing. In animal cells, the cell membrane contracts, or squeezes together, around the middle of the cell. Fibers around the center of the cell pull together. This forms a crease, called a furrow, in the middle of the cell. The furrow gets deeper and deeper until the cell membrane comes together and divides the cell. An animal cell undergoing cytokinesis is shown in **Figure 8**.

Cytokinesis in plants happens in a different way. As shown in **Figure 8**, a new cell wall forms in the middle of a plant cell. First, organelles called vesicles join together to form a membrane-bound disk called a cell plate. Then the cell plate grows outward toward the cell wall until two new cells form.

Reading Check Compare cytokinesis in plant and animal cells.

Results of Cell Division

Recall that the cell cycle results in two new cells. These daughter cells are genetically identical to each other and to the original cell that no longer exists. For example, a human cell has 46 chromosomes. When that cell divides, it will produce two new cells with 46 chromosomes each. The cell cycle is important for reproduction in some organisms, growth in multicellular organisms, replacement of worn out or damaged cells, and repair of damaged tissues.

(l)P.M. Motta & D. Palermo/Science Source; (t)Al Telser/McGraw-Hill Education

Reproduction

In some unicellular organisms, cell division is a form of reproduction. For example, an organism called a paramecium often reproduces by dividing into two new daughter cells or two new paramecia. Cell division is also important in other methods of reproduction in which the offspring are identical to the parent organism.

Growth

Cell division allows multicellular organisms, such as humans, to grow and develop from one cell (a fertilized egg). In humans, cell division begins about 24 hours after fertilization and continues rapidly during the first few years of life. It is likely that during the next few years you will go through another period of rapid growth and development. This happens because cells divide and increase in number as you grow and develop.

Replacement

Even after an organism is fully grown, cell division continues. It replaces cells that wear out or are damaged. The outermost layer of your skin is always rubbing or flaking off. A layer of cells below the skin's surface is constantly dividing. This produces millions of new cells daily to replace the ones that are rubbed off.

Repair

Cell division is also critical for repairing damage. When a bone breaks, cell division produces new bone cells that patch the broken pieces back together.

Not all damage can be repaired, however, because not all cells continue to divide. Recall that mature nerve cells stop the cell cycle in interphase. For this reason, injuries to nerve cells often cause permanent damage.

Key Concept Check Why is the result of the cell cycle important?

MiniLab   20 minutes

How does mitosis work?

The dolix is a mythical animal whose cells contain just two chromosomes. What happens to a dolix cell nucleus during mitosis?

1. Read and complete a lab safety form.

2. Form four 60-cm lengths of **yarn** into large circles on four separate sheets of **paper.** Each piece of paper represents one phase of mitosis, and the yarn represents the cell membrane.

3. On each sheet of paper, model one phase of mitosis using different colors of yarn to represent the nuclear membrane, the spindles, and the chromosomes. Use **twist ties** to represent centromeres. **Tape** the yarn in place.

4. Label your models, or develop a key to indicate which color is used for which part.

Analyze and Conclude

1. **Identify** If you were to model a dolix cell's nucleus before mitosis began, what would your model look like? Would you be able to see the individual chromosomes?

2. **Integrate** What would a model of your cell look like during the stage immediately following mitosis? What is this stage?

3. **Key Concept** How does your model of mitosis show how the cells in multicellular organisms make more cells for growth and repair?

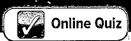
Visual Summary

During interphase, most cells go through periods of rapid growth and replication of organelles, copying DNA, and preparation for cell division.

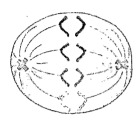

The nucleus and its contents divide during mitosis.

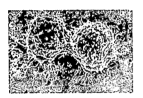

The cytoplasm and its contents divide during cytokinesis.

FOLDABLES

Use your lesson Foldable to review the lesson. Save your Foldable for the project at the end of the chapter.

What do you think

You first read the statements below at the beginning of the chapter.

1. Cell division produces two identical cells.

2. Cell division is important for growth.

3. At the end of the cell cycle, the original cell no longer exists.

Did you change your mind about whether you agree or disagree with the statements? Rewrite any false statements to make them true.

Use Vocabulary

1 Distinguish between mitosis and cytokinesis.

2 A duplicated chromosome is made of two _____.

3 Use the term *interphase* in a sentence.

Understand Key Concepts

4 Which is NOT part of mitosis?
   A. anaphase   **C.** prophase
   B. interphase   **D.** telophase

5 Construct a table to show the different phases of mitosis and what happens during each.

6 Give three examples of why the result of the cell cycle is important.

Interpret Graphics

7 Identify The animal cell on the right is in what phase of mitosis? Explain your answer.

8 Organize Copy and fill in the graphic organizer below to show the results of cell division.

Results of cell division

Critical Thinking

9 Predict what might happen to a cell if it were unable to divide by mitosis.

Math Skills   Math Practice

10 The mitotic phase of the human cell cycle takes approximately 1 hour. What percentage of the 24-hour cell cycle is the mitotic phase?

DNA Fingerprinting

▽ DNA

Solving Crimes One Strand at a Time

Every cell in your body has the same DNA in its nucleus. Unless you are an identical twin, your DNA is entirely unique. Identical twins have identical DNA because they begin as one cell that divides and separates. When your cells begin mitosis, they copy their DNA. Every new cell has the same DNA as the original cells. That is why DNA can be used to identify people. Just as no two people have the same fingerprints, your DNA belongs to you alone.

Using scientific methods to solve crimes is called forensics. DNA fingerprinting is now a basic tool in forensics. Samples collected from a crime scene can be compared to millions of samples previously collected and indexed in a computer.

Every day, everywhere you go, you leave a trail of DNA. It might be in skin cells. It might be in hair or in the saliva you used to lick an envelope. If you commit a crime, you will most likely leave DNA behind. An expert crime scene investigator will know how to collect that DNA.

DNA evidence can prove innocence as well. Investigators have reexamined DNA found at old crime scenes. Imprisoned persons have been proven not guilty through DNA fingerprinting methods that were not yet available when a crime was committed.

DNA fingerprinting can also be used to identify bodies that had previously been known only as a John or Jane Doe.

▼ The Federal Bureau of Investigation (FBI) has a nationwide index of DNA samples called CODIS (Combined DNA Index System).

(l)©SCIENCE PHOTO LIBRARY/age fotostock; (r)©Bananastock/Alamy

It's Your Turn

DISCOVER Your cells contain organelles called mitochondria. They have their own DNA, called mitochondrial DNA. Your mitochondrial DNA is identical to your mother's mitochondrial DNA. Find out how this information is used.

Reading Guide

Key Concepts 🔑

ESSENTIAL QUESTIONS

- How do unicellular and multicellular organisms differ?

- How does cell differentiation lead to the organization within a multicellular organism?

Vocabulary

cell differentiation p. 553

stem cell p. 554

tissue p. 555

organ p. 556

organ system p. 557

 Multilingual eGlossary

 BrainPOP®

 7.LS.1, 7.LS.2, 7.LS.3, SEPS.3, SEPS.6

Levels of Organization

Inquiry Scales on Wings?

This butterfly has a distinctive pattern of colors on its wings. The pattern is formed by clusters of tiny scales. In a similar way, multicellular organisms are made of many small parts working together.

(inset)Iain Lawrie/Getty Images; (bkgd)•IT Stock/age fotostock

Launch Lab

How is a system organized?

The places people live are organized in a system. Do you live in or near a city? Cities contain things such as schools and stores that enable them to function on their own. Many cities together make up another level of organization.

1. Read and complete a lab safety form.

2. Using a **metric ruler** and **scissors**, measure and cut squares of **construction paper** that are 4 cm, 8 cm, 12 cm, 16 cm, and 20 cm on each side. Use a different color for each square.

3. Stack the squares from largest to smallest, and glue them together.

4. Cut apart the *City, Continent, Country, County,* and *State* labels your teacher gives you.

5. Use a **glue stick** to attach the *City* label to the smallest square. Sort the remaining labels from smallest to largest, and glue to the corresponding square.

Think About This

1. What is the largest level of organization a city belongs to?

2. Can any part of the system function without the others? Explain.

3. **Key Concept** How do you think the system used to organize where people live is similar to how your body is organized?

Color-Enhanced SEM. Magnification: 12×

Life's Organization

You might recall that all matter is made of atoms and that atoms combine and form molecules. Molecules make up cells. A large animal, such as a Komodo dragon, is not made of one cell. Instead, it is composed of trillions of cells working together. Its skin, shown in Figure 9, is made of many cells that are specialized for protection. The Komodo dragon has other types of cells, such as blood cells and nerve cells, that perform other functions. Cells work together in the Komodo dragon and enable it to function. In the same way, cells work together in you and in other multicellular organisms.

Recall that some organisms are made of only one cell. These unicellular organisms carry out all the activities necessary to survive, such as absorbing nutrients and getting rid of wastes. But no matter their sizes, all organisms are made of cells.

Figure 9 Skin cells are only one of the many kinds of cells that make up a Komodo dragon.

Figure 10 Unicellular organisms carry out life processes within one cell.

Contractile vacuole

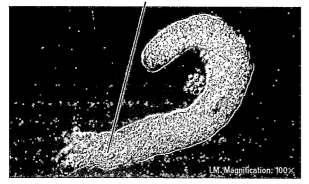

LM. Magnification: 100×

This unicellular amoeba captures algae for food.

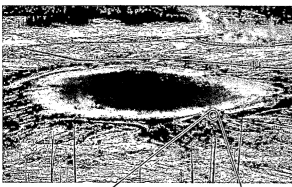

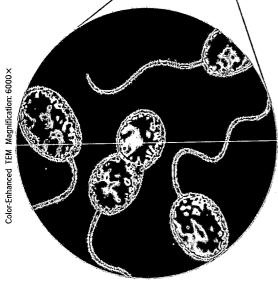

Color-Enhanced TEM Magnification: 6000×

These heat-loving bacteria are often found in hot springs as shown here. They get their energy to produce food from sulfur instead of from light like plants.

Unicellular Organisms

As you read on the previous page, some organisms have only one cell. Unicellular organisms do all the things needed for their survival within that one cell. For example, the amoeba in Figure 10 is ingesting another organism, a type of green algae called *Pandorina* spp., for food. Unicellular organisms also respond to their environment, get rid of waste, grow, and even reproduce on their own. Unicellular organisms include both prokaryotes and some eukaryotes.

Prokaryotes

Recall that a cell without a membrane-bound nucleus is a prokaryotic cell. In general, prokaryotic cells are smaller than eukaryotic cells and have fewer cell structures. A unicellular organism made of one prokaryotic cell is called a prokaryote. Some prokaryotes live in groups called colonies. Some can also live in extreme environments, as shown in Figure 10.

Eukaryotes

You might recall that a eukaryotic cell has a nucleus surrounded by a membrane and many other specialized organelles. For example, the amoeba shown in Figure 10 has an organelle called a contractile vacuole. It functions like a bucket that is used to bail water out of a boat. A contractile vacuole collects excess water from the amoeba's cytoplasm. Then it pumps the water out of the amoeba. This prevents the amoeba from swelling and bursting.

A unicellular organism that is made of one eukaryotic cell is called a eukaryote. There are thousands of different unicellular eukaryotes, such as algae that grow on the inside of an aquarium and the fungus that causes athlete's foot.

 Reading Check Give an example of a unicellular eukaryotic organism.

Multicellular Organisms

Multicellular organisms are made of many eukaryotic cells working together, like the crew on an airplane. Each member of the crew, from the pilot to the mechanic, has a specific job that is important for the plane's operation. Similarly, each type of cell in a multicellular organism has a specific job that is important to the survival of the organism.

 Key Concept Check. How do unicellular and multicellular organisms differ?

Cell Differentiation

As you read in the last lesson, all cells in a multicellular organism come from one cell–a fertilized egg. Cell division starts quickly after fertilization. The first cells made can become any type of cell, such as a muscle cell, a nerve cell, or a blood cell. *The process by which cells become different types of cells is called* **cell differentiation** (dihf uh ren shee AY shun).

You might recall that a cell's instructions are contained in its chromosomes. Also, nearly all the cells of an organism have identical sets of chromosomes. If an organism's cells have identical sets of instructions, how can cells be different? Different cell types use different parts of the instructions on the chromosomes. A few of the many different types of cells that can result from human cell differentiation are shown in **Figure 11.**

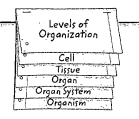

Make a layered book from three sheets of notebook paper. Label it as shown. Use your book to describe the levels of organization that make up organisms.

Figure 11 A fertilized egg produces cells that can differentiate into a variety of cell types.

 **Personal Tutor**

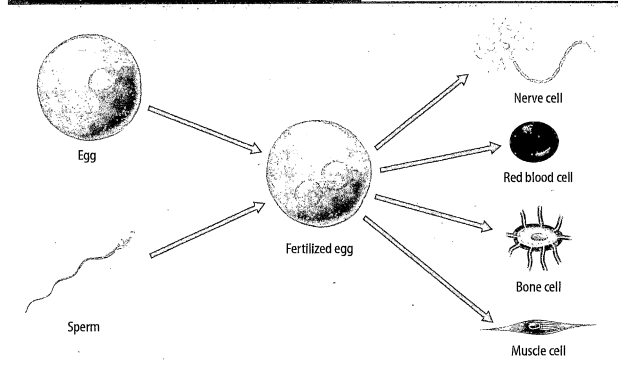

Cell Differentiation in Eukaryotes

Egg

Sperm

Fertilized egg

Nerve cell

Red blood cell

Bone cell

Muscle cell

Animal Stem Cells Not all cells in a developing animal differentiate. **Stem cells** *are unspecialized cells that are able to develop into many different cell types.* There are many stem cells in embryos but fewer in adult organisms. Adult stem cells are important for the cell repair and replacement you read about in Lesson 1. For example, stem cells in your bone marrow can produce more than a dozen different types of blood cells. These replace ones that are damaged or worn out. Stem cells have also been discovered in skeletal muscles. These stem cells can produce new muscle cells when the fibers that make up the muscle are torn.

Plant Cells Plants also have unspecialized cells similar to animal stem cells. These cells are grouped in areas of a plant called meristems (MER uh stemz). Meristems are in different areas of a plant, including the tips of roots and stems, as shown in **Figure 12.** Cell division in meristems produces different types of plant cells with specialized structures and functions, such as transporting materials, making food, storing food, or protecting the plant. These cells might become parts of stems, leaves, flowers, or roots.

SCIENCE USE V. COMMON USE
fiber
Science Use a long muscle cell

Common Use a thread

Figure 12 Plant meristems produce cells that can become part of stems, leaves, flowers, or roots.

Stem meristem

Root meristem

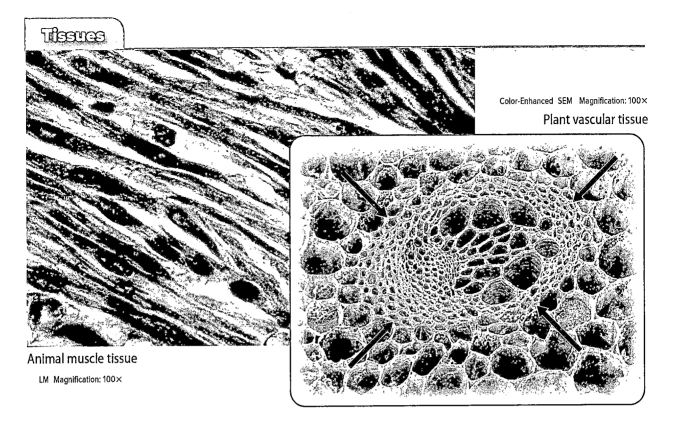

Color-Enhanced SEM Magnification: 100×
Plant vascular tissue

Animal muscle tissue

LM Magnification: 100×

Figure 13 Similar cells work together and form tissues such as this animal muscle tissue that contracts the stomach to help digestion. Plant vascular tissue, indicated by red arrows, moves water and nutrients throughout a plant.

Tissues

In multicellular organisms, similar types of cells are organized into groups. **Tissues** *are groups of similar types of cells that work together to carry out specific tasks.* Humans, like most other animals, have four main types of tissue—muscle, connective, nervous, and epithelial (eh puh THEE lee ul). For example, the animal tissue shown in **Figure 13** is smooth muscle tissue that is part of the stomach. Muscle tissue causes movement. Connective tissue provides structure and support and often connects other types of tissue together. Nervous tissue carries messages to and from the brain. Epithelial tissue forms the protective outer layer of the skin and the lining of major organs and internal body cavities.

Plants also have different types of tissues. The three main types of plant tissue are dermal, vascular (VAS kyuh lur), and ground tissue. Dermal tissue provides protection and helps reduce water loss. Vascular tissue, shown in **Figure 13**, transports water and nutrients from one part of a plant to another. Ground tissue provides storage and support and is where photosynthesis takes place.

 Reading Check Compare animal and plant tissues.

WORD ORIGIN
tissue
from Latin *texere*, means "weave"

(l)Biophoto Associates/Science Source, (r)Andrew Syred/Science Source

ACADEMIC VOCABULARY

complex
(adjective) made of two or more
parts

Organs

Complex jobs in organisms require more than one type of tissue. **Organs** *are groups of different tissues working together to perform a particular job.* For example, your stomach is an organ specialized for breaking down food. It is made of all four types of tissue: muscle, epithelial, nervous, and connective. Each type of tissue performs a specific function necessary for the stomach to work properly. Layers of muscle tissue contract and break up pieces of food, epithelial tissue lines the stomach, nervous tissue sends signals to indicate the stomach is full, and connective tissue supports the stomach wall.

Plants also have organs. The leaves shown in Figure 14 are organs specialized for photosynthesis. Each leaf is made of dermal, ground, and vascular tissues. Dermal tissue covers the outer surface of a leaf. The leaf is a vital organ because it contains ground tissue that produces food for the rest of the plant. Ground tissue is where photosynthesis takes place. The ground tissue is tightly packed on the top half of a leaf. The vascular tissue moves both the food produced by photosynthesis and water throughout the leaf and the rest of the plant.

 Reading Check List the tissues in a leaf organ.

Figure 14 A plant leaf is an organ made of several different tissues.

Visual Check Which plant tissue makes up the thinnest layer?

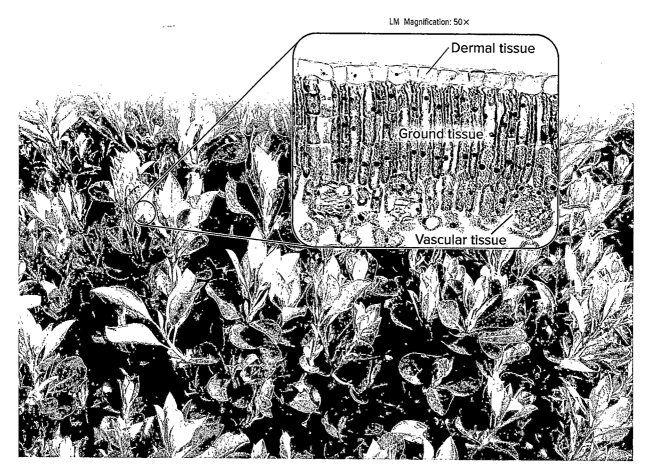

LM Magnification: 50×

Dermal tissue

Ground tissue

Vascular tissue

Organ Systems

Usually organs do not function alone. Instead, **organ systems** *are groups of different organs that work together to complete a series of tasks.* Human organ systems can be made of many different organs working together. For example, the human digestive system is made of many organs, including the stomach, the small intestine, the liver, and the large intestine. These organs and others all work together to break down food and take it into the body. Blood absorbs and transports nutrients from broken down food to cells throughout the body.

Plants have two major organ systems—the shoot system and the root system. The shoot system includes leaves, stems, and flowers. Food and water are transported throughout the plant by the shoot system. The root system anchors the plant and takes in water and nutrients.

 Reading Check What are the major organ systems in plants?

🦉 MiniLab
25 minutes

How do cells work together to make an organism?

In a multicellular organism, similar cells work together and make a tissue. A tissue can perform functions that individual cells cannot. Tissues are organized into organs, then organ systems, then organisms. How can you model the levels of organization in an organism?

① Read and complete a lab safety form.

② Your teacher will give you a **cardboard shape, macaroni,** and a **permanent marker.**

③ The macaroni represent cells. Use the marker to draw a small circle on each piece of macaroni. This represents the nucleus.

④ Arrange and **glue** enough macaroni on the blank side of the cardboard shape to cover it. Your group of similar cells represents a tissue.

⑤ One of the squares on the back of your shape is labeled *A, B, C,* or *D.* Find the group with a matching letter. Line up these squares, and use **tape** to connect the two tissues. This represents an organ.

⑥ Repeat step 4 with the squares labeled *E* or *F.* This represents an organ system.

⑦ Connect the organ systems by aligning the squares labeled *G* to represent an organism.

Analyze and Conclude

1. Each group had to work with other groups to make a model of an organism. Do cells, tissues, and organs need to work together in organisms? Explain.

2. 🔑 **Key Concept** How does your model show the levels of organization in living things?

Hutchings Photography/Digital Light Source

Organisms

Multicellular organisms usually have many organ systems. These systems work together to carry out all the jobs needed for the survival of the organisms. For example, the cells in the leaves and the stems of a plant need water to live. They cannot absorb water directly. Water diffuses into the roots and is transported through the stem to the leaves by the transport system.

In the human body, there are many major organ systems. Each organ system depends on the others and cannot work alone. For example, the cells in the muscle tissue of the stomach cannot survive without oxygen. The stomach cannot get oxygen without working together with the respiratory and circulatory systems. **Figure 15** will help you review how organisms are organized.

Key Concept Check How does cell differentiation lead to the organization within a multicellular organism?

Animation

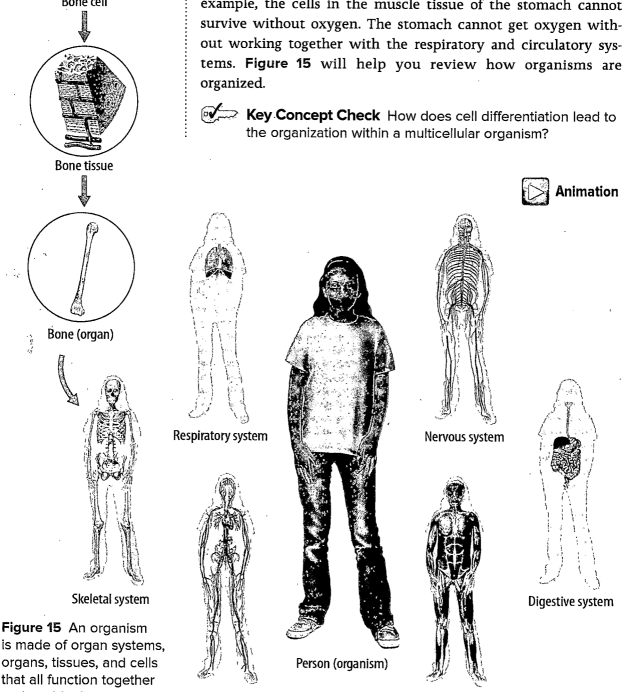

Bone cell

Bone tissue

Bone (organ)

Skeletal system

Respiratory system

Circulatory system

Person (organism)

Nervous system

Muscular system

Digestive system

Figure 15 An organism is made of organ systems, organs, tissues, and cells that all function together and enable the organism's survival.

Online Quiz

Virtual Lab

Visual Summary

A unicellular organism carries out all the activities necessary for survival within one cell.

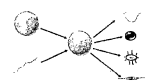

Cells become specialized in structure and function during cell differentiation.

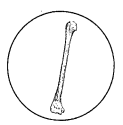

Organs are groups of different tissues that work together to perform a job.

FOLDABLES

Use your lesson Foldable to review the lesson. Save your Foldable for the project at the end of the chapter.

What do you think NOW?

You first read the statements below at the beginning of the chapter.

4. Unicellular organisms do not have all the characteristics of life.

5. All the cells in a multicellular organism are the same.

6. Some organs work together as part of an organ system.

Did you change your mind about whether you agree or disagree with the statements? Rewrite any false statements to make them true.

Michael Abbey/Science Source

Use Vocabulary

1 **Define** *cell differentiation* in your own words.

2 **Distinguish** between an organ and an organ system.

Understand Key Concepts

3 **Explain** the difference between a unicellular organism and a multicellular organism.

4 **Describe** how cell differentiation produces different types of cells in animals.

5 Which is the correct sequence of the levels of organization?
  A. cell, organ, tissue, organ system, organism
  B. organism, organ, organ system, tissue, cell
  C. cell, tissue, organ, organ system, organism
  D. tissue, organ, organism, organ system, cell

Interpret Graphics

6 **Organize** Copy and fill in the table below to summarize the characteristics of unicellular and multicellular organisms.

Organism Characteristics	
Unicellular	Multicellular

Critical Thinking

7 **Predict** A mistake occurs during mitosis of a muscle stem cell. How might this affect muscle tissue?

8 **Compare** the functions of a cell to the functions of an organism, such as getting rid of wastes.

Materials

cooked eggs

boiled
chicken leg

forceps

dissecting
scissors

plastic knife

paper towels

Safety

Cell Differentiation

It's pretty amazing that a whole chicken with wings, feet, beak, feathers, and internal organs can come from one cell, a fertilized egg. Shortly after fertilization, the cell begins to divide. The new cells in the developing embryo become specialized both in structure and function. The process by which cells become specialized is called cellular differentiation.

Question

How does a single cell become a multicellular organism?

Procedure

① Read and complete a lab safety form.

② Carefully examine the outside of your egg. Remove the shell.

③ Dissect the egg on a paper towel, cutting it in half from tip to rounded end. Examine the inside.

④ Record your observations in your Science Journal. Include a labeled drawing. Infer the function of each part.

⑤ Discard all your trash in the container provided.

⑥ Examine the outside of the chicken leg. Describe the skin and its functions.

③

Hutchings Photography/Digital Light Source

⑦ Carefully remove the skin using forceps and dissecting scissors. Put the skin in your discard container. Now you should see evidence of fat and muscles. You may also be able to see some blood vessels and tendons, but these are not always visible after cooking. Describe each part that you see and explain its function.

⑧ Peel back the muscles to reveal the bones. Tendons, ligaments, and cartilage holding the bones in place may also be evident.

⑨ Put all your trash in the discard container. Your teacher will give you instructions about cleaning up.

Analyze and Conclude

⑩ **The Big Idea** A single cell can become a multicellular organism through the process of cell differentiation. How do the organization of the egg and the chicken leg compare?

⑪ **Summarize** How many different types of cell differentiation did you observe in the chicken leg?

Lab Tips

☑ Work slowly and carefully on your dissections so as not to destroy any structures. Report any accidents to your teacher immediately. Cleaning up is important!

Communicate Your Results

Construct an explanation about how the cells of a chicken develop through differentiation to form specialized tissues and organs. Make a poster to share your explanation with others.

Examine a whole raw chicken or a raw chicken leg that is still attached to a thigh. You might be able to move the muscles in the legs or wings and see parts that were not visible in this lab. Be sure to wear gloves and to wash well with soap and water after touching the raw chicken.

Remember to use scientific methods.

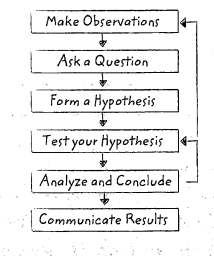

Make Observations

Ask a Question

Form a Hypothesis

Test your Hypothesis

Analyze and Conclude

Communicate Results

 Through cell division, one cell can produce new cells to grow and develop into a multicellular organism.

Key Concepts Summary

Lesson 1: The Cell Cycle and Cell Division

- The **cell cycle** consists of two phases. During **interphase,** a cell grows and its chromosomes and organelles replicate. During the mitotic phase of the cell cycle, the nucleus divides during **mitosis,** and the cytoplasm divides during **cytokinesis.**

- The cell cycle results in two genetically identical **daughter cells.** The original parent cell no longer exists.

- The cell cycle is important for growth in multicellular organisms, reproduction in some organisms, replacement of worn-out cells, and repair of damaged cells.

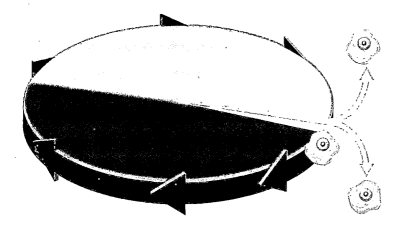

Vocabulary

cell cycle p. 539

interphase p. 540

sister chromatid p. 542

centromere p. 542

mitosis p. 543

cytokinesis p. 543

daughter cell p. 543

Lesson 2: Levels of Organization

- The one cell of a unicellular organism is able to obtain all the materials that it needs to survive.

- In a multicellular organism, cells cannot survive alone and must work together to provide the organism's needs.

- Through **cell differentiation,** cells become different types of cells with specific functions. Cell differentiation leads to the formation of **tissues, organs,** and **organ systems.**

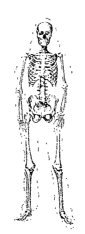

cell differentiation p. 553

stem cell p. 554

tissue p. 555

organ p. 556

organ system p. 557

Personal Tutor

Vocabulary eFlashcards
Vocabulary eGames

FOLDABLES Chapter Project

Assemble your lesson Foldables as shown to make a Chapter Project. Use the project to review what you have learned in this chapter.

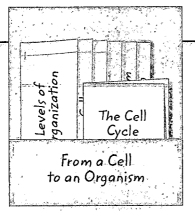

Levels of Organization

The Cell Cycle

From a Cell to an Organism

Use Vocabulary

1 Use the term *sister chromatids* in a sentence.

2 Define the term *centromere* in your own words.

3 The new cells formed by mitosis are called _____.

4 Use the term *cell differentiation* in a sentence.

5 Define the term *stem cell* in your own words.

6 Organs are groups of _____ working together to perform a specific task.

Link Vocabulary and Key Concepts

Interactive Concept Map

Copy this concept map, and then use vocabulary terms from the previous page and from the chapter to complete the concept map.

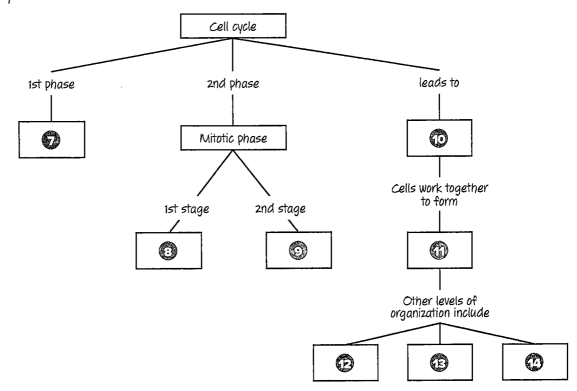

Understand Key Concepts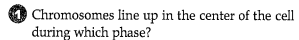

1 Chromosomes line up in the center of the cell during which phase?
- A. anaphase
- B. metaphase
- C. prophase
- D. telophase

2 Which stage of the cell cycle precedes cytokinesis?
- A. G_1
- B. G_2
- C. interphase
- D. mitosis

Use the figure below to answer questions 3 and 4.

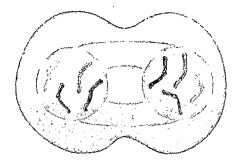

3 The figure represents which stage of mitosis?
- A. anaphase
- B. metaphase
- C. prophase
- D. telophase

4 What forms during this phase?
- A. centromere
- B. furrow
- C. sister chromatid
- D. two nuclei

5 What is the longest part of the cell cycle?
- A. anaphase
- B. cytokinesis
- C. interphase
- D. mitosis

6 A plant's root system is which level of organization?
- A. cell
- B. organ
- C. organ system
- D. tissue

7 Where is a meristem often found?
- A. liver cells
- B. muscle tissue
- C. tip of plant root
- D. unicellular organism

8 Which is NOT a type of human tissue?
- A. connective
- B. meristem
- C. muscle
- D. nervous

9 Which are unspecialized cells?
- A. blood cells
- B. muscle cells
- C. nerve cells
- D. stem cells

10 Which level of organization is shown in the figure below?
- A. cell
- B. organ
- C. organ system
- D. tissue

11 Which level of organization completes a series of tasks?
- A. cell
- B. organ
- C. organ system
- D. tissue

Critical Thinking

12 Sequence the events that occur during the phases of mitosis.

13 Explain how mitosis is related to cancer.

14 Create Use the figure below to create a cartoon that shows a duplicated chromosome separating into two sister chromatids.

15 Classify a leaf as a tissue or an organ. Explain your choice.

16 Distinguish between a tissue and an organ.

17 Construct a table that lists and defines the different levels of organization.

18 Summarize the differences between unicellular organisms and multicellular organisms.

Writing in Science

19 Write a five-sentence paragraph describing a human organ system. Include a main idea, supporting details, and a concluding statement.

REVIEW THE BIG IDEA

20 Why is cell division important for multicellular organisms?

21 The photo below shows a chick growing inside an egg. An egg begins as one cell. Explain how cells develop through differentiation into specialized tissues and organs as the one original cell becomes a chick.

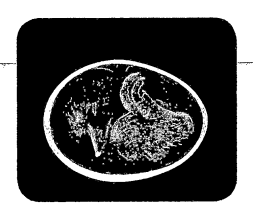

Math Skills ✕ ÷ ＋ Math Practice

Use Percentages

22 During an interphase lasting 23 hours, the S stage takes an average of 8.0 hours. What percentage of interphase is taken up by the S stage?

Use the following information to answer questions 23 through 25.

During a 23-hour interphase, the G_1 stage takes 11 hours and the S stage takes 8.0 hours.

23 What percentage of interphase is taken up by the G_1 and S stages?

24 What percentage of interphase is taken up by the G_2 phase?

25 How many hours does the G_2 phase last?

Record your answers on the answer sheet provided by your teacher or on a sheet of paper.

Multiple Choice

1 Which tissue carries messages to and from the brain?

   A connective

   B epithelial

   C muscle

   D nervous

Use the diagram below to answer question 2.

2 What is indicated by the arrow?

   A centromere

   B chromatid

   C chromosome

   D nucleus

3 In which stage of mitosis do spindle fibers form?

   A anaphase

   B metaphase

   C prophase

   D telophase

4 What structures separate during anaphase?

   A centromeres

   B chromatids

   C nuclei

   D organelles

Use the diagram below to answer question 5.

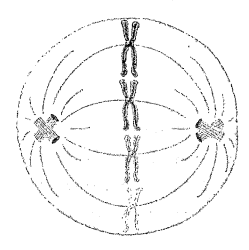

5 What stage of mitosis does the image above represent?

   A anaphase

   B metaphase

   C prophase

   D telophase

6 A plant's dermal tissue

   A produces food for the rest of the plant.

   B provides protection and helps reduce water loss.

   C takes in water and nutrients for use throughout the plant.

   D transports water and nutrients throughout the plant.

7 Which is the most accurate description of a leaf or your stomach?

   A a cell

   B an organ

   C an organ system

   D a tissue

Use the figure below to answer question 8.

8 Which does this figure illustrate?

   A an organ

   B an organism

   C an organ system

   D a tissue

9 If a cell has 30 chromosomes at the start of mitosis, how many chromosomes will be in each new daughter cell?

   A 10

   B 15

   C 30

   D 60

10 What areas of plants have unspecialized cells?

   A flowers

   B fruits

   C leaves

   D meristems

Constructed Response

Use the figure below to answer questions 11 and 12.

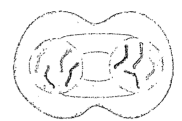

Figure A

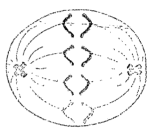

Figure B

11 The figures illustrate two phases of mitosis. Which occurs first: A or B? Explain your reasoning.

12 What stage of the mitotic phase follows those illustrated above? Explain how this stage differs between plant and animal cells.

13 What are some similarities and differences between the G_1 and S stages of interphase?

14 Are all human cells capable of mitosis and cell division? How does this affect the body's ability to repair itself? Support your answer with specific examples.

NEED EXTRA HELP?														
If You Missed Question...	1	2	3	4	5	6	7	8	9	10	11	12	13	14
Go to Lesson...	2	1	1	1	1	2	2	2	1	2	1	1	1	1

Chapter 16

Human Body Systems

THE BIG IDEA What are the functions of the human body systems?

(Inquiry) Part of a Human?

This is a photograph of a cross section through a human body. You can see the lower part of a human arm and part of the abdomen. In the abdomen, you might be able to pick out a vertebra, muscles, fat, and part of the intestine.

- What body systems can you identify here?

- What are the functions of the human body systems?

Get Ready to Read

What do you think?

Before you read, decide if you agree or disagree with each of these statements. As you read this chapter, see if you change your mind about any of the statements.

1. A human body has organ systems that carry out specific functions.

2. The body protects itself from disease.

3. All bones in the skeletal system are hollow.

4. The endocrine system makes hormones.

5. The testes produce sperm.

6. Puberty occurs during infancy.

connectED

Your one-stop online resource
connectED.mcgraw-hill.com

LearnSmart®

Chapter Resources Files, Reading Essentials, Get Ready to Read, Quick Vocabulary

Animations, Videos, Interactive Tables

Self-checks, Quizzes, Tests

Project-Based Learning Activities

Lab Manuals, Safety Videos, Virtual Labs & Other Tools

Vocabulary, Multilingual eGlossary, Vocab eGames, Vocab eFlashcards

Personal Tutors

Reading Guide

Key Concepts

ESSENTIAL QUESTIONS

- How do nutrients enter and leave the body?

- How do nutrients travel through the body?

- How does the body defend itself from harmful invaders?

Vocabulary

organ system p. 571

homeostasis p. 571

nutrient p. 573

Calorie p. 573

lymphocyte p. 579

immunity p. 580

 Multilingual·eGlossary

 BrainPOP®, Science Video, What's Science Got to do With It?

 7.LS.4

PBL Go to the resource tab in ConnectED to find the PBL *Building Body Systems.*

Transport and Defense

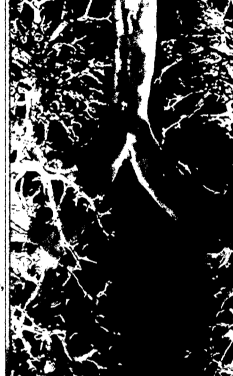

Inquiry Unusual Web?

This branching structure might look like a strange spider web, but it is actually a resin cast of human lungs. The purple-ish tubes that branch off from the main tube are large air passages, and smaller airways are shown in blue, pink, and white. Why do the lungs need these parts?

James Cavallini Science Source

Which tool can transport water quickly?

You need to transport materials throughout your body. Each cell must receive nutrients and oxygen and get rid of wastes. What kinds of tools do you think would be most effective in moving fluids such as water quickly?

1. Read and complete a lab safety form.
2. Choose one of the **tools** for moving water.
3. Have another student use a **stopwatch** to keep time for 30 s. Use your tool to transport as much water as you can in 30 s from the main **bowl** into a **beaker**.
4. Use a **graduated cylinder** to measure the amount of water you moved from the bowl to the beaker. Record the measurement in your Science Journal.
5. Trade roles with your partner. Repeat steps 2 through 4.
6. Repeat step 5 until you have used all of the tools.

Think About This

1. Which tool was most effective for moving water quickly? Which tool was least effective?

2. **Key Concept** Why do you think moving small items in fluid might be more effective than moving them all individually?

The Body's Organization

Have you ever tried to find a book in a library? Libraries have thousands of books grouped together by subject. Grouping books by subject in a library helps keep them organized and easier to find. Your body's organization helps it function.

All organisms have different parts with special functions. Recall that cells are the basic unit of all living organisms. Organized groups of cells that work together are tissues. Groups of tissues that perform a specific function are organs. *Groups of organs that work together and perform a specific task are* **organ systems.** Organ systems provide movement, transport substances, and perform many other functions that you will read about in this chapter.

Organ systems work together and maintain **homeostasis** (hoh mee oh STAY sus), *or steady internal conditions when external conditions change.* Have you ever jogged, jumped rope, or snowshoed, as shown in Figure 1, and started to sweat? When exercising, your body uses stored energy. Your body releases excess energy as thermal energy. Sweat, also called perspiration (pur spuh RAY shun), helps the body release thermal energy and maintain homeostasis.

Figure 1 Sweating helps the body maintain homeostasis by releasing excess thermal energy.

(t)Hutchings Photography/Digital Light Source, (b)John Terence Turner/Alamy

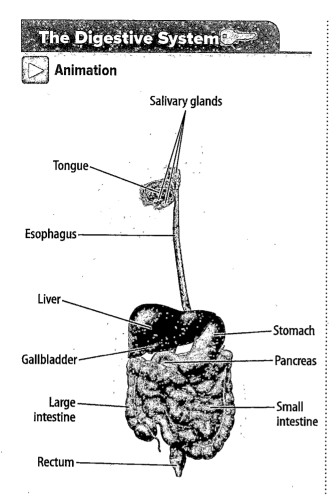

▷ **Animation**

Salivary glands

Tongue

Esophagus

Liver

Gallbladder

Large intestine

Rectum

Stomach

Pancreas

Small intestine

Figure 2 Food enters the digestive system through the mouth, and nutrients are absorbed by the small intestine.

FOLDABLES

Make three horizontal two-tab books. Label them with the body systems in this lesson, and glue them side by side to form a booklet with six tabs. Use your book to organize information about each body system in this lesson.

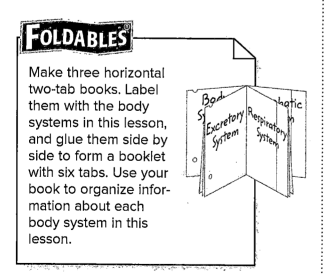

Digestion and Excretion

Humans need food, water, and oxygen to survive. Food contains energy that is processed by the body. The process by which food is broken down is called digestion. After digestion, substances that are not used by the body are removed through excretion (ihk SKREE shun).

The Digestive System

As shown in **Figure 2**, the digestive system is made up of several organs, composed of different types of cells and tissues. Food and water enter the digestive system through the mouth.

Digestion After food enters the mouth, chewing breaks food into smaller parts. Saliva, which contains enzymes, also helps the mouth break down food. Recall that enzymes are proteins that speed up chemical reactions.

When you swallow, food, water, and other liquids move into a hollow tube called the esophagus (ih SAH fuh gus). Muscle tissue helps move food through the esophagus to the stomach. Digestion continues as food leaves the esophagus and enters the stomach. The stomach is a flexible, baglike organ that contains cells that secrete enzymes that break down food so that the food can be used by the body.

✓ **Reading Check** Identify where food enters the body.

Absorption Next, food moves into the small intestine. By the time food gets to the small intestine, it is a soupy mixture. The small intestine is a tube that has two functions—digestion and absorption. The liver makes a substance called bile. The pancreas makes enzymes. Both bile and enzymes are used in the small intestine to break down food even more. Because the small intestine is very long, it takes food hours to move through it. During that time, particles of food and water are absorbed into the blood.

Excretion The large intestine, or colon (KOH lun), receives digested food that the small intestine did not absorb. The large intestine also absorbs water from the remaining waste material. Most foods are completely digested into smaller parts that can be easily absorbed by the small intestine. However, some foods travel through the entire digestive system without being digested or absorbed. For example, some types of fiber, called insoluble fiber, in vegetables and whole grains are not digested and leave the body through the rectum.

Nutrition

As you have read, one of the functions of the small intestine is absorption. **Nutrients** *are the parts of food used by the body to grow and survive.* There are several types of nutrients. Proteins, fats, carbohydrates, vitamins, and minerals are all nutrients. Nutrition labels on food, as shown in **Figure 3,** show the amount of each nutrient in that food. By looking at the labels on packaged foods, you can make sure you get the nutrients you need. Different people need different amounts of nutrients. For example, football players, swimmers, and other athletes need a lot of nutrients for energy. Pregnant women also need lots of nutrients to provide for their developing babies.

Digestion helps release energy from food. *A* **Calorie** *is the amount of energy it takes to raise the temperature of 1 kg of water by 1ºC.* The body uses Calories from proteins, fats, and carbohydrates, which each contain a different amount of energy.

 Reading Check Name five types of nutrients.

Figure 3 The information on a nutrition label can help you decide whether a food is healthful to eat.

 Visual Check How many servings are in this food container?

Math Skills ✕÷+

Use Proportions
A proportion is an equation of two equal ratios. You can solve a proportion for an unknown value. For example, a 50-g egg provides 70 Calories (C) of energy. How many Calories would you get from 125 g of scrambled eggs?

Write a proportion.
$$\frac{50\ g}{70\ C} = \frac{125\ g}{x}$$

Find the cross products.

$50\ g\ (x) = 70\ C \times 125\ g$

$50\ g\ (x) = 8{,}750\ C\ g$

Divide both sides by 50.
$$\frac{50\ g\ (x)}{50\ g} = \frac{8{,}750\ C\ g}{50\ g}$$
Simplify the equation.

$$x = 175\ C$$

Practice
The serving size of a large fast-food hamburger with cheese is 316 g. It contains 790 C of energy. How many Calories would you consume if you ate 100 g of the burger?

 Math Practice

 Personal Tutor

REVIEW VOCABULARY
protein
a long chain of amino acid molecules

How much water do you lose each day?

Most people lose an average of 2.5 L of water each day. You lose an average of 0.8 L through breathing, 1.5 L through urine, 0.1 L through sweating, and 0.1 L through feces.

① Read and complete a lab safety form.

② In your Science Journal, keep track of how much water you drink for 1 day. Include all the liquids you take in, and write down the sources as part of your list. Add and record the total.

③ Use the data above to figure out how much water you lost. First, subtract the amounts for breathing and feces.

④ Next, subtract the amount for sweating. If you did a physical activity that made you sweat, add another 0.5 L to this amount.

⑤ The remaining amount of water is lost as urine. Record this amount from the data above.

Analyze and Conclude

1. **Calculate** how much of the water you drank was used by your body, and display your data in a table. Did the amount of water lost equal the amount you drank? Why do you think this is so?

2. **Construct** a graph that shows, in percentages, how your body used the water you drank.

3. **Key Concept** Infer how the water you drank must be transported within your body for it to be used in each process.

The Excretory System

The excretory system removes solid, liquid, and gas waste materials from the body. The lungs, skin, liver, kidneys, bladder, and rectum all are parts of the excretory system.

The lungs remove carbon dioxide (CO_2) and excess water as water vapor when you breathe out, or exhale. The skin removes water and salt when you sweat.

The liver removes wastes from the blood. As you have read, the liver also is a part of the digestive system. The digestive and excretory systems work together to break down, absorb, and remove food.

When the liver breaks down proteins, urea forms. Urea is toxic if it stays in the body. The kidneys, shown in **Figure 4**, remove urea from the body by making urine. Urine contains water, urea, and other waste chemicals. Urine leaves each kidney through a tube, called the ureter (YOO ruh tur), and is stored in a flexible sac, called the bladder. Urine is removed from the body through a tube called the urethra (yoo REE thruh).

Like the liver, the rectum is part of the excretory system and the digestive system. Food substances that are not absorbed by the small intestine are mixed with other wastes and form feces. The rectum stores feces until it moves out of the body.

Key Concept Check How does food enter and leave the body?

Figure 4 The kidneys remove waste material from the body.

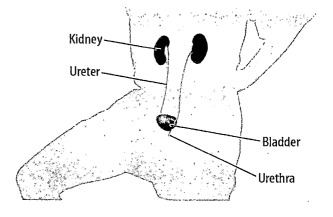

Thinkstock/Getty Images

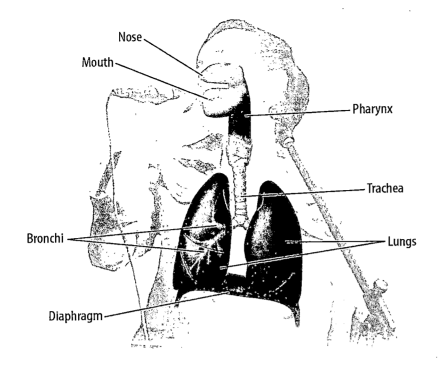

Nose

Mouth

Pharynx

Trachea

Bronchi

Lungs

Diaphragm

Figure 5 Air enters the respiratory system through the nose and the mouth. Oxygen enters the blood in the lungs.

Respiration and Circulation

You have read about how the body converts food into nutrients and how the small intestine absorbs nutrients. But how do the oxygen you breathe in and the nutrients absorbed by the small intestine get to the rest of the body? And how do waste products leave the body?

The Respiratory System

The respiratory system, shown in **Figure 5**, exchanges gases between the body and the environment. As air flows through the respiratory system, it passes through the nose and mouth, pharynx (FER ingks), trachea (TRAY kee uh), bronchi (BRAHN ki; singular, bronchus), and lungs. The parts of the respiratory system work together and supply the body with oxygen. They also rid the body of wastes, such as carbon dioxide.

Pharynx and Trachea Oxygen enters the body when you inhale, or breathe in. Carbon dioxide leaves the body when you exhale. When you inhale, air enters the nostrils and passes through the pharynx. Because the pharynx is part of the throat, it is a part of both the digestive and respiratory systems. Food goes through the pharynx to the esophagus. Air travels through the pharynx to the trachea. The trachea is also called the windpipe because it is a long, tubelike organ that connects the pharynx to the bronchi.

 Reading Check Which organ is part of both the digestive system and the respiratory system?

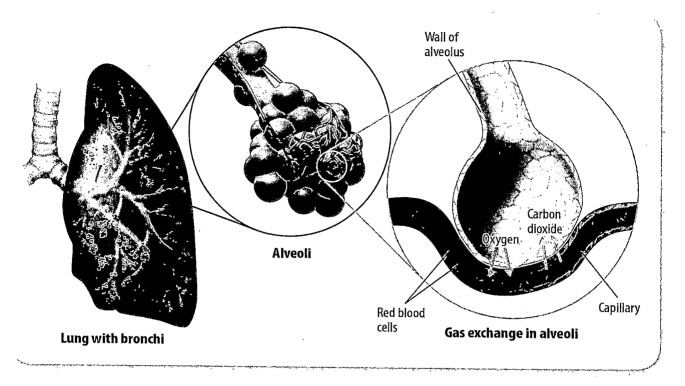

Wall of alveolus

Alveoli

Carbon dioxide

Oxygen

Red blood cells

Capillary

Gas exchange in alveoli

Lung with bronchi

Figure 6 Bronchi divide into smaller tubes that end in clusters of alveoli that are surrounded by capillaries.

 Visual Check Which gas leaves the alveoli and enters capillaries?

SCIENCE USE V. COMMON USE·

vessel
Science Use a tube in the body that carries fluid such as blood

Common Use a ship

Bronchi and Alveoli There are two bronchi; one enters the left lung, and one enters the right lung. As shown in **Figure 6**, the bronchi divide into smaller tubes that end in tiny groups of cells that look like bunches of grapes. These groups of cells are called alveoli (al VEE uh li). Inside each lung, there are more than 100 million alveoli. The alveoli are surrounded by blood vessels called capillaries. Oxygen in the alveoli enters the capillaries. The blood inside capillaries transports oxygen to the rest of the body

Reading Check What are alveoli, and what do they do?

Inhaling and exhaling require the movement of a thin muscle under the lungs called the diaphragm (DI uh fram). As the diaphragm contracts and moves down, air enters the lungs and you inhale. When the diaphragm relaxes and moves up, you exhale.

The Circulatory System

As shown in **Figure 7**, the heart, blood, and blood vessels make up the circulatory system. It transports nutrients, gases, wastes, and other substances through the body. Blood vessels transport blood to all organs in the body. Because your body uses oxygen and nutrients continually, your circulatory system transports blood between the heart, lungs, and other organs more than 1,000 times each day!

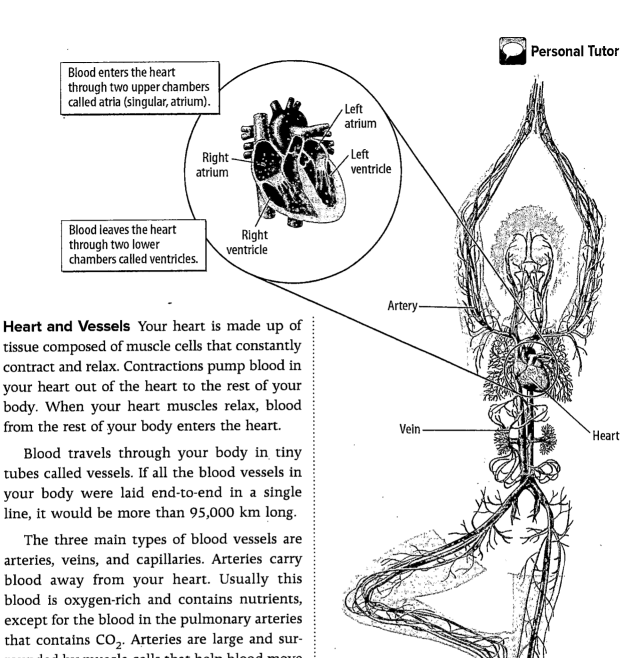

Blood enters the heart through two upper chambers called atria (singular, atrium).

Left atrium

Right atrium

Left ventricle

Blood leaves the heart through two lower chambers called ventricles.

Right ventricle

Artery

Vein

Heart

Heart and Vessels Your heart is made up of tissue composed of muscle cells that constantly contract and relax. Contractions pump blood in your heart out of the heart to the rest of your body. When your heart muscles relax, blood from the rest of your body enters the heart.

Blood travels through your body in tiny tubes called vessels. If all the blood vessels in your body were laid end-to-end in a single line, it would be more than 95,000 km long.

The three main types of blood vessels are arteries, veins, and capillaries. Arteries carry blood away from your heart. Usually this blood is oxygen-rich and contains nutrients, except for the blood in the pulmonary arteries that contains CO_2. Arteries are large and surrounded by muscle cells that help blood move through the vessels faster. Veins transport blood that contains CO_2 back to your heart, except for the blood in the pulmonary veins, which is oxygen-rich. Capillaries are very tiny vessels that enable oxygen, CO_2, and nutrients to move between your circulatory system and your entire body.

You just read that capillaries surround the alveoli in your lungs. Capillaries also surround the small intestine, where they absorb nutrients and transport them to the rest of the body.

 **Key Concept Check** How do nutrients travel through the body?

Figure 7 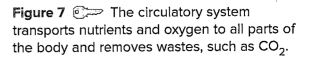 The circulatory system transports nutrients and oxygen to all parts of the body and removes wastes, such as CO_2.

Image Source/Jupiterimages

Table 1 Human Blood Types

Blood Type	Type A	Type B	Type AB	Type O
Antigens on red blood cells	(A antigens)	(B antigens)	(A and B antigens)	(no antigens)
Percentage of U.S. population with this blood type	42	10	4	44
Clumping proteins in plasma	anti-B	anti-A	none	anti-A and anti-B
Blood type(s) that can be RECEIVED in a transfusion	A or O	B or O	A, B, AB, or O	O only
This blood type can DONATE TO these blood types	A or AB	B or AB	AB only	A, B, AB, O

Table 1 The red blood cells of each blood type have different proteins on their surfaces.

◎ **Visual Check** To which blood group can type A donate?

Blood The blood that circulates through vessels has several parts. The liquid part of blood is called plasma and contains nutrients, water, and CO_2. Blood also contains red blood cells, platelets, and white blood cells. Red blood cells carry oxygen. Platelets help the body heal when you get a cut. White blood cells help the body defend itself from toxins and diseases. You will read more about white blood cells on the next page.

Everyone has red blood cells. However, different people have different proteins on the surfaces of their red blood cells, as shown in **Table 1.** Scientists classify these different red-blood-cell proteins into groups called blood types.

People with A proteins on their red blood cells have type A blood. People with B proteins on their red blood cells have type B blood. Some people have both A and B proteins on their red blood cells. They have type AB blood. People with type O blood have neither A nor B proteins on the surfaces of their red blood cells.

. Medical professionals use blood types to determine which type of blood a person can receive from a blood donor. For example, because people with type O blood have no proteins on the surfaces of their red blood cells, they can receive blood only from a donor who also has type O blood.

The Lymphatic System

Have you ever had a cold and found it painful to swallow? This can happen if your tonsils swell. Tonsils are small organs on both sides of your throat. They are part of the lymphatic (lihm FA tihk) system.

The spleen, the thymus, bone marrow, and lymph nodes also are parts of the lymphatic system. The spleen stores blood for use in an emergency. The thymus, the spleen, and bone marrow make white blood cells.

Your lymphatic system has three main functions: removing excess fluid around organs, producing white blood cells, and absorbing and transporting fats. The lymphatic system helps your body maintain fluid homeostasis. About 65 percent of the human body is water. Most of this water is inside cells. Sometimes, when water, wastes, and nutrients move between capillaries and organs, not all of the fluid is taken up by the organs. When fluid builds up around organs, swelling can occur. To prevent swelling, the lymphatic system removes the fluid.

Reading Check Identify a function of the lymphatic system.

Lymph vessels are all over your body, as shown in **Figure 8**. Fluid that travels through the lymph vessels flows into organs called lymph nodes. Humans have more than 500 lymph nodes. The lymph nodes work together and protect the body by removing toxins, wastes, and other harmful substances.

The lymphatic system makes white blood cells. They help the body defend against infection. There are many different types of white blood cells. A **lymphocyte** (LIHM fuh site) *is a type of white blood cell that is made in the thymus, the spleen, or a tissue called bone marrow.* Lymphocytes protect the body by traveling through the circulatory system, defending against infection.

C Squared Studios/Getty Images

Figure 8 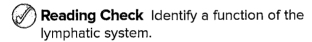 Lymph vessels are throughout your body.

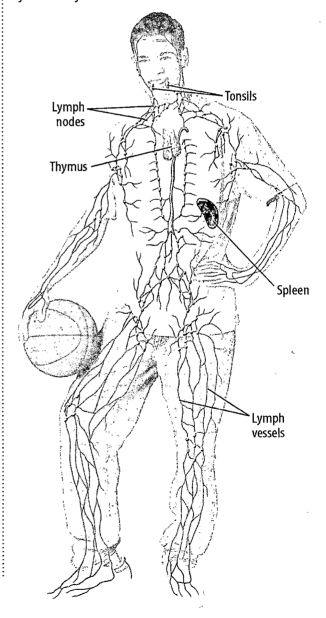

Tonsils

Lymph nodes

Thymus

Spleen

Lymph vessels

Immunity

The lymphatic system protects your body from harmful substances and infection. *The resistance to specific pathogens, or disease-causing agents, is called* **immunity.** The skeletal system produces immune cells, and the circulatory system transports them throughout the body. Immune cells include lymphocytes and other white blood cells. These cells detect viruses, bacteria, and other foreign substances that are not normally made in the body. The immune cells attack and destroy them, as shown in **Figure 9.**

If the body is exposed to the same bacteria, virus, or substance later, some immune cells remember and make proteins called antibodies. These antibodies recognize specific proteins on the harmful agent and help the body fight infection faster. Because there are many different types of bacteria and viruses, humans make billions of different types of antibodies. Each type of antibody responds to a different harmful agent.

ACADEMIC VOCABULARY

detect
(*verb*) to discover the presence of

Figure 9 Lymphocytes surround bacteria and destroy or remove them from the body.

📃 **Visual Check** How long did it take for the lymphocyte to completely surround the bacterium?

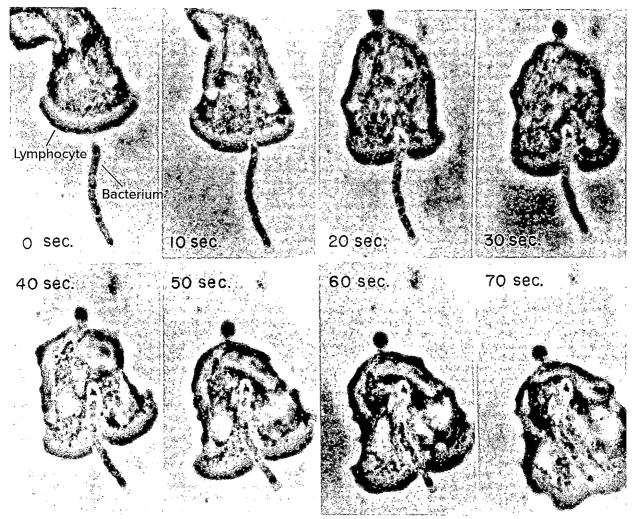

Lymphocyte

Bacterium

O sec.   10 sec.   20 sec.   30 sec.

40 sec.   50 sec.   60 sec.   70 sec.

Omikron/Science Source

Infectious Disease		Noninfectious Disease
Disease	Pathogen	
colds	virus	cancer
AIDS	virus	diabetes
strep throat	bacteria	heart disease
chicken pox	virus	allergy

Table 2 Examples of Diseases

Types of Diseases

There are two main groups of diseases—infectious and noninfectious—as shown in **Table 2.** Infectious diseases are caused by pathogens, such as bacteria and viruses. Infectious diseases are usually contagious, which means they can be spread from one person to another. The flu is an example of an infectious disease. Viruses that invade organ systems of the body, such as the respiratory system, cause infectious diseases.

A noninfectious disease is caused by the environment or a genetic disorder, not a pathogen. Skin cancer, diabetes, and allergies are examples of noninfectious diseases. Noninfectious diseases are not contagious and cannot be spread from one person to another.

Lines of Defense

The human body has many ways of protecting itself from viruses, bacteria, and harmful substances. Skin and mucus (MYEW kus) are parts of the first line of defense. They prevent toxins and other substances from entering the body. Mucus is a thick, gel-like substance in the nostrils, trachea, and lungs. Mucus traps harmful substances and prevents them from entering your body.

The second line of defense is the immune response. In the immune response, white blood cells attack and destroy harmful substances, as shown in **Figure 9.**

The third line of defense protects your body against substances that have infected the body before. As you have read, immune cells make antibodies that destroy the harmful substances. Vaccines are used to help the body develop antibodies against infectious diseases. For example, many people get an influenza vaccine annually to protect them against the flu.

Key Concept Check How does the body defend itself from harmful invaders?

Table 2 Diseases are classified into two main groups based on whether they are caused by pathogens.

Project-Based Learning Activity

Building Body Systems Go online to research and describe the functions and relationships between various cell types, tissues, and organs in the immune system, circulatory system, and digestive system of the human body.

Visual Summary

The kidneys remove liquid wastes from the body.

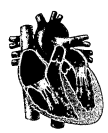

The circulatory system transports nutrients, gases, wastes, and other substances through the body.

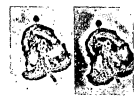

Immune cells detect and destroy viruses, bacteria, and other foreign substances.

FOLDABLES

Use your lesson Foldable to review the lesson. Save your Foldable for the project at the end of the chapter.

What do you think NOW?

You first read the statements below at the beginning of the chapter.

1. A human body has organ systems that carry out specific functions.

2. The body protects itself from disease.

Did you change your mind about whether you agree or disagree with the statements? Rewrite any false statements to make them true.

Use Vocabulary

1 Use the term *organ system* in a sentence.

2 Define *homeostasis* in your own words.

3 A(n) _____ is a type of white blood cell.

Understand Key Concepts

4 Organs are groups of _____ that work together.
  A. cells   C. systems
  B. organisms   D. tissues

5 Differentiate the role of the liver in the digestive system from its role in the excretory system.

6 Examine how the circulatory system and the respiratory system work together and move oxygen through the body.

7 Contrast infectious diseases and noninfectious diseases.

Interpret Graphics

8 Analyze the nutrition label below. How many Calories, carbohydrates, fats, and proteins are in a serving of this food?

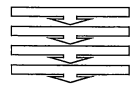

9 Summarize Copy and fill in the graphic organizer below to show how food travels through the digestive system.

Math Skills Math Practice

10 If 30.5 g of milk contains 18 C, how many Calories will you consume by drinking a glass of milk (244 g)?

(l)Omikron/Science Source; (r)Mark Dierker/McGraw-Hill Education

How can you model the function of blood cells?

Materials

toy cars and trucks

modeling clay

construction paper

scissors

glue stick

Safety

Your body has different types of cells that perform various functions in the blood. Red blood cells carry oxygen to all the other cells in your body. White blood cells destroy viruses and bacteria that can attack the body and make you sick.

Learn It

In science, a **model** is a representation of how something in the natural world works. A model can be used to demonstrate a process that is difficult to see in action.

Try It

1. Read and complete a lab safety form.

2. Cut out shapes from construction paper to represent the following organs: heart, lungs, stomach, and small intestine. Also cut out a shape to represent a body cell.

3. Draw an outline of a student on a large sheet of paper. Place the organs in the appropriate body position on the outline. Choose a location away from the center of the body, such as an arm or a leg, to place the body cell.

4. Use the modeling clay to create molecules of oxygen, food, and waste materials (carbon dioxide and water). Place the oxygen molecules in the lungs. Place the food molecules in the stomach.

5. Your body gets energy when oxygen helps break down food molecules. Waste products are released during the breakdown of food molecules. Think about how a body cell gets energy. Draw roads to connect the organs and the body cell so that the body cell can get the energy it needs. Select toy vehicles to represent red blood cells and white blood cells.

6. Draw a diagram of your model in your Science Journal.

Apply It

7. How does oxygen reach body cells? Use the appropriate vehicle to model how red blood cells carry oxygen to a body cell. Add the path of the oxygen molecules to your diagram.

8. How do food molecules reach body cells? Use the appropriate vehicle to model how food molecules reach a body cell. Add the path of the food molecules to your diagram.

9. Where are waste materials produced? Use the appropriate vehicle to model how waste materials leave the body. Add the path to your diagram.

10. **Key Concept** Explain why using police cars and red pickup trucks are appropriate models to represent white blood cells and red blood cells, respectively.

Structure, Movement, and Control

Reading Guide

Key Concepts 🔑
ESSENTIAL QUESTIONS

- How does the body move?

- How does the body respond to changes in its environment?

Vocabulary

compact bone p. 586

spongy bone p. 586

neuron p. 588

reflex p. 589

hormone p. 591

 Multilingual eGlossary

 BrainPOP®

6-8.LST.7.1

Inquiry Open wide?

When you have a dental checkup, you are asked to open your mouth. How are you able to open your mouth? What keeps your teeth from falling out when you chew food?

YOSHIKAZU TSUNO/AFP/Getty Images

Why is the skeletal system so important?

Your skeletal system protects your body's organs, provides support, helps you move, and stores necessary minerals.

1. Read and complete a lab safety form.
2. Obtain one of the **disassembled human figures** and a **kit of materials.**
3. Use the materials to build a backbone for your figure. Using your backbone, connect the head and the arms to the legs of the figure.

Think About This

1. Which materials did you find helpful in creating a backbone and skeletal structure for your figure? Which were not helpful?

2. What characteristics of the "skeleton" were important as you built it? What problems would be caused by not having a skeleton?

3. **Key Concept** Can you make your figure move? How does having a good support structure help it to move?

Structure and Movement

Have you ever had to open your mouth for a dental checkup as shown in the photo on the previous page? The human body can move in many different directions and perform a wide variety of tasks. It is able to do things that require many parts of the body to move, such as shooting a basketball into a hoop or swimming a lap in a pool. The human body also can remain very still, such as when posing for a picture or balancing on one leg.

In this lesson, you will read more about two organ systems—the skeletal system and the muscular system—that give the body structure, help the body move, and protect other organ systems.

The Skeletal System

The skeletal system has four major jobs. It protects internal organs, provides support, helps the body move, and stores minerals. The skeletal system is mostly bones. Adults have 206 bones. Ligaments, tendons, and cartilage are also parts of the skeletal system.

FOLDABLES

Make two horizontal two-tab books. Label them as shown, and glue them side by side to form a booklet with four tabs. Glue this section to the back of the one you made in Lesson 1. Use your book to organize information about the body systems in this lesson.

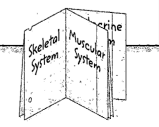

Hutchings Photography/Digital Light Source

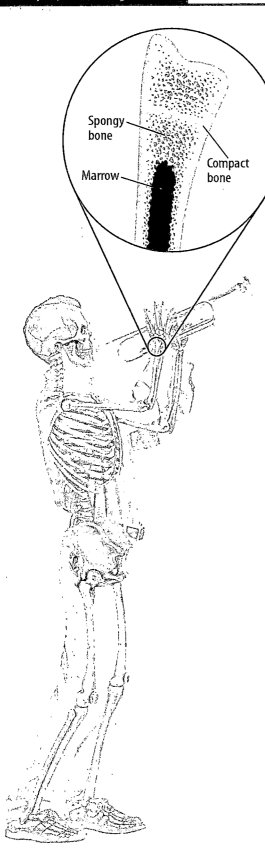

Spongy bone

Marrow

Compact bone

Figure 10 Bone is made up of a dense, hard exterior and a spongy interior.

Storage The skeletal system is also an important storage site for minerals such as calcium. Calcium is essential for life. It has many functions in the body. Muscles require calcium for contractions. The nervous system requires calcium for communication. Most of the calcium in the body is stored in bone. Calcium helps build stronger compact bone. Cheese and milk are good sources of calcium.

Reading Check What mineral is stored by the skeletal system?

Support Without a skeleton, your body would look like a beanbag. Your skeleton gives your body structure and support, as shown in **Figure 10.** Your bones help you stand, sit up, and raise your arms to play an instrument, such as a trumpet.

Protection Many of the bones in the body protect organs that are made of softer tissue. For example, the skull protects the soft tissue of the brain, and the rib cage protects the soft tissue of the lungs and heart.

Movement The skeletal system helps the body move by working with the muscular system. Bones can move because they are attached to muscles. You will read more about the interaction of the skeletal system and the muscular system later in this lesson.

Bone Types Bones are organs that contain two types of tissue. **Compact bone** *is the hard outer layer of bone.* **Spongy bone** *is the interior region of bone that contains many tiny holes.* As shown in **Figure 10,** spongy bone is inside compact bone. Some bones also contain bone marrow. Recall that bone marrow is a part of the lymphatic system and makes white blood cells.

Reading Check How do the two types of bone tissue differ?

The Muscular System

You might already know that there are muscle cells in your arms and legs. But did you know that there are muscle cells in your eyes, heart, and blood vessels? Without muscle cells you would not be able to talk, write, or run.

As shown in **Figure 11,** muscle cells are everywhere in the body. Almost one-half of your body mass is muscle cells. These muscle cells make up the muscular system. By working together, they help the body move.

The muscular system is made of three different types of muscle tissue–skeletal muscle, cardiac muscle, and smooth muscle. Skeletal muscle works with the skeletal system and helps you move. Tendons connect skeletal muscles to bones. Skeletal muscle also gives you the strength to lift heavy objects.

Another type of muscle tissue is cardiac muscle. Cardiac muscle is only in the heart. It continually contracts and relaxes and moves blood throughout your body.

Smooth muscle tissue moves materials through your body. Smooth muscle tissue is in organs such as the stomach and the bladder. Blood vessels also have smooth muscle tissue.

 Key Concept Check What systems help the body move?

Figure 11 Cardiac muscle is only in the heart. Organs, such as the stomach, have smooth muscle. Skeletal muscle moves your body.

Ⓥ **Visual Check** Which type of muscle is in your arms?

The Muscular System

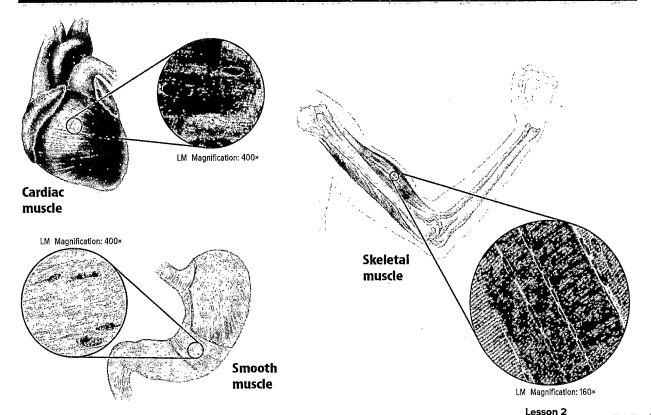

Cardiac muscle

LM Magnification: 400×

LM Magnification: 400×

Smooth muscle

Skeletal muscle

LM Magnification: 160×

(t, b)Al Telser/McGraw-Hill Education; (br)Innerspace Imaging/Science Source

▷ Animation

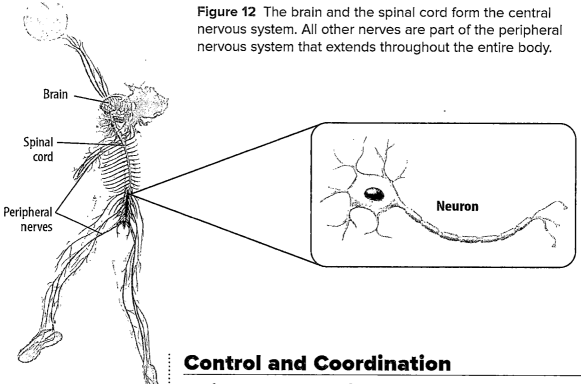

Brain

Spinal cord

Peripheral nerves

Figure 12 The brain and the spinal cord form the central nervous system. All other nerves are part of the peripheral nervous system that extends throughout the entire body.

Neuron

☐ Central nervous system (CNS)
■ Peripheral nervous system (PNS)

WORD ORIGIN ············
neuron
from Greek *neuron*, means
"a nerve cell with appendages"
·············

Control and Coordination

The nervous system, shown in **Figure 12**, and the endocrine system, which you·will read about later, receive and process information about your internal and external environments. These two systems control many functions, including movement, communication, and growth, by working with other systems in the body and help maintain homeostasis.

 Key Concept Check How does the body respond to changes in its environment?

The Nervous System

The nervous system is a group of organs and specialized cells that detect, process, and respond to information. The nervous system constantly receives information from your external environment and from inside your body. It can receive information, process it, and produce a response in less than 1 second.

Nerve cells, or **neurons,** *are the basic units of the nervous system.* Neurons can be many different lengths. In adults, some neurons are more than 1 m long. This is about as long as the distance between a toe and the spinal cord.

The nervous system includes the brain, the spinal cord, and nerves. The brain and the spinal cord form the central nervous system. Nerves outside the brain and the spinal cord make up the peripheral nervous system.

Doug Pensinger/Getty Images

Processing Information The central nervous system is protected by the skeletal system. Muscles and other organs surround the peripheral nervous system. Information enters the nervous system through neurons in the peripheral nervous system. Most of the information then is sent to the central nervous system for processing. After the central nervous system processes information, it signals the peripheral nervous system to respond.

Voluntary and Involuntary Control The body carries out many functions that depend on the nervous system. Some of these functions such as breathing and digestion are automatic, or involuntary. They do not require you to think about them to make them happen. The nervous system automatically controls these functions and maintains homeostasis.

Most of the other functions of the nervous system are not automatic. They require you to think about them to make them happen. Tasks such as reading, talking, and walking are voluntary. These tasks require input, processing, and a response.

Reflexes Have you ever touched a hot pan with your hand? Touching a hot object sends a rapid signal that your hand is in pain. The signal is so fast that you do not think about moving your hand; it just happens automatically. *Automatic movements in response to a signal are called* **reflexes.** The spinal cord receives and processes reflex signals, as shown in Figure 13. Processing the information in the spinal cord instead of the brain helps the body respond more quickly.

 **Personal Tutor**

Figure 13 Reflexes happen automatically.

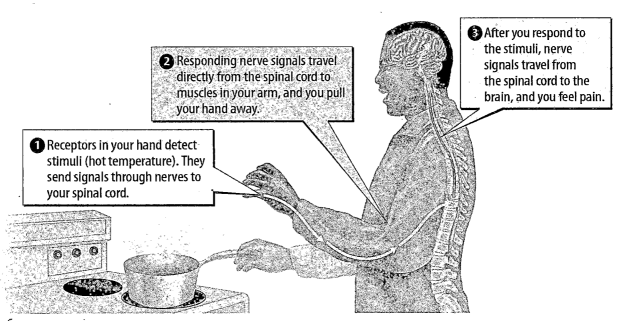

❷ Responding nerve signals travel directly from the spinal cord to muscles in your arm, and you pull your hand away.

❸ After you respond to the stimuli, nerve signals travel from the spinal cord to the brain, and you feel pain.

❶ Receptors in your hand detect stimuli (hot temperature). They send signals through nerves to your spinal cord.

🔍 **Visual Check** What detects heat when you touch a hot pan?

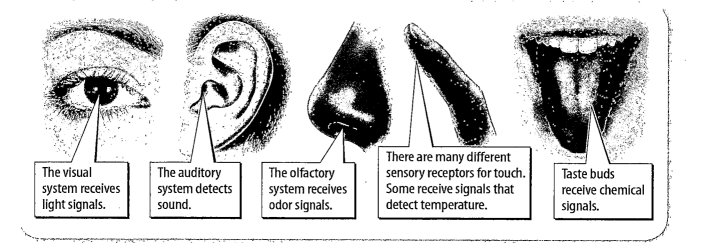

| The visual system receives light signals. | The auditory system detects sound. | The olfactory system receives odor signals. | There are many different sensory receptors for touch. Some receive signals that detect temperature. | Taste buds receive chemical signals. |

Figure 14 Each sense receives a different type of signal.

The Senses Humans detect their external environment with five senses—vision, hearing, smell, touch, and taste—as shown in **Figure 14**. Each of the five senses has specific neurons that receive signals from the environment. Information detected by the senses is sent to the spinal cord and then to the brain for processing and a response. Responses depend on the specific signal detected. Some responses cause muscles to contract and move such as when you touch a hot surface. The aroma of baking cookies might cause your mouth to produce saliva.

MiniLab
15 minutes

Does your sight help you keep your balance?

It can be hard to keep your balance when standing on one leg. Does shutting your eyes make this task easier or more difficult?

① Read and complete a lab safety form.

② Stand upright and lift your left leg, balancing yourself on your right leg. Hold your left arm out so it is over your left knee.

③ Move your left leg backward and forward while maintaining your balance. As you move your leg, move your left arm at the same time. Have another student nearby to help you if you lose your balance.

④ Count how many times you are able to move your arm and your leg together before you lose your balance. Record this number in your Science Journal.

⑤ Repeat steps 2–4 with your eyes closed.

Analyze and Conclude

1. **Compare** How many times were you able to swing your arm and your leg with your eyes open? With your eyes closed?

2. **Analyze** Was it easier to maintain your balance with your eyes open or closed? Explain your answer.

3. **Key Concept** Infer how your vision helps you maintain homeostasis.

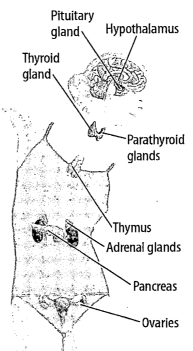

Pituitary gland

Hypothalamus

Thyroid gland

Parathyroid glands

Thymus

Adrenal glands

Pancreas

Ovaries

The Endocrine System

How tall were you in first grade? How tall are you now? From the time you were born until now, your body has changed. These changes are controlled by the endocrine system, shown in **Figure 15**. Like the nervous system, the endocrine system sends signals to the body. *Chemical signals released by the organs of the endocrine system are called* **hormones.** Hormones cause organ systems to carry out specific functions.

Why does your body need two organ systems to process information? The signals sent by the nervous system travel quickly through neurons. Hormones travel in blood through blood vessels in the circulatory system. These messages travel more slowly than nerve messages. A signal sent by the nervous system can travel from your head to your toes in less than 1 s, but a hormone will take about 20 s to make the trip. Although hormones take longer to reach their target organ system, their effects usually last longer.

Many of the hormones made by the endocrine system work with other organ systems and maintain homeostasis. For example, parathyroid hormone works with the skeletal system and controls calcium storage. Insulin is a hormone that is released from the pancreas that signals the digestive system to control nutrient homeostasis. Other hormones, such as growth hormone, work with many organ systems to help you grow. In the next lesson, you will read about another system that the endocrine system works with.

Figure 15 The endocrine system uses hormones to communicate with other organ systems.

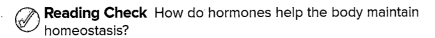

Reading Check How do hormones help the body maintain homeostasis?

Mark Andersen/Getty Images

Visual Summary

 The skeletal system protects organs, provides support, helps the body move, and stores minerals.

 Skeletal muscle works with the skeletal system and helps you move.

 Reflex signals are received by the spinal cord but are not processed by the brain. This helps the body respond quickly.

FOLDABLES

Use your lesson Foldable to review the lesson. Save your Foldable for the project at the end of the chapter.

What do you think NOW?

You first read the statements below at the beginning of the chapter.

3. All bones in the skeletal system are hollow.

4. The endocrine system makes hormones.

Did you change your mind about whether you agree or disagree with the statements? Rewrite any false statements to make them true.

Use Vocabulary

1 **Distinguish** between compact bone and spongy bone.

2 A chemical signal that is released by the endocrine system is a(n) _____.

3 **Use the term** *neuron* in a sentence.

Understand Key Concepts

4 An automatic movement in response to a signal is called a
- **A.** hormone.
- **C.** neuron.
- **B.** muscle.
- **D.** reflex.

5 **Compare** the role of tendons in helping the skeletal system and the muscular system work together to a bridge between two cities.

6 **Infer** How does the skeletal system protect other organ systems in the body?

Interpret Graphics

7 **Summarize** Copy and fill in the graphic organizer below to show the three types of muscle tissue.

8 **Predict** the effect of having less compact bone than normal on the strength of the skeletal system by examining the figure below.

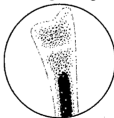

Critical Thinking

9 **Hypothesize** What would be the effect of losing one's sight on the ability to digest food? Explain your answer.

Bone Marrow Transplants

Why might you need new bone marrow?

Healthy blood cells are essential to overall health. Red blood cells carry oxygen throughout the body. Some white blood cells fight infections. Platelets help stop bleeding. A bone marrow transplant is sometimes necessary when a disease interferes with the body's ability to produce healthy blood cells.

Bone marrow is a tissue found inside some of the bones in your body. Healthy bone marrow contains cells that can develop into white blood cells, red blood cells, or platelets. Some diseases, such as leukemia and sickle cell disease, affect bone marrow. Replacing malfunctioning bone marrow with healthy bone marrow can help treat these diseases.

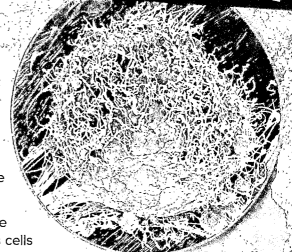

▲ In healthy bone marrow, a stem cell can develop into different types of blood cells.

A bone marrow transplant involves several steps. The patient receiving the bone marrow must have treatments to destroy his or her unhealthy bone marrow. Healthy bone marrow must be obtained for the transplant. Sometimes, the patient's own bone marrow can be treated and used for transplant. This transplant has the greatest chance of success. Other transplants involve healthy bone marrow donated by another person. The bone marrow must be tested to ensure that it is a good match for the patient.

The bone marrow donor undergoes a procedure called harvesting. Bone marrow is taken from the donor's pelvic bone. The donor's body replaces the harvested bone marrow, so there are no long-term effects for the donor.

The donated bone marrow is introduced into the patient's bloodstream. If the transplant is successful, the new bone marrow moves into the bone cavities and begins producing healthy blood cells.

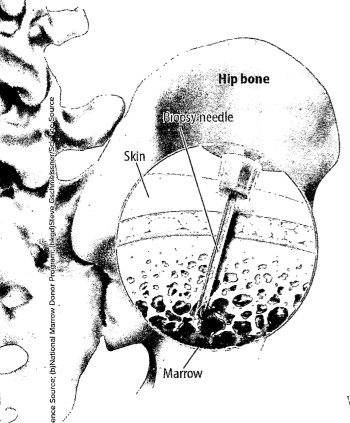

Hip bone

Biopsy needle

Skin

Marrow

▲ Bone marrow is harvested from the pelvic bone. An anesthetic is used to keep the donor from feeling pain during the procedure.

(t)Paul Gunning/Science Source; (b)National Marrow Donor Program; (bkgd)Steve Gschmeissner/Science Source

It's Your Turn

NATIONAL
MARROW
DONOR
PROGRAM

RESEARCH AND REPORT Find out more about bone marrow transplants. What other diseases can be treated using a bone marrow transplant? What is the National Marrow Donor Program? Present your findings to your class.

Reading Guide

Key Concepts 🔑

ESSENTIAL QUESTIONS

- What do the male and female reproductive systems do?

- How do humans grow and change?

Vocabulary

reproduction p. 595

gamete p. 595

sperm p. 595

ovum p. 595

fertilization p. 595

zygote p. 595

  Multilingual eGlossary

 BrainPOP®

6-8.LST.7.1, 6-8.LST.7.3

Reproduction and Development

Inquiry Strands of Hair?

The things that look like strands of hair are sperm, the male reproductive cells. The red structure is an egg, the female reproductive cell. Why are there so many sperm but only one egg?

David M. Phillips/Science Source

How do the sizes of egg and sperm cells compare?

A sperm cell combines with an egg cell to create a zygote that will eventually become a fetus and then a baby. The sperm and egg cells each contribute half the genetic material to the zygote.

1. Read and complete a lab safety form.

2. Select one of the **spheres** to use as a model of an egg cell. With a **ruler,** measure the diameter of the sphere. Record the measurement in your Science Journal.

3. If an average sperm cell is 3–6 microns in diameter, and an average egg cell is 120–150 microns in diameter, determine the diameter of a suitable model for a sperm cell.

4. Find another sphere that is approximately the size needed to create an accurate model to represent a sperm cell. Label both of your models.

Think About This

1. What were the sizes of the spheres you chose to model the sizes of the sperm and egg cells?

2. ✍️ **Key Concept** How do the egg cell and sperm cells interact in reproduction? How do you think size plays a role in this interaction?

Reproduction and Hormones

You have read how the endocrine system works with other organ systems and helps the body grow and maintain homeostasis. The endocrine system has another very important function—to ensure that humans can reproduce. Some of the organs of the endocrine system produce hormones that help humans reproduce. **Reproduction** *is the process by which new organisms are produced.* Reproduction is essential to the continuation of life on Earth.

A male and a female each have special organs for reproduction. Organs in the male reproductive system are different from those in the female reproductive system. *Human reproductive cells,* called **gametes** (GA meets), *are made by the male and female reproductive systems. Male gametes are called* **sperm.** *Female gametes are called* **ova** (OH vah; singular ovum), *or eggs.*

As shown in the photo at the beginning of the lesson, *a sperm joins with an egg in a reproductive process called* **fertilization.** *The cell that forms when a sperm cell fertilizes an egg cell is called a* **zygote** (ZI goht). A zygote is the first cell of a new human. It contains genetic information from both the sperm and the ovum. The zygote will grow and develop in the female's reproductive system.

✅ **Reading Check** How do gametes enable humans to reproduce?

FOLDABLES

Make a horizontal two-tab book. Label it as shown, and glue it side by side to the back of the booklet made in Lessons 1 and 2. Use the book to organize information about the male and female reproductive systems.

Male Reproductive System | Female Reproductive System

WORD ORIGIN

zygote
from Greek *zygoun*, means "to join"

Hutchings Photography/Digital Light Source

 **Animation**

Male Reproductive System

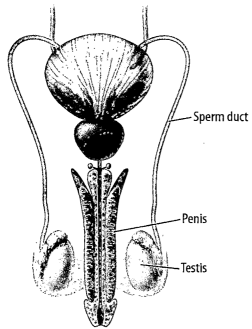

- Sperm duct
- Penis
- Testis

The organs of the male reproductive system produce sperm and deliver it to the female reproductive system.

Female Reproductive System

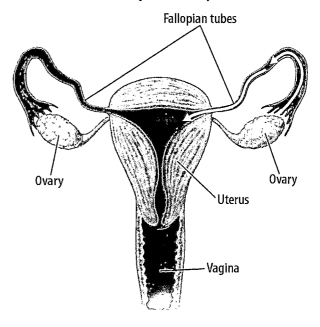

- Fallopian tubes
- Ovary
- Ovary
- Uterus
- Vagina

The female reproductive system produces eggs and provides a place for a new human to grow and develop before birth.

Figure 16 🔑 Males and females have specialized organs for reproduction.

The Male Reproductive System

The male reproductive system, shown in **Figure 16**, produces sperm and delivers it to the female reproductive system. Sperm are produced in the testes (TES teez; singular, testis). Sperm develop inside each testis and then are stored in tubes called sperm ducts. Sperm matures in the sperm ducts.

The testes also produce a hormone called testosterone. Testosterone helps sperm change from round cells to long, slender cells that can swim. Once sperm have fully developed, they can travel to the penis. The penis is a tubelike structure that delivers sperm to the female reproductive system. Sperm are transported in a fluid called semen (SEE mun). Semen contains millions of sperm and nutrients that provide the sperm with energy.

📝 **Key Concept Check** What does the male reproductive system do?

The Female Reproductive System

The female reproductive system contains two ovaries, as shown in **Figure 16**. Eggs grow and mature in the ovaries. Two hormones made by the ovaries, estrogen (ES truh jun) and progesterone (proh JES tuh rohn), help eggs mature. Once mature, eggs are released from the ovaries and enter the fallopian tubes. As shown in **Figure 16**, the fallopian tubes connect the ovaries to the uterus.

If sperm are also present in the fallopian tube, fertilization can occur as the egg enters the fallopian tube. Sperm enter the female reproductive system through the vagina, a tube-shaped organ that leads to the uterus. A fertilized egg, or zygote, can move through the fallopian tube and attach inside the uterus.

If there are no sperm in the fallopian tube, the egg will not be fertilized. However, it will still travel through the fallopian tube and uterus and then break down.

The Menstrual Cycle The endocrine system controls egg maturation and release and thickening of the lining of the uterus in a process called the menstrual (MEN stroo ul) cycle. The menstrual cycle takes about 28 days and has three parts.

During the first part of the cycle, eggs grow and mature and the thickened lining of the uterus leaves the body. In the second part of the cycle, mature eggs are released from the ovaries and the lining of the uterus thickens. In the third part of the cycle, unfertilized eggs and the thickened lining break down. The lining leaves the body in the first part of the next cycle.

 Key Concept Check What does the female reproductive system do?

Human Development

As shown in **Figure 17**, humans develop in many stages. You have read that when a sperm fertilizes an egg, a zygote forms. The zygote develops into an embryo (EM bree oh). An embryo is a ball-shaped structure that attaches inside the uterus and continues to grow.

The embryo develops into a fetus, the last stage before birth. It takes about 38 weeks for a fertilized egg to fully develop. This developmental period is called pregnancy. During this period, the organ systems of the fetus will develop and the fetus will get larger. Pregnancy ends with birth. During birth, the endocrine system releases hormones that help the uterus push the fetus through the vagina and out of the body.

Figure 17 During pregnancy, a unicellular zygote develops into a fetus.

Visual Check When is the heart fully formed?

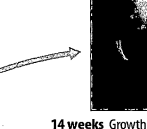

14 weeks Growth and development continue. The fetus is about 6 cm long.

8 weeks The embryo is about 2.5 cm long. The heart is fully formed and beating, bones are beginning to harden, and nearly all muscles have appeared.

16 weeks The fetus is about 15 cm long and about 140 g. The fetus can make a fist and has a range of facial expressions.

5 weeks The embryo is about 7 mm long. The heart and other organs have started to develop. The arms and legs are beginning to bud.

22 weeks The fetus is about 27 cm long and about 430 g. Footprints and fingerprints are forming.

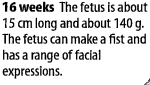

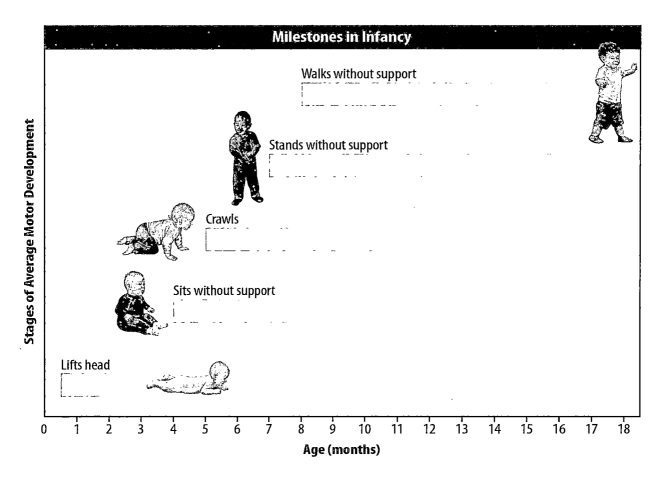

Milestones in Infancy

Stages of Average Motor Development

Walks without support

Stands without support

Crawls

Sits without support

Lifts head

0   1   2   3   4   5   6   7   8   9   10   11   12   13   14   15   16   17   18

Age (months)

△ **Figure 18** During infancy, a human learns to crawl and walk.

🔍 **Visual Check** When does an infant usually crawl?

Figure 19 🔑
Humans continue to change during adolescence and adulthood. ▼

From Birth Through Childhood

The first life stage after birth is infancy, the first 2 years of life. During infancy, the muscular and nervous systems develop and an infant begins walking, as shown in **Figure 18.** Growth and development continue in childhood, which is from about 2 years to about 12 years of age. Bones in the skeletal system grow longer and stronger, and the lymphatic system matures.

Adolescence Through Adulthood

Adolescence follows childhood. During adolescence, growth of the skeletal and muscular systems continues. Organs such as the lungs and kidneys get larger. As the endocrine system develops, the male and female reproductive systems mature. The period of time during which the reproductive system matures is called puberty.

After adolescence is adulthood, as shown in **Figure 19.** During adulthood, humans continue to change. In later adulthood, hair turns gray, wrinkles might form in the skin, and bones become weaker in a process called aging. Aging is a slow process that can last for decades.

✏️ **Key Concept Check** How do humans change during adulthood?

Digital Vision

Visual Summary

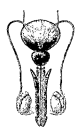 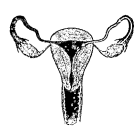

Sperm are produced in the testes, develop inside each testis, and then are stored in sperm ducts.

Eggs grow and mature in the ovaries.

During pregnancy, a zygote develops into an embryo and then into a fetus.

FOLDABLES

Use your lesson Foldable to review the lesson. Save your Foldable for the project at the end of the chapter.

What do you think NOW?

You first read the statements below at the beginning of the chapter.

5. The testes produce sperm.

6. Puberty occurs during infancy.

Did you change your mind about whether you agree or disagree with the statements? Rewrite any false statements to make them true.

Use Vocabulary

1 Sperm and ova are types of _____.

2 **Distinguish** between an ovum and a zygote.

3 **Define** *fertilization* in your own words.

Understand Key Concepts

4 The period between birth and 2 years is called
A. adolescence.   C. childhood.
B. adulthood.   D. infancy.

5 **Compare** the functions of the ovaries and the testes.

6 **Distinguish** between a zygote and a fetus.

Interpret Graphics

7 **Summarize** Copy and fill in the graphic organizer below to show the stages of life.

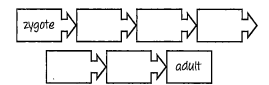

zygote → ☐ → ☐ → ☐
☐ → ☐ → adult

8 **Evaluate** the changes in aging using the photo below.

Critical Thinking

9 **Hypothesize** why development before birth takes a long time, about 38 weeks.

Materials

presentation materials

Model the Body Systems

You have learned about the functions of the different systems of the body. Your task is to find a real-life example of something that can be used as a model for the entire body, including all of its organ systems. You will illustrate this model and use it to describe how the various systems all work together to help the body function as a whole.

Question

What other real-life systems can be used to model the systems of the human body?

Procedure

1. Read and complete a lab safety form.

2. Think about the different systems that make up your body. In your Science Journal, make a table such as the one below. List each body system, and write a description of the role of each system in the body.

3. Discuss a model of the entire body with your teacher and the rest of the class. Note how each system is modeled in the example and how all the systems work together in the model as well.

4. Think of an example of your own. Write out a description of this model in your Science Journal.

5. Complete the last column of your table for the example you chose. Be creative and descriptive.

6. Create a visual display that illustrates your model. Use photos and other pictures to illustrate the different parts of the model system you created. Label each of these pictures to describe which body system they represent. Include a description of the function of each system on the labels.

7. Use the visual of your model to describe how the systems work together and maintain homeostasis. List the events that occur in your model as each system does its job properly.

Body System	Description of Activity	Model System
Circulatory	transport materials	

⑧ Use the information in your display to predict how your model would be affected if one of the systems did not function properly.

⑨ Use the model to explain how the entire model would be affected if one of the "body systems" did not work properly. Write out a list of events for this scenario.

Analyze and Conclude

⑩ **Analyze** Is there a system that is not included in your model? Explain why some functions are easier to model than others.

⑪ **Assess** How do the systems in your model respond to changes in the environment?

⑫ **Evaluate** How successful was your model in illustrating the effects of having parts of the system break down?

⑬ **The Big Idea** How do all of the systems in your model work together to help the model as a whole?

Communicate Your Results

Share your model with the class. Discuss the parts of your model with other students, and compare the ways you chose to model the same systems.

In real life, human body systems might have problems that cause them to fail. Doctors often fix a body system that no longer functions by replacing failing organs with donated ones. Investigate how doctors use donated organs. Look for a recent news article in which someone's life was saved by one of these procedures. Write a brief summary of what you found, and describe the procedure using your model.

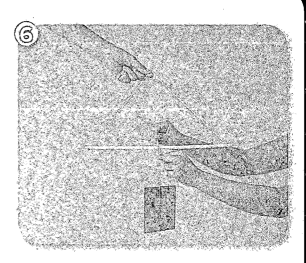

Lab Tips

☑ Use the descriptions in your table to help you come up with the different parts of your model. Remember that your model represents general functions.

☑ Use magazines, pictures, or other visuals to illustrate your model. Don't forget to label the parts of the model. Be as descriptive as possible with the labels.

☑ Make sure the parts of your model connect to each other as part of the larger picture.

Remember to use scientific methods.

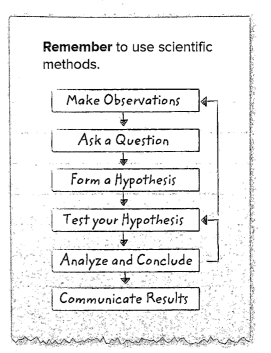

Make Observations
↓
Ask a Question
↓
Form a Hypothesis
↓
Test your Hypothesis
↓
Analyze and Conclude
↓
Communicate Results

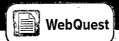 WebQuest

Human body systems transport materials; defend against pathogens; provide structure, movement, and control; and enable the species to survive.

Key Concepts Summary

Vocabulary

Lesson 1: Transport and Defense

- Nutrients enter the body through the digestive system. Wastes and water leave the body through the excretory system. Oxygen enters the body and carbon dioxide leaves the body through the respiratory system.
- Substances such as **nutrients** and oxygen reach the body's cells through the circulatory system.
- The lymphatic system helps the body defend itself against harmful invaders.

organ system p. 571

homeostasis p. 571

nutrient p. 573

Calorie p. 573

lymphocyte p. 579

immunity p. 580

Lesson 2: Structure, Movement, and Control

- The muscular system and the skeletal system work together and help the body move. The skeletal system provides the body with structure and protects other organ systems.
- The nervous system and the endocrine system work together and help the body respond to changes in the environment.

compact bone p. 586

spongy bone p. 586

neuron p. 588

reflex p. 589

hormone p. 591

Lesson 3: Reproduction and Development

- The male and female reproductive systems ensure survival of the human species.
- Humans develop and grow both before and after birth.

reproduction p. 595

gamete p. 595

sperm p. 595

ovum p. 595

fertilization p. 595

zygote p. 595

FOLDABLES® Chapter Project

Assemble your lesson Foldables as shown to make a Chapter Project. Use the project to review what you have learned in this chapter.

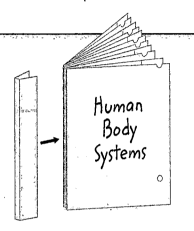

Human Body Systems

Use Vocabulary

1 Carbohydrates, fats, and proteins are all _____ and contain _____.

2 The thymus and the spleen produce white blood cells called _____.

3 Bones in the skeletal system are made of a hard exterior called _____.

4 Define the term *hormone* in your own words.

5 Use the terms *reproduction* and *fertilization* in a sentence.

6 Distinguish between ova and sperm.

Link Vocabulary and Key Concepts

▷ **Interactive Concept Map**

Copy this concept map, and then use vocabulary terms from the previous page to complete the concept map.

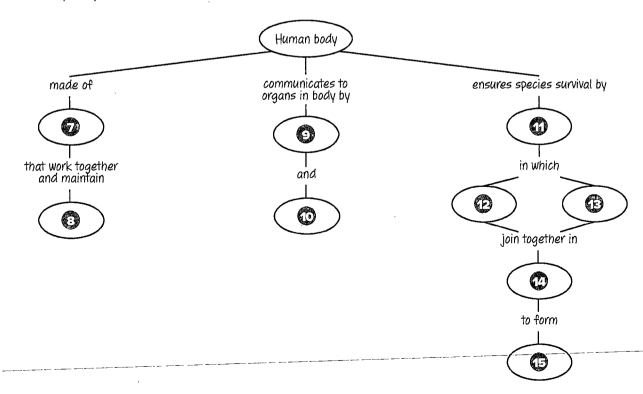

Understand Key Concepts

1 Which body system removes carbon dioxide and waste?
A. circulatory
B. digestive
C. excretory
D. lymphatic

2 Which body system makes immune cells?
A. circulatory
B. digestive
C. excretory
D. lymphatic

3 Which are bundles of cells in the lungs that take in oxygen?
A. alveoli
B. bronchi
C. nostrils
D. trachea

4 Which are proteins that recognize specific proteins on bacteria?
A. antibodies
B. enzymes
C. nutrients
D. receptors

5 Which part of the nervous system is shown below?

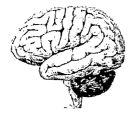

A. brain
B. neuron
C. peripheral nerve
D. spinal cord

6 Which is NOT a type of blood vessel?
A. artery
B. capillary
C. spleen
D. vein

7 Which is NOT a type of muscle tissue?
A. cardiac
B. lymphatic
C. skeletal
D. smooth

8 Which is a part of the skeletal system?
A. ligament
B. spleen
C. thymus
D. trachea

9 Which hormone helps the cells produced in the system below mature?

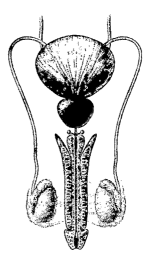

A. estrogen
B. insulin
C. progesterone
D. testosterone

10 Which connects the ovaries to the uterus?
A. bladder
B. cervix
C. fallopian tubes
D. seminiferous tubules

11 Which system works with the reproductive system?
A. endocrine
B. excretory
C. respiratory
D. skeletal

Critical Thinking

12 **Relate** the body's organization to how homeostasis is maintained.

13 **Describe** the roles of the structure shown below in digestion.

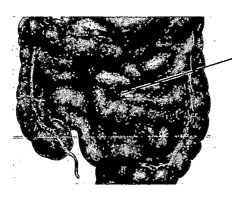

Small intestine

14 **Compare** the functions of lymphatic vessels and blood vessels.

15 **Hypothesize** how an injury to the spinal cord might affect the ability of the nervous system to sense and respond to a change in the environment.

16 **Assess** how the nervous system helps the muscular system control heart rate, digestion, and respiration.

17 **Relate** the organs of the lymphatic system to immunity.

18 **Assess** the role of the skeletal system in the storage of nutrients.

19 **Summarize** the role of puberty in the transition from adolescence to adulthood.

20 **Compare** the functions of the male and female reproductive systems.

Writing in Science

21 **Write** a five-sentence paragraph that distinguishes the two main types of diseases. Be sure to include a topic sentence and a concluding sentence in your paragraph.

REVIEW THE BIG IDEA

22 How do organ systems help the body function?

23 The photo below shows parts of the digestive system, the skeletal system, the muscular system, and the nervous system. What are the functions of these systems?

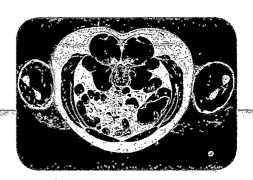

Math Skills

Math Practice

Use Proportions

24 Which type of chicken in the table below has the fewest Calories per gram?

Food	Mass (g)	Calories (C)
$\frac{1}{2}$ chicken breast, baked	86	140
1 chicken leg, baked	52	112

25 A small 140-g apple and a 100-g banana each provide 70 C of energy. How many Calories would there be in a 200-g serving of fruit salad that contained equal amounts of apple and banana? [Hint: Add the values for the apple and the banana first.]

Record your answers on the answer sheet provided by your teacher or on a sheet of paper.

Multiple Choice

1. In which part of the digestive system does absorption of nutrients occur?

   A. esophagus

   B. liver

   C. small intestine

   D. stomach

2. After food enters the mouth, which path does it travel through the digestive system?

   A. esophagus → stomach → small intestine → large intestine → rectum

   B. large intestine → small intestine → stomach → esophagus → rectum

   C. small intestine → large intestine → esophagus → stomach → pancreas

   D. stomach → esophagus → small intestine → large intestine → liver

Use the diagram below to answer question 3.

3. What body system is made of the basic unit shown in the diagram?

   A. circulatory system

   B. endocrine system

   C. muscular system

   D. nervous system

4. Which body system provides protection from infection and toxins?

   A. circulatory system

   B. digestive system

   C. excretory system

   D. lymphatic system

5. Which two systems work together to make your body move?

   A. digestive system and skeletal system

   B. lymphatic system and digestive system

   C. nervous system and excretory system

   D. skeletal system and muscular system

Use the image below to answer question 6.

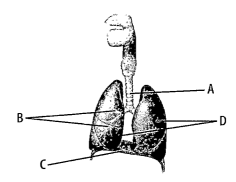

6. Which letter shows the muscle that contracts during inhalation and relaxes during exhalation?

   A. A

   B. B

   C. C

   D. D

7. What role do alveoli play in the body?

   A. They form urea.

   B. They produce lymphocytes.

   C. They connect the right atrium to the right ventricle

   D. They move oxygen into the circulatory system.

8. What is the human development period between 2 years and 12 years called?

   A. adolescence

   B. adulthood

   C. childhood

   D. infancy

Use the diagram below to answer question 9.

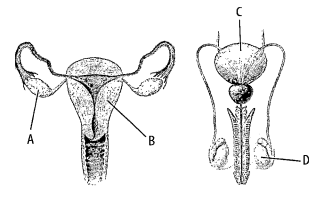

9. Which structure produces male gametes?

   A. A

   B. B

   C. C

   D. D

Constructed Response

Use the figure below to answer questions 10 and 11.

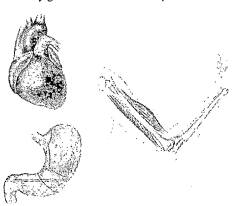

10. Identify the type of muscle shown in each image above.

11. Which muscles are under voluntary control of the nervous system? Which are involuntary? Explain your answer.

12. Which body system would be most likely affected by a diet that includes too little calcium? Explain your answer.

13. Describe how the endocrine system and reproductive system are related.

NEED EXTRA HELP?													
If You Missed Question...	1	2	3	4	5	6	7	8	9	10	11	12	13
Go to Lesson...	1	1	2	1	2	1	1	3	3	2	2	1, 2	2, 3

Student Resources

For Students and Parents/Guardians

These resources are designed to help you achieve success in science. You will find useful information on laboratory safety, math skills, and science skills. In addition, science reference materials are found in the Reference Handbook. You'll find the information you need to learn and sharpen your skills in these resources.

Table of Contents

Scientific Methods

Scientists use an orderly approach called the scientific method to solve problems. This includes organizing and recording data so others can understand them. Scientists use many variations in this method when they solve problems.

Identify a Question

The first step in a scientific investigation or experiment is to identify a question to be answered or a problem to be solved. For example, you might ask which gasoline is the most efficient.

Gather and Organize Information

After you have identified your question, begin gathering and organizing information. There are many ways to gather information, such as researching in a library, interviewing those knowledgeable about the subject, and testing and working in the laboratory and field. Fieldwork is investigations and observations done outside of a laboratory.

Researching Information Before moving in a new direction, it is important to gather the information that already is known about the subject. Start by asking yourself questions to determine exactly what you need to know. Then you will look for the information in various reference sources, like the student is doing in **Figure 1.** Some sources may include textbooks, encyclopedias, government documents, professional journals, science magazines, and the Internet. Always list the sources of your information.

Figure 1 The Internet can be a valuable research tool.

Evaluate Sources of Information Not all sources of information are reliable. You should evaluate all of your sources of information, and use only those you know to be dependable. For example, if you are researching ways to make homes more energy efficient, a site written by the U.S. Department of Energy would be more reliable than a site written by a company that is trying to sell a new type of weatherproofing material. Also, remember that research always is changing. Consult the most current resources available to you. For example, a 1985 resource about saving energy would not reflect the most recent findings.

Sometimes scientists use data that they did not collect themselves, or conclusions drawn by other researchers. This data must be evaluated carefully. Ask questions about how the data were obtained, if the investigation was carried out properly, and if it has been duplicated exactly with the same results. Would you reach the same conclusion from the data? Only when you have confidence in the data can you believe it is true and feel comfortable using it.

Interpret Scientific Illustrations As you research a topic in science, you will see drawings, diagrams, and photographs to help you understand what you read. Some illustrations are included to help you understand an idea that you can't see easily by yourself, like the tiny particles in an atom in **Figure 2.** A drawing helps many people to remember details more easily and provides examples that clarify difficult concepts or give additional information about the topic you are studying. Most illustrations have labels or a caption to identify or to provide more information.

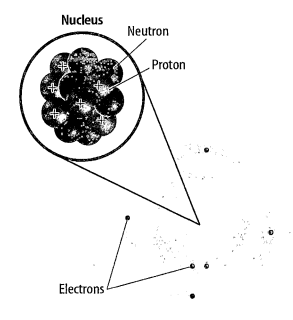

Figure 2 This drawing shows an atom of carbon with its six protons, six neutrons, and six electrons.

Concept Maps One way to organize data is to draw a diagram that shows relationships among ideas (or concepts). A concept map can help make the meanings of ideas and terms more clear, and help you understand and remember what you are studying. Concept maps are useful for breaking large concepts down into smaller parts, making learning easier.

Network Tree A type of concept map that not only shows a relationship, but how the concepts are related is a network tree, shown in **Figure 3.** In a network tree, the words are written in the ovals, while the description of the type of relationship is written across the connecting lines.

When constructing a network tree, write down the topic and all major topics on separate pieces of paper or notecards. Then arrange them in order from general to specific. Branch the related concepts from the major concept and describe the relationship on the connecting line. Continue to more specific concepts until finished.

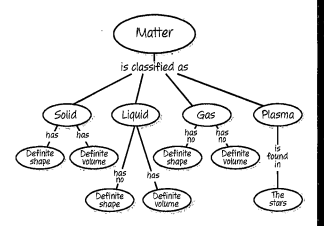

Figure 3 A network tree shows how concepts or objects are related.

Events Chain Another type of concept map is an events chain. Sometimes called a flow chart, it models the order or sequence of items. An events chain can be used to describe a sequence of events, the steps in a procedure, or the stages of a process.

When making an events chain, first find the one event that starts the chain. This event is called the initiating event. Then, find the next event and continue until the outcome is reached, as shown in **Figure 4** on the next page.

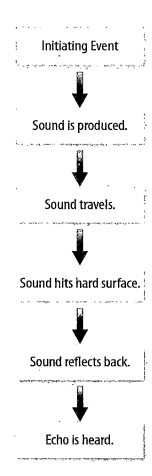

Figure 4 Events-chain concept maps show the order of steps in a process or event. This concept map shows how a sound makes an echo.

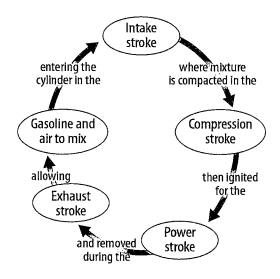

Figure 5 A cycle map shows events that occur in a cycle.

Cycle Map A specific type of events chain is a cycle map. It is used when the series of events do not produce a final outcome, but instead relate back to the beginning event, such as in **Figure 5.** Therefore, the cycle repeats itself.

To make a cycle map, first decide what event is the beginning event. This is also called the initiating event. Then list the next events in the order that they occur, with the last event relating back to the initiating event. Words can be written between the events that describe what happens from one event to the next. The number of events in a cycle map can vary, but usually contain three or more events.

Spider Map A type of concept map that you can use for brainstorming is the spider map. When you have a central idea, you might find that you have a jumble of ideas that relate to it but are not necessarily clearly related to each other. The spider map on sound in **Figure 6** shows that if you write these ideas outside the main concept, then you can begin to separate and group unrelated terms so they become more useful.

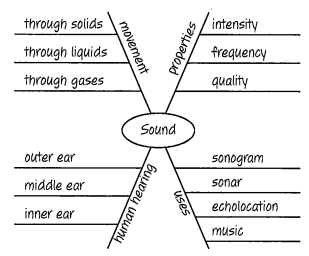

Figure 6 A spider map allows you to list ideas that relate to a central topic but not necessarily to one another.

SCIENCE SKILL HANDBOOK

MATH SKILL HANDBOOK

FOLDABLES HANDBOOK

REFERENCE HANDBOOK

GLOSSARY/ GLOSARIO

INDEX

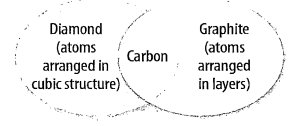

Figure 7 This Venn diagram compares and contrasts two substances made from carbon.

Venn Diagram To illustrate how two subjects compare and contrast you can use a Venn diagram. You can see the characteristics that the subjects have in common and those that they do not, shown in **Figure 7.**

To create a Venn diagram, draw two overlapping ovals that are big enough to write in. List the characteristics unique to one subject in one oval, and the characteristics of the other subject in the other oval. The characteristics in common are listed in the overlapping section.

Make and Use Tables One way to organize information so it is easier to understand is to use a table. Tables can contain numbers, words, or both.

To make a table, list the items to be compared in the first column and the characteristics to be compared in the first row. The title should clearly indicate the content of the table, and the column or row heads should be clear. Notice that in **Table 1** the units are included.

Table 1 Recyclables Collected During Week			
Day of Week	Paper (kg)	Aluminum (kg)	Glass (kg)
Monday	5.0	4.0	12.0
Wednesday	4.0	1.0	10.0
Friday	2.5	2.0	10.0

Make a Model One way to help you better understand the parts of a structure, the way a process works, or to show things too large or small for viewing is to make a model. For example, an atomic model made of a plastic-ball nucleus and chenille stem electron shells can help you visualize how the parts of an atom relate to each other. Other types of models can be devised on a computer or represented by equations.

Form a Hypothesis

A possible explanation based on previous knowledge and observations is called a hypothesis. After researching gasoline types and recalling previous experiences in your family's car, you form a hypothesis—our car runs more efficiently because we use premium gasoline. To be valid, a hypothesis has to be something you can test by using an investigation.

Predict When you apply a hypothesis to a specific situation, you predict something about that situation. A prediction makes a statement in advance, based on prior observation, experience, or scientific reasoning. People use predictions to make everyday decisions. Scientists test predictions by performing investigations. Based on previous observations and experiences, you might form a prediction that cars are more efficient with premium gasoline. The prediction can be tested in an investigation.

Design an Experiment A scientist needs to make many decisions before beginning an investigation. Some of these include: how to carry out the investigation, what steps to follow, how to record the data, and how the investigation will answer the question. It also is important to address any safety concerns.

SCIENCE SKILL HANDBOOK

MATH SKILL HANDBOOK

FOLDABLES HANDBOOK

REFERENCE HANDBOOK

GLOSSARY/ GLOSARIO

INDEX

SCIENCE SKILL HANDBOOK

MATH SKILL HANDBOOK

FOLDABLES HANDBOOK

REFERENCE HANDBOOK

GLOSSARY/ GLOSARIO

INDEX

Test the Hypothesis

Now that you have formed your hypothesis, you need to test it. Using an investigation, you will make observations and collect data, or information. This data might either support or not support your hypothesis. Scientists collect and organize data as numbers and descriptions.

Follow a Procedure In order to know what materials to use, as well as how and in what order to use them, you must follow a procedure. **Figure 8** shows a procedure you might follow to test your hypothesis.

Procedure
Step 1   Use regular gasoline for two weeks.
Step 2   Record the number of kilometers between fill-ups and the amount of gasoline used.
Step 3   Switch to premium gasoline for two weeks.
Step 4   Record the number of kilometers between fill-ups and the amount of gasoline used.

Figure 8 A procedure tells you what to do step-by-step.

Identify and Manipulate Variables and Controls In any experiment, it is important to keep everything the same except for the item you are testing. The one factor you change is called the independent variable. The change that results is the dependent variable. Make sure you have only one independent variable, to assure yourself of the cause of the changes you observe in the dependent variable. For example, in your gasoline experiment the type of fuel is the independent variable. The dependent variable is the efficiency.

Many experiments also have a control— an individual instance or experimental subject for which the independent variable is not changed. You can then compare the test results to the control results. To design a control you must have two cars of the same type. The control car uses regular gasoline for four weeks. After you are done with the test, you can compare the experimental results to the control results.

Collect Data

Whether you are carrying out an investigation or a short observational experiment, you will collect data, as shown in **Figure 9.** Scientists collect data as numbers and descriptions and organize them in specific ways.

Observe Scientists observe items and events, then record what they see. When they use only words to describe an observation, it is called qualitative data. Scientists' observations also can describe how much there is of something. These observations use numbers, as well as words, in the description and are called quantitative data. For example, if a sample of the element gold is described as being "shiny and very dense" the data are qualitative. Quantitative data on this sample of gold might include "a mass of 30 g and a density of 19.3 g/cm^3."

Figure 9 Collecting data is one way to gather information directly.

Figure 10 Record data neatly and clearly so it is easy to understand.

When you make observations, you should examine the entire object or situation first, and then look carefully for details. It is important to record observations accurately and completely. Always record your notes immediately as you make them, so you do not miss details or make a mistake when recording results from memory. Never put unidentified observations on scraps of paper. Instead they should be recorded in a notebook, like the one in **Figure 10.** Write your data neatly so you can easily read it later. At each point in the experiment, record your observations and label them. That way, you will not have to determine what the figures mean when you look at your notes later. Set up any tables that you will need to use ahead of time, so you can record any observations right away. Remember to avoid bias when collecting data by not including personal thoughts when you record observations. Record only what you observe.

Estimate Scientific work also involves estimating. To estimate is to make a judgment about the size or the number of something without measuring or counting. This is important when the number or size of an object or population is too large or too difficult to accurately count or measure.

Sample Scientists may use a sample or a portion of the total number as a type of estimation. To sample is to take a small, representative portion of the objects or organisms of a population for research. By making careful observations or manipulating variables within that portion of the group, information is discovered and conclusions are drawn that might apply to the whole population. A poorly chosen sample can be unrepresentative of the whole. If you were trying to determine the rainfall in an area, it would not be best to take a rainfall sample from under a tree.

Measure You use measurements every day. Scientists also take measurements when collecting data. When taking measurements, it is important to know how to use measuring tools properly. Accuracy also is important.

Length The SI unit for length is the meter (m). Smaller measurements might be measured in centimeters or millimeters.

Length is measured using a metric ruler or meterstick. When using a metric ruler, line up the 0-cm mark with the end of the object being measured and read the number of the unit where the object ends. Look at the metric ruler shown in **Figure 11.** The centimeter lines are the long, numbered lines, and the shorter lines are millimeter lines. In this instance, the length would be 4.50 cm.

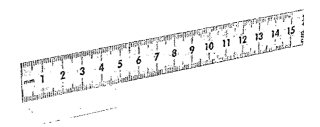

Figure 11 This metric ruler has centimeter and millimeter divisions.

SCIENCE SKILL HANDBOOK

MATH SKILL HANDBOOK

FOLDABLES HANDBOOK

REFERENCE HANDBOOK

GLOSSARY/ GLOSARIO

INDEX

Mass The SI unit for mass is the kilogram (kg). Scientists can measure mass using units formed by adding metric prefixes to the unit gram (g), such as milligram (mg). To measure mass, you might use a triple-beam balance similar to the one shown in **Figure 12.** The balance has a pan on one side and a set of beams on the other side. Each beam has a rider that slides on the beam.

When using a triple-beam balance, place an object on the pan. Slide the largest rider along its beam until the pointer drops below zero. Then move it back one notch. Repeat the process for each rider proceeding from the larger to smaller until the pointer swings an equal distance above and below the zero point. Sum the masses on each beam to find the mass of the object. Move all riders back to zero when finished.

Instead of putting materials directly on the balance, scientists often take a tare of a container. A tare is the mass of a container into which objects or substances are placed for measuring their masses. To find the mass of objects or substances, find the mass of a clean container. Remove the container from the pan, and place the object or substances in the container. Find the mass of the container with the materials in it. Subtract the mass of the empty container from the mass of the filled container to find the mass of the materials you are using.

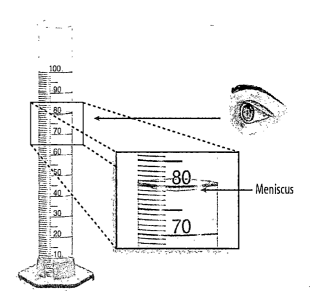

Figure 13 Graduated cylinders measure liquid volume.

Liquid Volume The SI unit for measuring liquids is the liter (l). When a smaller unit is needed, scientists might use a milliliter. Because a milliliter takes up the volume of a cube measuring 1 cm on each side it also can be called a cubic centimeter ($cm^3 = cm \times cm \times cm$).

You can use beakers and graduated cylinders to measure liquid volume. A graduated cylinder, shown in **Figure 13,** is marked from bottom to top in milliliters. In lab, you might use a 10-mL graduated cylinder or a 100-mL graduated cylinder. When measuring liquids, notice that the liquid has a curved surface. Look at the surface at eye level, and measure the bottom of the curve. This is called the meniscus. The graduated cylinder in **Figure 13** contains 79.0 mL, or 79.0 cm^3, of a liquid.

Temperature Scientists often measure temperature using the Celsius scale. Pure water has a freezing point of 0°C and boiling point of 100°C. The unit of measurement is degrees Celsius. Two other scales often used are the Fahrenheit and Kelvin scales.

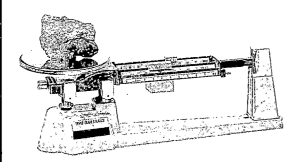

Figure 12 A triple-beam balance is used to determine the mass of an object.

SCIENCE SKILL HANDBOOK

MATH SKILL HANDBOOK

FOLDABLES HANDBOOK

REFERENCE HANDBOOK

GLOSSARY/ GLOSARIO

INDEX

StudiOhio

Figure 14 A thermometer measures the temperature of an object.

Scientists use a thermometer to measure temperature. Most thermometers in a laboratory are glass tubes with a bulb at the bottom end containing a liquid such as colored alcohol. The liquid rises or falls with a change in temperature. To read a glass thermometer like the thermometer in **Figure 14,** rotate it slowly until a red line appears. Read the temperature where the red line ends.

Form Operational Definitions

An operational definition defines an object by how it functions, works, or behaves. For example, when you are playing hide and seek and a tree is home base, you have created an operational definition for a tree.

Objects can have more than one operational definition. For example, a ruler can be defined as a tool that measures the length of an object (how it is used). It can also be a tool with a series of marks used as a standard when measuring (how it works).

Analyze the Data

To determine the meaning of your observations and investigation results, you will need to look for patterns in the data. Then you must think critically to determine what the data mean. Scientists use several approaches when they analyze the data they have collected and recorded. Each approach is useful for identifying specific patterns.

Interpret Data

The word *interpret* means "to explain the meaning of something." When analyzing data from an experiment, try to find out what the data show. Identify the control group and the test group to see whether changes in the independent variable have had an effect. Look for differences in the dependent variable between the control and test groups.

Classify

Sorting objects or events into groups based on common features is called classifying. When classifying, first observe the objects or events to be classified. Then select one feature that is shared by some members in the group, but not by all. Place those members that share that feature in a subgroup. You can classify members into smaller and smaller subgroups based on characteristics. Remember that when you classify, you are grouping objects or events for a purpose. Keep your purpose in mind as you select the features to form groups and subgroups.

Compare and Contrast

Observations can be analyzed by noting the similarities and differences between two or more objects or events that you observe. When you look at objects or events to see how they are similar, you are comparing them. Contrasting is looking for differences in objects or events.

Recognize Cause and Effect A cause is a reason for an action or condition. The effect is that action or condition. When two events happen together, it is not necessarily true that one event caused the other. Scientists must design a controlled investigation to recognize the exact cause and effect.

Draw Conclusions

When scientists have analyzed the data they collected, they proceed to draw conclusions about the data. These conclusions are sometimes stated in words similar to the hypothesis that you formed earlier. They may confirm a hypothesis, or lead you to a new hypothesis.

Infer Scientists often make inferences based on their observations. An inference is an attempt to explain observations or to indicate a cause. An inference is not a fact, but a logical conclusion that needs further investigation. For example, you may infer that a fire has caused smoke. Until you investigate, however, you do not know for sure.

Apply When you draw a conclusion, you must apply those conclusions to determine whether the data supports the hypothesis. If your data do not support your hypothesis, it does not mean that the hypothesis is wrong. It means only that the result of the investigation did not support the hypothesis. Maybe the experiment needs to be redesigned, or some of the initial observations on which the hypothesis was based were incomplete or biased. Perhaps more observation or research is needed to refine your hypothesis. A successful investigation does not always come out the way you originally predicted.

Avoid Bias Sometimes a scientific investigation involves making judgments. When you make a judgment, you form an opinion. It is important to be honest and not to allow any expectations of results to bias your judgments. This is important throughout the entire investigation, from researching to collecting data to drawing conclusions.

Communicate

The communication of ideas is an important part of the work of scientists. A discovery that is not reported will not advance the scientific community's understanding or knowledge. Communication among scientists also is important as a way of improving their investigations.

Scientists communicate in many ways, from writing articles in journals and magazines that explain their investigations and experiments, to announcing important discoveries on television and radio. Scientists also share ideas with colleagues on the Internet or present them as lectures, like the student is doing in **Figure 15.**

Figure 15 A student communicates to his peers about his investigation.

Aaron Haupt

These safety symbols are used in laboratory and field investigations in this book to indicate possible hazards. Learn the meaning of each symbol and refer to this page often. *Remember to wash your hands thoroughly after completing lab procedures.*

PROTECTIVE EQUIPMENT Do not begin any lab without the proper protection equipment.

GOGGLES	Proper eye protection must be worn when performing or observing science activities that involve items or conditions as listed below.	**APRON** Wear an approved apron when using substances that could stain, wet, or destroy cloth.	**SOAP** Wash hands with soap and water before removing goggles and after all lab activities.	**GLOVES** Wear gloves when working with biological materials, chemicals, animals, or materials that can stain or irritate hands.

LABORATORY HAZARDS

Symbols	Potential Hazards	Precaution	Response
DISPOSAL	contamination of classroom or environment due to improper disposal of materials such as chemicals and live specimens	• DO NOT dispose of hazardous materials in the sink or trash can. • Dispose of wastes as directed by your teacher.	• If hazardous materials are disposed of improperly, notify your teacher immediately.
EXTREME TEMPERATURE	skin burns due to extremely hot or cold materials such as hot glass, liquids, or metals; liquid nitrogen; dry ice	• Use proper protective equipment, such as hot mitts and/or tongs, when handling objects with extreme temperatures.	• If injury occurs, notify your teacher immediately.
SHARP OBJECTS	punctures or cuts from sharp objects such as razor blades, pins, scalpels, and broken glass	• Handle glassware carefully to avoid breakage. • Walk with sharp objects pointed downward, away from you and others.	• If broken glass or injury occurs, notify your teacher immediately.
ELECTRICAL	electric shock or skin burn due to improper grounding, short circuits, liquid spills, or exposed wires	• Check condition of wires and apparatus for fraying or uninsulated wires, and broken or cracked equipment. • Use only GFCI-protected outlets	• DO NOT attempt to fix electrical problems. Notify your teacher immediately.
CHEMICAL	skin irritation or burns, breathing difficulty, and/or poisoning due to touching, swallowing, or inhalation of chemicals such as acids, bases, bleach, metal compounds, iodine, poinsettias, pollen, ammonia, acetone, nail polish remover, heated chemicals, mothballs, and any other chemicals labeled or known to be dangerous	• Wear proper protective equipment such as goggles, apron, and gloves when using chemicals. • Ensure proper room ventilation or use a fume hood when using materials that produce fumes. • NEVER smell fumes directly. • NEVER taste or eat any material in the laboratory.	• If contact occurs, immediately flush affected area with water and notify your teacher. • If a spill occurs, leave the area immediately and notify your teacher.
FLAMMABLE	unexpected fire due to liquids or gases that ignite easily such as rubbing alcohol	• Avoid open flames, sparks, or heat when flammable liquids are present.	• If a fire occurs, leave the area immediately and notify your teacher.
OPEN FLAME	burns or fire due to open flame from matches, Bunsen burners, or burning materials	• Tie back loose hair and clothing. • Keep flame away from all materials. • Follow teacher instructions when lighting and extinguishing flames. • Use proper protection, such as hot mitts or tongs, when handling hot objects.	• If a fire occurs, leave the area immediately and notify your teacher.
ANIMAL SAFETY	injury to or from laboratory animals	• Wear proper protective equipment such as gloves, apron, and goggles when working with animals. • Wash hands after handling animals.	• If injury occurs, notify your teacher immediately.
BIOLOGICAL	infection or adverse reaction due to contact with organisms such as bacteria, fungi, and biological materials such as blood, animal or plant materials	• Wear proper protective equipment such as gloves, goggles, and apron when working with biological materials. • Avoid skin contact with an organism or any part of the organism. • Wash hands after handling organisms.	• If contact occurs, wash the affected area and notify your teacher immediately.
FUME	breathing difficulties from inhalation of fumes from substances such as ammonia, acetone, nail polish remover, heated chemicals, and mothballs	• Wear goggles, apron, and gloves. • Ensure proper room ventilation or use a fume hood when using substances that produce fumes. • NEVER smell fumes directly.	• If a spill occurs, leave area and notify your teacher immediately.
IRRITANT	irritation of skin, mucous membranes, or respiratory tract due to materials such as acids, bases, bleach, pollen, mothballs, steel wool, and potassium permanganate	• Wear goggles, apron, and gloves. • Wear a dust mask to protect against fine particles.	• If skin contact occurs, immediately flush the affected area with water and notify your teacher.
RADIOACTIVE	excessive exposure from alpha, beta, and gamma particles	• Remove gloves and wash hands with soap and water before removing remainder of protective equipment.	• If cracks or holes are found in the container, notify your teacher immediately.

Safety in the Science Laboratory

Introduction to Science Safety

The science laboratory is a safe place to work if you follow standard safety procedures. Being responsible for your own safety helps to make the entire laboratory a safer place for everyone. When performing any lab, read and apply the caution statements and safety symbol listed at the beginning of the lab.

General Safety Rules

1. Complete the *Lab Safety Form* or other safety contract BEFORE starting any science lab.

2. Study the procedure. Ask your teacher any questions. Be sure you understand safety symbols shown on the page.

3. Notify your teacher about allergies or other health conditions that can affect your participation in a lab.

4. Learn and follow use and safety procedures for your equipment. If unsure, ask your teacher.

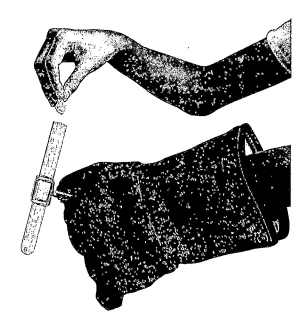

5. Never eat, drink, chew gum, apply cosmetics, or do any personal grooming in the lab. Never use lab glassware as food or drink containers. Keep your hands away from your face and mouth.

6. Know the location and proper use of the safety shower, eye wash, fire blanket, and fire alarm.

Prevent Accidents

1. Use the safety equipment provided to you. Goggles and a safety apron should be worn during investigations.

2. Do NOT use hair spray, mousse, or other flammable hair products. Tie back long hair and tie down loose clothing.

3. Do NOT wear sandals or other open-toed shoes in the lab.

4. Remove jewelry on hands and wrists. Loose jewelry, such as chains and long necklaces, should be removed to prevent them from getting caught in equipment.

5. Do not taste any substances or draw any material into a tube with your mouth.

6. Proper behavior is expected in the lab. Practical jokes and fooling around can lead to accidents and injury.

7. Keep your work area uncluttered.

Laboratory Work

1. Collect and carry all equipment and materials to your work area before beginning a lab.

2. Remain in your own work area unless given permission by your teacher to leave it.

KS Studios

3. Always slant test tubes away from yourself and others when heating them, adding substances to them, or rinsing them.

4. If instructed to smell a substance in a container, hold the container a short distance away and fan vapors toward your nose.

5. Do NOT substitute other chemicals/substances for those in the materials list unless instructed to do so by your teacher.

6. Do NOT take any materials or chemicals outside of the laboratory.

7. Stay out of storage areas unless instructed to be there and supervised by your teacher.

Laboratory Cleanup

1. Turn off all burners, water, and gas, and disconnect all electrical devices.

2. Clean all pieces of equipment and return all materials to their proper places.

3. Dispose of chemicals and other materials as directed by your teacher. Place broken glass and solid substances in the proper containers. Never discard materials in the sink.

4. Clean your work area.

5. Wash your hands with soap and water thoroughly BEFORE removing your goggles.

Emergencies

1. Report any fire, electrical shock, glassware breakage, spill, or injury, no matter how small, to your teacher immediately. Follow his or her instructions.

2. If your clothing should catch fire, STOP, DROP, and ROLL. If possible, smother it with the fire blanket or get under a safety shower. NEVER RUN.

3. If a fire should occur, turn off all gas and leave the room according to established procedures.

4. In most instances, your teacher will clean up spills. Do NOT attempt to clean up spills unless you are given permission and instructions to do so.

5. If chemicals come into contact with your eyes or skin, notify your teacher immediately. Use the eyewash, or flush your skin or eyes with large quantities of water.

6. The fire extinguisher and first-aid kit should only be used by your teacher unless it is an extreme emergency and you have been given permission.

7. If someone is injured or becomes ill, only a professional medical provider or someone certified in first aid should perform first-aid procedures.

SCIENCE SKILL HANDBOOK

MATH SKILL HANDBOOK

FOLDABLES HANDBOOK

REFERENCE HANDBOOK

GLOSSARY/ GLOSARIO

INDEX

Math Review

Use Fractions

A fraction compares a part to a whole. In the fraction $\frac{2}{3}$, the 2 represents the part and is the numerator. The 3 represents the whole and is the denominator.

Reduce Fractions To reduce a fraction, you must find the largest factor that is common to both the numerator and the denominator, the greatest common factor (GCF). Divide both numbers by the GCF. The fraction has then been reduced, or it is in its simplest form.

Example

Twelve of the 20 chemicals in the science lab are in powder form. What fraction of the chemicals used in the lab are in powder form?

Step 1 Write the fraction.

$$\frac{part}{whole} = \frac{12}{20}$$

Step 2 To find the GCF of the numerator and denominator, list all of the factors of each number.

Factors of 12: 1, 2, 3, 4, 6, 12 (the numbers that divide evenly into 12)

Factors of 20: 1, 2, 4, 5, 10, 20 (the numbers that divide evenly into 20)

Step 3 List the common factors.

1, 2, 4

Step 4 Choose the greatest factor in the list. The GCF of 12 and 20 is 4.

Step 5 Divide the numerator and denominator by the GCF.

$$\frac{12 \div 4}{20 \div 4} = \frac{3}{5}$$

In the lab, $\frac{3}{5}$ of the chemicals are in powder form.

Practice Problem At an amusement park, 66 of 90 rides have a height restriction. What fraction of the rides, in its simplest form, has a height restriction?

Add and Subtract Fractions with Like Denominators

To add or subtract fractions with the same denominator, add or subtract the numerators and write the sum or difference over the denominator. After finding the sum or difference, find the simplest form for your fraction.

Example 1

In the forest outside your house, $\frac{1}{8}$ of the animals are rabbits, $\frac{3}{8}$ are squirrels, and the remainder are birds and insects. How many are mammals?

Step 1 Add the numerators.

$$\frac{1}{8} + \frac{3}{8} = \frac{(1 + 3)}{8} = \frac{4}{8}$$

Step 2 Find the GCF.

$$\frac{4}{8} \text{ (GCF, 4)}$$

Step 3 Divide the numerator and denominator by the GCF.

$$\frac{4 \div 4}{8 \div 4} = \frac{1}{2}$$

$\frac{1}{2}$ of the animals are mammals.

Example 2

If $\frac{7}{16}$ of the Earth is covered by freshwater, and $\frac{1}{16}$ of that is in glaciers, how much freshwater is not frozen?

Step 1 Subtract the numerators.

$$\frac{7}{16} - \frac{1}{16} = \frac{(7 - 1)}{16} = \frac{6}{16}$$

Step 2 Find the GCF.

$$\frac{6}{16} \text{ (GCF, 2)}$$

Step 3 Divide the numerator and denominator by the GCF.

$$\frac{6 \div 2}{16 \div 2} = \frac{3}{8}$$

$\frac{3}{8}$ of the freshwater is not frozen.

Practice Problem A bicycle rider is riding at a rate of 15 km/h for $\frac{4}{9}$ of his ride, 10 km/h for $\frac{2}{9}$ of his ride, and 8 km/h for the remainder of the ride. How much of his ride is he riding at a rate greater than 8 km/h?

SCIENCE SKILL HANDBOOK

MATH SKILL HANDBOOK

FOLDABLES HANDBOOK

REFERENCE HANDBOOK

GLOSSARY/ GLOSARIO

INDEX

Add and Subtract Fractions with Unlike Denominators To add or subtract fractions with unlike denominators, first find the least common denominator (LCD). This is the smallest number that is a common multiple of both denominators. Rename each fraction with the LCD, and then add or subtract. Find the simplest form if necessary.

Example 1

A chemist makes a paste that is $\frac{1}{2}$ table salt (NaCl), $\frac{1}{3}$ sugar ($C_6H_{12}O_6$), and the remainder is water (H_2O). How much of the paste is a solid?

Step 1 Find the LCD of the fractions.

$\frac{1}{2} + \frac{1}{3}$ (LCD, 6)

Step 2 Rename each numerator and each denominator with the LCD.

Step 3 Add the numerators.

$\frac{3}{6} + \frac{2}{6} = \frac{(3+2)}{6} = \frac{5}{6}$

$\frac{5}{6}$ of the paste is a solid.

Example 2

The average precipitation in Grand Junction, CO, is $\frac{7}{10}$ inch in November, and $\frac{3}{5}$ inch in December. What is the total average precipitation?

Step 1 Find the LCD of the fractions.

$\frac{7}{10} + \frac{3}{5}$ (LCD, 10)

Step 2 Rename each numerator and each denominator with the LCD.

Step 3 Add the numerators.

$\frac{7}{10} + \frac{6}{10} = \frac{(7+6)}{10} = \frac{13}{10}$

$\frac{13}{10}$ inches total precipitation, or $1\frac{3}{10}$ inches.

Practice Problem On an electric bill, about $\frac{1}{8}$ of the energy is from solar energy and about $\frac{1}{10}$ is from wind power. How much of the total bill is from solar energy and wind power combined?

Example 3

In your body, $\frac{7}{10}$ of your muscle contractions are involuntary (cardiac and smooth muscle tissue). Smooth muscle makes $\frac{3}{15}$ of your muscle contractions. How many of your muscle contractions are made by cardiac muscle?

Step 1 Find the LCD of the fractions.

$\frac{7}{10} - \frac{3}{15}$ (LCD, 30)

Step 2 Rename each numerator and each denominator with the LCD.

$\frac{7 \times 3}{10 \times 3} = \frac{21}{30}$

$\frac{3 \times 2}{15 \times 2} = \frac{6}{30}$

Step 3 Subtract the numerators.

$\frac{21}{30} - \frac{6}{30} = \frac{(21-6)}{30} = \frac{15}{30}$

Step 4 Find the GCF.

$\frac{15}{30}$ (GCF, 15)

$\frac{1}{2}$

$\frac{1}{2}$ of all muscle contractions are cardiac muscle.

Example 4

Tony wants to make cookies that call for $\frac{3}{4}$ of a cup of flour, but he only has $\frac{1}{3}$ of a cup. How much more flour does he need?

Step 1 Find the LCD of the fractions.

$\frac{3}{4} - \frac{1}{3}$ (LCD, 12)

Step 2 Rename each numerator and each denominator with the LCD.

$\frac{3 \times 3}{4 \times 3} = \frac{9}{12}$

$\frac{1 \times 4}{3 \times 4} = \frac{4}{12}$

Step 3 Subtract the numerators.

$\frac{9}{12} - \frac{4}{12} = \frac{(9-4)}{12} = \frac{5}{12}$

$\frac{5}{12}$ of a cup of flour

Practice Problem Using the information provided to you in Example 3 above, determine how many muscle contractions are voluntary (skeletal muscle).

Multiply Fractions To multiply with fractions, multiply the numerators and multiply the denominators. Find the simplest form if necessary.

Example

Multiply $\frac{3}{5}$ by $\frac{1}{3}$.

Step 1 Multiply the numerators and denominators.

$$\frac{3}{5} \times \frac{1}{3} = \frac{(3 \times 1)}{(5 \times 3)} \quad \frac{3}{15}$$

Step 2 Find the GCF.

$$\frac{3}{15} \text{ (GCF, 3)}$$

Step 3 Divide the numerator and denominator by the GCF.

$$\frac{3 \div 3}{15 \div 3} = \frac{1}{5}$$

$\frac{3}{5}$ multiplied by $\frac{1}{3}$ is $\frac{1}{5}$.

Practice Problem Multiply $\frac{3}{14}$ by $\frac{5}{16}$.

Find a Reciprocal Two numbers whose product is 1 are called multiplicative inverses, or reciprocals.

Example

Find the reciprocal of $\frac{3}{8}$.

Step 1 Inverse the fraction by putting the denominator on top and the numerator on the bottom.

$$\frac{8}{3}$$

The reciprocal of $\frac{3}{8}$ is $\frac{8}{3}$.

Practice Problem Find the reciprocal of $\frac{4}{9}$.

Divide Fractions To divide one fraction by another fraction, multiply the dividend by the reciprocal of the divisor. Find the simplest form if necessary.

Example 1

Divide $\frac{1}{9}$ by $\frac{1}{3}$.

Step 1 Find the reciprocal of the divisor.

The reciprocal of $\frac{1}{3}$ is $\frac{3}{1}$.

Step 2 Multiply the dividend by the reciprocal of the divisor.

$$\frac{\frac{1}{9}}{\frac{1}{3}} = \frac{1}{9} \times \frac{3}{1} = \frac{(1 \times 3)}{(9 \times 1)} = \frac{3}{9}$$

Step 3 Find the GCF.

$$\frac{3}{9} \text{ (GCF, 3)}$$

Step 4 Divide the numerator and denominator by the GCF.

$$\frac{3 \div 3}{9 \div 3} = \frac{1}{3}$$

$\frac{1}{9}$ divided by $\frac{1}{3}$ is $\frac{1}{3}$.

Example 2

Divide $\frac{3}{5}$ by $\frac{1}{4}$.

Step 1 Find the reciprocal of the divisor.

The reciprocal of $\frac{1}{4}$ is $\frac{4}{1}$.

Step 2 Multiply the dividend by the reciprocal of the divisor.

$$\frac{\frac{3}{5}}{\frac{1}{4}} = \frac{3}{5} \times \frac{4}{1} = \frac{(3 \times 4)}{(5 \times 1)} = \frac{12}{5}$$

$\frac{3}{5}$ divided by $\frac{1}{4}$ is $\frac{12}{5}$ or $2\frac{2}{5}$.

Practice Problem Divide $\frac{3}{11}$ by $\frac{7}{10}$.

SCIENCE SKILL HANDBOOK

MATH SKILL HANDBOOK

FOLDABLES HANDBOOK

REFERENCE HANDBOOK

GLOSSARY/ GLOSARIO

INDEX

Use Ratios

When you compare two numbers by division, you are using a ratio. Ratios can be written 3 to 5, 3:5, or $\frac{3}{5}$. Ratios, like fractions, also can be written in simplest form.

Ratios can represent one type of probability, called odds. This is a ratio that compares the number of ways a certain outcome occurs to the number of possible outcomes. For example, if you flip a coin 100 times, what are the odds that it will come up heads? There are two possible outcomes, heads or tails, so the odds of coming up heads are 50:100. Another way to say this is that 50 out of 100 times the coin will come up heads. In its simplest form, the ratio is 1:2.

Example 1

A chemical solution contains 40 g of salt and 64 g of baking soda. What is the ratio of salt to baking soda as a fraction in simplest form?

Step 1 Write the ratio as a fraction.

$$\frac{salt}{baking\ soda} = \frac{40}{64}$$

Step 2 Express the fraction in simplest form. The GCF of 40 and 64 is 8.

$$\frac{40}{64} = \frac{40 \div 8}{64 \div 8} = \frac{5}{8}$$

The ratio of salt to baking soda in the chemical solution is 5:8.

Example 2

Sean rolls a 6-sided die 6 times. What are the odds that the side with a 3 will show?

Step 1 Write the ratio as a fraction.

$$\frac{number\ of\ sides\ with\ a\ 3}{number\ of\ possible\ sides} = \frac{1}{6}$$

Step 2 Multiply by the number of attempts.

$\frac{1}{6} \times 6$ attempts $= \frac{6}{6}$ attempts $= 1$ attempt

1 attempt out of 6 will show a 3.

Practice Problem Two metal rods measure 100 cm and 144 cm in length. What is the ratio of their lengths in simplest form?

Use Decimals

A fraction with a denominator that is a power of ten can be written as a decimal. For example, 0.27 means $\frac{27}{100}$. The decimal point separates the ones place from the tenths place.

Any fraction can be written as a decimal using division. For example, the fraction $\frac{5}{8}$ can be written as a decimal by dividing 5 by 8. Written as a decimal, it is 0.625.

Add or Subtract Decimals When adding and subtracting decimals, line up the decimal points before carrying out the operation.

Example 1

Find the sum of 47.68 and 7.80.

Step 1 Line up the decimal places when you write the numbers.

```
  47.68
   7.80
```

Step 2 Add the decimals.

```
  47.68
   7.80
  55.48
```

The sum of 47.68 and 7.80 is 55.48.

Example 2

Find the difference of 42.17 and 15.85.

Step 1 Line up the decimal places when you write the number.

```
  42.17
 −15.85
```

Step 2 Subtract the decimals.

```
  42.17
 −15.85
  26.32
```

The difference of 42.17 and 15.85 is 26.32.

Practice Problem Find the sum of 1.245 and 3.842.

SCIENCE SKILL HANDBOOK

MATH SKILL HANDBOOK

FOLDABLES HANDBOOK

REFERENCE HANDBOOK

GLOSSARY/ GLOSARIO

INDEX

SCIENCE SKILL HANDBOOK

MATH SKILL HANDBOOK

FOLDABLES HANDBOOK

REFERENCE HANDBOOK

GLOSSARY/GLOSARIO

INDEX

Multiply Decimals To multiply decimals, multiply the numbers like numbers without decimal points. Count the decimal places in each factor. The product will have the same number of decimal places as the sum of the decimal places in the factors.

Example

Multiply 2.4 by 5.9.

Step 1 Multiply the factors like two whole numbers.

$24 \times 59 = 1416$

Step 2 Find the sum of the number of decimal places in the factors. Each factor has one decimal place, for a sum of two decimal places.

Step 3 The product will have two decimal places.

14.16

The product of 2.4 and 5.9 is 14.16.

Practice Problem Multiply 4.6 by 2.2.

Divide Decimals When dividing decimals, change the divisor to a whole number. To do this, multiply both the divisor and the dividend by the same power of ten. Then place the decimal point in the quotient directly above the decimal point in the dividend. Then divide as you do with whole numbers.

Example

Divide 8.84 by 3.4.

Step 1 Multiply both factors by 10.

$3.4 \times 10 = 34, 8.84 \times 10 = 88.4$

Step 2 Divide 88.4 by 34.

```
        2.6
   34)88.4
      -68
       204
      -204
         0
```

8.84 divided by 3.4 is 2.6.

Practice Problem Divide 75.6 by 3.6.

Use Proportions

An equation that shows that two ratios are equivalent is a proportion. The ratios $\frac{2}{4}$ and $\frac{5}{10}$ are equivalent, so they can be written as $\frac{2}{4} = \frac{5}{10}$. This equation is a proportion.

When two ratios form a proportion, the cross products are equal. To find the cross products in the proportion $\frac{2}{4} = \frac{5}{10}$, multiply the 2 and the 10, and the 4 and the 5. Therefore $2 \times 10 = 4 \times 5$, or $20 = 20$.

Because you know that both ratios are equal, you can use cross products to find a missing term in a proportion. This is known as solving the proportion.

Example

The heights of a tree and a pole are proportional to the lengths of their shadows. The tree casts a shadow of 24 m when a 6-m pole casts a shadow of 4 m. What is the height of the tree?

Step 1 Write a proportion.

$$\frac{\text{height of tree}}{\text{height of pole}} = \frac{\text{length of tree's shadow}}{\text{length of pole's shadow}}$$

Step 2 Substitute the known values into the proportion. Let h represent the unknown value, the height of the tree.

$$\frac{h}{6} \times \frac{24}{4}$$

Step 3 Find the cross products.

$h \times 4 = 6 \times 24$

Step 4 Simplify the equation.

$4h = 144$

Step 5 Divide each side by 4.

$$\frac{4h}{4} = \frac{144}{4}$$

$h = 36$

The height of the tree is 36 m.

Practice Problem The ratios of the weights of two objects on the Moon and on Earth are in proportion. A rock weighing 3 N on the Moon weighs 18 N on Earth. How much would a rock that weighs 5 N on the Moon weigh on Earth?

Use Percentages

The word *percent* means "out of one hundred." It is a ratio that compares a number to 100. Suppose you read that 77 percent of Earth's surface is covered by water. That is the same as reading that the fraction of Earth's surface covered by water is $\frac{77}{100}$. To express a fraction as a percent, first find the equivalent decimal for the fraction. Then, multiply the decimal by 100 and add the percent symbol.

Example 1

Express $\frac{13}{20}$ as a percent.

Step 1   Find the equivalent decimal for the fraction.

$$\begin{array}{r} 0.65 \\ 20\overline{)13.00} \\ \underline{12\ 0} \\ 1\ 00 \\ \underline{1\ 00} \\ 0 \end{array}$$

Step 2   Rewrite the fraction $\frac{13}{20}$ as 0.65.

Step 3   Multiply 0.65 by 100 and add the % symbol.

$$0.65 \times 100 = 65 = 65\%$$

So, $\frac{13}{20} = 65\%$.

This also can be solved as a proportion.

Example 2

Express $\frac{13}{20}$ as a percent.

Step 1   Write a proportion.

$$\frac{13}{20} = \frac{x}{100}$$

Step 2   Find the cross products.

$$1300 = 20x$$

Step 3   Divide each side by 20.

$$\frac{1300}{20} = \frac{20x}{20}$$

$$65 = x = 65\%$$

So, $\frac{13}{20} = 65\%$.

Practice Problem In one year, 73 of 365 days were rainy in one city. What percent of the days in that city were rainy?

Solve One-Step Equations

A statement that two expressions are equal is an equation. For example, $A = B$ is an equation that states that A is equal to B.

An equation is solved when a variable is replaced with a value that makes both sides of the equation equal. To make both sides equal the inverse operation is used. Addition and subtraction are inverses, and multiplication and division are inverses.

Example 1

Solve the equation $x - 10 = 35$.

Step 1   Find the solution by adding 10 to each side of the equation.

$$x - 10 = 35$$
$$x - 10 + 10 = 35 + 10$$
$$x = 45$$

Step 2   Check the solution.

$$x - 10 = 35$$
$$45 - 10 = 35$$
$$35 = 35$$

Both sides of the equation are equal, so $x = 45$.

Example 2

In the formula $a = bc$, find the value of c if $a = 20$ and $b = 2$.

Step 1   Rearrange the formula so the unknown value is by itself on one side of the equation by dividing both sides by b.

$$a = bc$$
$$\frac{a}{b} = \frac{bc}{b}$$
$$\frac{a}{b} = c$$

Step 2   Replace the variables a and b with the values that are given.

$$\frac{a}{b} = c$$
$$\frac{20}{2} = c$$
$$10 = c$$

Step 3   Check the solution.

$$a = bc$$
$$20 = 2 \times 10$$
$$20 = 20$$

Both sides of the equation are equal, so $c = 10$ is the solution when $a = 20$ and $b = 2$.

Practice Problem In the formula $h = gd$, find the value of d if $g = 12.3$ and $h = 17.4$.

SCIENCE SKILL HANDBOOK

MATH SKILL HANDBOOK

FOLDABLES HANDBOOK

REFERENCE HANDBOOK

GLOSSARY/ GLOSARIO

INDEX

SCIENCE SKILL HANDBOOK

MATH SKILL HANDBOOK

FOLDABLES HANDBOOK

REFERENCE HANDBOOK

GLOSSARY/ GLOSARIO

INDEX

Use Statistics

The branch of mathematics that deals with collecting, analyzing, and presenting data is statistics. In statistics, there are three common ways to summarize data with a single number—the mean, the median, and the mode.

The **mean** of a set of data is the arithmetic average. It is found by adding the numbers in the data set and dividing by the number of items in the set.

The **median** is the middle number in a set of data when the data are arranged in numerical order. If there were an even number of data points, the median would be the mean of the two middle numbers.

The **mode** of a set of data is the number or item that appears most often.

Another number that often is used to describe a set of data is the range. The **range** is the difference between the largest number and the smallest number in a set of data.

Example

The speeds (in m/s) for a race car during five different time trials are 39, 37, 44, 36, and 44.

To find the mean:

Step 1   Find the sum of the numbers.

$39 + 37 + 44 + 36 + 44 = 200$

Step 2   Divide the sum by the number of items, which is 5.

$200 \div 5 = 40$

The mean is 40 m/s.

To find the median:

Step 1   Arrange the measures from least to greatest.

36, 37, 39, 44, 44

Step 2   Determine the middle measure.

36, 37, <u>39</u>, 44, 44

The median is 39 m/s.

To find the mode:

Step 1   Group the numbers that are the same together.

44, 44, 36, 37, 39

Step 2   Determine the number that occurs most in the set.

<u>44, 44,</u> 36, 37, 39

The mode is 44 m/s.

To find the range:

Step 1   Arrange the measures from greatest to least.

44, 44, 39, 37, 36

Step 2   Determine the greatest and least measures in the set.

<u>44,</u> 44, 39, 37, <u>36</u>

Step 3   Find the difference between the greatest and least measures.

$44 - 36 = 8$

The range is 8 m/s.

Practice Problem Find the mean, median, mode, and range for the data set 8, 4, 12, 8, 11, 14, 16.

A **frequency table** shows how many times each piece of data occurs, usually in a survey. **Table 1** below shows the results of a student survey on favorite color.

Table 1 Student Color Choice		
Color	Tally	Frequency
red	ℍℕ	4
blue	IIII	5
black	II	2
green	III	3
purple	ℍℕ II	7
yellow	ℍℕ I	6

Based on the frequency table data, which color is the favorite?

Use Geometry

The branch of mathematics that deals with the measurement, properties, and relationships of points, lines, angles, surfaces, and solids is called geometry.

Perimeter The **perimeter** (P) is the distance around a geometric figure. To find the perimeter of a rectangle, add the length and width and multiply that sum by two, or $2(l + w)$. To find perimeters of irregular figures, add the length of all the sides.

Example 1

Find the perimeter of a rectangle that is 3 m long and 5 m wide.

Step 1   You know that the perimeter is 2 times the sum of the width and length.

$P = 2(3 \text{ m} + 5 \text{ m})$

Step 2   Find the sum of the width and length.

$P = 2(8 \text{ m})$

Step 3   Multiply by 2.

$P = 16 \text{ m}$

The perimeter is 16 m.

Example 2

Find the perimeter of a shape with sides measuring 2 cm, 5 cm, 6 cm, 3 cm.

Step 1   You know that the perimeter is the sum of all the sides.

$P = 2 + 5 + 6 + 3$

Step 2   Find the sum of the sides.

$P = 2 + 5 + 6 + 3$

$P = 16$

The perimeter is 16 cm.

Practice Problem Find the perimeter of a rectangle with a length of 18 m and a width of 7 m.

Practice Problem Find the perimeter of a triangle measuring 1.6 cm by 2.4 cm by 2.4 cm.

Area of a Rectangle The **area** (A) is the number of square units needed to cover a surface. To find the area of a rectangle, multiply the length times the width, or $l \times w$. When finding area, the units also are multiplied. Area is given in square units.

Example

Find the area of a rectangle with a length of 1 cm and a width of 10 cm.

Step 1   You know that the area is the length multiplied by the width.

$A = (1 \text{ cm} \times 10 \text{ cm})$

Step 2   Multiply the length by the width. Also multiply the units.

$A = 10 \text{ cm}^2$

The area is 10 cm².

Practice Problem Find the area of a square whose sides measure 4 m.

Area of a Triangle To find the area of a triangle, use the formula:

$A = \frac{1}{2}(\text{base} \times \text{height})$

The base of a triangle can be any of its sides. The height is the perpendicular distance from a base to the opposite endpoint, or vertex.

Example

Find the area of a triangle with a base of 18 m and a height of 7 m.

Step 1   You know that the area is $\frac{1}{2}$ the base times the height.

$A = \frac{1}{2}(18 \text{ m} \times 7 \text{ m})$

Step 2   Multiply $\frac{1}{2}$ by the product of 18 × 7. Multiply the units.

$A = \frac{1}{2}(126 \text{ m}^2)$

$A = 63 \text{ m}^2$

The area is 63 m².

Practice Problem Find the area of a triangle with a base of 27 cm and a height of 17 cm.

SCIENCE SKILL HANDBOOK

MATH SKILL HANDBOOK

FOLDABLES HANDBOOK

REFERENCE HANDBOOK

GLOSSARY/ GLOSARIO

INDEX

SCIENCE SKILL HANDBOOK

MATH SKILL HANDBOOK

FOLDABLES HANDBOOK

REFERENCE HANDBOOK

GLOSSARY/ GLOSARIO

INDEX

Circumference of a Circle The **diameter** (d) of a circle is the distance across the circle through its center, and the **radius** (r) is the distance from the center to any point on the circle. The radius is half of the diameter. The distance around the circle is called the **circumference** (C). The formula for finding the circumference is:

$C = 2\pi r$ or $C = \pi d$

The circumference divided by the diameter is always equal to 3.1415926... This nonterminating and nonrepeating number is represented by the Greek letter π (pi). An approximation often used for π is 3.14.

Example 1

Find the circumference of a circle with a radius of 3 m.

Step 1 You know the formula for the circumference is 2 times the radius times π.

$C = 2\pi(3)$

Step 2 Multiply 2 times the radius.

$C = 6\pi$

Step 3 Multiply by π.

$C \approx 19$ m

The circumference is about 19 m.

Example 2

Find the circumference of a circle with a diameter of 24.0 cm.

Step 1 You know the formula for the circumference is the diameter times π.

$C = \pi(24.0)$

Step 2 Multiply the diameter by π.

$C \approx 75.4$ cm

The circumference is about 75.4 cm.

Practice Problem Find the circumference of a circle with a radius of 19 cm.

Area of a Circle The formula for the area of a circle is: $A = \pi r^2$

Example 1

Find the area of a circle with a radius of 4.0 cm.

Step 1 $A = \pi(4.0)^2$

Step 2 Find the square of the radius.

$A = 16\pi$

Step 3 Multiply the square of the radius by π.

$A \approx 50$ cm^2

The area of the circle is about 50 cm^2.

Example 2

Find the area of a circle with a radius of 225 m.

Step 1 $A = \pi(225)^2$

Step 2 Find the square of the radius.

$A = 50625\pi$

Step 3 Multiply the square of the radius by π.

$A \approx 159043.1$

The area of the circle is about 159043.1 m^2.

Example 3

Find the area of a circle whose diameter is 20.0 mm.

Step 1 Remember that the radius is half of the diameter.

$A = \pi\left(\dfrac{20.0}{2}\right)^2$

Step 2 Find the radius.

$A = \pi(10.0)^2$

Step 3 Find the square of the radius.

$A = 100\pi$

Step 4 Multiply the square of the radius by π.

$A \approx 314$ mm^2

The area of the circle is about 314 mm^2.

Practice Problem Find the area of a circle with a radius of 16 m.

Volume The measure of space occupied by a solid, is the **volume** (V). To find the volume of a rectangular solid, multiply the length times width times height, or $V = l \times w \times h$. It is measured in cubic units, such as cubic centimeters (cm^3).

Example

Find the volume of a rectangular solid with a length of 2.0 m, a width of 4.0 m, and a height of 3.0 m.

Step 1 You know the formula for volume is the length times the width times the height.

$$V = 2.0 \text{ m} \times 4.0 \text{ m} \times 3.0 \text{ m}$$

Step 2 Multiply the length times the width times the height.

$$V = 24 \text{ m}^3$$

The volume is 24 m^3.

Practice Problem Find the volume of a rectangular solid that is 8 m long, 4 m wide, and 4 m high.

To find the volume of other solids, multiply the area of the base times the height.

Example 1

Find the volume of a solid that has a triangular base with a length of 8.0 m and a height of 7.0 m. The height of the entire solid is 15.0 m.

Step 1 You know that the base is a triangle, and the area of a triangle is $\frac{1}{2}$ the base times the height, and the volume is the area of the base times the height.

$$V = \left[\frac{1}{2}(b \times h)\right] \times 15$$

Step 2 Find the area of the base.

$$V = \left[\frac{1}{2}(8 \times 7)\right] \times 15$$
$$V = \left(\frac{1}{2} \times 56\right) \times 15$$

Step 3 Multiply the area of the base by the height of the solid.

$$V = 28 \times 15$$
$$V = 420 \text{ m}^3$$

The volume is 420 m^3.

Example 2

Find the volume of a cylinder that has a base with a radius of 12.0 cm, and a height of 21.0 cm.

Step 1 You know that the base is a circle, and the area of a circle is the square of the radius times π, and the volume is the area of the base times the height.

$$V = (\pi r^2) \times 21$$
$$V = (\pi 12^2) \times 21$$

Step 2 Find the area of the base.

$$V = 144\pi \times 21$$
$$V = 452 \times 21$$

Step 3 Multiply the area of the base by the height of the solid.

$$V \approx 9{,}500 \text{ cm}^3$$

The volume is about 9,500 cm^3.

Example 3

Find the volume of a cylinder that has a diameter of 15 mm and a height of 4.8 mm.

Step 1 You know that the base is a circle with an area equal to the square of the radius times π. The radius is one-half the diameter. The volume is the area of the base times the height.

$$V = (\pi r^2) \times 4.8$$
$$V = \left[\pi\left(\frac{1}{2} \times 15\right)^2\right] \times 4.8$$
$$V = (\pi 7.5^2) \times 4.8$$

Step 2 Find the area of the base.

$$V = 56.25\pi \times 4.8$$
$$V \approx 176.71 \times 4.8$$

Step 3 Multiply the area of the base by the height of the solid.

$$V \approx 848.2$$

The volume is about 848.2 mm^3.

Practice Problem Find the volume of a cylinder with a diameter of 7 cm in the base and a height of 16 cm.

SCIENCE SKILL HANDBOOK

MATH SKILL HANDBOOK

FOLDABLES HANDBOOK

REFERENCE HANDBOOK

GLOSSARY/ GLOSARIO

INDEX

Science Applications

Measure in SI

The metric system of measurement was developed in 1795. A modern form of the metric system, called the International System (SI), was adopted in 1960 and provides the standard measurements that all scientists around the world can understand.

The SI system is convenient because unit sizes vary by powers of 10. Prefixes are used to name units. Look at **Table 2** for some common SI prefixes and their meanings.

Table 2 Common SI Prefixes

Prefix	Symbol	Meaning	
kilo–	k	1,000	thousandth
hecto–	h	100	hundred
deka–	da	10	ten
deci–	d	0.1	tenth
centi–	c	0.01	hundredth
milli–	m	0.001	thousandth

Example

How many grams equal one kilogram?

Step 1 Find the prefix *kilo–* in **Table 2.**

Step 2 Using **Table 2,** determine the meaning of *kilo–*. According to the table, it means 1,000. When the prefix *kilo–* is added to a unit, it means that there are 1,000 of the units in a "kilounit."

Step 3 Apply the prefix to the units in the question. The units in the question are grams. There are 1,000 grams in a kilogram.

Practice Problem Is a milligram larger or smaller than a gram? How many of the smaller units equal one larger unit? What fraction of the larger unit does one smaller unit represent?

Dimensional Analysis

Convert SI Units In science, quantities such as length, mass, and time sometimes are measured using different units. A process called dimensional analysis can be used to change one unit of measure to another. This process involves multiplying your starting quantity and units by one or more conversion factors. A conversion factor is a ratio equal to one and can be made from any two equal quantities with different units. If 1,000 mL equal 1 L then two ratios can be made.

$$\frac{1,000 \text{ mL}}{1 \text{ L}} = \frac{1 \text{ L}}{1,000 \text{ mL}} = 1$$

One can convert between units in the SI system by using the equivalents in **Table 2** to make conversion factors.

Example

How many cm are in 4 m?

Step 1 Write conversion factors for the units given. From **Table 2,** you know that 100 cm = 1 m. The conversion factors are

$$\frac{100 \text{ cm}}{1 \text{ m}} \quad and \quad \frac{1 \text{ m}}{100 \text{ cm}}$$

Step 2 Decide which conversion factor to use. Select the factor that has the units you are converting from (m) in the denominator and the units you are converting to (cm) in the numerator.

$$\frac{100 \text{ cm}}{1 \text{ m}}$$

Step 3 Multiply the starting quantity and units by the conversion factor. Cancel the starting units with the units in the denominator. There are 400 cm in 4 m.

$$4 \text{ m} = \frac{100 \text{ cm}}{1 \text{ m}} = 400 \text{ cm}$$

Practice Problem How many milligrams are in one kilogram? (Hint: You will need to use two conversion factors from **Table 2.**)

SCIENCE SKILL HANDBOOK

MATH SKILL HANDBOOK

FOLDABLES HANDBOOK

REFERENCE HANDBOOK

GLOSSARY/ GLOSARIO

INDEX

Table 3 Unit System Equivalents

Type of Measurement	Equivalent
Length	1 in = 2.54 cm 1 yd = 0.91 m 1 mi = 1.61 km
Mass and weight*	1 oz = 28.35 g 1 lb = 0.45 kg 1 ton (short) = 0.91 tonnes (metric tons) 1 lb = 4.45 N
Volume	$1 \text{ in}^3 = 16.39 \text{ cm}^3$ 1 qt = 0.95 L 1 gal = 3.78 L
Area	$1 \text{ in}^2 = 6.45 \text{ cm}^2$ $1 \text{ yd}^2 = 0.83 \text{ m}^2$ $1 \text{ mi}^2 = 2.59 \text{ km}^2$ 1 acre = 0.40 hectares
Temperature	$°C = \frac{(°F - 32)}{1.8}$ $K = °C + 273$

*Weight is measured in standard Earth gravity.

Convert Between Unit Systems Table 3 gives a list of equivalents that can be used to convert between English and SI units.

Example

If a meterstick has a length of 100 cm, how long is the meterstick in inches?

Step 1 Write the conversion factors for the units given. From **Table 3,** 1 in = 2.54 cm.

$$\frac{1 \text{ in}}{2.54 \text{ cm}} \text{ and } \frac{2.54 \text{ cm}}{1 \text{ in}}$$

Step 2 Determine which conversion factor to use. You are converting from cm to in. Use the conversion factor with cm on the bottom.

$$\frac{1 \text{ in}}{2.54 \text{ cm}}$$

Step 3 Multiply the starting quantity and units by the conversion factor. Cancel the starting units with the units in the denominator. Round your answer to the nearest tenth.

$$100 \text{ cm} \times \frac{1 \text{ in}}{2.54 \text{ cm}} = 39.37 \text{ in}$$

The meterstick is about 39.4 in long.

Practice Problem 1 A book has a mass of 5 lb. What is the mass of the book in kg?

Practice Problem 2 Use the equivalent for in and cm (1 in = 2.54 cm) to show how 1 in3 ≈ 16.39 cm3.

SCIENCE SKILL HANDBOOK

MATH SKILL HANDBOOK

FOLDABLES HANDBOOK

REFERENCE HANDBOOK

GLOSSARY/ GLOSARIO

INDEX

Precision and Significant Digits

When you make a measurement, the value you record depends on the precision of the measuring instrument. This precision is represented by the number of significant digits recorded in the measurement. When counting the number of significant digits, all digits are counted except zeros at the end of a number with no decimal point such as 2,050, and zeros at the beginning of a decimal such as 0.03020. When adding or subtracting numbers with different precision, round the answer to the smallest number of decimal places of any number in the sum or difference. When multiplying or dividing, the answer is rounded to the smallest number of significant digits of any number being multiplied or divided.

Example

The lengths 5.28 and 5.2 are measured in meters. Find the sum of these lengths and record your answer using the correct number of significant digits.

Step 1 Find the sum.

5.28 m	2 digits after the decimal
+ 5.2 m	1 digit after the decimal
10.48 m	

Step 2 Round to one digit after the decimal because the least number of digits after the decimal of the numbers being added is 1.

The sum is 10.5 m.

Practice Problem 1 How many significant digits are in the measurement 7,071,301 m? How many significant digits are in the measurement 0.003010 g?

Practice Problem 2 Multiply 5.28 and 5.2 using the rule for multiplying and dividing. Record the answer using the correct number of significant digits.

Scientific Notation

Many times numbers used in science are very small or very large. Because these numbers are difficult to work with, scientists use scientific notation. To write numbers in scientific notation, move the decimal point until only one non-zero digit remains on the left. Then count the number of places you moved the decimal point and use that number as a power of ten. For example, the average distance from the Sun to Mars is 227,800,000,000 m. In scientific notation, this distance is 2.278×10^{11} m. Because you moved the decimal point to the left, the number is a positive power of ten.

The mass of an electron is about 0.000 000 000 000 000 000 000 000 000 000 911 kg. Expressed in scientific notation, this mass is 9.11×10^{-31} kg. Because the decimal point was moved to the right, the number is a negative power of ten.

Example

Earth is 149,600,000 km from the Sun. Express this in scientific notation.

Step 1 Move the decimal point until one non-zero digit remains on the left.

1.496 000 00

Step 2 Count the number of decimal places you have moved. In this case, eight.

Step 2 Show that number as a power of ten, 10^8.

Earth is 1.496×10^8 km from the Sun.

Practice Problem 1 How many significant digits are in 149,600,000 km? How many significant digits are in 1.496×10^8 km?

Practice Problem 2 Parts used in a high performance car must be measured to 7×10^{-6} m. Express this number as a decimal.

Practice Problem 3 A CD is spinning at 539 revolutions per minute. Express this number in scientific notation.

Make and Use Graphs

Data in tables can be displayed in a graph—a visual representation of data. Common graph types include line graphs, bar graphs, and circle graphs.

Line Graph A line graph shows a relationship between two variables that change continuously. The independent variable is changed and is plotted on the *x*-axis. The dependent variable is observed, and is plotted on the *y*-axis.

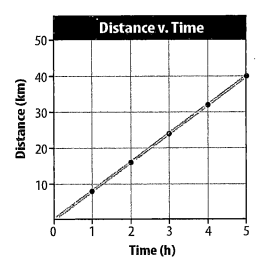

Figure 8 This line graph shows the relationship between distance and time during a bicycle ride.

Practice Problem A puppy's shoulder height is measured during the first year of her life. The following measurements were collected: (3 mo, 52 cm), (6 mo, 72 cm), (9 mo, 83 cm), (12 mo, 86 cm). Graph this data.

Example

Draw a line graph of the data below from a cyclist in a long-distance race.

Table 4 Bicycle Race Data

Time (h)	Distance (km)
0	0
1	8
2	16
3	24
4	32
5	40

Step 1 Determine the *x*-axis and *y*-axis variables. Time varies independently of distance and is plotted on the *x*-axis. Distance is dependent on time and is plotted on the *y*-axis.

Step 2 Determine the scale of each axis. The *x*-axis data ranges from 0 to 5. The *y*-axis data ranges from 0 to 50.

Step 3 Using graph paper, draw and label the axes. Include units in the labels.

Step 4 Draw a point at the intersection of the time value on the *x*-axis and corresponding distance value on the *y*-axis. Connect the points and label the graph with a title, as shown in **Figure 8.**

Find a Slope The slope of a straight line is the ratio of the vertical change, rise, to the horizontal change, run.

$$\text{Slope} = \frac{\text{vertical change (rise)}}{\text{horizontal change (run)}} = \frac{\text{change in } y}{\text{change in } x}$$

Example

Find the slope of the graph in **Figure 8**.

Step 1 You know that the slope is the change in *y* divided by the change in *x*.

$$\text{Slope} = \frac{\text{change in } y}{\text{change in } x}$$

Step 2 Determine the data points you will be using. For a straight line, choose the two sets of points that are the farthest apart.

$$\text{Slope} = \frac{(40 - 0) \text{ km}}{(5 - 0) \text{ h}}$$

Step 3 Find the change in *y* and *x*.

$$\text{Slope} = \frac{40 \text{ km}}{5 \text{ h}}$$

Step 4 Divide the change in *y* by the change in *x*.

$$\text{Slope} = \frac{8 \text{ km}}{\text{h}}$$

The slope of the graph is 8 km/h.

SCIENCE SKILL HANDBOOK

MATH SKILL HANDBOOK

FOLDABLES HANDBOOK

REFERENCE HANDBOOK

GLOSSARY/ GLOSARIO

INDEX

Bar Graph To compare data that does not change continuously you might choose a bar graph. A bar graph uses bars to show the relationships between variables. The *x*-axis variable is divided into parts. The parts can be numbers such as years, or a category such as a type of animal. The *y*-axis is a number and increases continuously along the axis.

Example

A recycling center collects 4.0 kg of aluminum on Monday, 1.0 kg on Wednesday, and 2.0 kg on Friday. Create a bar graph of this data.

Step 1 Select the *x*-axis and *y*-axis variables. The measured numbers (the masses of aluminum) should be placed on the *y*-axis. The variable divided into parts (collection days) is placed on the *x*-axis.

Step 2 Create a graph grid like you would for a line graph. Include labels and units.

Step 3 For each measured number, draw a vertical bar above the *x*-axis value up to the *y*-axis value. For the first data point, draw a vertical bar above Monday up to 4.0 kg.

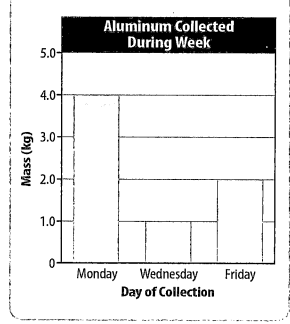

Practice Problem Draw a bar graph of the gases in air: 78% nitrogen, 21% oxygen, 1% other gases.

Circle Graph To display data as parts of a whole, you might use a circle graph. A circle graph is a circle divided into sections that represent the relative size of each piece of data. The entire circle represents 100%, half represents 50%, and so on.

Example

Air is made up of 78% nitrogen, 21% oxygen, and 1% other gases. Display the composition of air in a circle graph.

Step 1 Multiply each percent by 360° and divide by 100 to find the angle of each section in the circle.

$$78\% \times \frac{360°}{100} = 280.8°$$

$$21\% \times \frac{360°}{100} = 75.6°$$

$$1\% \times \frac{360°}{100} = 3.6°$$

Step 2 Use a compass to draw a circle and to mark the center of the circle. Draw a straight line from the center to the edge of the circle.

Step 3 Use a protractor and the angles you calculated to divide the circle into parts. Place the center of the protractor over the center of the circle and line the base of the protractor over the straight line.

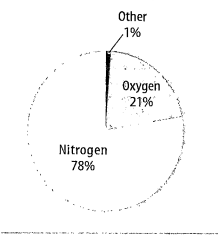

Practice Problem Draw a circle graph to represent the amount of aluminum collected during the week shown in the bar graph to the left.

SCIENCE SKILL HANDBOOK

MATH SKILL HANDBOOK

FOLDABLES HANDBOOK

REFERENCE HANDBOOK

GLOSSARY/ GLOSARIO

INDEX

Student Study Guides & Instructions
By Dinah Zike

1. You will find suggestions for Study Guides, also known as Foldables or books, in each chapter lesson and as a final project. Look at the end of the chapter to determine the project format and glue the Foldables in place as you progress through the chapter lessons.

2. Creating the Foldables or books is simple and easy to do by using copy paper, art paper, and internet printouts. Photocopies of maps, diagrams, or your own illustrations may also be used for some of the Foldables. Notebook paper is the most common source of material for study guides and 83% of all Foldables are created from it. When folded to make books, notebook paper Foldables easily fit into 11" × 17" or 12" × 18" chapter projects with space left over. Foldables made using photocopy paper are slightly larger and they fit into Projects, but snugly. Use the least amount of glue, tape, and staples needed to assemble the Foldables.

3. Seven of the Foldables can be made using either small or large paper. When 11" × 17" or 12" × 18" paper is used, these become projects for housing smaller Foldables. Project format boxes are located within the instructions to remind you of this option.

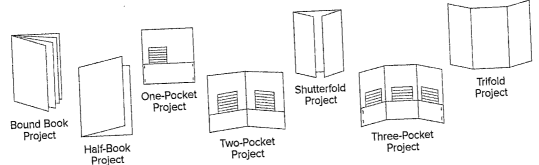

Bound Book Project

Half-Book Project

One-Pocket Project

Two-Pocket Project

Shutterfold Project

Three-Pocket Project

Trifold Project

4. Use one-gallon self-locking plastic bags to store your projects. Place strips of two-inch clear tape along the left, long side of the bag and punch holes through the taped edge. Cut the bottom corners off the bag so it will not hold air. Store this Project Portfolio inside a three-hole binder. To store a large collection of project bags, use a giant laundry-soap box. Holes can be punched in some of the Foldable Projects so they can be stored in a three-hole binder without using a plastic bag. Punch holes in the pocket books before gluing or stapling the pocket.

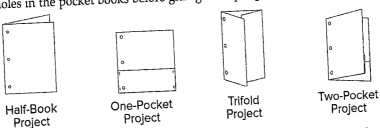

Half-Book Project

One-Pocket Project

Trifold Project

Two-Pocket Project

5. Maximize the use of the projects by collecting additional information and placing it on the back of the project and other unused spaces of the large Foldables.

SCIENCE SKILL HANDBOOK

MATH SKILL HANDBOOK

FOLDABLES HANDBOOK

REFERENCE HANDBOOK

GLOSSARY/GLOSARIO

INDEX

SCIENCE SKILL HANDBOOK

MATH SKILL HANDBOOK

FOLDABLES HANDBOOK

REFERENCE HANDBOOK

GLOSSARY/ GLOSARIO

INDEX

Half-Book Foldable® By Dinah Zike

Step 1 Fold a sheet of notebook or copy paper in half.

Label the exterior tab and use the inside space to write information.

PROJECT FORMAT
Use 11" X 17" or 12" X 18" paper on the horizontal axis to make a large project book.

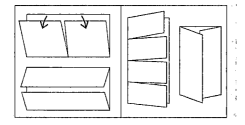

Variations

Paper can be folded horizontally, like a *hamburger* or vertically, like a *hot dog*.

C Half-books can be folded so that one side is ½ inch longer than the other side. A title or question can be written on the extended tab.

Worksheet Foldable or Folded Book® By Dinah Zike

Step 1 Make a half-book (see above) using work sheets, internet printouts, diagrams, or maps.

Step 2 Fold it in half again.

Variations

A This folded sheet as a small book with two pages can be used for comparing and contrasting, cause and effect, or other skills.

B When the sheet of paper is open, the four sections can be used separately or used collectively to show sequences or steps.

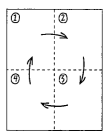

Two-Tab and Concept-Map Foldable® By Dinah Zike

 Step 1 Fold a sheet of notebook or copy paper in half vertically or horizontally.

 Step 2 Fold it in half again, as shown.

Step 3 Unfold once and cut along the fold line or valley of the top flap to make two flaps.

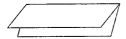

Variations

A Concept maps can be made by leaving a ½ inch tab at the top when folding the paper in half. Use arrows and labels to relate topics to the primary concept.

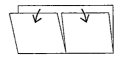

B Use two sheets of paper to make multiple page tab books. Glue or staple books together at the top fold.

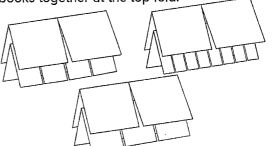

. . . .

Three-Quarter Foldable® By Dinah Zike

 Step 1 Make a two-tab book (see above) and cut the left tab off at the top of the fold line.

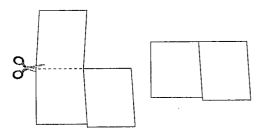

Variations

A Use this book to draw a diagram or a map on the exposed left tab. Write questions about the illustration on the top right tab and provide complete answers on the space under the tab.

B Compose a self-test using multiple choice answers for your questions. Include the correct answer with three wrong responses. The correct answers can be written on the back of the book or upside down on the bottom of the inside page.

SCIENCE SKILL HANDBOOK

MATH SKILL HANDBOOK

FOLDABLES HANDBOOK

REFERENCE HANDBOOK

GLOSSARY/ GLOSARIO

INDEX

Three-Tab Foldable® By Dinah Zike

 Fold a sheet of paper in half horizontally.

 Fold into thirds.

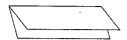 Unfold and cut along the folds of the top flap to make three sections.

Variations

Ⓐ Before cutting the three tabs draw a Venn diagram across the front of the book.

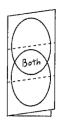

Ⓑ Make a space to use for titles or concept maps by leaving a ½ inch tab at the top when folding the paper in half.

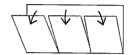

· ·

Four-Tab Foldable® By Dinah Zike

 Fold a sheet of paper in half horizontally.

 Fold in half and then fold each half as shown below.

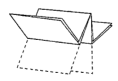

Unfold and cut along the fold lines of the top flap to make four tabs.

Variations

Ⓐ Make a space to use for titles or concept maps by leaving a ½ inch tab at the top when folding the paper in half.

Ⓑ Use the book on the vertical axis, with or without an extended tab.

Folding Fifths for a Foldable® By Dinah Zike

 Step 1 Fold a sheet of paper in half horizontally.

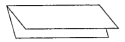

 Step 2 Fold again so one-third of the paper is exposed and two-thirds are covered.

Step 3 Fold the two-thirds section in half.

Step 4 Fold the one-third section, a single thickness, backward to make a fold line.

Variations

A Unfold and cut along the fold lines to make five tabs.

B Make a five-tab book with a ½ inch tab at the top (see two-tab instructions).

C Use 11" × 17" or 12" × 18" paper and fold into fifths for a five-column and/or row table or chart.

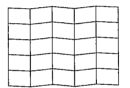

Folded Table or Chart, and Trifold Foldable® By Dinah Zike

Step 1 Fold a sheet of paper in the required number of vertical columns for the table or chart.

Step 2 Fold the horizontal rows needed for the table or chart.

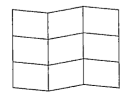

PROJECT FORMAT
Use 11" × 17" or 12" × 18" paper and fold it to make a large trifold project book or larger tables and charts.

Variations

A Make a trifold by folding the paper into thirds vertically or horizontally.

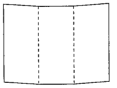

B Make a trifold book. Unfold it and draw a Venn diagram on the inside.

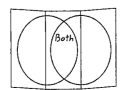

SCIENCE SKILL HANDBOOK

MATH SKILL HANDBOOK

FOLDABLES HANDBOOK

REFERENCE HANDBOOK

GLOSSARY/ GLOSARIO

INDEX

Two or Three-Pockets Foldable® By Dinah Zike

Step 1 Fold up the long side of a horizontal sheet of paper about 5 cm.

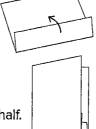

Step 2 Fold the paper in half.

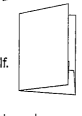

Step 3 Open the paper and glue or staple the outer edges to make two compartments.

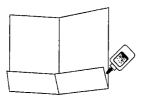

Variations

A Make a multi-page booklet by gluing several pocket books together.

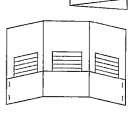

B Make a three-pocket book by using a trifold (see previous instructions).

PROJECT FORMAT
Use 11" × 17" or 12" × 18" paper and fold it horizontally to make a large multi-pocket project.

- -

Matchbook Foldable® By Dinah Zike

Step 1 Fold a sheet of paper almost in half and make the back edge about 1–2 cm longer than the front edge.

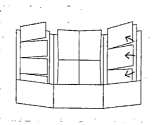

Step 2 Find the midpoint of the shorter flap.

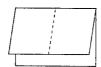

Step 3 Open the paper and cut the short side along the midpoint making two tabs.

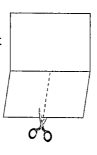

Step 4 Close the book and fold the tab over the short side.

Variations

A Make a single-tab matchbook by skipping Steps 2 and 3.

B Make two smaller matchbooks by cutting the single-tab matchbook in half.

Shutterfold Foldable® By Dinah Zike

 Begin as if you were folding a vertical sheet of paper in half, but instead of creasing the paper, pinch it to show the midpoint.

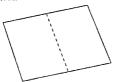

PROJECT FORMAT
Use 11" × 17" or 12" × 18" paper and fold it to make a large shutterfold project.

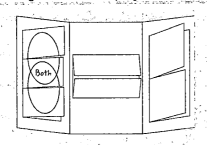

 Step 2 Fold the top and bottom to the middle and crease the folds.

Variations

A Use the shutterfold on the horizontal axis.

B Create a center tab by leaving .5–2 cm between the flaps in Step 2.

Four-Door Foldable® By Dinah Zike

 Make a shutterfold (see above).

Step 2 Fold the sheet of paper in half.

Step 3 Open the last fold and cut along the inside fold lines to make four tabs.

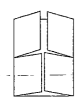

Variations

A Use the four-door book on the opposite axis.

B Create a center tab by leaving .5–2 cm between the flaps in Step 1.

Bound Book Foldable® By Dinah Zike

Step 1 Fold three sheets of paper in half. Place the papers in a stack, leaving about .5 cm between each top fold. Mark all three sheets about 3 cm from the outer edges.

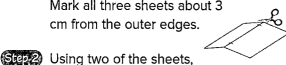

Step 2 Using two of the sheets, cut from the outer edges to the marked spots on each side. On the other sheet, cut between the marked spots.

Step 3 Take the two sheets from Step 1 and slide them through the cut in the third sheet to make a 12-page book.

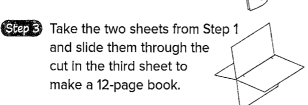

Step 4 Fold the bound pages in half to form a book.

Variation

A Use two sheets of paper to make an eight-page book, or increase the number of pages by using more than three sheets.

PROJECT FORMAT

Use two or more sheets of 11" × 17" or 12" × 18" paper and fold it to make a large bound book project.

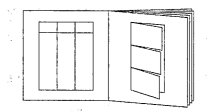

- -

Accordion Foldable® By Dinah Zike

Step 1 Fold the selected paper in half vertically, like a *hamburger*.

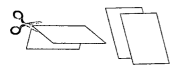

Step 2 Cut each sheet of folded paper in half along the fold lines.

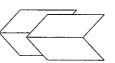

Step 3 Fold each half-sheet almost in half, leaving a 2 cm tab at the top.

Step 4 Fold the top tab over the short side, then fold it in the opposite direction.

Variations

A Glue the straight edge of one paper inside the tab of another sheet. Leave a tab at the end of the book to add more pages.

B Tape the straight edge of one paper to the tab of another sheet, or just tape the straight edges of nonfolded paper end to end to make an accordion.

C Use whole sheets of paper to make a large accordion.

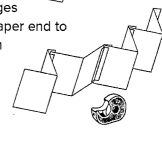

SCIENCE SKILL HANDBOOK

MATH SKILL HANDBOOK

FOLDABLES HANDBOOK

REFERENCE HANDBOOK

GLOSSARY/GLOSARIO

INDEX

Layered Foldable® By Dinah Zike

Step 1 Stack two sheets of paper about 1–2 cm apart. Keep the right and left edges even.

Step 2 Fold up the bottom edges to form four tabs. Crease the fold to hold the tabs in place.

Step 3 Staple along the folded edge, or open and glue the papers together at the fold line.

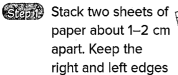

Variations

A Rotate the book so the fold is at the top or to the side.

B Extend the book by using more than two sheets of paper.

• •

Envelope Foldable® By Dinah Zike

Step 1 Fold a sheet of paper into a *taco*. Cut off the tab at the top.

Step 2 Open the *taco* and fold it the opposite way making another *taco* and an X-fold pattern on the sheet of paper.

Step 3 Cut a map, illustration, or diagram to fit the inside of the envelope.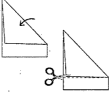

Step 4 Use the outside tabs for labels and inside tabs for writing information.

Variations

A Use 11" × 17" or 12" × 18" paper to make a large envelope.

B Cut off the points of the four tabs to make a window in the middle of the book.

SCIENCE SKILL HANDBOOK

MATH SKILL HANDBOOK

FOLDABLES HANDBOOK

REFERENCE HANDBOOK

GLOSSARY/ GLOSARIO

INDEX

Sentence Strip Foldable® By Dinah Zike

Step 1 Fold two sheets of paper in half vertically, like a *hamburger*.

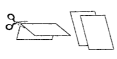

Step 2 Unfold and cut along fold lines making four half sheets.

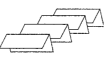

Step 3 Fold each half sheet in half horizontally, like a *hot dog*.

Step 4 Stack folded horizontal sheets evenly and staple together on the left side.

Step 5 Open the top flap of the first sentence strip and make a cut about 2 cm from the stapled edge to the fold line. This forms a flap that can be raised and lowered. Repeat this step for each sentence strip.

Variations

A Expand this book by using more than two sheets of paper.

B Use whole sheets of paper to make large books.

- -

Pyramid Foldable® By Dinah Zike

Step 1 Fold a sheet of paper into a *taco*. Crease the fold line, but do not cut it off.

Step 2 Open the folded sheet and refold it like a *taco* in the opposite direction to create an X-fold pattern.

Step 3 Cut one fold line as shown, stopping at the center of the X-fold to make a flap.

Step 4 Outline the fold lines of the X-fold. Label the three front sections and use the inside spaces for notes. Use the tab for the title.

Step 5 Glue the tab into a project book or notebook. Use the space under the pyramid for other information.

Step 6 To display the pyramid, fold the flap under and secure with a paper clip, if needed.

Single-Pocket or One-Pocket Foldable® By Dinah Zike

 Using a large piece of paper on a vertical axis, fold the bottom edge of the paper upwards, about 5 cm.

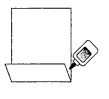

 Glue or staple the outer edges to make a large pocket.

PROJECT FORMAT
Use 11" × 17" or 12" × 18" paper and fold it vertically or horizontally to make a large pocket project.

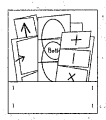

Variations

A Make the one-pocket project using the paper on the horizontal axis.

B To store materials securely inside, fold the top of the paper almost to the center, leaving about 2–4 cm between the paper edges. Slip the Foldables through the opening and under the top and bottom pockets.

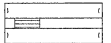

Multi-Tab Foldable® By Dinah Zike

 Fold a sheet of notebook paper in half like a *hot dog*.

 Open the paper and on one side cut every third line. This makes ten tabs on wide ruled notebook paper and twelve tabs on college ruled.

 Label the tabs on the front side and use the inside space for definitions or other information.

Variation

A Make a tab for a title by folding the paper so the holes remain uncovered. This allows the notebook Foldable to be stored in a three-hole binder.

SCIENCE SKILL HANDBOOK

MATH SKILL HANDBOOK

FOLDABLES HANDBOOK

REFERENCE HANDBOOK

GLOSSARY/ GLOSARIO

INDEX

PERIODIC TABLE OF THE ELEMENTS

Element — Hydrogen
Atomic number — 1
Symbol — H
Atomic mass — 1.01
State of matter

Gas
Liquid
Solid
Synthetic

A column in the periodic table is called a **group**.

A row in the periodic table is called a **period**.

1

1
Hydrogen
1
H
1.01

2
Lithium
3
Li
6.94

Beryllium
4
Be
9.01

3
Sodium
11
Na
22.99

Magnesium
12
Mg
24.31

2

3

4

5

6

7

8

9

4
Potassium
19
K
39.10

Calcium
20
Ca
40.08

Scandium
21
Sc
44.96

Titanium
22
Ti
47.87

Vanadium
23
V
50.94

Chromium
24
Cr
52.00

Manganese
25
Mn
54.94

Iron
26
Fe
55.85

Cobalt
27
Co
58.93

5
Rubidium
37
Rb
85.47

Strontium
38
Sr
87.62

Yttrium
39
Y
88.91

Zirconium
40
Zr
91.22

Niobium
41
Nb
92.91

Molybdenum
42
Mo
95.96

Technetium
43
Tc
(98)

Ruthenium
44
Ru
101.07

Rhodium
45
Rh
102.91

6
Cesium
55
Cs
132.91

Barium
56
Ba
137.33

Lanthanum
57
La
138.91

Hafnium
72
Hf
178.49

Tantalum
73
Ta
180.95

Tungsten
74
W
183.84

Rhenium
75
Re
186.21

Osmium
76
Os
190.23

Iridium
77
Ir
192.22

7
Francium
87
Fr
(223)

Radium
88
Ra
(226)

Actinium
89
Ac
(227)

Rutherfordium
104
Rf
(267)

Dubnium
105
Db
(268)

Seaborgium
106
Sg
(271)

Bohrium
107
Bh
(272)

Hassium
108
Hs
(270)

Meitnerium
109
Mt
(276)

The number in parentheses is the mass number of the longest lived isotope for that element.

Lanthanide series

Cerium
58
Ce
140.12

Praseodymium
59
Pr
140.91

Neodymium
60
Nd
144.24

Promethium
61
Pm
(145)

Samarium
62
Sm
150.36

Europium
63
Eu
151.96

Actinide series

Thorium
90
Th
232.04

Protactinium
91
Pa
231.04

Uranium
92
U
238.03

Neptunium
93
Np
(237)

Plutonium
94
Pu
(244)

Americium
95
Am
(243)

Metal

Metalloid

Nonmetal

Recently discovered

			13	**14**	**15**	**16**	**17**	**18**
								Helium 2 He 4.00
			Boron 5 B 10.81	Carbon 6 C 12.01	Nitrogen 7 N 14.01	Oxygen 8 O 16.00	Fluorine 9 F 19.00	Neon 10 Ne 20.18
10	**11**	**12**	Aluminum 13 Al 26.98	Silicon 14 Si 28.09	Phosphorus 15 P 30.97	Sulfur 16 S 32.07	Chlorine 17 Cl 35.45	Argon 18 Ar 39.95
Nickel 28 Ni 58.69	Copper 29 Cu 63.55	Zinc 30 Zn 65.38	Gallium 31 Ga 69.72	Germanium 32 Ge 72.64	Arsenic 33 As 74.92	Selenium 34 Se 78.96	Bromine 35 Br 79.90	Krypton 36 Kr 83.80
Palladium 46 Pd 106.42	Silver 47 Ag 107.87	Cadmium 48 Cd 112.41	Indium 49 In 114.82	Tin 50 Sn 118.71	Antimony 51 Sb 121.76	Tellurium 52 Te 127.60	Iodine 53 I 126.90	Xenon 54 Xe 131.29
Platinum 78 Pt 195.08	Gold 79 Au 196.97	Mercury 80 Hg 200.59	Thallium 81 Tl 204.38	Lead 82 Pb 207.20	Bismuth 83 Bi 208.98	Polonium 84 Po (209)	Astatine 85 At (210)	Radon 86 Rn (222)
Darmstadtium 110 Ds (281)	Roentgenium 111 Rg (280)	Copernicium 112 Cn (285)	Ununtrium * 113 Uut (284)	Flerovium 114 Fl (289)	Ununpentium * 115 Uup (288)	Livermorium 116 Lv (293)	Ununseptium * 117 Uus (294)	Ununoctium * 118 Uuo (294)

* The names and symbols for elements 113, 115, 117, and 118 are temporary. Final names will be approved by IUPAC (International Union of Pure and Applied Chemistry)

Gadolinium 64 Gd 157.25	Terbium 65 Tb 158.93	Dysprosium 66 Dy 162.50	Holmium 67 Ho 164.93	Erbium 68 Er 167.26	Thulium 69 Tm 168.93	Ytterbium 70 Yb 173.05	Lutetium 71 Lu 174.97
Curium 96 Cm (247)	Berkelium 97 Bk (247)	Californium 98 Cf (251)	Einsteinium 99 Es (252)	Fermium 100 Fm (257)	Mendelevium 101 Md (258)	Nobelium 102 No (259)	Lawrencium 103 Lr (262)

SCIENCE SKILL HANDBOOK

MATH SKILL HANDBOOK

FOLDABLES HANDBOOK

REFERENCE HANDBOOK

GLOSSARY/ GLOSARIO

INDEX

SCIENCE SKILL HANDBOOK

MATH SKILL HANDBOOK

FOLDABLES HANDBOOK

REFERENCE HANDBOOK

GLOSSARY/ GLOSARIO

INDEX

Diversity of Life: Classification of Living Organisms

A six-kingdom system of classification of organisms is used today. Two kingdoms—Kingdom Archaebacteria and Kingdom Eubacteria—contain organisms that do not have a nucleus and that lack membrane-bound structures in the cytoplasm of their cells. The members of the other four kingdoms have a cell or cells that contain a nucleus and structures in the cytoplasm, some of which are surrounded by membranes. These kingdoms are Kingdom Protista, Kingdom Fungi, Kingdom Plantae, and Kingdom Animalia.

Kingdom Archaebacteria

one-celled; some absorb food from their surroundings; some are photosynthetic; some are chemosynthetic; many are found in extremely harsh environments including salt ponds, hot springs, swamps, and deep-sea hydrothermal vents

Kingdom Eubacteria

one-celled; most absorb food from their surroundings; some are photosynthetic; some are chemosynthetic; many are parasites; many are round, spiral, or rod-shaped; some form colonies

Kingdom Protista

Phylum Euglenophyta one-celled; photosynthetic or take in food; most have one flagellum; euglenoids

Kingdom Eubacteria
Bacillus anthracis

Phylum Bacillariophyta one-celled; photosynthetic; have unique double shells made of silica; diatoms

Phylum Dinoflagellata one-celled; photosynthetic; contain red pigments; have two flagella; dinoflagellates

Phylum Chlorophyta one-celled, many-celled, or colonies; photosynthetic; contain chlorophyll; live on land, in freshwater, or salt water; green algae

Phylum Rhodophyta most are many-celled; photosynthetic; contain red pigments; most live in deep, saltwater environments; red algae

Phylum Phaeophyta most are many-celled; photosynthetic; contain brown pigments; most live in saltwater environments; brown algae

Phylum Rhizopoda one-celled; take in food; are free-living or parasitic; move by means of pseudopods; amoebas

Phylum Chlorophyta
Desmid

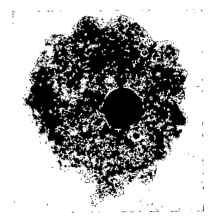

Amoeba

Phylum Zoomastigina one-celled; take in food; free-living or parasitic; have one or more flagella; zoomastigotes

Phylum Ciliophora one-celled; take in food; have large numbers of cilia; ciliates

Phylum Sporozoa one-celled; take in food; have no means of movement; are parasites in animals; sporozoans

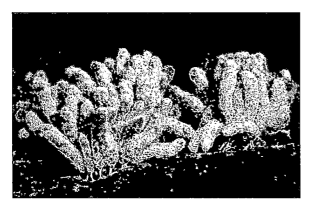

Phylum Myxomycota
Slime mold

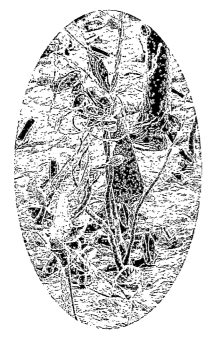

Phylum Oomycota
Phytophthora infestans

Phyla Myxomycota and Acrasiomycota one- or many-celled; absorb food; change form during life cycle; cellular and plasmodial slime molds

Phylum Oomycota many-celled; are either parasites or decomposers; live in freshwater or salt water; water molds, rusts and downy mildews

Kingdom Fungi

Phylum Zygomycota many-celled; absorb food; spores are produced in sporangia; zygote fungi; bread mold

Phylum Ascomycota one- and many-celled; absorb food; spores produced in asci; sac fungi; yeast

Phylum Basidiomycota many-celled; absorb food; spores produced in basidia; club fungi; mushrooms

Phylum Deuteromycota members with unknown reproductive structures; imperfect fungi; Penicillium

Phylum Mycophycota organisms formed by symbiotic relationship between an ascomycote or a basidiomycote and green alga or cyanobacterium; lichens

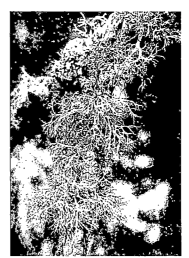

Lichens

SCIENCE SKILL HANDBOOK

MATH SKILL HANDBOOK

FOLDABLES HANDBOOK

REFERENCE HANDBOOK

GLOSSARY/ GLOSARIO

INDEX

SCIENCE SKILL HANDBOOK

MATH SKILL HANDBOOK

FOLDABLES HANDBOOK

REFERENCE HANDBOOK

GLOSSARY/ GLOSARIO

INDEX

Kingdom Plantae

Divisions Bryophyta (mosses), **Anthocerophyta** (hornworts), **Hepaticophyta** (liverworts), **Psilophyta** (whisk ferns) many-celled nonvascular plants; reproduce by spores produced in capsules; green; grow in moist, land environments

Division Lycophyta many-celled vascular plants; spores are produced in conelike structures; live on land; are photosynthetic; club mosses

Division Arthrophyta vascular plants; ribbed and jointed stems; scalelike leaves; spores produced in conelike structures; horsetails

Division Pterophyta vascular plants; leaves called fronds; spores produced in clusters of sporangia called sori; live on land or in water; ferns

Division Ginkgophyta deciduous trees; only one living species; have fan-shaped leaves with branching veins and fleshy cones with seeds; ginkgoes

Division Cycadophyta palmlike plants; have large, featherlike leaves; produces seeds in cones; cycads

Division Coniferophyta deciduous or evergreen; trees or shrubs; have needlelike or scalelike leaves; seeds produced in cones; conifers

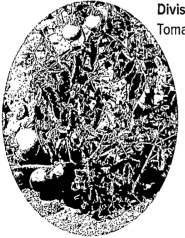

Division Anthophyta
Tomato plant

Phylum
Platyhelminthes
Flatworm

Division Gnetophyta shrubs or woody vines; seeds are produced in cones; division contains only three genera; gnetum

Division Anthophyta dominant group of plants; flowering plants; have fruits with seeds

Kingdom Animalia

Phylum Porifera aquatic organisms that lack true tissues and organs; are asymmetrical and sessile; sponges

Phylum Cnidaria radially symmetrical organisms; have a digestive cavity with one opening; most have tentacles armed with stinging cells; live in aquatic environments singly or in colonies; includes jellyfish, corals, hydra, and sea anemones

Phylum Platyhelminthes bilaterally symmetrical worms; have flattened bodies; digestive system has one opening; parasitic and free-living species; flatworms

Division Bryophyta
Liverwort

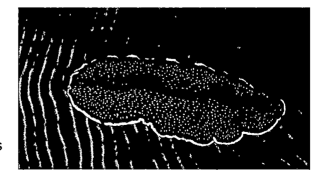

Phylum Chordata

Phylum Nematoda round, bilaterally symmetrical body; have digestive system with two openings; free-living forms and parasitic forms; roundworms

Phylum Mollusca soft-bodied animals, many with a hard shell and soft foot or footlike appendage; a mantle covers the soft body; aquatic and terrestrial species; includes clams, snails, squid, and octopuses

Phylum Annelida bilaterally symmetrical worms; have round, segmented bodies; terrestrial and aquatic species; includes earthworms, leeches, and marine polychaetes

Phylum Arthropoda largest animal group; have hard exoskeletons, segmented bodies, and pairs of jointed appendages; land and aquatic species; includes insects, crustaceans, and spiders

Phylum Echinodermata marine organisms; have spiny or leathery skin and a water-vascular system with tube feet; are radially symmetrical; includes sea stars, sand dollars, and sea urchins

Phylum Chordata organisms with internal skeletons and specialized body systems; most have paired appendages; all at some time have a notochord, nerve cord, gill slits, and a post-anal tail; include fish, amphibians, reptiles, birds, and mammals

SCIENCE SKILL HANDBOOK

MATH SKILL HANDBOOK

FOLDABLES HANDBOOK

REFERENCE HANDBOOK

GLOSSARY/ GLOSARIO

INDEX

SCIENCE SKILL HANDBOOK

MATH SKILL HANDBOOK

FOLDABLES HANDBOOK

REFERENCE HANDBOOK

GLOSSARY/ GLOSARIO

INDEX

Use and Care of a Microscope

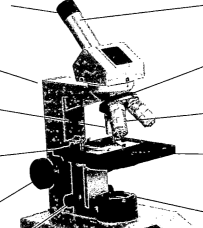

Eyepiece Contains magnifying lenses you look through.

Arm Supports the body tube.

Low-power objective Contains the lens with the lowest power magnification.

Stage clips Hold the microscope slide in place.

Coarse adjustment Focuses the image under low power.

Fine adjustment Sharpens the image under high magnification.

Body tube Connects the eyepiece to the revolving nosepiece.

Revolving nosepiece Holds and turns the objectives into viewing position.

High-power objective Contains the lens with the highest magnification.

Stage Supports the microscope slide.

Light source Provides light that passes upward through the diaphragm, the specimen, and the lenses.

Base Provides support for the microscope.

Caring for a Microscope

1. Always carry the microscope holding the arm with one hand and supporting the base with the other hand.

2. Don't touch the lenses with your fingers.

3. The coarse adjustment knob is used only when looking through the lowest-power objective lens. The fine adjustment knob is used when the high-power objective is in place.

4. Cover the microscope when you store it.

Using a Microscope

1. Place the microscope on a flat surface that is clear of objects. The arm should be toward you.

2. Look through the eyepiece. Adjust the diaphragm so light comes through the opening in the stage.

3. Place a slide on the stage so the specimen is in the field of view. Hold it firmly in place by using the stage clips.

4. Always focus with the coarse adjustment and the low-power objective lens first. After the object is in focus on low power, turn the nosepiece until the high-power objective is in place. Use ONLY the fine adjustment to focus with the high-power objective lens.

Making a Wet-Mount Slide

1. Carefully place the item you want to look at in the center of a clean, glass slide. Make sure the sample is thin enough for light to pass through.

2. Use a dropper to place one or two drops of water on the sample.

3. Hold a clean coverslip by the edges and place it at one edge of the water. Slowly lower the coverslip onto the water until it lies flat.

4. If you have too much water or a lot of air bubbles, touch the edge of a paper towel to the edge of the coverslip to draw off extra water and draw out unwanted air.

Matt Meadows

Glossary/Glosario

SCIENCE SKILL HANDBOOK

MATH SKILL HANDBOOK

FOLDABLES HANDBOOK

REFERENCE HANDBOOK

GLOSSARY/ GLOSARIO

INDEX

Multilingual eGlossary

A science multilingual glossary is available on ConnectEd.
The glossary includes the following languages:

Arabic	Hmong	Tagalog
Bengali	Korean	Urdu
Chinese	Portuguese	Vietnamese
English	Russian	
Haitian Creole	Spanish	

Cómo usar el glosario en español:
1. Busca el término en inglés que desees encontrar.
2. El término en español, junto con la definición, se encuentran en la columna de la derecha.

Pronunciation Key

Use the following key to help you sound out words in the glossary:

a	back (BAK)	ew	food (FEWD)
ay	day (DAY)	yoo	pure (PYOOR)
ah	father (FAH thur)	yew	few (FYEW)
ow	flower (FLOW ur)	uh	comma (CAH muh)
ar	car (CAR)	u (+ con)	rub (RUB)
e	less (LES)	sh	shelf (SHELF)
ee	leaf (LEEF)	ch	nature (NAY chur)
ih	trip (TRIHP)	g	gift (GIHFT)
i (i + con + e)	idea (i DEE uh)	j	gem (JEM)
oh	go (GOH)	ing	sing (SING)
aw	soft (SAWFT)	zh	vision (VIH zhun)
or	orbit (OR buht)	k	cake (KAYK)
oy	coin (COYN)	s	seed, cent (SEED, SENT)
oo	foot (FOOT)	z	zone, raise (ZOHN, RAYZ)

English — A — Español

abrasion/adaptation   **abrasión/adaptación**

abrasion: the grinding away of rock or other surfaces as particles carried by wind, water, or ice scrape against them. (p. 282)

accuracy: a description of how close a measurement is to an accepted or true value. (p. NOS 20)

acid precipitation: precipitation that has a lower pH than that of normal rainwater (p. 444)

active transport: the movement of substances through a cell membrane using the cell's energy. (p. 518)

adaptation (a dap TAY shun): an inherited trait that increases an organism's chance of surviving and reproducing in a particular environment. (p. 402)

abrasión: desgaste de una roca o de otras superficies a medida que las partículas transportadas por el viento, el agua o el hielo las raspan. (pág. 282)

exactitud: descripción de qué tan cerca está una medida a un valor aceptable. (pág. NOS 20)

precipitación ácida: precipitación que tiene un pH más bajo que el del agua de la lluvia normal. (5.6) (pág. 444)

transporte activo: movimiento de sustancias a través de la membrana celular usando la energía de la célula. (pág. 518)

adaptación: rasgo heredado que aumenta la oportunidad de un organismo de sobrevivir y reproducirse en su medioambiente. (pág. 402)

Archean (ar KEE un) eon: the time from about 4 to 2.5 million years ago. (p. 394)

asthenosphere (as THEN uh sfihr): the partially melted portion of the mantle below the lithosphere. (p. 208)

atom: a small particle that is the building block of matter. (pp. 161, 151)

atomic number: the number of protons in an atom of an element. (p. 178)

eón arcaico: tiempo desde hace cerca de 4 a 2.5 millones de años. (pág. 394)

astenosfera: parte parcialmente fundida del manto por debajo de la lithoshpere. (pág. 208)

átomo: partícula pequeña que es el componente básico de la materia. (pág. 161, 151)

número atómico: número de protones en el átomo de un elemento. (pág. 178)

B

balanced forces: forces acting on an object that combine and form a net force of zero. (p. 20)

basin: area of subsidence; region with low elevation. (p. 369)

binomial nomenclature: a naming system that gives each organism a two-word scientific name. (p. 475)

biomass energy: energy produced by burning organic matter, such as wood, food scraps, and alcohol. (p. 429)

Boyle's Law: the law that pressure of a gas increases if the volume decreases and pressure of a gas decreases if the volume increases, when temperature is constant. (p. 146)

fuerzas en equilibrio: fuerzas que actúan sobre un objeto, se combinan y forman una fuerza neta de cero. (pág. 20)

cuenca: área de hundimiento; región de elevación baja. (pág. 369)

nomenclatura binomial: sistema de nombrar que le da a cada organismo un nombre científico de dos palabras. (pág. 475)

energía de biomasa: energía producida por la combustión de materia orgánica, como la madera, las sobras de comida y el alcohol. (pág. 429)

Ley de Boyle: ley que afirma que la presión de un gas aumenta si el volumen disminuye y que la presión de un gas disminuye si el volumen aumenta, cuando la temperatura es constante. (pág. 146)

C

Calorie: the amount of energy it takes to raise the temperature of 1 kg of water by 1°C. (p. 573)

carbohydrate (kar boh HI drayt): a macromolecule made up of one or more sugar molecules, which are composed of carbon, hydrogen, and oxygen; usually the body's major source of energy. (p. 501)

cell cycle: a cycle of growth, development, and division that most cells in an organism go through. (p. 539)

cell differentiation (dihf uh ren shee AY shun): the process by which cells become different types of cells. (p. 553)

cell membrane: a flexible covering that protects the inside of a cell from the environment outside the cell. (p. 506)

caloría: cantidad de energía necesaria para aumentar la temperatura de 1 kg de agua en 1°C. (pág. 573)

carbohidrato: macromolécula constituida de una o más moléculas de azúcar, las cuales están compuestas de carbono, hidrógeno y oxígeno; usualmente es la mayor fuente de energía del cuerpo. (pág. 501)

ciclo celular: ciclo de crecimiento, desarrollo y división por el que pasan la mayoría de células de un organismo. (pág. 539)

diferenciación celular: proceso por el cual las células se convierten en diferentes tipos de células. (pág. 553)

membrana celular: cubierta flexible que protege el interior de una célula del ambiente externo de la célula. (pág. 506)

SCIENCE SKILL HANDBOOK

MATH SKILL HANDBOOK

FOLDABLES HANDBOOK

REFERENCE HANDBOOK

GLOSSARY/ GLOSARIO

INDEX

cell theory: the theory that states that all living things are made of one or more cells, the cell is the smallest unit of life, and all new cells come from preexisting cells. (p. 498)

cell wall: a stiff structure outside the cell membrane that protects a cell from attack by viruses and other harmful organisms. (p. 506)

cell: the smallest unit of life. (p. 464)

cellular respiration: a series of chemical reactions that convert the energy in food molecules into a usable form of energy called ATP. (p. 523)

centripetal (sen TRIH puh tuhl) force: in circular motion, a force that acts perpendicular to the direction of motion, toward the center of the curve. (p. 30)

centromere: a structure that holds sister chromatids together. (p. 542)

Charles's Law: the law that volume of a gas increases with increasing temperature, if the pressure is constant. (p. 147)

chemical change: a change in matter in which the substances that make up the matter change into other substances with different chemical and physical properties. (p. 108)

chemical energy: energy that is stored in and released from the bonds between atoms. (p. 52)

chemical property: the ability or inability of a substance to combine with or change into one or more new substances. (p. 99)

chloroplast (KLOR uh plast): a membrane-bound organelle that uses light energy and makes food—a sugar called glucose— from water and carbon dioxide in a process known as photosynthesis. (p. 511)

circular motion: any motion in which an object is moving along a curved path. (p. 30)

cladogram: a branched diagram that shows the relationships among organisms, including common ancestors. (p. 477)

cleavage: the breaking of a mineral along a smooth, flat surface. (p. 237)

closed system: a system that does not exchange matter or energy with the environment. (p. 63)

teoría celular: teoría que establece que todos los seres vivos están constituidos de una o más células (la célula es la unidad más pequeña de vida) y que las células nuevas provienen de células preexistentes. (pág.498)

pared celular: estructura rígida en el exterior de la membrana celular que protege la célula del ataque de virus y otros organismos dañinos. (pág. 506)

célula: unidad más pequeña de vida. (pág. 464)

respiración celular: serie de reacciones químicas que convierten la energía de las moléculas de alimento en una forma de energía utilizable llamada ATP. (pág. 523)

fuerza centrípeta: en movimiento circular, la fuerza que actúa de manera perpendicular a la dirección del movimiento, hacia el centro de la curva. (pág. 30)

centrómero: estructura que mantiene unidas las cromátidas hermanas. (pág. 542)

Ley de Charles: ley que afirma que el volumen de un gas aumenta cuando la temperatura aumenta, si la presión es constante. (pág. 147)

cambio químico: cambio de la materia en el cual las sustancias que componen la materia se transforman en otras sustancias con propi-edades químicas y físicas diferentes. (pág. 108)

energía química: energía almacenada en y liberada por los enlaces entre los átomos. (pág. 52)

propiedad química: capacidad o incapacidad de una sustancia para combinarse con una o más sustancias o transformarse en una o más sustancias. (pág. 99)

cloroplasto: organelo limitado por una membrana que usa la energía lumínica para producir alimento –un azúcar llamado glucosa– del agua y del dióxido de carbono en un proceso llamado fotosíntesis. (pág. 511)

movimiento circular: cualquier movimiento en el cual un objeto se mueve a lo largo de una trayectoria curva. (pág. 30)

cladograma: diagrama de brazos que muestra las relaciones entre los organismos, incluidos los ancestros comunes. (pág. 477)

exfoliación: rompimiento de un mineral en láminas o superficies planas. (pág. 237)

sistema cerrado: sistema que no intercambia materia o energía con el ambiente. (pág. 63)

SCIENCE SKILL HANDBOOK

MATH SKILL HANDBOOK

FOLDABLES HANDBOOK

REFERENCE HANDBOOK

GLOSSARY/ GLOSARIO

INDEX

compact bone: the hard outer layer of bone. (p. 586)

compound microscope: a light microscope that uses more than one lens to magnify an object. (p. 482)

compound: a substance containing atoms of two or more different elements chemically bonded together. (p. 164)

compression: the squeezing force at a convergent boundary. (p. 345)

condensation: the change of state from a gas to a liquid. (p. 138)

conduction (kuhn DUK shun): the transfer of thermal energy due to collisions between particles. (p. 73)

constants: the factors in an experiment that remain the same. (p. NOS 26)

contact force: a push or a pull on one object by another object that is touching it. (p. 9)

continental drift: the movement of Earth's continents over time. (p. 307)

convection: the circulation of particles within a material caused by differences in thermal energy and density. (p. 328)

convection: the transfer of thermal energy by the movement of particles from one part of a material to another. (p. 73)

convergent boundary: the boundary between two plates that move toward each other. (p. 325)

core: the dense metallic center of Earth. (p. 210)

critical thinking: comparing what you already know with information you are given in order to decide whether you agree with it. (p. NOS 10)

crust: the brittle, rocky outer layer of Earth. (p. 207)

crystal structure: the orderly, repeating pattern of atoms in a crystal. (p. 234)

crystallization: the process by which atoms form a solid with an orderly, repeating pattern. (p. 235)

cytokinesis (si toh kuh NEE sus): a process during which the cytoplasm and its contents divide. (p. 543)

cytoplasm: the liquid part of a cell inside the cell membrane; contains salts and other molecules. (p. 507)

hueso compacto: capa externa y dura del hueso. (pág. 586)

microscopio compuesto: microscopio de luz que usa más de un lente para aumentar la imagen de un objeto. (pág. 482)

compuesto: sustancia que contiene átomos de dos o más elementos diferentes unidos químicamente. (pág. 164)

compresión: tensión en un límite convergente. (pág. 345)

condensación: cambio de estado gaseoso a líquido. (pág. 138)

conducción: transferencia de energía térmica debido a colisiones entre partículas. (pág. 73)

constantes: factores en un experimento que permanecen iguales. (pág. NOS 26)

fuerza de contacto: empuje o arrastre ejercido sobre un objeto por otro que lo está tocando. (pág. 9)

deriva continental: el desplazamiento de los continentes trás tiempo. (pág. 307)

convección: circulación de partículas dentro de un material causado por diferencias en la energía térmica y densidad. (pág. 328)

convección: transferencia de energía térmica por el movimiento de partículas de una parte de la materia a otra. (pág. 73)

límite convergente de placas: límite entre dos placas que se mueven uno hacia el otro. (pág. 325)

núcleo: centro de la Tierra denso y metálico. (pág. 210)

pensamiento crítico: comparación que se hace cuando se sabe algo acerca de información nueva, y se decide si se está o no de acuerdo con ella. (pág. NOS 10)

corteza: capa frágil y rocosa superficial de la Tierra. (pág. 207)

estructura del cristal: patrón repetitivo y ordenado de los átomos en un cristal. (pág. 234)

cristalización: proceso por el cual los átomos forman un sólido con un patrón ordenado y repetitivo. (pág. 235)

citocinesis: proceso durante el cual el citoplasma y sus contenidos se dividen. (pág. 543)

citoplasma: fluido en el interior de una célula que contiene sales y otras moléculas. (pág. 507)

cytoskeleton: a network of threadlike proteins joined together that gives a cell its shape and helps it move. (p. 507)

citoesqueleto: red de proteínas en forma de filamentos unidos que le da forma a la célula y le ayuda a moverse. (pág. 507)

D

daughter cells: the two new cells that result from mitosis and cytokinesis. (p. 543)

deforestation: the removal of large areas of forests for human purposes. (p. 438)

delta: a large deposit of sediment that forms where a stream enters a large body of water. (p. 280)

density: the mass per unit volume of a substance. (pp. 201, 97)

dependent variable: the factor a scientist observes or measures during an experiment. (p. NOS 26)

deposition: the laying down or settling of eroded material. (p. 253)

deposition: the laying down or settling of eroded material. (p. 271)

deposition: the process of changing directly from a gas to a solid. (p. 138)

description: a spoken or written summary of an observation. (p. NOS 18)

dichotomous key: a series of descriptions arranged in pairs that leads the user to the identification of an unknown organism. (p. 476)

diffusion: the movement of substances from an area of higher concentration to an area of lower concentration. (p. 516)

divergent boundary: the boundary between two plates that move away from each other. (p. 325)

dune: a pile of windblown sand. (p. 282)

células hija: las dos células nuevas que resultan de la mitosis y la citocinesis. (pág. 543)

deforestación: eliminación de grandes áreas de bosques con propósitos humanos. (pág. 438)

delta: depósito grande de sedimento que se forma donde una corriente entra a un cuerpo grande de agua. (pág. 280)

densidad: de masa por unidad de volumen de una sustancia. (pág. 201, 97)

variable dependiente: factor que el científico observa o mide durante un experimento. (pág. NOS 26)

deposición: establecimiento o asentamiento de material erosionado. (pág. 253)

deposición: establecimiento o asentamiento de material erosionado. (pág. 271)

deposición: proceso de cambiar directamente de gas a sólido. (pág. 138)

descripción: resumen oral o escrito de una observación de. (pág. NOS 18)

clave dicotómica: serie de descripciones organizadas en pares que dan al usuario la identificación de un organismo desconocido. (pág. 476)

difusión: movimiento de sustancias de un área de mayor concentración a un área de menor concentración. (pág. 516)

límite divergente de placas: límite entre dos placas que se alejan unas de otras. (pág. 325)

duna: montón de arena que el viento transporta. (pág. 282)

E

electric energy: energy carried by an electric current. (p. 53)

electron cloud: the region surrounding an atom's nucleus where one or more electrons are most likely to be found. (p. 177)

electron microscope: a microscope that uses a magnetic field to focus a beam of electrons through an object or onto an object's surface. (p. 483)

energía eléctrica: energía transportada por una corriente eléctrica. (pág. 53)

nube de electrones: región que rodea el núcleo de un átomo en donde es más probable encontrar uno o más electrones. (pág. 177)

microscopio electrónico: microscopio que usa un campo magnético para enfocar un haz de electrones a través de un objeto o sobre la superficie de un objeto. (pág. 483)

SCIENCE SKILL HANDBOOK

MATH SKILL HANDBOOK

FOLDABLES HANDBOOK

REFERENCE HANDBOOK

GLOSSARY/ GLOSARIO

INDEX

electron: a negatively charged particle that occupies the space in an atom outside the nucleus. (p. 176)

element: a substance that consists of only one type of atom. (p. 163)

endocytosis (en duh si TOH sus): the process during which a cell takes in a substance by surrounding it with the cell membrane. (p. 518)

energy transfer: the process of moving energy from one object to another without changing form. (p. 61)

energy transformation: the conversion of one form of energy to another. (p. 61)

energy: the ability to cause change. (p. 51)

erosion: the moving of weathered material, or sediment, from one location to another. (p. 269)

evaporation: the process of a liquid changing to a gas at the surface of the liquid. (p. 138)

exocytosis (ek soh si TOH sus): the process during which a cell's vesicles release their contents outside the cell. (p. 518)

explanation: an interpretation of observations. (p. NOS 18)

extinct: all of the members of a species have died. (p. 402)

extrusive rock: igneous rock that forms when volcanic material erupts, cools, and crystallizes on Earth's surface. (p. 252)

electrón: partícula cargada negativamente que ocupa el espacio por fuera del núcleo de un átomo. (pág. 176)

elemento: sustancia que consiste de un sólo tipo de átomo. (pág. 163)

endocitosis: proceso durante el cual una célula absorbe una sustancia rodeándola con la membrana celular. (pág. 518)

transferencia de energía: proceso por el cual se mueve energía de un objeto a otro sin cambiar de forma. (pág. 61)

transformación de energía: conversión de una forma de energía a otra. (pág. 61)

energía: capacidad de ocasionar cambio. (pág. 51)

erosión: traslado de material meteorizado, o de los sedimentos, de un lugar a otro. (pág. 269)

evaporación: proceso por el cual un líquido cambia a gas en la superficie de dicho líquido. (pág. 138)

exocitosis: proceso durante el cual las vesículas de una célula liberan sus contenidos fuera de la célula. (pág. 518)

explicación: interpretación que se hace de las observaciones. (pág. NOS 18)

extinto: especie en la cual todos los miembros han muerto. (pág. 402)

roca extrusiva: roca ígnea que se forma cuando el material volcánico sale, se enfría y se cristaliza en la superficie de la Tierra. (pág. 252)

F

facilitated diffusion: the process by which molecules pass through a cell membrane using special proteins called transport proteins. (p. 517)

fault zone: an area of many fractured pieces of crust along a large fault. (p. 355)

fault-block mountain: parallel ridge that forms where blocks of crust move up or down along faults. (p. 362)

fermentation: a reaction that eukaryotic and prokaryotic cells can use to obtain energy from food when oxygen levels are low. (p. 524)

fertilization (fur tuh luh ZAY shun): a reproductive process in which a sperm joins with an egg. (p. 595)

difusión facilitada: proceso por el cual las moléculas pasan a través de la membrana celular usando proteínas especiales, llamadas proteínas de transporte. (pág. 517)

zona de falla: área de muchos pedazos fracturados de corteza en una falla extensa. (pág. 355)

montaña de bloques fallados: dorsal paralela que se forma donde los bloques de corteza se mueven hacia arriba o hacia abajo en las fallas. (pág. 362)

fermentación: reacción que las células eucarióticas y procarióticas usan para obtener energía del alimento cuando los niveles de oxígeno son bajos. (pág. 524)

fertilización: proceso reproductivo en el cual un espermatozoide se une con un óvulo. (pág. 595)

folded mountain: mountain made of layers of rocks that are folded. (p. 361)

foliation [foh lee AY shun]: rock texture that forms when uneven pressures cause flat minerals to line up, giving the rock a layered appearance. (p. 247)

force pair: the forces two objects apply to each other. (p. 35)

force: a push or a pull on an object. (p. 9)

fossil: the preserved remains or evidence of past living organisms. (p. 384)

fracture: the breaking of a mineral along a rough or irregular surface. (p. 237)

friction: a contact force that resists the sliding motion of two surfaces that are touching. (p. 13)

montaña plegada: montaña constituida de capas de rocas plegadas. (pág. 361)

foliación: textura de la roca que se forma cuando presiones disparejas causan que los minerales planos se alineen, dándole a la roca una apariencia de capas. (pág. 247)

par de fuerzas: fuerzas que dos objetos se aplican entre sí. (pág. 35)

fuerza: empuje o arrastre ejercido sobre un objeto. (pág. 9)

fósil: restos conservados o evidencia de organismos vivos del pasado. (pág. 384)

fractura: rompimiento de un mineral en una superficie desigual o irregular. (pág. 237)

fricción: fuerza de contacto que resiste el movimiento de dos superficies que están en contacto. (pág. 13)

G

gamete (GA meet): human reproductive cell. (p. 595)

gas: matter that has no definite volume and no definite shape. (p. 130, 94)

genus (JEE nus): a group of similar species. (p. 475)

geologic time scale: a chart that divides Earth's history into different time units based on changes in the rocks and fossils. (p. 386)

geosphere: the solid part of Earth. (p. 198)

geothermal energy: thermal energy from Earth's interior. (p. 429)

glacier: a large mass of ice, formed by snow accumulation on land, that moves slowly across Earth's surface. (p. 289)

glycolysis: a process by which glucose, a sugar, is broken down into smaller molecules. (p. 523)

grain: an individual particle in a rock. (p. 243)

gravity: an attractive force that exists between all objects that have mass. (pp. 199, 11)

gameto: célula reproductora humana. (pág. 595)

gas: materia que no tiene volumen ni forma definidos. (pág. 130, 94)

género: grupo de especies similares. (pág. 475)

escala de tiempo geológico: tabla que divide la historia de la Tierra en diferentes unidades de tiempo, basado en los cambios en las rocas y fósiles. (pág. 386)

geosfera: parte sólida de la Tierra. (pág. 198)

energía geotérmica: energía térmica del interior de la Tierra. (pág. 429)

glaciar: masa enorme de hielo, formado por la acumulación de nieve en la tierra, que se mueve lentamente por la superficie de la Tierra. (pág. 289)

glucólisis: proceso por el cual la glucosa, un azúcar, se divide en moléculas más pequeñas. (pág. 523)

grano: partícula individual de una roca. (pág. 243)

gravedad: fuerza de atracción que existe entre todos los objetos que tienen masa. (pág. 199, 11)

H

Hadean (hay DEE un) eon: the first 640 million years of Earth history. (p. 392)

half-life: the time required for half of the amount of a radioactive parent element to decay into a stable daughter element. (p. 385)

eón hadeano: los primeros 640 millones de años de la historia de la Tierra. (pág. 392)

vida media: tiempo requerido para que la mitad de cierta cantidad de un elemento radiactivo se desintegre en otro elemento estable. (pág. 385)

heat: the movement of thermal energy from a region of higher temperature to a region of lower temperature. (p. 72)

heterogeneous mixture: a mixture in which substances are not evenly mixed. (p. 167)

homeostasis (hoh mee oh STAY sus): an organism's ability to maintain steady internal conditions when outside conditions change. (pp. 571, 467)

homogeneous mixture: a mixture in which two or more substances are evenly mixed but not bonded together. (p. 168)

hormone: a chemical signal that is produced by an endocrine gland in one part of an organism and carried in the bloodstream to another part of the organism. (p. 591)

hydroelectric power: electricity produced by flowing water. (p. 428)

hypothesis: a possible explanation for an observation that can be tested by scientific investigations. (p. NOS 6)

calor: movimiento de energía térmica desde una región de alta temperatura a una región de baja temperatura. (pág. 72)

mezcla heterogénea: mezcla en la cual las sustancias no están mezcladas de manera uniforme. (pág. 167)

homeostasis: capacidad de un organismo de mantener las condiciones internas estables cuando las condiciones externas cambian. (pág. 571, 467)

mezcla homogénea: mezcla en la cual dos o más sustancias están mezcladas de manera uniforme, pero no están unidas químicamente. (pág. 168)

hormona: señal química producido por una glándula endocrina en una parte de un organismo y llevado en la corriente sanguínea a otra parte del organismo. (pág. 591)

energía hidroeléctrica: electricidad producida por agua que fluye. (pág. 428)

hipótesis: explicación posible de una observación que se puede probar por medio de investigaciones científicas. (pág. NOS 6)

I

immunity: the resistance to specific pathogens, or disease-causing agents. (p. 580)

independent variable: the factor that is changed by the investigator to observe how it affects a dependent variable. (p. NOS 26)

inertia (ihn UR shuh): the tendency of an object to resist a change in its motion. (p. 22)

inference: a logical explanation of an observation that is drawn from prior knowledge or experience. (p. NOS 6)

International System of Units (SI): the internationally accepted system of measurement. (p. NOS 18)

interphase: the period during the cell cycle of a cell's growth and development. (p. 540)

intrusive rock: igneous rock that forms as magma cools underground. (p. 252)

ion (I ahn): an atom that is no longer neutral because it has gained or lost electrons. (p. 179)

isostasy (i SAHS tuh see): the equilibrium between continental crust and the denser mantle below it. (p. 344)

inmunidad: resistencia a patógenos específicos o a agentes causantes de enfermedades. (pág. 580)

variable independiente: factor que el investigador cambia para observar cómo afecta la variable dependiente. (pág. NOS 26)

inercia: tendencia de un objeto a resistirse al cambio en su movimiento. (pág. 22)

inferencia: explicación lógica de una observación que se extrae de un conocimiento previo o experiencia. (pág. NOS 6)

Sistema Internacional de Unidades (SI): sistema de medidas aceptado internacionalmente. (pág. NOS 18)

interfase: período durante el ciclo celular del crecimiento y desarrollo de una célula. (pág. 540)

roca intrusiva: roca ígnea que se forma cuando el magma se enfría bajo el suelo. (pág. 252)

ión: átomo que no es neutro porque ha ganado o perdido electrones. (pág. 179)

isostasia: equilibrio entre la corteza continental y el manto más denso debajo de la corteza. (pág. 344)

isotopes (I suh tohps): atoms of the same element that have different numbers of neutrons. (p. 179)

isótopos: átomos del mismo elemento que tienen diferente número de neutrones. (pág. 179)

Ⓚ

kinetic (kuh NEH tik) energy: energy due to motion. (p. 134)

kinetic energy: energy due to motion. (p. 53)

kinetic molecular theory: an explanation of how particles in matter behave. (p. 144)

energía cinética: energía debida al movimiento. (pág. 134)

energía cinética: energía debida al movimiento. (pág. 53)

teoría cinética molecular: explicación de cómo se comportan las partículas en la materia. (pág. 144)

Ⓛ

landform: a topographic feature formed by processes that shape Earth's surface. (p. 216)

landslide: rapid, downhill movement of soil, loose rocks, and boulders. (p. 287)

lava: magma that erupts onto Earth's surface. (p. 244)

law of conservation of energy: law that states that energy can be transformed from one form to another, but it cannot be created or destroyed. (p. 60)

law of conservation of mass: law that states that the total mass of the reactants before a chemical reaction is the same as the total mass of the products after the chemical reaction. (p. 111)

law of conservation of momentum: a principle stating that the total momentum of a group of objects stays the same unless outside forces act on the objects. (p. 38)

lens: a transparent object with at least one curved side that causes light to change direction.

light microscope: a microscope that uses light and lenses to enlarge an image of an object. (p. 482)

lipid: a large macromolecule that does not dissolve in water. (p. 501)

liquid: matter with a definite volume but no definite shape. (pp. 94, 128)

lithification: the process through which sediment turns into rock. (p. 245)

lithosphere (LIH thuh sfihr): the rigid outermost layer of Earth that includes the uppermost mantle and crust. (pp. 208, 324)

accidente geográfico: característica topográfica formada por procesos que moldean la superficie de la Tierra. (pág. 216)

deslizamiento de tierra: movimiento rápido del suelo, rocas sueltas y canto rodado, pendiente abajo. (pág. 287)

lava: magma que llega a la superficie de la Tierra. (pág. 244)

ley de la conservación de la energía: ley que plantea que la energía puede transformarse de una forma a otra, pero no puede crearse ni destruirse. (pág. 60)

ley de la conservación de la masa: ley que plantea que la masa total de los reactivos antes de una reacción química es la misma que la masa total de los productos después de la reacción química. (pág. 111)

ley de la conservación del momentum: principio que establece que el momentum total de un grupo de objetos permanece constante a menos que fuerzas externas actúen sobre los objetos. (pág. 38)

lente: un objeto transparente con al menos un lado curvo que hace que la luz para cambiar de dirección.

microscopio de luz: microscopio que usa luz y lentes para aumentar la imagen de un objeto. (pág. 482)

lípido: macromolécula extensa que no se disuelve en agua. (pág. 501)

líquido: materia con volumen definido y forma indefinida. (pág. 94, 128)

litificación: proceso mediante el cual el sedimento se vuelve roca. (pág. 245)

litosfera: capa rígida más externa de la Tierra formada por la corteza y el manto superior. (pág. 208, 324)

SCIENCE SKILL HANDBOOK

MATH SKILL HANDBOOK

FOLDABLES HANDBOOK

REFERENCE HANDBOOK

GLOSSARY/GLOSARIO

INDEX

loess (LUHS): a crumbly, windblown deposit of silt and clay. (p. 282)

longshore current: a current that flows parallel to the shoreline. (p. 279)

luster: the way a mineral reflects or absorbs light at its surface. (p. 237)

lymphocyte (LIHM fuh site): a type of white blood cell that is made in the thymus, the spleen, and bone marrow. (p. 579)

loess: depósito quebradizo de limo y arcilla transportados por el viento. (pág. 282)

corriente costera: corriente que fluye paralela a la costa. (pág. 279)

brillo: forma en que un mineral refleja o absorbe la luz en su superficie. (pág. 237)

linfocito: tipo de glóbulos blancos que se producen en el timo, el bazo y la médula del hueso. (pág. 579)

macromolecule: substance in cells that forms when many small molecules join together. (p. 499)

magma: molten rock stored beneath Earth's surface. (p. 244)

magnetic reversal: an event that causes a magnetic field to reverse direction. (p. 318)

magnetosphere: the outer part of Earth's magnetic field that interacts with charged particles. (p. 211)

mantle: the thick middle layer in the solid part of Earth. (p. 208)

mass wasting: the downhill movement of a large mass of rocks or soil due to gravity. (p. 286)

mass: the amount of matter in an object. (p. 11, 96)

matter: anything that has mass and takes up space. (p. 161)

meander: a broad, C-shaped curve in a stream. (p. 278)

mechanical energy: sum of the potential energy and the kinetic energy in a system. (p. 54)

mid-ocean ridge: long, narrow mountain range on the ocean floor; formed by magma at divergent plate boundaries. (p. 315)

mineral: a solid that is naturally occurring, inorganic, and has a crystal structure and definite chemical composition. (p. 233)

mitosis (mi TOH sus): a process during which the nucleus and its contents divide. (p. 543)

mixture: matter that can vary in composition. (p. 166)

molecule (MAH lih kyewl): two or more atoms that are held together by covalent bonds and act as a unit. (p. 163)

macromolécula: sustancia en las células que se forma cuando mucha moléculas pequeñas se unen. (pág. 499)

magma: roca derretida almacenada debajo de la superficie de la Tierra. (pág. 244)

inversión magnética: evento que causa que un campo magnético invierta su dirección. (pág. 318)

magnetosfera: parte externa del campo magnético de la Tierra que interactúa con partículas cargadas. (pág. 211)

manto: capa delgada central de la parte sólida de la Tierra. (pág. 208)

transporte en masa: movimiento de gran cantidad de roca o suelo debido a la fuerza de gravedad, pendiente abajo. (pág. 286)

masa: cantidad de materia en un objeto. (pág. 11, 96)

materia: cualquier cosa que tiene masa y ocupa espacio. (pág. 161)

meandro: curva pronunciada en forma de C en un arroyo. (pág. 278)

energía mecánica: suma de la energía potencial y de la energía cinética en un sistema. (pág. 54)

dorsal oceánica: de largo, cordillera estrecha en el fondo del océano; formada por magma en los límites de placas divergentes. (pág. 315)

mineral: sólido inorgánico que se encuentra en la naturaleza, tiene una estructura cristalina y una composición química definida. (pág. 233)

mitosis: proceso durante el cual el núcleo y sus contenidos se divide. (pág. 543)

mezcla: materia que puede variar en composición. (pág. 166)

molécula: dos o más átomos que están unidos mediante enlaces covalentes y actúan como una unidad. (pág. 163)

SCIENCE SKILL HANDBOOK

MATH SKILL HANDBOOK

FOLDABLES HANDBOOK

REFERENCE HANDBOOK

GLOSSARY/GLOSARIO

INDEX

SCIENCE SKILL HANDBOOK

MATH SKILL HANDBOOK

FOLDABLES HANDBOOK

REFERENCE HANDBOOK

GLOSSARY/GLOSARIO

INDEX

momentum: a measure of how hard it is to stop a moving object. (p. 37)

moraine: a mound or ridge of unsorted sediment deposited by a glacier. (p. 290)

mountain: landform with high relief and high elevation. (p. 219)

multicellular: a living thing that is made up of two or more cells. (p. 464)

momentum: medida de qué tan difícil es detener un objeto en movimiento. (pág. 37)

morrena: monte o colina de sedimento sin clasificar depositado por un glacial. (pág. 290)

montaña: accidente geográfico de alto relieve y elevación alta. (pág. 219)

pluricelular: ser vivo formado por dos o más células. (pág. 464)

N

net force: the combination of all the forces acting on an object. (p. 19)

neuron (NOO rahn): the basic functioning unit of the nervous system; a nerve cell. (p. 588)

neutron: a neutral particle in the nucleus of an atom. (p. 176)

Newton's first law of motion: law that states that if the net force acting on an object is zero, the motion of the object does not change. (p. 21)

Newton's second law of motion: law that states that the acceleration of an object is equal to the net force exerted on the object divided by the object's mass. (p. 29)

Newton's third law of motion: law that states that for every action there is an equal and opposite reaction. (p. 35)

noncontact force: a force that one object applies to another object without touching it. (p. 10)

nonrenewable energy resource: an energy resource that is available in limited amounts or that is used faster than it can be replaced in nature. (p. 66)

nonrenewable resource: a natural resource that is being used up faster than it can be replaced by natural processes. (p. 417)

normal polarity: when magnetized objects, such as compass needles, orient themselves to point north. (p. 318)

nuclear energy: energy stored in and released from the nucleus of an atom. (p. 421)

nuclear energy: energy stored in and released from the nucleus of an atom. (p. 52)

nucleic acid: a macromolecule that forms when long chains of molecules called nucleotides join together. (p. 500)

fuerza neta: combinación de todas las fuerzas que actúan sobre un objeto. (pág. 19)

neurona: unidad básica de funcionamiento del sistema nervioso; célula nerviosa. (pág. 588)

neutrón: partícula neutra en el núcleo de un átomo. (pág. 176)

primera ley del movimiento de Newton: ley que establece que si la fuerza neta ejercida sobre un objeto es cero, el movimiento de dicho objeto no cambia. (pág. 21)

segunda ley del movimiento de Newton: ley que establece que la aceleración de un objeto es igual a la fuerza neta que actúa sobre él divida por su masa. (pág. 29)

tercera ley del movimiento de Newton: ley que establece que para cada acción hay una reacción igual en dirección opuesta. (pág. 35)

fuerza de no contacto: fuerza que un objeto puede aplicar sobre otro sin tocarlo. (pág. 10)

recurso energético no renovable: recurso energético disponible en cantidades limitadas o que se usa más rápido de lo que se repone en la naturaleza. (pág. 66)

recurso no renovable: recurso natural que se está agotando más rápidamente de lo que se puede reemplazar mediante procesos naturales. (pág. 417)

polaridad normal: ocurre cuando los objetos magnetizados, tales como las agujas de la brújula, se orientan a sí mismas para apuntar al norte. (pág. 318)

energía nuclear: energía almacenada y emitidas desde el núcleo de un átomo. (pág. 421)

energía nuclear: energía almacenada en y liberada por el núcleo de un átomo. (pág. 52)

ácido nucléico: macromolécula que se forma cuando cadenas largas de moléculas llamadas nucleótidos se unen. (pág. 500)

nucleus: part of a eukaryotic cell that directs cell activity and contains genetic information stored in DNA. (p. 509)

nucleus: the region in the center of an atom where most of an atom's mass and positive charge is concentrated. (p. 176)

nutrient: a part of food used by the body to grow and survive. (p. 573)

núcleo: parte de la célula eucariótica que gobierna la actividad celular y contiene la información genética almacenada en el ADN. (pág. 509)

núcleo: región en el centro de un átomo donde se concentra la mayor cantidad de masa y las cargas positivas. (pág. 176)

nutriente: parte del alimento que el cuerpo usa para crecer y vivir. (pág. 573)

---

observation: the act of using one or more of your senses to gather information and take note of what occurs. (p. NOS 6)

ocean trench: a deep, underwater trough created by one plate subducting under another plate at a convergent plate boundary. (p. 352)

open system: a system that exchanges matter or energy with the environment. (p. 63)

ore: a deposit of minerals that is large enough to be mined for a profit. (p. 239)

ore: a deposit of minerals that is large enough to be mined for a profit. (p. 437)

organ system: a group of organs that work together and perform a specific task. (p. 557)

organ system: a group of organs that work together and perform a specific task. (p. 571)

organ: a group of different tissues working together to perform a particular job. (p. 556)

organelle: membrane-surrounded component of a eukaryotic cell with a specialized function. (p. 508)

organism: something that has all the characteristics of life. (p. 463)

osmosis: the diffusion of water molecules only through a membrane. (p. 516)

outwash: layered sediment deposited by streams of water that flow from a melting glacier. (p. 290)

ovum (OH vum): female reproductive cell, or gamete. (p. 595)

observación: acción de usar uno o más sentidos para reunir información y tomar notar de lo que ocurre. (pág. NOS 6)

fosa oceánica: depresión profunda debajo del agua formada por una placa que se desliza debajo de otra placa, en un límite de placas convergentes. (pág. 352)

sistema abierto: sistema que intercambia materia o energía con el ambiente. (pág. 63)

mena: depósito de minerales suficientemente grandes como para ser explotados con un beneficio. (pág. 239)

mena: depósito de minerales suficientemente grandes como para ser explotados con un beneficio. (pág. 437)

sistema de órganos: grupo de órganos que trabajan juntos y realizar una función específica. (pág. 557)

sistema de órganos: grupo de órganos que trabajan juntos para realizar una tarea específica. (pág. 571)

órgano: grupo de diferentes tejidos que trabajan juntos para realizar una función específica. (pág. 556)

organelo: componente de una célula eucariótica rodeado de una membrana con una función especializada. (pág. 508)

organismo: algo que tiene todas las características de la vida. (pág. 463)

ósmosis: difusión de las moléculas de agua únicamente a través de una membrana. (pág. 516)

sandur: capas de sedimentos depositados por las corrientes de agua que fluyen de un glaciar en deshielo. (pág. 290)

óvulo: célula reproductora femenina, o gameto. (pág. 595)

P

Pangaea (pan JEE uh): name given to a supercontinent that began to break apart approximately 290 million years ago. (p. 307)

passive transport: the movement of substances through a cell membrane without using the cell's energy. (p. 515)

Phanerozoic (FAN uh ruh ZO ihk) eon: the time in Earth's history from 542 million years ago to the present. (p. 401)

photochemical smog: air pollution that forms from the interaction between chemicals in the air and sunlight. (p. 444)

photosynthesis (foh toh SIHN thuh sus): a series of chemical reactions that convert light energy, water, and carbon dioxide into the food-energy molecule glucose and give off oxygen. (p. 525)

physical change: a change in the size, shape, form, or state of matter that does not change the matter's identity. (p. 106)

physical property: a characteristic of matter that you can observe or measure without changing the identity of the matter. (p. 96)

plain: landform with low relief and low elevation. (pp. 218, 369)

plate tectonics: theory that Earth's surface is broken into large, rigid pieces that move with respect to each other. (p. 323)

plateau: an area with low relief and high elevation. (pp. 219, 370)

potential (puh TEN chul) energy: stored energy due to the interactions between objects or particles. (p. 51)

precision: a description of how similar or close measurements are to each other. (p. NOS 20)

prediction: a statement of what will happen next in a sequence of events. (p. NOS 7)

pressure: the amount of force per unit area applied to an object's surface. (p. 145)

principle of superposition: principle that states that in rock layers that have not been folded or deformed, the oldest rock layers are on the bottom. (p. 384)

Pangea: nombre dado a un supercontinente que empezó a separarse hace aproximadamente 290 millones de años. (pág. 307)

transporte pasivo: movimiento de sustancias a través de una membrana celular sin usar la energía de la célula. (pág. 515)

eón fanerozoico: tiempo en la historia de la Tierra desde hace 542 millones de años hasta el presente. (pág. 401)

smog fotoquímico: polución del aire que se forma de la interacción entre los químicos en el aire y la luz solar. (pág. 444)

fotosíntesis: serie de reacciones químicas que convierte la energía lumínica, el agua y el dióxido de carbono en glucosa, una molécula de energía alimentaria, y libera oxígeno. (pág. 525)

cambio físico: cambio en el tamaño, la forma o estado de la materia en el que no cambia la identidad de la materia. (pág. 106)

propiedad física: característica de la materia que puede observarse o medirse sin cambiar la identidad de la materia. (pág. 96)

plano: accidente geográfico de bajo relieve y elevación baja. (pág. 218, 369)

tectónica de placas: teoría que afirma que la superficie de la Tierra está formada por bloques rígidos de roca o placas, que se mueven una con respecto a la otra. (pág. 323)

meseta: área de bajo relieve y alta elevación. (pág. 219, 370)

energía potencial: energía almacenada debido a las interacciones entre objetos o partículas. (pág. 51)

precisión: sescripción de qué tan similar o cercana están las mediciones una de otra. (pág. NOS 20)

predicción: afirmación de lo que ocurrirá a continuación en una secuencia de eventos. (pág. NOS 7)

presión: cantidad de fuerza por unidad de área aplicada a la superficie de un objeto. (pág. 145)

principio de superposición: principio que establece que en las capas de las rocas que no se han doblado ni deformado, las rocas más viejas se encuentran en la parte inferior. (pág. 384)

SCIENCE SKILL HANDBOOK

MATH SKILL HANDBOOK

FOLDABLES HANDBOOK

REFERENCE HANDBOOK

GLOSSARY/ GLOSARIO

INDEX

protein: a long chain of amino acid molecules; contains carbon, hydrogen, oxygen, nitrogen, and sometimes sulfur (p. 501)

Proterozoic (PROH ter oh zoh ihk) eon: the time from 2.5 to 0.542 billion years ago. (p. 396)

protocontinents: small, early continents. (p. 394)

proton: a positively charged particle in the nucleus of an atom. (p. 176)

proteína: larga cadena de aminoácidos; contiene carbono, hidrógeno, oxígeno, nitrógeno y, algunas veces, sulfuro. (pág. 501)

eón proterozoico: tiempo desde hace 2.5 a 0.542 mil millones de años. (pág. 396)

protocontinentes: continentes pequeños y antiguos. (pág. 394)

protón: partícula cargada positivamente en el núcleo de un átomo. (pág. 176)

R

radiant energy: energy carried by an electromagnetic wave. (p. 56)

radiation: the transfer of thermal energy by electromagnetic waves. (p. 73)

radioactive decay: the process by which an unstable element naturally changes into another element that is stable. (p. 385)

reclamation: a process in which mined land must be recovered with soil and replanted with vegetation. (p. 423)

reflex: an automatic movement in response to a stimulus. (p. 589)

renewable energy resource: an energy resource that is replaced as fast as, or faster than, it is used. (p. 64)

renewable resource: a natural resource that can be replenished by natural processes at least as quickly as it is used. (p. 417)

reproduction: the process by which new organisms are produced. (p. 595)

reversed polarity: when magnetized objects reverse direction and orient themselves to point south. (p. 318)

ridge push: the process that results when magma rises at a mid-ocean ridge and pushes oceanic plates in two different directions away from the ridge. (p. 329)

rock cycle: the series of processes that change one type of rock into another type of rock. (p. 251)

rock: a naturally occurring solid composed of minerals, rock fragments, and sometimes other materials such as organic matter. (p. 243)

energía radiante: energía que transporta una onda electromagnética. (pág. 56)

radiación: transferencia de energía térmica por ondas electromagnéticas. (pág. 73)

desintegración radiactiva: proceso mediante el cual un elemento inestable cambia naturalmente en otro elemento que es estable. (pág. 385)

recuperación: proceso por el cual las tierras explotadas se deben recubrir con suelo y se deben replantar con vegetación. (pág. 423)

reflejo: movimiento automático en respuesta a un estímulo. (pág. 589)

recurso energético renovable: recurso energético que se repone tan rápido, o más rápido, de lo que se consume. (pág. 64)

recurso renovable: recurso natural que se reabastece mediante procesos naturales tan rápidamente como se usa. (pág. 417)

reproducción: proceso por el cual se producen nuevos organismos. (pág. 595)

polaridad inversa: ocurre cuando los objetos magnetizados invierten la dirección y se orientan a sí mismos para apuntar al sur. (pág. 318)

empuje de dorsal: proceso que resulta cuando el magma se levanta en la dorsal oceánica y empuja las placas oceánicas en dos direcciones diferentes, lejos de la dorsal. (pág. 329)

ciclo geológico: series de procesos que cambian un tipo de roca en otro tipo de roca. (pág. 251)

roca: sólido de origen natural compuesto de minerales, acumulación de fragmentos y algunas veces de otros materiales como materia orgánica. (pág. 243)

S

scientific law: a rule that describes a pattern in nature. (p. NOS 9)

ley científica: regla que describe un patrón dado en la naturaleza. (pág. NOS 9)

scientific theory: an explanation of observations or events that is based on knowledge gained from many observations and investigations. (p. NOS 9)

seafloor spreading: the process by which new oceanic crust forms along a mid-ocean ridge and older oceanic crust moves away from the ridge. (p. 316)

sediment: rock material that forms when rocks are broken down into smaller pieces or dissolved in water as rocks erode. (p. 245)

shear: parallel forces acting in opposite directions at a transform boundary. (p. 345)

significant digits: the number of digits in a measurement that are known with a certain degree of reliability. (p. NOS 21)

sister chromatids: two identical chromosomes that make up a duplicated chromosome. (p. 542)

slab pull: the process that results when a dense oceanic plate sinks beneath a more buoyant plate along a subduction zone, pulling the rest of the plate that trails behind it. (p. 329)

solar energy: energy from the Sun. (p. 427)

solid: matter that has a definite shape and a definite volume. (p. 94)

solid: matter that has a definite shape and a definite volume. (p. 127)

solubility (sahl yuh BIH luh tee): the maximum amount of solute that can dissolve in a given amount of solvent at a given temperature and pressure. (p. 98)

sound energy: energy carried by sound waves. (p. 55)

species (SPEE sheez): a group of organisms that have similar traits and are able to produce fertile offspring. (p. 475)

sperm: a male reproductive, or sex, cell; forms in a testis. (p. 595)

sphere: a ball shape with all points on the surface at an equal distance from the center. (p. 197)

spongy bone: the interior region of bone that contains many tiny holes. (p. 586)

stem cell: an unspecialized cell that is able to develop into many different cell types. (p. 554)

teoría científica: explicación de observaciones o eventos con base en conocimiento obtenido de muchas observaciones e investigaciones. (pág. NOS 9)

expansión del lecho marino: proceso mediante el cual se forma corteza oceánica nueva en la dorsal oceánica, y la corteza oceánica vieja se aleja de la dorsal. (pág. 316)

sedimento: material rocoso que se forma cuando las rocas se rompen en piezas pequeñas o cuando se disuelven en agua al erosionarse. (pág. 245)

cizalla: fuerzas paralelas que actúan en direcciones opuestas en un límite transformante. (pág. 345)

cifras significativas: número de dígitos que se conoce con cierto grado de fiabilidad en una medida. (pág. NOS 21)

cromátidas hermanas: dos cromosomas idénticos que constituyen un cromosoma duplicado. (pág. 542)

convergencia de placas: proceso que resulta cuando una placa oceánica densa se hunde debajo de una placa flotante en una zona de subducción, arrastrando el resto de la placa detrás suyo. (pág. 329)

energía solar: energía proveniente del Sol. (pág. 427)

sólido: materia con forma y volumen definidos. (pág. 94)

sólido: materia con forma y volumen definidos. (pág. 127)

solubilidad: cantidad máxima de soluto que puede disolverse en una cantidad dada de solvente a temperatura y presión dadas. (pág. 98)

energía sonora: energía que transportan las ondas sonoras. (pág. 55)

especie: grupo de organismos que tienen rasgos similares y que están en capacidad de producir crías fértiles. (pág. 475)

espermatozoide: célula reproductora masculina o sexual; forma en un testículo. (pág. 595)

esfera: figura de bola cuyos puntos en la superficie están ubicados a una distancia igual del centro. (pág. 197)

hueso esponjoso: región interior de un hueso que contiene muchos huecos diminutos. (pág. 586)

célula madre: célula no especializada que tiene la capacidad de desarrollarse en diferentes tipos de células. (pág. 554)

strain: a change in the shape of rock caused by stress. (p. 346)

streak: the color of a mineral's powder. (p. 237)

subduction: the process that occurs when one tectonic plate moves under another tectonic plate. (p. 325)

sublimation: the process of changing directly from a solid to a gas. (p. 138)

subsidence: the downward vertical motion of Earth's surface. (p. 345)

substance: matter with a composition that is always the same. (p. 162)

surface tension: the uneven forces acting on the particles on the surface of a liquid. (p. 129)

deformación: cambio en la forma de una roca causado por la presión. (pág. 346)

raya: color del polvo de un mineral. (pág. 237)

subducción: el proceso que ocurre cuando uno se mueve bajo otra placa tectónica de las placas tectónicas. (pág. 325)

sublimación: proceso de cambiar directamente de sólido a gas. (pág. 138)

hundimiento: movimiento vertical hacia abajo de la superficie de la Tierra. (pág. 345)

sustancia: materia cuya composición es siempre la misma. (pág. 162)

tensión superficial: fuerzas desiguales que actúan sobre las partículas en la superficie de un líquido. (pág. 129)

T

talus: a pile of angular rocks and sediment from a rockfall. (p. 287)

technology: the practical use of scientific knowledge, especially for industrial or commercial use. (p. NOS 8)

temperature: the measure of the average kinetic energy of the particles in a material. (p. 134)

temperature: the measure of the average kinetic energy of the particles in a material. (p. 71)

tension: the pulling force at a divergent boundary. (p. 345)

texture: a rock's grain size and the way the grains fit together. (p. 244)

thermal conductor: a material through which thermal energy flows quickly. (p. 76)

thermal energy: the sum of the kinetic energy and the potential energy of the particles that make up an object. (p. 54)

thermal energy: the sum of the kinetic energy and the potential energy of the particles that make up an object. (p. 135)

thermal insulator: a material through which thermal energy flows slowly. (p. 76)

till: a mixture of various sizes of sediment that has been deposited by a glacier. (p. 290)

tissue: a group of similar types of cells that work together to carry out specific tasks. (p. 555)

transform boundary: the boundary between two plates that slide past each other. (p. 325)

talus: montón de rocas angulares y sedimentos de un derrumbe de montaña. (pág. 287)

tecnología: uso práctico del conocimiento científico, especialmente para uso industrial o comercial. (pág. NOS 8)

temperatura: medida de la energía cinética promedio de las partículas de un material. (pág. 134)

temperatura: medida de la energía cinética promedio de las partículas de un material. (pág. 71)

tensión: fuerza de tracción en un límite divergente. (pág. 345)

textura: tamaño del grano de una roca y la forma como los granos encajan. (pág. 244)

conductor térmico: material en el cual la energía térmica se mueve con rapidez. (pág. 76)

energía térmica: suma de la energía cinética y potencial de las partículas que componen un objeto. (pág. 54)

energía térmica: suma de la energía cinética y potencial de las partículas que forman un objeto (pág. 135)

aislante térmico: material a través del cual la energía térmica fluye con lentitud. (pág. 76)

till: mezcla de varios tamaños de sedimento depositado por un glaciar. (pág. 290)

tejido: grupo de tipos similares de células que trabajan juntas para llevar a cabo diferentes funciones. (pág. 555)

límite de placas transcurrente: límite entre dos placas que se deslizan una sobre otra. (pág. 325)

transform fault: fault that forms where tectonic plates slide horizontally past each other. (p. 355)

falla transformante: falla que se forma donde las placas tectónicas se deslizan horizontalmente una con respecto a la otra. (pág. 355)

unbalanced forces: forces acting on an object that combine and form a net force that is not zero. (p. 20)

unicellular: a living thing that is made up of only one cell. (p. 464)

uplift: the process that moves large bodies of Earth materials to higher elevations. (p. 252)

uplift: the process that moves large bodies of Earth materials to higher elevations. (p. 345)

fuerzas no balanceadas: fuerzas que actúan sobre un objeto, se combinan y forman una fuerza neta diferente de cero. (pág. 20)

unicelular: ser vivo formado por una sola célula. (pág. 464)

levantamiento: proceso por el cual se mueven grandes cuerpos de materiales de la Tierra hacia elevaciones mayores. (pág. 252)

levantamiento: proceso por el cual se mueven grandes cuerpos de materiales de la Tierra hacia elevaciones mayores. (pág. 345)

vapor: the gas state of a substance that is normally a solid or a liquid at room temperature. (p. 130)

vaporization: the change in state from a liquid to a gas. (p. 137)

vaporization: the change of state from a liquid to a gas. (p. 75)

variable: any factor that can have more than one value. (p. NOS 26)

viscosity (vihs KAW sih tee): a measurement of a liquid's resistance to flow. (p. 128)

volcanic arc: a curved line of volcanoes that forms parallel to a plate boundary. (p. 353)

volume: the amount of space a sample of matter occupies. (p. 94)

vapor: estado gaseoso de una sustancia que normalmente es sólida o líquida a temperatura ambiente. (pág. 130)

vaporización: cambio de estado líquido a gaseoso. (pág. 137)

vaporización: cambio de estado líquido a gaseoso. (pág. 75)

variable: cualquier factor que tenga más de un valor. (pág. NOS 26)

viscosidad: medida de la resistencia de un líquido a fluir. (pág. 128)

arco volcánico: línea curva de volcanes que se forman paralelos al límite de una placa. (pág. 353)

volumen: cantidad de espacio que ocupa la materia. (pág. 94)

wave: a disturbance that transfers energy from one place to another without transferring matter. (p. 55)

weight: the gravitational force exerted on an object. (p. 12)

wind farm: a group of wind turbines that produce electricity. (p. 428)

work: the amount of energy used as a force moves an object over a distance. (p. 61)

onda: perturbación que transfiere energía de un lugar a otro sin transferir materia. (pág. 55)

peso: fuerza gravitacional ejercida sobre un objeto. (pág. 12)

parque eólico: grupo de turbinas de viento que produce electricidad. (pág. 428)

trabajo: cantidad de energía usada como fuerza que mueve un objeto a cierta distancia. (pág. 61)

zygote (ZI goht): the cell that forms when a sperm cell fertilizes an egg cell. (p. 595)

zigoto: célula nueva que se forma cuando un espermatozoide fertiliza un óvulo. (pág. 595)

SCIENCE SKILL HANDBOOK

MATH SKILL HANDBOOK

FOLDABLES HANDBOOK

REFERENCE HANDBOOK

GLOSSARY/GLOSARIO

INDEX

Abrasion

Italic numbers = illustration/photo   **Bold numbers** = vocabulary term
lab = indicates entry is used in a lab on this page

Cambrian Explosion

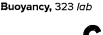

SCIENCE SKILL HANDBOOK

MATH SKILL HANDBOOK

FOLDABLES HANDBOOK

REFERENCE HANDBOOK

GLOSSARY/ GLOSARIO

INDEX

SCIENCE SKILL HANDBOOK

MATH SKILL HANDBOOK

FOLDABLES HANDBOOK

REFERENCE HANDBOOK

GLOSSARY/GLOSARIO

INDEX

SCIENCE SKILL HANDBOOK

MATH SKILL HANDBOOK

FOLDABLES HANDBOOK

REFERENCE HANDBOOK

GLOSSARY/ GLOSARIO

INDEX

X

Y

Z